*The Motorola*
*Microprocessor Family: 68000, 68008,*
*68010, 68020, 68030, and 68040:*
  *Programming and*
  *Interfacing with Applications*

# The Saunders College Publishing Series in Electronics Technology

# The Motorola Microprocessor Family: 68000, 68008, 68010, 68020, 68030, and 68040: Programming and Interfacing with Applications

Barry B. Brey

*DeVry Institute of Technology*
Columbus, Ohio

SAUNDERS COLLEGE PUBLISHING

*A Harcourt Brace Jovanovich College Publisher*

Ft. Worth   Philadelphia   San Diego   Chicago   San Francisco
New York   Orlando   Austin   San Antonio   Montreal   Toronto
London   Sydney   Tokyo

Text Typeface: Times Roman
Compositor: The Composing Room of Michigan, Inc.
Acquisitions Editor: Barbara Gingery
Assistant Editor: Laura Shur
Managing Editor: Carol Field
Project Editor: Barbara A. Chernow
Copy Editor: Brenda Griffing
Manager of Art and Design: Carol Bleistine
Art Director: Doris Bruey
Art and Design Coordinator: Caroline McGowan
Text Designer: Rebecca Lemna
Cover Designer: Laurence Didona
Text Artwork: Textbook Art Associates
Director of EDP: Tim Frelick
Production Manager: Charlene Squibb


**Library of Congress Cataloging-in-Publication Data**

Brey, Barry B.
   The Motorola microprocessor family : 68000, 68008, 68010, 68020, 68030, and 68040 : programming and interfacing with applications / Barry B. Brey.
      p.   cm.
   Includes index.
   ISBN 0-03-026423-5
   1. Motorola 68000 series microprocessors.   I. Title.
QA76.8.M6895B73   1991
004.165—dc20                                        91-27473


Printed in the United States of America

THE MOTOROLA MICROPROCESSOR FAMILY

0-03-026423-5

Library of Congress Catalog Card Number: 91-27473

0123 0016987654321

*This text is dedicated to Gary S. Citron. May you continue to sparkle and bring joy to our family as you grow and mature.*

# Preface

This text is written for the student in a course of study that requires a thorough knowledge of the Motorola family of microprocessors. It is a very practical reference text for anyone interested in all aspects of this microprocessor family. Today, anyone functioning or striving to function in a field of study that uses computers must understand this important 32-bit family of microprocessor. The Motorola microprocessors have gained wide acceptance in many areas of electronics, communications, and particularly in control systems.

This text is a direct result of my frustrated search for teaching support for the Motorola microprocessor family. Textbooks featuring the Motorola family fall short by only including the 68000 or, at best, the 68000 and 68020. Today we all need to know and understand the operation of all family members from the 68000, the first of the series, to the latest from Motorola, the 68040. Intervening members, including the 8-bit bus version, the 68008—an ideal controller because of its 8-bit data bus width—are also important for understanding existing equipment. This text explains the operation, programming, and interfacing of the 68000 and 68008 in great depth. After these basic family members are understood, the newest members (68010, 68020, 68030, and 68040) are introduced and any differences and new features that exist are highlighted. The operation and programming of the 68881/68882 family of floating-point coprocessors is also explained.

## Organization and Coverage

In order to cultivate a comprehensive approach to learning, each chapter of the text begins with a set of objectives that briefly define the contents of the chapter. Also listed are key terms that appear throughout the chapter. This is followed by the body of the chapter, which includes many programming and hardware application examples that illustrate the main topics. At the end of each chapter, a numerical summary, which doubles as a study guide, is used to review the information presented in the chapter. Finally, questions are provided to promote practice and mental exercise with the concepts presented in the chapter. Without this practice, less information is retained from the chapter.

This text is divided into two main parts. The first presents the microprocessor as a programmable device. Chapters 1–5 explain the function of each instruction and also illustrate many example programs. Example programs, using the 68000 assembler program, provide an opportunity to learn how to program the 68000 family of microprocessors. This foundation of programming is required to understand the second part of the text (Chapters 6–12), which explains how the microprocessor functions with its system and how to interface the microprocessor to a variety of peripheral devices. This interfacing, which encompasses both machines and humans, is essential to a complete understanding of the microprocessor and its application. Through this comprehensive approach, the student will become proficient in microprocessor programming, interfacing, and application.

## Approach

Because the Motorola family of microprocessors is quite diverse, this text initially concentrates on the components of this line of microprocessors, the 68000 and the 68008 versions. The other family members, which include the 68010, 68020, 68030, and 68040, are compared and contrasted with the 68000 and 68008 in Chapters 12 and 13. This entire series of microprocessors includes machines that are internally 32-bit microprocessors with nearly identical programming models. Each of these microprocessors executes data transfer, arithmetic, and logic operations on 8-, 16-, and 32-bit data. Each can be interfaced to virtually any other machine or to humans through diverse sets of programmable input/output interfacing components that are explained in depth in Chapters 6–12.

In addition to fully explaining the programming, operation, and interfacing of the microprocessor, this text also explains the programming and operation of the *numeric coprocessor* (68881/68882). The numeric coprocessor functions in a system to provide access to *floating-point calculations* that are important in such applications as control systems, video graphics, and CAD (computer aided design). The numeric coprocessor allows a program access to complex arithmetic operations that are otherwise difficult to achieve with normal programming techniques.

Through this approach—operation of the microprocessor, programming, interfacing, and the advanced members—a working and practical background is attainable. On completion of a course of study based on this text, you should be able to:

1. Easily develop software to control an application interfaced to any member of the Motorola family of microprocessors.

2. Program the numeric coprocessor (68881/68882) to solve equations.

3. Interface memory subsystems to the microprocessor.

4. Interface peripheral devices to the microprocessor to control I/O devices using direct, interrupt, and DMA techniques as they apply.

5. Explain the differences between the family members and highlight the features of each member.

## Content Overview

Chapter 1 introduces the Motorola family of microprocessors with an emphasis on the 68000 and 68008. This chapter serves to introduce the microprocessor, its operation, and the method used to store data in the microprocessor-based system. Once an understanding of the basic machine is achieved, Chapters 2–4 explain how each instruction functions with the 68000/68008 microprocessor and its system. As instructions are explained, simple applications are presented to illustrate the operation of the instructions and to develop basic programming concepts.

Once the basis for programming is developed, Chapter 5 explains the operation and application of the *assembler program*. The assembler program is then utilized in software examples that provide the main building blocks of programming. The programs presented demonstrate techniques that are required to interface the microprocessor to I/O devices discussed in later chapters. The programs also illustrate basic *data transfer* and *arithmetic manipulation* as well as *code conversion, table lookup, time delays, sorting,* and *diagnostic software.*

Chapter 6 provides the first concise coverage of the microprocessor as a component in a digital system. This chapter provides detail on the connection of the microprocessor to the bus system through buffers. It also provides detail on ancillary components required to construct a functional microprocessor-based system. This includes the generation and application of the $\overline{\text{DTACK}}$ signal, a clock signal for the microprocessor, and a reset signal to initialize it. The electrical characteristics of the microprocessor are provided so it can be interfaced to other system components.

Once the operation, pinout, and electrical characteristics of the microprocessor are understood, Chapter 7 interfaces the microprocessor to the memory system. Memory interface is implemented through the use of *TTL decoders, PROM decoders,* and *PAL*[1] *decoders*. Both *fully-decoded* and *partially decoded* memory systems are illustrated for the 68000 and 68008 microprocessors. This chapter describes how to interface the most common memory components such as *EPROM* (erasable programmable read-only memory), *SRAM* (static RAM), and *DRAM* (dynamic RAM) to the microprocessor.

Chapters 8, 9, and 10 provide a complete coverage of I/O interfacing. The first of these chapters investigates common I/O devices that are used to interface both *parallel* and *serial* data to the microprocessor. It also again describes decoding, with an emphasis on *I/O address decoding*. Common basic I/O systems that are explained include *keyboards* and *segmented numeric display systems*. We also include a coverage of *analog-to-digital* (ADC) and *digital-to-analog* (DAC) conversions so the microprocessor can be interfaced to the human world, which is an analog world. Because microprocessors often provide systems with control ability, we present interface to *stepper motors* and *DC motors*.

Chapter 9 introduces interrupt processed I/O devices, which are an extension of the devices and techniques described in Chapter 8. This chapter develops applications such as *printer interfaces* and *real-time clocks*, which are often interrupt processed. It also introduces interrupt expansion using mechanisms such as a *daisy-chain*. The last section provides a detailed description of the *68230 parallel interface and timer* with applications.

Chapter 10 explains the final form of I/O called *direct memory access* or DMA using the 68450 family of DMA controllers. It also describes *disk memory systems*

---

[1]PAL is a programmable array logic device that is a register trademark of Monolithic Memories, Inc.

and *video display systems*. Disk memory and video displays are applications of DMA controlled devices found connected to computer systems.

More advanced material exists in Chapters 11, 12, and 13, which explain the operation and programming of the *68881/68882 numeric coprocessor* and the advanced *68010, 68020, 68030, and 68040 microprocessors family members*. These advanced versions of the 68000/68008 are explained with an understanding that the first ten chapters of this text are understood. Advanced techniques such as *memory management* and *cache memory* are also detailed in the last few chapters.

The appendices provide a wealth of information that includes:

1. A complete listing of the 68000/68008 instruction set for reference as programs are developed.

2. A complete summary of the 68881/68882 instruction set used to program the numeric coprocessor.

3. A listing of instruction execution times so programs that require execution time calculations can be written.

4. The *VMEbus* is described so this popular bus system is understood. The VMEbus finds wide application in dedicated systems used for just about any purpose.

5. Answers to selected, end-of-chapter questions so the student can check on his progress.

6. A glossary that details the frequently appearing new terminology that applies to this ever changing field of microprocessors.

## Instructor's Manual

An instructor's manual provides solutions and answers to the end-of-chapter questions not provided in Appendix F of the text. The instructor's manual is designed to assist the instructor and provide a more thorough understanding of the text by providing solutions to the many application-oriented questions in the text. The manual provides programming examples produced using the assembler program and also schematics of hardware interfacing examples.

## Acknowledgments

I would like to individually acknowledge all of the people involved in developing this project, but there are too many to mention in the space provided. In addition, thanks go to past, present, and future students, who have probably taught, and will continue to teach, me more than they realize about programming, microprocessors, and interfacing. The past and current trends in this area of electronics are amazing, from the microprocessors used in 1974 (6800/8080), through the steady progression of newer and improved microprocessors and techniques over the years (68000/8086), to the present (68040/80486) and the exciting prospects for the future (68050/80586).

The following colleagues helped prepare the manuscript by their honest and encouraging critiques:

James Hallam, Spokane Community College

Robert Samuels, Catawba Valley Community College

Sohil Anwar, Luzerne County Community College

Gary Johnsey, University of Southern Mississippi

Richard Bernstein, Harper Community College

Steve Yelton, Cincinnati Technical College

I would like to also thank the people at Saunders for their dedication and hard work producing this text. I especially wish to acknowledge:

Barbara Gingery, Senior Acquisitions Editor

Laura Shur, Assistant Editor

Charlene Squibb, Production Manager

Barbara Chernow and the people at Chernow Editorial Services

Finally, thanks to the unsung heroes of the computer world, who provided the software that made this textbook possible. All of the people who wrote operating systems, word processors, CAD packages, and assembler programs that make the task of developing anything possible and relatively pain free.

Barry B. Brey
December 1991

# Contents

## Chapter 4
Program Control Instructions  98

## Chapter 5
Assembly Language Programming  128

## Chapter 9
Interrupt Processed I/O    322

# Introduction to Microprocessors and the 68000 Family

1

**OBJECTIVES**

Upon completion of this chapter, you will be able to:

- Explain the purpose of the microprocessor.
- Describe the operation of the microprocessor in a computer system.
- Define various microprocessor related terms, such as data bus, control bus, address bus, software, and hardware.
- Draw the block diagram of a computer system and detail the operation of each block.
- Draw the programming model of the 68000 microprocessor and explain the purpose of each internal register.
- Explain the purpose of the memory and I/O system as they apply to the microprocessor.
- Show how unsigned and signed integers are stored in the memory.
- Show the form of ASCII code, BCD code, and floating-point numbers.

**KEY TERMS**

| | | |
|---|---|---|
| microprocessor | bus | interrupt |
| intelligent controller | bus transfer | stack |
| microcomputer | program counter | $ |
| byte | data registers | unsigned integer |
| bit | address registers | signed binary integer |
| stored program | user stack pointer | Binary-coded decimal |
| logical memory | supervisor stack | floating-point |
| hexadecimal | pointer | ASCII |
| memory locations | stack pointer register | parity |
| input device | sign extension | floating-point number |
| output device | housekeeping | |
| controlling element | registers | |

T HE microprocessor is a vital component that is used in the fields of electronics, computer science, and electrical engineering. Today, the microprocessor is found in almost every piece of modern electronic equipment. For this reason, no field of technical education can escape the study of this device. The microprocessor has truly become paramount to the study of electronics, computer science, and electrical engineering.

In this first chapter, the role of the microprocessor is presented as it applies to the fields just mentioned. The 68000 family of microprocessors, which is an important modern family of microprocessors and also the focus of this text, is also introduced. This family currently consists of the 68000, 68008, 68010, 68020, 68030, and 68040.

## 1-1  What Is a Microprocessor?

What is a microprocessor? A *microprocessor* is a digital machine that is programmed to perform arithmetic, logic, and data transfers. In addition, it makes simple decisions. The term "microprocessor" was conceived to describe a processing unit that, today, is placed on a single integrated circuit or microchip. Because the microprocessor is programmable, it functions in an infinite number of ways in almost any situation imaginable. Probably one of the microprocessor's greatest contributions is its use to emulate any machine or system in existence, usually for far less money than any other method or technique!

For example, a very popular use of the microprocessor is to replace discrete digital logic circuitry. This saves space and money for the manufacturer. It also reduces the physical size of a system because a microprocessor-based system requires less energy to operate. The reduced component count also makes a system simpler for the field service organization to repair.

Another, more recent, application uses the microprocessor as an intelligent controller. An *intelligent controller* is a device that makes decisions and corrections as it controls a system. Corrections are made by sampling events in real time (time as it happens). An intelligent controller uses the microprocessor to calculate the result with a program and adjust parameters to control the system. This type of intelligent controller is playing a much more important role in artificial intelligence (AI) applications.

Systems built upon the microprocessor are often called microcomputers. A *microcomputer* is a system that uses the microprocessor as its controlling member. The microcomputer consists of the microprocessor, a memory, and an I/O (input/output) device or devices. (Microcomputer integrated circuit chips are also available with the microprocessor, memory, and I/O collectively integrated onto one circuit component.)

In the block diagram of a computer system shown in Figure 1-1, the microprocessor uses the memory to store data and also programs. The I/O system is used to communicate to other machines or to humans through a variety of I/O devices. Interconnecting the microprocessor to the memory and I/O are the buses, which serve to transfer data, select memory or I/O, and cause the reading or writing of data to the memory or I/O.

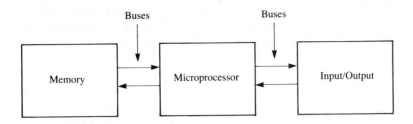

**Figure 1-1** The block diagram of a computer system.

## 1-1.1 Memory

The memory system of a computer consists of a group of storage elements, each of which holds a byte or more of binary information. (One *byte* is generally equal to 8 binary bits of information. A *bit* or binary digit is either a logic one or a logic zero.) Memory is used to store (1) the data that the program either generates or uses during its normal course of operation and (2) the program itself.

Because the program is stored in the memory system, the microprocessor executes it at a very high rate of speed. This *stored program* concept is one of the main reasons that the computer system has gained wide acceptance for many applications. Once a program has been installed in the memory system, it may be executed at lightning speed with predictable results as many times as required. This makes repetitive tasks, such as processing pay checks and telephone bills, more efficient once the programs have been written and placed in the memory system.

Figure 1-2 illustrates the organization of the logical memory system used by the Motorola 68000 microprocessor. The term *logical memory* is applied to the memory system as seen by the programmer. The organization of the logical memory does not necessarily match that of the actual physical memory. In the 68000 microprocessor, logical memory is always a byte wide, with each byte of the memory addressable via the program. Notice that each memory location, in this illustration, contains a byte of data and that the memory is numbered from 000000 through FFFFFF (hexadecimal). This means that the 68000 microprocessor addresses 16M bytes of memory. (Hexadecimal numbers are used with computers today. A *hexadecimal* digit is a number that ranges in value from 0 to F. The letters A–F are used to represent values 10–15.)

Also notice from Figure 1-2 that each of the memory locations is numbered. These numbers are called memory *addresses* or *memory locations*. Addresses are used to reference locations in the memory via a program in much the same way as a letter carrier locates your home.

The 68000 microprocessor was first produced and made available by Motorola in about 1980. Soon after, many other versions were developed as a result of the growing demand for this popular microprocessor. The 68000 is also available in the 68008, 68010, 68020, 68030, and 68040 versions. The 68008 addresses 1M bytes within a memory address range of 00000–FFFFF, the 68010 addresses 16M bytes within a memory address range of 000000–FFFFFF, and each of the other micro-

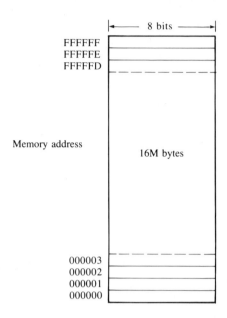

**Figure 1-2   The memory system of the 68008 microprocessor as viewed by the programmer.**

processors (the 68020, 68030, and 68040) addresses an astounding 4G bytes of memory within a memory address range of 00000000–FFFFFFFF! (1K = 1024, M = 1024K, and G = 1024M.)

Just to express what the size of memory means: a byte of memory holds one printed character of information; it takes about 4K bytes to hold a printed, single-spaced typewritten page of information; thus a 4G memory stores 1,000,000 printed pages of information. With this incredible amount of memory, there is virtually no task that cannot be manipulated with ease by the 68020, 68030, or 68040 microprocessor.

The physical memory systems of the 68000 family of microprocessors appear in Figure 1-3. Notice that these physical memory maps are not all identical. The physical memory map for the 68008 is 8 bits wide; for the 68000 and 68010, it is 16 bits wide; and for the 68020, 68030, and 68040, the memory is 32 bits wide. The physical maps are of different widths because each of these microprocessors transfers data of different widths between itself and the memory and I/O structure.

For example, the 68020 transfers up to 4 bytes (32 bits) of information at a time, while the 68008 only transfers 1 byte (8 bits) at a time. If the microprocessor is used in applications that require mostly 8-bit data, then the 68008 is often the best choice, provided not too much memory is required. If a system requires greater data widths, either the 68000, 68010, 68020, 68030, or 68040 is a better choice. The application usually dictates which of these microprocessors is best suited to a particular task. Selection criteria usually include memory size, memory width, and microprocessor speed.

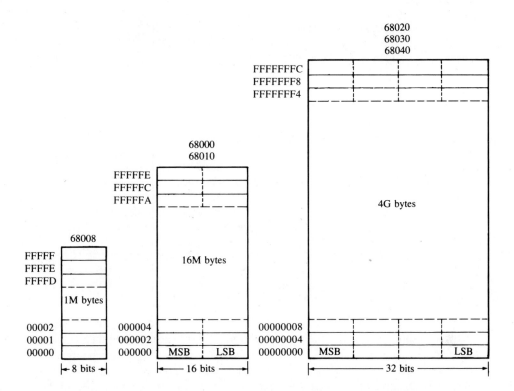

**Figure 1-3**   The physical memory maps of the 68000, 68008, 68010, 68020, 68030, and 68040 microprocessors. Note that the memory for the 68000 and 68010 contains 2 bytes per location. The memory for the 68020, 68030, and 68040 contains 4 bytes per location. As mentioned, each byte is numbered.

### 1-1.2   Input/Output Devices

Input/output (I/O) devices are used by the microprocessor to communicate its needs and also information between itself and the exterior world. Communication is accomplished between the microprocessor and another computer system or between itself and another machine. Communication is also accomplished between the microprocessor and humans. Without I/O devices, a computer would be of little use to humans.

Today a wide variety of equipment is used as I/O devices. Table 1-1 lists an assortment of I/O devices and their functions in computer systems. An *input device* allows data to be entered into the computer system from some external source. Input data consist of just about anything from keyboard data to an analog electrical signal that is converted to a digital code.

An *output device* accepts data from the microprocessor. Output data are sent to printers or other devices that accept data. Output data consist of digital data that are converted into essentially any type of electrical signal. This electrical signal can cause physical movement through motors and solenoids or speech through speakers.

**Table 1-1   Some Common I/O Devices**

| Name | Type | Function |
|------|------|----------|
| Printer | Output | Lists data and programs. |
| Keyboard | Input | Enters data or programs. |
| Switch | Input | Senses events or enters signals to a computer. |
| Plotter | Output | Draws images on paper. |
| Solenoid | Output | Moves things for a short distance. |
| Motor | Output | Can be ac, dc, or a stepper motor; used to move anything for long distances when compared to a solenoid. |
| DAC | Output | Digital-to-analog converters translate a digital code into an analog voltage that is used to control analog devices. |
| ADC | Input | Analog-to-digital converters translate analog voltages that come from analog devices into digital codes processed by the microprocessor. |

## 1-2  The Function of the Microprocessor

The microprocessor is the *controlling element* in a computer system. Its main purpose is to retrieve the programs that are stored in its memory and then execute them. As it executes these programs, the microprocessor uses data, which it fetches from the memory or internal registers, to generate new data. The new data, in turn, are stored in registers or in the memory, or are transferred between the microprocessor itself and the I/O devices in the system. Much of the microprocessor's time is spent transferring the program, and each of its instructions, from the memory to an internal instruction register for interpretation.

Once the instruction has been placed in the instruction register, it is examined (decoded), and the microprocessor executes it. When an instruction has been executed, the microprocessor may retrieve or store additional information in the memory or it may transfer data to or from the I/O devices in the system. At times it also performs some arithmetic or logic operations on the data that reside in either its memory or its internal register set.

Another operation performed by the microprocessor is a decision. The microprocessor makes some limited decisions based upon numerical facts. One of the main reasons a microprocessor is so powerful lies in its ability to make decisions. This decision-making ability can be used to cause the microprocessor to perform intelligent actions.

### 1-2.1  Buses

The microprocessor interacts with its memory and I/O through a series of bus connections. A *bus* is a common set of wires or a data path that contains common information. The bus is threaded to all the blocks in a computer system. Most modern microprocessor-based computer systems contain three buses: the address bus, the data bus, and the control bus. These buses interconnect the microprocessor and its I/O and memory.

## Address Bus

The address bus in the 68000 family of microprocessors is used to specify the memory address for the memory system or the I/O address for the I/O system. The memory address is used to select a particular byte or wider memory location, and the I/O address is used to select a single I/O device. Memory address information is anywhere from 20 bits wide in the 68008 to a full 32 bits wide in the 68020, 68030, or 68040. The 68000 and 69010 each contain a 24-bit address bus.

Table 1-2 lists the different 68000 family members and the size of their respective address and data buses. Also listed is the number of memory bytes that each type of microprocessor can directly address.

## Data Bus

The data bus is used by the microprocessor to transfer information between itself and the memory or I/O. Data transfers occur a byte at a time in the 68008. Data transfers are a byte or word (2 bytes) in the 68000 and 68010. A byte, word, or long-word (4 bytes) is transferred in the 68020, 68030, and 68040. All 680XX (680XX is used in this text to denote any 68000 family member) microprocessors are capable of transferring 8, 16, or 32 bits of data. The 68008 must use one, two, or four data bus transfers to accomplish this; the 68000 and 68010 must use one or two transfers; and the 68020, 68030, and 68040 are able to transfer any of these data sizes with one transfer. (A *bus transfer* refers to the time that it takes to transfer one piece of data through the data bus.)

For example, if 32-bit data are transferred with the 68008, it takes four bus transfers, whereas if transferred with the 68020, one transfer is sufficient. This means that the 68020 can transfer a 32-bit number four times faster than the 68008. Wider data buses usually mean that more bytes of data can be transferred per second. This makes the overall speed of the system greater if many of the data are 32 bits in width. If only 8-bit data are to be transferred, any 680XX family member is capable of the transfer in one bus transfer cycle.

**Table 1-2   Address, Data Bus, and Memory Size**

| Member | Address bus | Data bus | Memory size (bytes) |
| --- | --- | --- | --- |
| 68000 | 24 bit | 16 bit | 16M |
| 60008D | 20 bit | 8 bit | 1M |
| 68008Q | 22 bit | 8 bit | 4M |
| 68010 | 24 bit | 16 bit | 16M |
| 68020 | 32 bit | 32 bit | 4G |
| 68030 | 32 bit | 32 bit | 4G |
| 68040 | 32 bit | 32 bit | 4G |

NOTE: There are two versions of the 68008 microprocessor, with different supporting memory sizes.

*Control Bus*

The control bus is used to command the memory or I/O to do one of two possible tasks: read or write. To accomplish these control operations, the 680XX microprocessor contains an R/$\overline{W}$ (read/write) signal. If the R/$\overline{W}$ signal is a logic one, the memory or I/O is commanded to read data from the address that appears on the address bus. The data are then transferred through the data bus to the microprocessor. If the R/$\overline{W}$ signal is a logic zero, data are transferred (written) to the I/O device or memory location addressed by the address bus. The data travel through the data bus toward the memory or I/O from the microprocessor. The R/$\overline{W}$ signal is qualified with the $\overline{DS}$ (data strobe) signal. The R/$\overline{W}$ is only valid when the $\overline{DS}$ signal is a logic zero.

The control bus contains many other control signals in addition to R/$\overline{W}$ and $\overline{DS}$. A discussion at this point would not be appropriate. Additional control bus signals are discussed in Chapters 6, 7, and 8, which deal with the microprocessor, memory, and I/O.

### 1-2.2   Microprocessor Function

The microprocessor performs two basic tasks during its normal sequence of operation: (1) it fetches instructions from the memory and (2) it executes the instructions that it fetches. This sequence of events is performed endlessly as the microprocessor executes a program.

*Fetch*

An instruction is fetched from the memory when the microprocessor sends out the address of the instruction, on its address bus, and issues a memory read signal (R/$\overline{W}$ = 1). Instructions in the 680XX microprocessor are always stored in multiples of 2 bytes. For example, an instruction can be 2, 4, 6, 8, or 10 bytes in length.

To keep track of the program and the location of the next instruction in the program, the microprocessor uses a program counter (PC). The *program counter* is a register that counts up through the memory so that the next sequential instruction can be located at the next higher memory location.

In the 680XX microprocessor, the program counter is 32 bits in width. Not all versions of the 680XX microprocessor use all 32 bits of the program counter. The 68008 uses 20 or 22 bits, and the 68000 and 68010 use 24 bits; only the 68020, 68030, and 68040 use the full 32 bits of the program counter. Once the instruction has been removed from the memory and placed into an internal instruction register, the microprocessor decodes the instruction and enters the execution phase of its operation.

*Execution*

The microprocessor performs three main tasks as it executes instructions: (1) data transfer, (2) arithmetic and logic, and (3) decisions. Data transfers, which include fetching instructions, encompass most of the microprocessor's operation. Data transfers occur between the microprocessor and the memory, between the microprocessor and the I/O, and between the internal registers of the microprocessor.

Arithmetic and logic operations are performed on data in the memory or in the internal registers. The 680XX series of microprocessors can accomplish arithmetic and logic operations on 8-, 16-, or 32-bit data. Some of the major arithmetic and logic operations that the 680XX is capable of performing are listed in Table 1-3. Notice that the 680XX is capable of simple arithmetic and logic operations. If more complicated operations (sine, cosine, etc.) are required, a program must be written to accomplish them. In a system that intensely relies on complicated arithmetic, a floating-point numeric coprocessor is often added to accomplish complicated arithmetic rapidly, without the need to write software procedures. The floating-point numeric coprocessor performs these tasks at up to 100 times the rate required by software (a program).

Decisions, the last type of operation described here, are probably one of the most important operations accomplished by the microprocessor. Two things make the computer system important and powerful in today's society: (1) its ability to execute a program stored in its memory at a high rate of speed and (2) its ability to make decisions. Without either of these two elements, the computer would be no better than a simple four-function calculator, which relies on the operator's memory to store the program and also make all decisions.

The decision-making capability of the microprocessor at first seems simple. Refer to Table 1-4 for a list of the decisions that the 680XX microprocessor achieves. Note that all decisions are based on simple numeric tests or facts. A number can be tested for zero, its arithmetic sign, an arithmetic overflow, or for a carry or borrow after an addition or subtraction. It is with these extremely simple tests that a microprocessor is used to accomplish some very difficult tasks, including artificial intelligence (AI) applications.

How can a simple numerical test be used in an AI scheme? At this point, not every possible use can be explained. An example is illustrated to give some idea of how artificial intelligence is performed with a microprocessor.

**Table 1-3   Arithmetic and Logic Operations**

| Operation | Comment |
| --- | --- |
| Addition | |
| Subtraction | |
| Multiplication | |
| Division | |
| AND | Logical multiplication |
| OR | Logical addition |
| Exclusive-OR | |
| Shift | Moving a number left or right |
| Rotate | Rotating a number left or right |
| NOT | Logical inversion |
| Negate | Arithmetic sign change |

**Table 1-4     680XX Decisions**

| Type | Test condition |
| --- | --- |
| Zero | Zero value |
| Not zero | Not equal to zero |
| Negative | Negative value |
| Positive | Positive value |
| Overflow | Arithmetic overflow |
| No overflow | No arithmetic overflow |
| Carry | Carry after addition, borrow after subtraction |
| No carry | No carry or borrow |

Suppose that your program must ask a yes–no question. The program prompts the person at the keyboard to type a Y or an N. How can the program determine whether a Y was typed? The letter Y has a code (ASCII) value of 59 hexadecimal in most systems. To detect this value, all that is needed is to subtract a 59 hexadecimal from the letter typed. If the result is a zero, a Y was typed. If the decision that checks to see whether a number is zero is the result after the subtraction, you have detected the letter Y.

You can use this technique to detect any key typed on a keyboard. Building on this strategy, a program can be written to detect any word or phrase that is typed on the keyboard. Based on the word or phrase typed, a program can be executed that makes the computer appear intelligent.

## 1-3     The Programming Model

Before a program is written or any instruction is investigated, the programming model of the microprocessor must be understood. Figure 1-4 illustrates the programming model of the 68000/68008 microprocessor. The programming models for the 68010, 68020, 68030, and 68040 differ slightly and are presented in Chapters 12 and 13, which cover these microprocessors and their differences.

The register storage contains a series of 32-bit registers categorized into three main groups: data registers, address registers, and housekeeping registers. The only register that isn't 32 bits in width is the status register, which is 16 bits wide.

### 1-3.1     Data Registers

The *data registers* are general-purpose registers that are used to store byte (8-bit), word (16-bit), or long-word (32-bit) numbers. Whenever any of the eight data registers is referred to in a program, it is called D0–D7. The instruction itself determines whether the register is used as a byte, word, or long-word register. Notice that if a data register is 8 bits wide, only the right-most eight bits are used; if a data register is a word (16-bit) register, only the right-most 16 bits are used by the program; and if a data register is used to hold a 32-bit (long-word) number, then all 32 bits are used for the number.

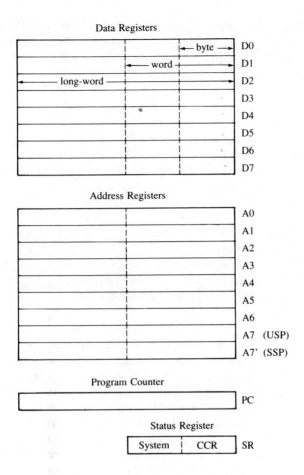

Figure 1-4   The programming model of the 68000/68008 microprocessor.

What type of information is normally found in a data register? Data registers hold general-purpose temporary data. The data types often found include unsigned binary integers, signed binary integers, ASCII coded characters, BCD (binary-coded decimal) numbers, and floating-point numbers. Because of the nature of the data registers, only the developer of the program ever knows exactly what is in them at any given instant. The value of the data stored in a register is no indication of data type because all data basically look the same. All data are binary.

## 1-3.2   Address Registers

The *address registers* are different from the data registers in two aspects: (1) address registers only hold 16- or 32-bit numbers, while the data registers hold 8-, 16-, or 32-bit numbers, and (2) address registers are not normally used to hold general-purpose data. Address registers are used to hold memory addresses. In most cases an address register is used to hold the operand address for an instruction. The *operand address* is the memory address of the data (operand) to be used by a particular instruction.

Address registers are referred to by A0–A6 and SP (stack pointer). A7 is a special register because it acts as a stack pointer (SP) register. In fact, A7 has two forms: A7 is the USP and A7' is the SSP. The USP is the *user stack pointer,* and it is active for most programs when the 680XX is operated in the user mode. The SSP (*supervisor stack pointer*) is active whenever the 680XX is operated in the supervisor mode. The supervisor mode is designed so that multiple users cannot gain access to the system hardware because certain instructions will function only in the supervisor mode. These two modes of operations are discussed in much more detail later in this text. When a program is written, A7 or A7' is referred to as SP, the stack pointer. You may use A7 in place of SP, but this is not normally done.

A *stack pointer register* is a register that holds the current memory address of the stack. A *stack* is a special way of organizing the memory: data are stored without regard to the memory address, except that initially the stack pointer is loaded with the address of the top of the stack. Stack memory is useful for linking to and returning from procedures or subroutines, as discussed later. It is also used for storing data temporarily.

If 16-bit data are stored in an address register, the data are sign-extended into a full 32-bit number. *Sign extension* occurs in address registers only when a word is stored. Sign extension does not occur in a data register. If a word is stored in a data register, only the least significant 16 bits of the register change. If a word is stored in an address register, the contents of the left-most bit of the word (sign bit) is copied into the remaining 16 bits of the address register. More detail on this feature is provided in the next chapter when addressing modes of the microprocessor are covered.

### 1-3.3   Housekeeping Registers

The 68000 has two housekeeping registers: the PC (program counter) and the SR (status register). The term *housekeeping* usually refers to a register or registers that are important in the operation of the microprocessor but are not directly accessed by the programmer. Both the PC and the SR are not normally directly accessed by the programmer. Instead they are used by the microprocessor during its normal execution of a program.

#### Program Counter

As mentioned earlier, the program counter is used by the microprocessor to locate the next instruction in a program. Each time an instruction is fetched from the memory, the program counter is incremented to the next instruction's memory location. This happens automatically, without the intervention of the program. The program counter may also at times be changed with a branch or jump instruction that allows the program to continue at another location in the memory.

*Status Register*

The status register (refer to Figure 1-5) contains two halves: the CCR (condition code register) and the system byte. The CCR contains bits of information that indicate the condition of the most recently executed instruction. The CCR contains the following condition code bits or indicators:

**X (extend).**   Indicates that a carry has occurred after an addition or that a borrow has occurred during a subtraction. The X-CCR bit is used with instructions that add or subtract the carry or borrow that it holds. X-CCR is also affected by rotate and shift instructions. (Note that a one in the X-CCR bit indicates that the carry or borrow has occurred, while a zero indicates no carry or no borrow.)

**C (carry).**   In most cases changes with the X-CCR bit and is used during a few of the rotate instructions and branches. As with the X-CCR bit, a one in the C-CCR bit indicates that a carry or borrow has occurred.

**V (overflow).**   Changes whenever the signed outcome of an addition or subtraction exceeds the precision of the answer. For example, suppose that two 8-bit signed numbers are added. The answer may exceed the 8-bit space left for it. When this occurs, the overflow CCR bit is set to indicate an overflow condition. A logic one in the V-CCR bit indicates that the overflow has occurred.

**Z (zero).**   Indicates that the result from the most recent instruction is zero. A logic one in the Z-CCR bit indicates that the outcome was a zero, while a zero indicates a nonzero result.

**N (negative).**   Indicates that the result from the most recent instruction is negative. A logic one in the N-CCR bit indicates that the result was negative, while a zero indicates positive.

The system byte of the SR contains information for and about the system. The system byte controls the interrupt structure, selects supervisor or user mode, and starts and stops the trace mode of operation. Following are brief descriptions of these bits.

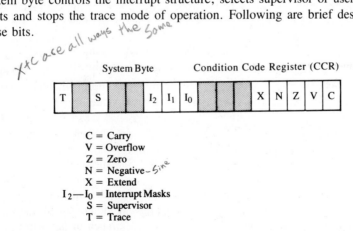

C = Carry
V = Overflow
Z = Zero
N = Negative
X = Extend
$I_2 - I_0$ = Interrupt Masks
S = Supervisor
T = Trace

**Figure 1-5   The status register illustrating both the CCR and system byte.**

**I2, I1, and I0.**    The interrupt control bits mask off a particular level of interrupt and all lower levels. For example, if a 101 (5) is placed in these bits, level 5 through level 1 interrupts are disabled or masked off. An *interrupt* is an interruption in the execution of the program caused by an external event. The only exception to this is that level 7 cannot be disabled.

**S.**    The supervisor bit selects supervisor operation when it is a logic one and user operation when it is a logic zero. Supervisor mode is entered when the 680XX is reset or whenever an interrupt occurs. At all other times the 680XX normally operates in the user mode.

**T.**    The trace bit enables single-instruction tracing when it is placed at its logic one level. Otherwise, the microprocessor processes instructions at full speed. If the trace bit is placed at a logic one level, the 680XX microprocessor interrupts the program and uses a subroutine. The subroutine used by a trace often displays the contents of the registers.

## 1-4   Microprocessor Data

Before the instruction set of the microprocessor is examined and used to accomplish any useful task, let us explore how information is stored in the registers and memory. This section details how the more common types of data, used with microprocessors, are stored in the memory and registers. Common types of data include signed and unsigned binary integers, BCD (binary-coded decimal), ASCII (American Standard Code for Information Interchange), and binary floating-point numbers.

### 1-4.1   Unsigned Binary Integers

One of the more common ways that numbers are stored in the computer is as unsigned integers. An *unsigned integer* is a binary number that occupies a byte, a word, or a long-word. It has no arithmetic sign. The byte-sized unsigned integer can range in value from 0 to 255 (decimal) or $00 to $FF (hexadecimal). Notice that the dollar sign ($) precedes a hexadecimal value. This convention is used for Motorola microprocessors throughout this text and also throughout Motorola literature and the industry. Word-sized unsigned integers range in decimal value from 0 to 65,535 or $0000 to $FFFF. Long-word unsigned integers range in decimal value from 0 to 4,294,967,295 or $00000000 to $FFFFFFFF. Figure 1-6 illustrates all three forms of the unsigned integers, with the weights of each position noted. Conversion from a number or to a number is handled easily by adding together the weights as listed. For example, to convert a 0010 0111 from binary to decimal, just add the $1 + 2 + 4 + 32 = 39$. Conversion from decimal to binary is handled by dividing the decimal number by a 2. After each division, the remainder becomes a significant digit in the result and the quotient is again divided by 2 until it is a zero. Example 1-1 illustrates how a decimal 50 is converted to binary.

E X A M P L E   1 - 1

Convert 50 decimal to binary.

$2\overline{)50}\ r = 0 \qquad q = 25$

$2\overline{)25}\ r = 1 \qquad q = 12$

$2\overline{)12}\ r = 0 \qquad q = 6$

$2\overline{)6}\ r\ = 0 \qquad q = 3$

$2\overline{)3}\ r\ = 1 \qquad q = 1$

$2\overline{)1}\ r\ = 1 \qquad q = 0$

$50 = 110010$

Notice from this example that the first remainder ($r$) is the least significant binary bit position of the answer and the quotient ($q$) is divided by 2 until it becomes a zero.

Figure 1-7 illustrates how long-word data are stored in the memory and also in a register. Notice that the numbers are normally stored in a register or memory location with their most significant byte stored first. The lowest numbered memory

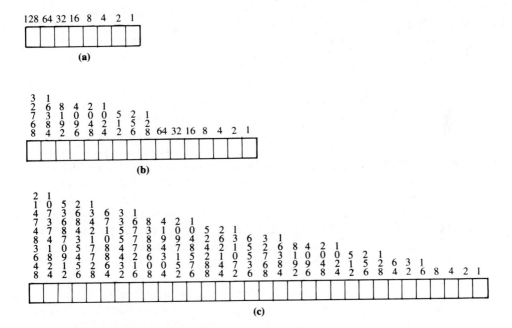

Figure 1-6  Unsigned integers (a) byte, (b) word, and (c) long-word.

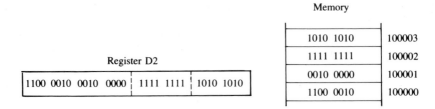

**Figure 1-7**   A $C220FFAA stored in both register D2 and memory locations $100000–$100003. Notice how the most significant byte is stored at the lowest numbered location in memory.

location always contains the most significant byte of a multiple-byte number. The left-most part of a register contains the most significant byte.

Unsigned integers are most often byte, word, or long-word, but they can be of any length. For example, if you need to store decimal 5,000,000,000 in the memory as an unsigned integer and it doesn't fit into the long-word format, you can store it in a 5-byte section of the memory and develop the software that is required to operate on it. There is no limit to the number of bytes used to store numbers in the memory system. If the number is wider than 32 bits, however, software must be developed for addition, subtraction, and all other operations.

### 1-4.2   Signed Binary Integers

*Signed binary integers* are used to store numbers that require an arithmetic plus or minus sign. Most computer systems today store signed numbers using the true form for a positive value and the two's complement form for a negative value. The Motorola 680XX series of microprocessors is no exception to this rule.

The true (positive) form of a +12 (decimal) or $0C is a 0000 1100 in binary. The two's complement (negative) form is 1111 0100 or $F4 ($-12$). Notice that the very left-most bit position contains the sign of the number. If the left-most bit is a one, the number is negative and is stored in the two's complement form. If the left-most bit is a zero, the number is positive and is stored in its true form. Whenever a number is two's-complemented, its arithmetic sign is changed. A negative number will become positive and a positive number will become negative after being two's-complemented.

In Example 1-2 the number 20 is first converted to binary by dividing it by 2. Because this example requires a byte-wide number, the binary equivalent, 10100, is expanded to 8 bits by adding leading zeros. To convert +20 to the two's complement (negative) form, each bit is inverted to 11101011 and then a 00000001 is added.

**E  X  A  M  P  L  E      1 - 2**

Convert a $-20$ to an 8-bit binary signed integer.

$$
\begin{array}{lll}
2\overline{)20} & r = 0 & q = 10 \\
2\overline{)10} & r = 0 & q = 5 \\
2\overline{)5} & r = 1 & q = 2 \\
2\overline{)2} & r = 0 & q = 1 \\
2\overline{)1} & r = 1 & q = 0 \\
\end{array}
$$

$$+20 = 00010100$$

$$
\begin{array}{r}
11101011 \\
+\quad\quad 1 \\
\hline
-20 = \overline{11101100}
\end{array}
$$

Another, more graphic, method can be used to two's-complement a number. Write the number down (from the right to the left) until you come to the first logic one. Write down the first logic one and then invert all the remaining bits. Example 1-3 illustrates this graphic technique.

E X A M P L E    1 - 3

|  | |
|---|---|
|  | 00010100 = +20 |
| write until first 1; | 00 |
| write first 1; | 100 |
| then invert all other bits; | 11101100 = −20 |

Figure 1-8 illustrates the byte, word, and long-word sized signed integers most often used with the 680XX microprocessor. Notice that the weight of the left-most bit position is negative. An 8-bit signed integer of 1000 0001 therefore has a value of −127. This same method of determining the value of a signed integer is used for any positive or negative number. A 0001 0000 has a value of +16 because there is no −128 and only a +16 to be added together. A 1000 1000 has a value of −120 because a −128 and an 8 equals −120.

### 1-4.3 BCD (Binary-Coded Decimal)

Binary-coded decimal (BCD) numbers are used in applications that are not math intensive. Example systems that use BCD data include point-of-sales terminals (cash registers) and many simple applications. *Binary-coded decimal numbers* are binary numbers ranging in value from 0000 to 1001 (0–9). If you wish to represent a number larger than a 9, two or more BCD digits are necessary. For example, 94 appears as a 1001 0100 in BCD.

BCD numbers are stored in two forms in the microprocessor: packed and unpacked. The *unpacked* form uses a byte for each BCD digit of a number. The *packed* form places two BCD digits in each byte. Table 1-5 illustrates several decimal numbers and their equivalents in packed and unpacked BCD form.

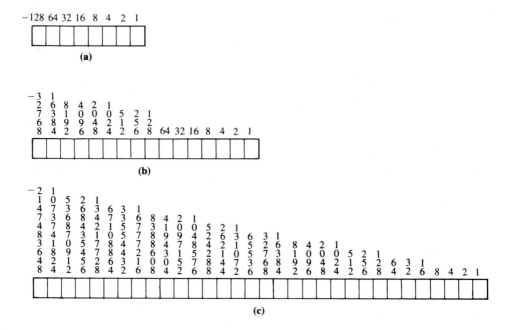

**Figure 1-8** Signed integers (a) byte, (b) word, and (c) long-word. Notice that the left-most bit is negative.

Data are normally input from a numeric keyboard in the unpacked BCD form and converted to packed BCD form for storage and arithmetic operations in the microprocessor. Once the packed BCD data have been processed, they are again converted to unpacked form for use in numeric displays. Displays either require BCD data or, in most cases, require that BCD data be converted from unpacked form to seven-segment code. This conversion is accomplished with a program or with digital logic circuitry.

### 1-4.4    ASCII

*ASCII (American Standard Code for Information Interchange)* is a code that is used to store both alphabetic and numeric data in a computer system's memory. It is also used to store special characters such as commas and colons. ASCII is standard to virtually all computer peripheral equipment manufactured in the United States, Japan, and many other countries of the world. Table 1-6 illustrates the entire ASCII

**Table 1-5    Packed and Unpacked BCD**

| Decimal | Unpacked | | | Packed | |
|---------|----------|----------|----------|--------|----------|
| 45      | 0000 0100 | 0000 0101 | | 0100 0101 | |
| 121     | 0000 0001 | 0000 0010 | 0000 0001 | 0000 0001 | 0010 0001 |
| 6       | 0000 0110 | | | 0000 0110 | |
| 306     | 0000 0011 | 0000 0000 | 0000 0110 | 0000 0011 | 0000 0110 |

code. Notice that ASCII is a 7-bit code, with the eighth bit remaining available to the system. The eighth bit is used to hold parity information in a data communications environment, to indicate graphic characters for some printers, or as an extension to the standard characters in many home computers.

*Parity* is a count of the number of ones, expressed as even or odd. For example, if the count of ones is 3, the number has odd parity; if there are 2 ones, the number has even parity. The parity bit is encoded so that the data always have either even or odd parity. In many data communications environments, the ASCII code is always sent with even parity.

Table 1-6 can be used to convert a character to ASCII code. For example, to find the ASCII code equivalent of the letter p, first locate the p. Next look horizontally to the left in the same row to find the first hexadecimal digit of the ASCII coded character. Then look up the p's column to find the second digit. Preface these digits with a $, to indicate hexadecimal, and you see that the letter p has an ASCII coded value of $70. Converting from ASCII to a character is accomplished in a similar fashion. To convert a $4E from ASCII to a character, look to the left-hand column of numbers for a 4. Then follow across the row until you come to the character under the letter E, which is the letter N.

The first 32 ASCII codes ($00–$1F) are used to encode control information for a printer or data communications environment. These control characters are often not printed on a printer or displayed on a terminal. For example, the $0D code is used for a carriage return (CR). A carriage return moves the printhead back to the left-hand margin of the printed page. It moves the VDT (video display terminal) cursor back to the left-hand side of the screen. The line feed code, $0A or LF, is another often used code; it serves to move the printed page up a line or the cursor down one line on the video screen.

Following the special codes are the letters, numbers, and special characters that are encoded in the ASCII code. Characters are obtained on a keyboard by typing the letter or number desired. If you need a code of less than $20, the special characters, it is obtained by holding the control key down while typing another character. For example, control A is code $01, control B is $02, and so forth. The $00 code is often obtained by holding down the control key and, usually, typing the @ symbol.

**Table 1-6   The ASCII Code**

| First | Second | | | | | | | | | | | | | | | |
|---|---|---|---|---|---|---|---|---|---|---|---|---|---|---|---|---|
| | 0 | 1 | 2 | 3 | 4 | 5 | 6 | 7 | 8 | 9 | A | B | C | D | E | F |
| 0 | NUL | SOH | STX | ETX | EOT | ENQ | ACK | BEL | BS | HT | LF | VT | FF | CR | SO | SI |
| 1 | DLE | DC1 | DC2 | DC3 | DC4 | NAK | SYN | ETB | CAN | EM | SUB | ESC | FS | GS | RS | US |
| 2 | SP | ! | " | # | $ | % | & | , | ( | ) | * | + | , | - | . | / |
| 3 | 0 | 1 | 2 | 3 | 4 | 5 | 6 | 7 | 8 | 9 | : | ; | < | = | > | ? |
| 4 | @ | A | B | C | D | E | F | G | H | I | J | K | L | M | N | O |
| 5 | P | Q | R | S | T | U | V | W | X | Y | Z | [ | \ | ] | ^ | _ |
| 6 | ` | a | b | c | d | e | f | g | h | i | j | k | l | m | n | o |
| 7 | p | q | r | s | t | u | v | w | x | y | z | { | \| | } | ~ | |

### 1-4.5   Binary Floating-Point Numbers

Binary floating-point numbers are very important in high level language programming such as BASIC, C-Language, or Pascal. A *floating-point number* is often referred to as binary scientific notation. In floating-point form, a number is represented as a normalized binary fraction raised to a power of 2. Example 1-4 illustrates several decimal numbers converted to standard floating-point form.

E  X  A  M  P  L  E     1 - 4

| Decimal Normalized | | S | Exponent | Fraction |
|---|---|---|---|---|
| 100    | $= 1.1001 \times 2^6$ | 0 | 1000 0101 | 1001 0000 0000 0000 0000 000 |
| $-12$  | $= -1.1 \times 2^3$ | 1 | 1000 0010 | 1000 0000 0000 0000 0000 000 |
| 14.75  | $= 1.11011 \times 2^3$ | 0 | 1000 0010 | 1101 1000 0000 0000 0000 000 |
| 0      | $= 0.0 \times 2^0$ | 0 | 0000 0000 | 0000 0000 0000 0000 0000 000 |
| $-0.125$ | $= -1.0 \times 2^{-3}$ | 1 | 0111 1100 | 0000 0000 0000 0000 0000 000 |

In this example, notice that the number is first converted to a normalized binary floating-point number. (A normalized number is written as a 1.XXXXXX raised to a some power of 2.) Next the number is converted to the standard 4-byte form used by almost all high level language programs today. The first bit is the sign bit (S). If S is a one, the number is negative, and if S is a zero the number is positive. The next 8 bits contain the biased exponent. The exponent is biased by a $7F. If the actual exponent is a 6, as in the first number in this example, then the biased exponent is an $85 (1000 0101) or $06 + $7F = $85.

Following the biased exponent is a 23-bit fraction. Notice that the 1. portion is not stored with the fraction. The 1. part is implied and is not actually stored in the floating-point form number. That means that a binary fraction of 1.111 is stored as 1110 0000 0000 0000 0000 000. Look at the examples to make sure that you understand this format.

Two exceptions to this rule are: zero, which is stored as 32 zeros, and infinity, which is stored as 32 ones. A more complete coverage of floating-point numbers appears in Chapter 11, which details the MC68881/MC68882 floating-point coprocessor.

*Converting from Decimal to Floating-Point Format*

To convert a decimal number into floating-point format, follow the steps outlined below:

**1.** Convert the decimal number to binary.

**2.** Normalize this binary number as $1.XXXXX \times 2^y$.

**3.** Place the sign of the number in the first bit.

**4.** Add a $7F to the exponent to arrive at the biased exponent.

**5.** Store the fraction minus the 1. in the next 23 bits.

Example 1-5 illustrates how to convert the number $-34.1875$ from decimal to floating-point form. Notice how each of the five steps is used for this conversion.

E X A M P L E   1 - 5

Convert a decimal, $-34.1875$, to floating-point form.

Step 1. $-34.1875_{10} = 100010.0011_2$

Step 2. $-1.000100011 \times 2^5$

Step 3. Sign (S) $= 1$ for negative

Step 4. Biased exponent $= \$7F + 5 = \$84$

Step 5. Fraction $= 0001\ 0001\ 1000\ 0000\ 0000\ 000$

```
S   exponent    fraction
1   1000 0100   0001 0001 1000 0000 0000 000
```

## Converting from Floating-Point Form to Decimal

To convert from the floating-point form to decimal, the 4-byte number is broken into its three fields: sign, biased exponent, and fraction. Once this has been accomplished, the following steps will aid you in converting the number to decimal.

**1.** Convert the number to three fields.

**2.** Subtract a $\$7F$ from the biased exponent to obtain the actual exponent.

**3.** Write the fraction with a 1.0 in front of it raised to the exponent power of 2.

**4.** Un-normalize the 1.XXXXXX fraction raised to $2^y$.

**5.** Convert the binary number to decimal and place the appropriate sign in front of it.

Example 1-6 illustrates how a floating-point number is converted to decimal. Notice that the five steps outlined are followed for this conversion.

E X A M P L E   1 - 6

Convert a $\$C0F80000$ into decimal.

```
         S   exponent    fraction
Step 1:  1   1000 0001   1111 0000 0000 0000 0000 000
Step 2:  $81 − $7F = 2
Step 3:  1.1111 × 2²
Step 4:  111.11
Step 5:  −7.75
```

## Summary

1. The microprocessor is a programmable controller that executes software that is stored in its memory system. The microprocessor performs simple arithmetic and logic operations, data transfers, and decisions that are based on numeric facts. Microprocessors are an important portion of electronics because they save considerable money when they replace discrete analog and digital systems.

2. The microcomputer is a computer system that is constructed around the micro-processor. A microcomputer contains the microprocessor, memory, and I/O. Some microcomputers are available on a single integrated circuit.

3. The memory of a computer system contains storage locations that are often a byte wide, with each location numbered with a hexadecimal address. Memory is used by a computer to store the program and the data used by the program.

4. The logical memory in a computer system is usually a byte in width; it is the memory as the programmer views it. The physical memory, the actual hardware configuration of the memory system, may be up to 32 bits wide in modern microprocessors.

5. The I/O (input/output) devices provide data to the computer and accept data from the computer. A keyboard is an example of an input device. A printer is an example of an output device.

6. The microprocessor communicates to its memory and I/O systems through a series of three buses: address, data, and control. The address bus contains the memory address or I/O address; the data bus conveys the data between the microprocessor and memory or I/O; and the control bus causes a read or write to occur.

7. The microprocessor performs two tasks during its normal sequence of operation: it fetches instructions from the program stored in the memory, and it executes these instructions.

8. The microprocessor executes instructions of three main types: data transfer, arithmetic and logic, and decision making.

9. The 68000 microprocessor contains registers of three main types: data registers, address registers, and housekeeping registers. The eight data registers (D0–D7) hold a byte, word, or long-word and are used for general-purpose operations. The eight address registers (A0–A6 and SP) hold either a word or a long-word and store the operand address of the memory data. The housekeeping registers PC (program counter) and SR (status register) are not normally directly accessible with a program. Instead, the program counter is used by the microprocessor to locate the next instruction in the program, and the status register is used to indicate conditions with its CCR (condition code register) and also to control the microprocessor with the system byte.

10. Binary integers are used to store most numbers in the 680XX microprocessor; they are either signed or unsigned. The unsigned integer is a whole number

without any arithmetic sign. It is stored as a byte, word, or long-word. The signed integer uses its left-most bit position to indicate the arithmetic sign of the number. If the sign bit contains a zero, the sign is positive; if it contains a one, the sign is negative. Positive signed numbers are stored in true form, while negative signed numbers are stored in two's complement form.

11. BCD (binary-coded decimal) numbers are stored as either one BCD digit per byte (unpacked) or as two BCD digits per byte (packed). A BCD digit is a grouping of 4 bits that contain the values 0000–1001 (0–9).

12. ASCII (American Standard Code for Information Interchange) is a 7-bit code that is used to store the letters of the alphabet, numbers, and special characters. It also contains 32 special characters as its first 32 codes. The left-most (eighth) bit holds parity for data communications or information for a printer.

13. Fractional, mixed, very large, or very small numbers require a special storage technique called the floating-point system. A floating-point number consists of a number 4 bytes wide, containing three fields of information: sign, biased exponent, and fraction. The sign is the arithmetic sign of the number. The biased exponent is a power of 2 that is biased by adding a $7F to it. The fraction is a normalized number equal to 1.XXXXXXX, where XXXXXXX is the fractional part and the 1. is implied and not stored.

## Questions

1. What is a microprocessor?

2. What is a microcomputer?

3. Draw the block diagram of a computer system. Make sure that you label all blocks and interconnecting paths.

4. Why has the stored program concept made the computer the powerful device that it is today?

5. What two objects are normally stored in the memory of a computer system?

6. What is the difference between the logical memory system and the physical memory system?

7. There are _____ bits in a byte.

8. The 68000 microprocessor addresses _____ bytes of memory.

9. The 68008 addresses _____ bytes of memory.

10. The 68020 can directly address 32-bit long-words of data. (*true* or *false*)

11. List three different I/O devices. Make sure to identify them as input or output devices.

12. What is a bus?

13. What is the purpose of the address bus?

14. What is the purpose of the data bus?

15. The data bus of the 68000 is _____ bits wide.

16. What is the purpose of the control bus?

17. The memory or I/O will write data if R/$\overline{\text{W}}$ = _____.

18. During normal operation, the microprocessor will perform two main tasks. What are these tasks?

19. What three major categories of instructions can be executed by the microprocessor?

20. Bytes of data are addressed in which 680XX registers?

21. Which 680XX registers are addressable only as words or long-words?

22. What is the purpose of the address register?

23. The SSP is actually one of the _____ registers.

24. What is the purpose of the program counter?

25. List the CCR bits and give a brief description of what each bit indicates.

26. The status register contains two bytes. What are these bytes named?

27. Convert the following decimal numbers into unsigned 8-bit integers.
    (a) 22    (b) 37    (c) 88    (d) 202    (e) 254

28. Convert the following unsigned binary integers into decimal numbers.
    (a) 0001 0011    (b) 0011 1111    (c) 0101 0111

29. Convert to decimal the following unsigned hexadecimal numbers of varying lengths.
    (a) $F4    (b) $33    (c) $020D    (d) $10000000

30. Convert the following signed decimal numbers to 8-bit binary signed integers.
    (a) −12    (b) +98    (c) −106    (d) +126

31. Convert the following signed binary integers to signed decimal numbers.
    (a) 0001 1011    (b) 1001 1111    (c) 1000 0000

32. If a $3456ABCD is stored as a long-word in 4 bytes of memory beginning at $200000, then $200000 = _____, $200001 = _____, $200002 = _____, and $200003 + _____. location

33. Show how the following decimal numbers are stored in both packed and unpacked BCD forms.
    (a) 12    (b) 894    (c) 1005

34. Convert the word SOMEHOW into a series of ASCII characters.

35. Convert into alphabetic characters the ASCII series: $48, $45, $4C, $4C, $4F.

**36.** Convert the following decimal numbers into floating-point numbers.
    **(a)** $+120.625$     **(b)** $-0.125$     **(c)** $+3000.3125$

**37.** Convert the following floating-point numbers into decimal numbers.
    **(a)** 1100 0011 0111 1111 0000 0000 0000 0000
    **(b)** 0011 1111 1000 0000 0000 0000 0000 0000
    **(c)** 1100 0000 1000 1111 0000 0000 0000 0000

# 2

# *Data Transfer Instructions*

## OBJECTIVES

Upon completion of this chapter, you will be able to:

- Understand and use the addressing modes available to the 680XX microprocessor.

- Learn how to convert symbolic machine language into hexadecimal machine language.

- Use the MOVE instruction to transfer data to any register or memory location.

- Describe the operation of the other data transfer instructions, such as MOVEM (move multiple register), EXG (exchange), and SWAP.

## KEY TERMS

| | | |
|---|---|---|
| MOVE | memory addressing | program counter |
| source | scratchpad memory | addressing (relative |
| destination | indirect addressing | addressing) |
| .B, .W, .L | indirect addressing | machine language |
| addressing mode | with postincrement | native |
| constant | indirect addressing | size field |
| # | with predecrement | destination field |
| direct register | displacement | source field |
| addressing | indirect (addressing) | register field |
| absolute short/long | with index | mode field |

T HIS IS the first of three chapters that explain the instruction set of the 680XX microprocessor. Before the instructions are examined, the way the 680XX microprocessor addresses data must be understood. The first part of this chapter develops a comprehension of how data are addressed in both the internal register set and the external memory system. The addressing techniques learned are used throughout the remainder of the text whenever programs are written or investigated. After addressing has been presented in detail, the data transfer instructions are described.

Data transfer instructions include a fairly large portion of the instruction set of the 680XX, and they also represent a major part of the instructions found in many programs with any microprocessor. Because of this, it is important that they be fully investigated and completely understood.

Once addressing modes have become intuitive, and the MOVE instruction has been learned, the techniques used to place these instructions in the memory can be explained. Two methods are commonly employed for placing a program in the memory for later execution: machine language and assembly language. Machine language programming is described in this chapter. Chapter 5 includes a thorough description of assembly language programming and the operation of the assembler.

## 2-1 Addressing Modes

Before any instruction can be completely understood, the way in which data are addressed must be discussed. This section of the text uses the MOVE instruction to explain the various addressing modes available to the 680XX microprocessor and most of its instructions.

### 2-1.1 The MOVE Instruction

Before any addressing mode is discussed, an instruction that can use all the addressing modes must be learned. One of the easiest instructions to understand is *MOVE*. The MOVE instruction is not normally used by itself. Instead, MOVE is almost always used with an extension that identifies the size and type of move.

Associated with the MOVE instruction are two operands called the *source* and the *destination*. (An *operand* is the data operated on by the *opcode*—the instruction to the microprocessor—such as the MOVE instruction being discussed here.) Figure 2-1 illustrates the normal symbolic form of the MOVE instruction, showing the extension, source operand, and destination operand. In this example the extension is .B (byte), the source is D2, and the destination is D1. The instruction copies the byte portion of register D2 into the byte portion of register D1.

In general, the MOVE instruction takes the data specified in the source operand and moves it into the destination operand. The data are copied from the source operand, and only the destination operand changes as a result of a MOVE instruc-

**Figure 2-1** The MOVE instruction illustrating the opcode (MOVE), extension (.B), source (D2), and destination (D1). This example moves a copy of the byte contents of register D2 into the byte portion of register D1.

tion. The source operand does not change. This is true for most instructions in the 680XX. Only the destination operand will change.

## Extension

The extensions *.B*, *.W*, and *.L* are required by most, but not all instructions. The MOVE instruction is used as a MOVE.B to move 8-bit bytes of data, a MOVE.W to move 16-bit words, and a MOVE.L to move 32-bit long-words of data. Some assembler programs do not require this extension with a word move, but allow it. This text will always include a .W for any instruction that operates on words of data, to prevent confusion as to operand size. (An *assembler* is a program that converts symbolic instructions, such as the MOVE instruction, into hexadecimal machine language. See Chapter 5.)

E  X  A  M  P  L  E     2 - 1
_____

Choose an instruction that will move the byte contents of register D2 into register D3.

```
001000     1602     MOVE.B     D2,D3
```
_____

The instruction illustrated in example 2-1 is a byte move because the extension .B follows the opcode MOVE. The instruction itself will move a byte of data from the source operand (register D2) to the destination operand (register D3). Here the contents (byte-sized) of D2 are transferred into D3. Whenever data are moved, the number is copied from the source operand into the destination operand. The source never changes. The only thing that changes is the contents of the destination operand. In this example, the right-most 8 bits of register D3 will change and the remaining 24 bits will not change because this is a byte-sized MOVE.

### 2-1.2    The Addressing Modes

The 680XX instruction set allows many addressing modes. Each is discussed in complete detail along with its operation using the MOVE instruction. *Addressing modes* specify how the 680XX treats the data identified by the operand. An operand can be data, the contents of a register, the contents of memory addressed by the operand address, or the contents of memory indirectly addressed by an address register or by the program counter. Table 2-1 illustrates all the allowable addressing modes for the 680XX microprocessor. Note that these addressing modes apply to the 68000, 68008, 68010, 68020, 68030, and 68040. The 68020, 68030, and 68040 have additional addressing modes, as discussed in Chapters 12 and 13, which detail their differences.

## Immediate Addressing

The term *immediate* implies that the data follow without interruption the opcode in the memory. This is shown later in this chapter when conversions to hexadecimal

**Table 2-1  680XX Addressing Modes**

| Mode | Syntax |
|---|---|
| Data register direct | Dn |
| Address register direct | An |
| Address register indirect | (An) |
| Address register indirect with postincrement | (An)+ |
| Address register indirect with predecrement | −(An) |
| Address register indirect with displacement | (d16,An) or d16(An) |
| Address register indirect with index | (d8,An,Xn) or d8(An,Xn) |
| Absolute short | XXX.W |
| Absolute long | XXX.L |
| Program counter indirect with displacement | (d16,PC) or d16(PC) |
| Program counter indirect with index | (d8,PC,Xn) or d8(PC,Xn) |
| Immediate | #XXX |

*push*
*pop*
*source only*

NOTES: d8 = 8-bit displacement, d16 = 16-bit displacement, An = A0–A7, Dn = D0–D7, Xn = A0–A7/D0–D7, and XXX = any value.

machine language are discussed. Immediate data are *constants*, which are placed into or operated on with registers or memory locations by an instruction.

Example 2-2 illustrates an instruction that places a 12 hexadecimal ($12) into the 8-bit (byte) portion of the D4 register. Notice that the extension is a .B, which designates a byte operation, that the source operand is immediate data 12 hexadecimal, and that the destination operand is D4. Also notice that immediate data are indicated by the # symbol and that the $ is used to designate a hexadecimal quantity. Figure 2-2 graphically illustrates the execution and result of this instruction.

**E X A M P L E   2 - 2**

Write an instruction that will place a $12 into the byte portion of D4.

```
001000   183C0012    MOVE.B  #$12,D4
```

**E X A M P L E   2 - 3**

Write an instruction that will place a 300 decimal into the word portion of the D7 register.

```
001000   3E3C012C    MOVE.W  #300,D7
```

Example 2-3 illustrates how a decimal number is moved immediately into a word register. Notice here that the $ is missing because the number 300 is decimal

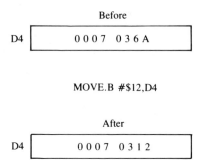

Before

D4   0 0 0 7   0 3 6 A

MOVE.B #$12,D4

After

D4   0 0 0 7   0 3 1 2

**Figure 2-2** The effect of a MOVE.B #$12,D4 instruction on the contents of register D4.

and not hexadecimal. Immediate addressing is used to load constants into registers or memory locations, while other addressing modes are used to specify variable data in the memory or a register. Example 2-4 shows how a long-word is placed into an address register.

E  X  A  M  P  L  E     2 - 4

Select an instruction that will place a $12345678 into the A6 register.

```
001000   2C7C12345678   MOVE.L   #$12345678,A6
```

Table 2-2 illustrates various instructions that use the immediate addressing mode. All these examples use the MOVE instruction. Notice that the immediate data always constitute the source operand and may never be the destination operand in any instruction.

*Direct Register Addressing*

Notice from Table 2-1 there are two forms of *direct register addressing*. One addresses data in a data register and the other addresses data in an address register. It is very important to recall from Chapter 1 that if a data register is specified, byte, word, or long-word data may be used, whereas if an address register is specified, only word and long-word data may be used. It is also important to note that we

**Table 2-2** Various Immediate Addressed Instructions

| Instruction | Description |
| --- | --- |
| MOVE.L #10,D5 | Places a 10 decimal into all 32 bits of D5. |
| MOVE.W #$10,D2 | Places a 10 hexadecimal into the right-most 16 bits of D2. |
| MOVE.B #$FE,D0 | Places an FE hexadecimal into the right-most 8 bits of D0. |

normally use SP (stack pointer) in place of A7 in programs. Although A7 is the stack pointer register, it is normally designated as an SP in a program. The program makes no distinction between the user stack pointer (USP) and the supervisor stack pointer (SSP). This is determined by the current mode of operation as set by the supervisor bit in the system byte of the status register. If user mode is selected, then the USP is active; if supervisor mode is selected, SSP is active.

Example 2-5 illustrates an instruction that will copy the contents of the word-sized D2 register into the word-sized D5 register. Note that only the right-most 16 bits of register D5 will change with this instruction. The left-most 16 bits are not changed. Figure 2-3 illustrates the path of data for the instruction of Example 2-5.

E  X  A  M  P  L  E      2 - 5

---

Choose an instruction that will copy a word from D2 into D5.

```
001000    3A02    MOVE.W    D2,D5
```

---

If an address register is to receive data, and it happens to receive 16 bits of data, the data are automatically *sign-extended* into a 32-bit number. The sign-extended number fills the remaining 16 bits of the address register. For example, if the instruction of Example 2-6 is executed with a $1000 in D2, then the outcome in A2 will be $00001000. This is because the sign bit (left-most binary bit) of the $1000 is a logic zero. This logic zero in the sign bit is copied into each bit of the most significant word of A2.

On the other hand, if D2 is an $8000, the outcome in A2 is $FFFF8000. This happens because the sign bit of $8000 is a logic one, and it is copied into each bit of the most significant portion of A2. Notice that any number moved into any word-sized *address register* is always sign-extended into a 32-bit value. If the sign of the word moved is positive (values of $0000–$7FFF), the most significant part of the result in the address register is a $0000. If the sign is negative (values of $8000–$FFFF), the most significant part of the result is a $FFFF. More detail on the reason for sign extension is provided in connection with absolute memory addressing.

Before

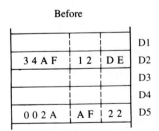

After

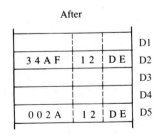

**Figure 2-3   Notice how the MOVE.W D2,D5 instruction copies the word contents of D2 into the word portion of D5.**

E  X  A  M  P  L  E     2 - 6

Write an instruction that will copy the word in D2 to A2.

```
001000    3442    MOVE.W    D2,A2
```

Example 2-7 illustrates using the SP register as an operand in a MOVE instruction. Here the entire 32 bits of the SP are copied into address register A3.

E  X  A  M  P  L  E     2 - 7

Select an instruction that will copy the SP into A3.

```
001000    264F    MOVE.L    SP,A3
```

Table 2-3 illustrates many instructions that use direct addressing. Notice that the SP register is used in place of A7 and that any 16-bit data moved into an address register is always sign-extended.

Example 2-8 shows how a short sequence of instructions is used to place a logic zero into all of the internal data registers. The first instruction uses the MOVE immediate instruction to place a $00000000 into register D0. Following this are direct register MOVE instructions that copy the zero in D0 to all the other data registers.

E  X  A  M  P  L  E     2 - 8

Write a sequence of instructions that place a $00000000 into all the data registers.

```
001000    7000              MOVE.L    #0,D0
001002    2200              MOVE.L    D0,D1
001004    2400              MOVE.L    D0,D2
001006    2600              MOVE.L    D0,D3
001008    2800              MOVE.L    D0,D4
00100A    2A00              MOVE.L    D0,D5
00100C    2C00              MOVE.L    D0,D6
00100E    2E00              MOVE.L    D0,D7
```

**Table 2-3   Example Direct Addressed Instructions**

| Instruction | Description |
| --- | --- |
| MOVE.B D2,D3 | Copies a byte from D2 into D3. |
| MOVE.W A4,A5 | Copies a word from A4 into A5. |
| MOVE.L D2,A4 | Copies a long-word from D2 into A4. |
| MOVE.L A5,D3 | Copies a long-word from A5 into D3. |
| MOVE.L SP,D1 | Copies a long-word from SP (A7) into D1. |

## Absolute Memory Addressing

*Absolute memory addressing* is used whenever the data are in a known memory location. Suppose that you wish to copy the byte contents of memory location $001000 into the D2 data register. This is accomplished by using absolute memory addressing. Absolute memory addressing is available in two distinct forms: *absolute short* and *absolute long*.

The absolute short form uses a 16-bit memory address to access either the bottom 32K bytes of memory ($000000–$007FFF) or the top 32K bytes ($FF8000–$FFFFFF). If absolute short memory addressing is used, the 680XX automatically sign-extends the address to a full 32 bits. It is because of this sign extension that only the bottom 32K or the top 32K of memory are available through this type of addressing. A word that is moved into an address register is sign-extended also because this allows a short (word) address to be moved into an address register.

Example 2-9 illustrates how the short address is used to access memory location $001000. Note that the .W (as illustrated in Table 2-1) is missing after the $1000. This is because most assemblers recognize that the memory address falls within the range of a short address and assembles the instructions as a short absolute address. Figure 2-4 illustrates how the address is formed as the machine executes an instruction that uses the short absolute form of addressing memory data.

E  X  A  M  P  L  E        2 - 9

Choose an instruction that will copy the byte contents of memory location $001000 into D2.

```
    002000      14381000     MOVE.B     $1000,D2
```

Absolute long memory addressing allows the programmer to access any memory location in the entire 680XX memory system. The absolute long address is a full 32-bit memory address. Example 2-10 illustrates how the word data at memory location $200000 are moved into the word portion of register D5 using absolute long memory addressing. Note that this instruction will copy the contents of memory locations $200000 and $200001 into the right-most 16 bits of D5. The left-most 16 bits of D5 remain unchanged, as well as the contents of the two memory locations.

The contents of $200000 are transferred into bit positions 15–8, and the contents of $200001 are transferred into bit positions 7–0 of D5. As with the short addressing form, the .L is missing because most assemblers will recognize that the $200000 requires a long address. Refer to Figure 2-5 for a graphical illustration of absolute long memory addressing in relation to the operation of Example 2-10.

E  X  A  M  P  L  E        2 - 10

Select an instruction that copies a word of data from memory location $200000 into D5.

```
    001000      3A390020000   MOVE.B     $200000,D5
```

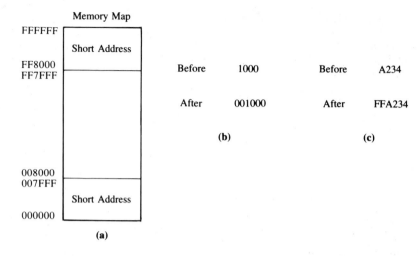

**Figure 2-4** Short absolute memory addressing (a) illustrating the range of addresses available with a short address, (b) showing how a short address or $1000 is sign-extended into address $001000, and (c) showing how a short address of $A234 is sign-extended into address $FFA234.

In normal programming, absolute addressing usually doesn't require that you specify a numeric address as in Examples 2-9 and 2-10. The reason is that we normally refer to a memory location by a name or label. Example 2-11 shows how the word contents of a memory location named DATA are transferred into register D5. Notice that .W or .L does not follow the word DATA. An assembler, which normally is used to create a program, will determine whether the memory location DATA needs a short or long address.

E  X  A  M  P  L  E    2 - 11

Write an instruction that copies the word contents of memory location DATA into D5.

```
001000    3A3900001006    MOVE.W    DATA,D5
```

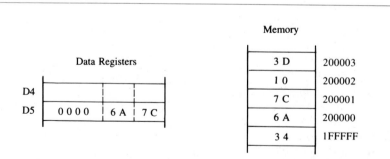

**Figure 2-5** The transfer by the MOVE.W $200000,D5 instruction of a word from memory into the word portion of D5.

**Table 2-4** Absolute Memory Addressed Instructions

| Instruction | Description |
|---|---|
| MOVE.B D2,$9000 | Copies a byte from D2 into memory location $FF9000 using a short address. |
| MOVE.W $009000,D4 | Copies a word from memory beginning at location $009000 into register D4. This instruction uses a long address. |
| MOVE.L A3,MEMORY | Copies a long-word from A3 into memory location MEMORY. |
| MOVE.B NUMBER,D7 | Copies a byte from memory location NUMBER into D7. |

Table 2-4 illustrates various absolute memory addressed instructions. Please recall that whenever an absolute short address is used to address memory data, the actual memory address generated and used by the instruction is sign-extended to a full 32 bits. The absolute long form requires no such sign extension because it is already a 32-bit address.

Suppose that it is required to place a $6F into memory location $30000, a $55 into $30001, and a $FF into $30002. This is accomplished by the program illustrated in Example 2-12, in which the immediate form of addressing is combined with the absolute form.

E X A M P L E    2 - 12

Write a program that places a $6F into $30000, a $55 into $30001, and a $FF into $30002.

```
001000   13FC006F00030000   MOVE.B   #$6F,$30000
001008   13FC005500030001   MOVE.B   #$55,$30001
001010   13FC006F00030002   MOVE.B   #$FF,$30002
```

Absolute short addressing is used as much as possible in a program, to ensure that the amount of memory used to store the program remains as small as possible. It takes 2 bytes of memory to store a short address (16-bit address) and 4 bytes to store a long address (32-bit address). Short addressing gives the programmer access to 64K bytes of scratchpad memory. Long addressing allows data at any location to be accessed. A *scratchpad memory* is a memory that can be accessed quickly and holds commonly used data. A short address is accessed more quickly than a long address because the short address requires 2 bytes of memory, while the long address requires 4 bytes of memory. The microprocessor can fetch 2 bytes from memory in half the time needed to retrieve 4 bytes.

## Indirect Addressing

As you noticed in Table 2-1, there are quite a few forms of indirect addressing available in the 680XX. The first form is the easiest to understand because it uses an address register to indirectly address memory data. When used this way, the address register contains the address of the memory data, not the data. Recall that an address register is loaded with either a word address (short) or a long-word address (long). This allows the address register to access any memory location or any scratchpad memory location.

Address register *indirect addressing* uses an address register to hold the memory location to be accessed by the instruction. In Example 2-13, which illustrates this type of instruction, the byte contents of D2 are moved into the memory location addressed by address register A3. Notice that the parentheses surrounding A3 cause the 680XX assembler to use the indirect form of memory addressing. Figure 2-6 illustrates how the address in address register A3 is used to access a location in the memory for the instruction of Example 2-13.

E  X  A  M  P  L  E    2 - 13

Write an instruction that will store the byte portion of D2 into the memory location addressed by address register A3.

        001000    1682    MOVE.B    D2,(A3)

Suppose that you must store the contents of register D5 at memory location $300000. This can be accomplished in two ways. The first way uses the long absolute addressing mode, and the second way uses the register indirect method. Example 2-14 shows two instructions that are used to accomplish this data transfer using the address register indirect technique. Notice that the first instruction places a $300000 into address register A4 and the second instruction uses indirect addressing to move the contents of D5 to the memory location addressed by address register A4 (in this example, location $300000).

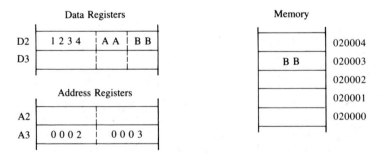

**Figure 2-6   The MOVE.B D2,(A3) instruction as it addresses memory.**

EXAMPLE 2-14

Store D5 into memory location $300000.

```
001000    287C00300000    MOVE,L    #$300000,A4
001008    2885            MOVE,L    D5,(A4)
```

Table 2-5 illustrates some instructions that use the indirect form of addressing memory data. Notice that A7 is not used to indirectly address memory data. In its place we use SP. The stack pointer (A7) is used to indirectly address stack data. Notice that the last example in the table is an instruction that transfers data from one memory location to another.

### Indirect with Postincrement Addressing

Another form of indirect addressing is address register *indirect addressing* with *postincrement*. This form of addressing functions similarly to the address register indirect mode except that after the data have been transferred, the contents of the address register are automatically incremented. If the operation is a byte, it is incremented by a 1; a word operation causes an increment by 2; and a long-word operation causes an increment by 4. The reason that the address register is incremented by 1, 2, or 4 is that .B is a byte, .W is a word (2 bytes), and .L is a longword (4 bytes).

This addressing mode permits data stored in blocks or arrays to be manipulated by software. If the address is automatically incremented to the next datum in a block, it makes it easier for the programmer to access the next datum in an array. The indirect with postincrement form of addressing is invaluable when a program requires data to be accessed in an array.

Example 2-15 illustrates a MOVE instruction that causes byte data from register D6 to be transferred to the memory location addressed by address register A1. Suppose that A1 contains a $001000. The byte contents of D6 will be stored in memory location $001000. After it has been stored, the contents of A1 are incremented by a 1 to $001001. The plus sign, following the closing parenthesis sur-

**Table 2-5** Indirect Addressed Instructions

| Instruction | Description |
| --- | --- |
| MOVE.B (A2),D3 | Copies the byte of data from the memory location addressed by A2 into D3. |
| MOVE.W D2,(A3) | Copies the word contents of D2 into the memory beginning at the location addressed by A3. |
| MOVE.L A2,(SP) | Copies the long-word from A2 into the memory beginning at the location addressed by the SP (A7). |
| MOVE.B (A2),(A3) | Copies a byte of data from the memory location addressed by A2 into the memory location addressed by A3. |

rounding A1, causes the 680XX to automatically increment the contents of A1 by a one after the move. Refer to Figure 2-7 to see how this instruction (Example 2-15) accesses memory and then increments the address register.

E  X  A  M  P  L  E    2 - 15

Transfer the byte contents of D6 to the memory location addressed by A1 and then increment A1.

```
001000    12C6    MOVE.B    D6,(A1)+
```

Example 2-16 illustrates the same instruction, only this time notice that it is a long-word move. This means that after the transfer of all 32 bits of data in D6, the contents of A1 will be incremented by a 4. If A1 were a $001000, as in Example 2-14, it would change to a $001004 after execution of the instruction. Why does the long-word transfer cause the address register to be incremented by a 4? This happens because a long-word transfer stores 4 bytes of data in the memory. The next long-word–sized memory location is therefore 4 bytes ahead. When the address register is incremented by 4, the next long-word is accessible by the address register. This is why the address register is automatically incremented by a 4 for a long-word transfer.

E  X  A  M  P  L  E    2 - 16

Copy the long-word in D6 to the memory location addressed by A1 and then increment the contents of A1 by 4.

```
001000   22C6   MOVE.L   D6,(A1)+
```

Table 2-6 depicts some additional examples of addressing memory data using the postincrement form of indirect addressing. This form is most often used to sequentially address long lists or arrays of memory data.

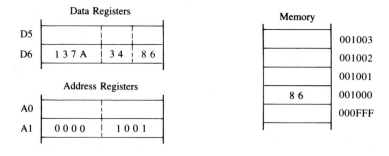

**Figure 2-7**    Notice that A1 is changed to $00001001 after the execution of the MOVE.B D6,(A1)+ instruction.

**Table 2-6   Examples of Postincrement Indirect Addressing**

| Instruction | Description |
|---|---|
| MOVE.B D2,(A6)+ | Copies the byte contents of D2 into the memory location addressed by A6 and then adds one to A6. |
| MOVE.W (A2)+,D3 | Copies the word contents of memory address by A2 into D3 and then adds 2 to A2. |
| MOVE.L A4,(SP)+ | Copies the long-word contents of A4 into the stack and then adds 4 to the SP. |
| MOVE.L (A2)+,(A3)+ | Copies the long-word contents of the memory addressed by A2 to the memory addressed by A3 and then adds 4 to both A2 and A3. |

## Indirect with Predecrement Addressing

Another method of indirectly addressing the memory is the indirect with *predecrement* mode. This form is similar to indirect with postincrement addressing except that the address register is decremented before a data transfer occurs.

Suppose that address register A4 contains a $00004000 and the word data are moved indirectly to memory through A4 from data register D2. (See Example 2-17.) First A4 is decremented by a 2. Then the data (D2) are moved to memory location $003FFE and $003FFF. If the move is a byte move, the address register is decremented by 1; if it is a long-word move, it is decremented by 4. Figure 2-8 shows how an address register is decremented before it is used to address memory data.

E  X  A  M  P  L  E      2 - 17

Choose an instruction that will copy the word contents of D2 into the memory location addressed by A4, but first decrement A4 by 2.

```
  001000     3902     MOVE.W     D2,-(A4)
```

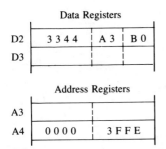
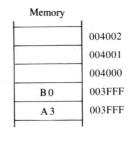

**Figure 2-8**   Notice how address register A4 points to the next lower word in memory after the MOVE.W D2,-(A4) instruction is executed. The A4 register initially addressed location $004000.

Table 2-7 illustrates some instructions that use the predecrement form of indirect memory addressing.

### Indirect with Displacement Addressing

At times memory data are addressed using an address register and a displacement. In the most common application of this addressing mode, the displacement is used to point to an element of an array of data. Suppose that you address the beginning of a byte array of data with address register A4. The first element of the array is addressed by A4, the second is at the location contained in A4 plus 1, the third is at A4 plus 2, and so on. The *displacement* is a distance. If you wish to address the second element, then the displacement is a 1. This is because the second element is at the location addressed by A4 plus 1.

Example 2-18 illustrates how the contents of the second element of the array addressed by A4 can be transferred into the byte portion of D3. Figure 2-9, which illustrates how the displacement is added to the contents of the address register before the memory data are accessed, uses the instruction presented in Example 2-18.

E  X  A  M  P  L  E    2 - 18

Address element 2 of the array pointed to by A4.
```
001000     162C0001    MOVE.B    1(A4),D3
```

Suppose that the A4 address register is still addressing the same array of data, but now you wish to copy the byte contents of D3 to array element 312. Example 2-19 illustrates how you can accomplish this operation.

E  X  A  M  P  L  E    2 - 19

Address element 312 of the array pointed to by A4.
```
001000     19430137    MOVE.B    D3,311(A4)
```

Table 2-7   Indirect Predecrement Instructions

| Instruction | Description |
|---|---|
| MOVE.B (A2)+,−(A3) | Subtracts 1 from A3, moves a byte of data from the memory location addressed by A2 to the location addressed by A3, and then adds 1 to A2. |
| MOVE.L #32,−(SP) | Subtracts 4 from SP and then places a 32 decimal into the long-word now addressed by SP. |
| MOVE.W D2,−(A6) | Decrements A6 by 2 and then copies the word contents of D2 into this new location in the memory. |

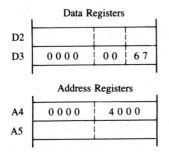
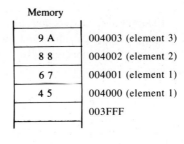

**Figure 2-9** Notice how the MOVE.B 1(A4),D3 instruction addresses the second element (location $004001) of the array beginning at location $004000.

The value of the displacement must range between +32,767 and -32,768. This means that the data may be placed above the memory location addressed by the address register or below it. Never may the data be farther away than ±32K if you wish to use this form of addressing.

When an array contains word elements, you must use a 2 for the second element, a 4 for the third, a 6 for the fourth, and so on. Likewise if the array contains long-words of data, you must use 4 as a multiplier. The displacement is always a count of bytes of memory, not words or long-words. So the displacement must also be expressed as bytes rather than words or long-words. See Table 2-8 for some additional examples of indirect with displacement addressing.

### Indirect with Indexing

The last form of address register indirect addressing is called *indirect with index*. This form uses the sum of an 8-bit displacement, an address register, and the contents of any word or long-word address or data register to develop the address of the data. Suppose that you point to a memory array with the address that you store in A2. You can access a byte element in that array by placing the element number in another register such as D2. Using this form of addressing will add the contents of A2 to D2 plus the displacement to form the address of the data.

**Table 2-8** Examples of Indirect with Displacement Addressing

| Instruction | Description |
|---|---|
| MOVE.B 450(A2),(A3) | Copies the byte contents of the memory location addressed by A2 plus 450 decimal to the location addressed by A3. |
| MOVE.W $30(A1),D2 | Copies the word contents of the memory location addressed by A1 plus 30 hexadecimal to D2. |
| MOVE.L D1,$1000(A6) | Copies the long-word from D1 to the memory location addressed by A6 plus 1000 hexadecimal. |
| MOVE.B -12(A2),D1 | Copies the byte from the memory location addressed by A6 minus 12 decimal into D1. |

Example 2-20 shows how this instruction is formed to load the byte portion of D3 with the data from the memory location addressed by the sum of A2 plus D2. Notice that the displacement listed is a zero. The displacement must be present for this form of addressing in most assemblers. In this case, because the displacement is zero, a zero must be typed. This is not true for indirect with displacement addressing, if the displacement is not required. Example 2-20 is graphically illustrated in Figure 2-10. Notice how the address register and the data registers are added before memory data are addressed.

E  X  A  M  P  L  E      2 - 20

Form an instruction that will access the memory location addressed by the sum of A2 plus D2 and place the byte transferred from that location into the D3 register.
```
001000   16322800   MOVE.B   0(A2,D2,L),D3
```

Notice that the data register specified in Example 2-20 has a .L following it. This is done because the 680XX allows you to choose either a word index register or a long-word index register. If the word form is chosen, the 680XX will sign-extend it into a 32-bit number before adding it to the address register to form the memory access address. The long-word form is already a 32-bit number, so no sign extension is required.

Suppose that D5 contains a $00008000 and A4 contains a $00010000. If the instruction illustrated in Example 2-21 is executed, the byte contents of D0 are stored in memory location $008000. How is this possible? The value of D5 is sign-extended before it is added to A4 to generate the memory access address. If an $8000 is sign-extended, the 32-bit result is $FFFF8000. When $FFFF8000 is added to $00010000, the address used is $008000.

E  X  A  M  P  L  E      2 - 21

Access address $008000 using indexed addressing.
```
001000   19805000   MOVE.B   D0,0(A4,D5,W)
```

Table 2-9 illustrates some other possible instructions that use the indirect with index form of addressing the memory data. Notice that some contain a displacement and some do not. Some assemblers require that a displacement be present even if it is a zero.

## Program Counter Addressing

The final form of addressing memory data is *program counter addressing,* often called *relative addressing* because the data are relative to the program's location in the memory. This is because the program counter, which always points to the next

Data Registers

| D2 | 0 0 0 0 | 0 0 | 0 3 |
| D3 | 1 2 3 4 | 5 6 | 7 8 |

Address Registers

| A2 | 0 0 0 1 | 0 0 0 0 |
| A3 | | |

Memory

| 3 D | 010004 |
| 7 8 | 010003 |
| A A | 010002 |
| 1 8 | 010001 |
| 4 4 | 010000 |

**Figure 2-10** The MOVE.B 0(A2,D2.L),D3 instruction addresses memory location $010003 in this example because the $010000 in A2 is added to the $000003 in D2.

instruction in the program, is used to address the memory data. Relative addressing is most often used when *relocatable* modules of software are written. Because the data are relative to the position of the program, the program can be moved to any place in the memory and still function correctly without changing any address. This ability to move or relocate a program is important when software packages are written for general use by many programs. In many cases subroutines that are common to many programs are written with relocatable code such as program counter addressing.

In the 680XX microprocessor, relative addressing is available in two forms: program counter addressing with a displacement and program counter with an index. Some assembler programs require that the address be followed by (PC), as illustrated in row 1 of Example 2-22, whereas some assemblers require just the label DATA because the label DATA is defined as relocatable (see row 2, Example 2-22). Yet another form for this type of addressing appears in row 3 of Example 2-22. Here the asterisk is used to tell the assembler that program counter addressing is to be used with, in this example, a displacement of +$30. Refer to your assembly language programming manual for the precise form used with your assembler.

**Table 2-9** Examples of Indirect with Index Addressing

| Instruction | Description |
| --- | --- |
| MOVE.B D1,2(A1,A2.W) | Copies the byte contents of D1 to the memory location addressed by the sum of A1 plus a sign-extended A2 plus a displacement of 2. |
| MOVE.B 2(A1,D2.L),D3 | Copies the byte contents of the memory location addressed by the sum of A1 plus D2 plus 2 to register D3. |
| MOVE.L (A1)+,0(A2,A3.L) | Copies the long-word addressed by A1 into the memory areas addressed by the sum of A2 plus A3. After the transfer, adds 4 to A1. |

NOTE: Even though a displacement is not desired, see the last entry: a zero must be included in most assemblers.

Figure 2-11 illustrates program counter addressing using a displacement of $30 as shown in row 3 of Example 2-22.

E  X  A  M  P  L  E     2 - 22

Write an instruction that will store the byte in D2 at the relative address DATA.

```
001000    143A000E    MOVE.B    DATA(PC),D2
001000    143A000E    MOVE.B    DATA,D2
001000    143A0030    MOVE.B    *+$30,D2
```

Notice from Figure 2-11 that the program counter consists of the address of the second word of the instruction. Here the program counter contents of $1002 are added to the displacement of $0030 to form memory address $1032.

The other version of addressing data with the program counter uses an index register and an 8-bit displacement. The index register can be any register (D0–D7, A0–A6, or SP). Example 2-23 illustrates a few cases of this form of addressing memory data. As with Example 2-22, three common forms for program counter addressing with index are shown. For the exact form used by the assembler in your possession, review the literature that came with your assembler.

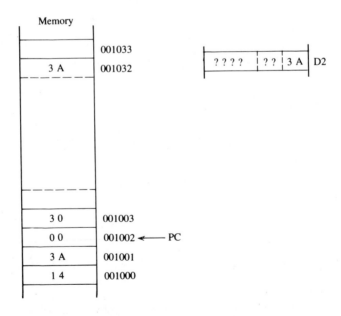

**Figure 2-11**   **The MOVE.B *+$30,D2 instruction uses a displacement of $0030 that is added to the contents of the program counter to address memory location $001032 in this example. Note that the program counter always contains the address of the second word of the instruction for this form of addressing.**

Examples using program counter with index addressing.

```
001000   163B2005   MOVE.B   5(PC),D2.W),D3
001004   163B2000   MOVE.B   (A3.L),D3
001008   11C00000   MOVE.B   *+$30(A3,W),D3
```

## 2-2 Machine Language Programming

Before instructions can be coded in machine language, the use of Appendix B must be discussed, as well as the format that machine language instructions can take in the 680XX microprocessor. *Machine language* is the language the microprocessor understands; it is in binary, but usually it is written as hexadecimal.

### 2-2.1 What Is Machine Language?

Machine language is the language that is *native* to the microprocessor. Just as we might view English as our main conversational language, the microprocessor views machine language as its main conversational language. The difference is that the microprocessor is procedure oriented rather than conversation oriented, like humans. For a microprocessor this native language takes the form of binary numbers that represent operation codes (*opcodes*) to the microprocessor. In the 680XX microprocessor these opcodes are 16 bits in width and are sometimes followed by other data or addresses for certain instructions and addressing modes. Appendix B illustrates all the instructions of the 68000 microprocessor and includes the machine language opcode and form for each.

### The Opcode

Figure 2-12 illustrates the opcode for a MOVE instruction. Notice that only the first two binary bits of this instruction are defined. The remaining bits are divided into three distinct fields of information: size, destination, and source. The *size field* specifies the size of the data transfer in bytes, words, or long-words. The *destina-*

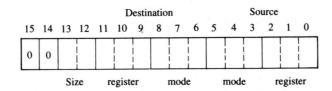

**Figure 2-12** **The opcode portion of the MOVE instruction. Note that this instruction contains a size field, a destination field, and a source field. Both the destination and source fields contain a register field and a mode field.**

*tion field* specifies the location to which the data are to be moved with the MOVE instruction. The *source field* specifies the location from which the data are to be moved with the MOVE instruction.

## Size Field

Notice that the size of the data is specified with a 2-bit binary number for most instructions. With most instructions that include a size field, these two bits are 01 for byte, 11 for word, and 10 for long-word operations. Table 2-10 lists these pairs of bits for later reference. If a choice of a word or a long-word only occurs, as with some of the instructions that use address registers only, a 1-bit field specifies word (0) or long-word (1).

## Destination/Source Field

The destination and source fields are broken into two parts: register and mode. The *register field* indicates which register, if any, is used, for the destination or source. Table 2-11 lists the registers and the numbers used with each field. There are actually two sets of registers listed—the address register set and the data register set—because some instructions use address registers and some use data registers for destinations or sources.

The *mode field* specifies how the data of the destination or source are addressed by the instruction. The various bit patterns for this 3-bit field and their meanings, along with the register bit field, are represented in Table 2-12. Notice that the register field does not always indicate one of the registers. It at times indicates a difference in the way that memory data are addressed.

By inspection of this table, it becomes clear how to encode most of the MOVE instructions except those that use an index register as the addressing mode. For example, the d8(A2,D2.W) mode of addressing memory data is unclear from Table 2-12. Here the first word is the opcode, and it specifies the register number of the address register A2 in the register field. The byte of memory following the opcode specifies the index register. The first four bits represent the index number: 0–7 for D0–D7 and 8–F for A0–SP. The next bit selects long-word (1) or word (0) forms for the index register. The 8-bit displacement for the instruction is stored in the fourth byte. Refer to Example 2-24 for a MOVE instruction and its equivalent using this addressing mode.

E  X  A  M  P  L  E     2 - 24

Example MOVE instruction illustrating a displacement.
```
      001000   14321008   MOVE.B   8(A2,D1.W),D2
```

```
                      dest        source
                ss  reg      mode  mode reg
Word one: 00 01 010     000   110   010   ($1432)
                reg  L         disp  (8-bit)
Word two:     0   001  0 000   0000  1000   ($1008)
```

**Table 2-10   The Size Field of an Opcode**

| Bits | Function  |
|------|-----------|
| 00   | not used  |
| 01   | byte      |
| 10   | long-word |
| 11   | word      |

Notice from Example 2-24 that the first word is the opcode and, with this instruction, the second word contains the displacement and an extension to the opcode. The size is a byte because ss = 01; the destination is a data register because the mode of the destination field mode contains a 000. The destination register is a 010 or D2. The source mode is 110, which indicates index addressing via an address register. Here the address register is A2 because the register field contains a 010. The next byte or the extension to the opcode contains the register number used as the index register and also a bit that indicates word or long-word form for this register. The L bit is a one for long-word form and a zero for word form. The fourth byte of the instruction contains the 8-bit displacement of 8 in this example.

Appendix A illustrates all these instructions, along with the addressing modes that are allowed for each one. It also shows the changes that occur in the CCR for each of these instructions. In perusing this appendix, you will notice that not all the instructions allow the same addressing modes for the source and destination. You must be careful to follow this appendix and observe the allowed addressing modes when writing software. Of course the assembler program will indicate any invalid addressing modes that you choose, but it is important to familiarize yourself with what is allowed before you write a program. If you are writing programs using machine language, it is very important to learn the binary bit patterns as described in Tables 2-11 and 2-12, because you will be referencing this material as you code each of the instructions in your program. Let us hope that you have an assembler

**Table 2-11   Register Field Bit Patterns**

| Bits | Address register | Data register |
|------|------------------|---------------|
| 000  | A0               | D0            |
| 001  | A1               | D1            |
| 010  | A2               | D2            |
| 011  | A3               | D3            |
| 100  | A4               | D4            |
| 101  | A5               | D5            |
| 110  | A6               | D6            |
| 111  | SP               | D7            |

NOTE: A7 is called the SP (stack pointer). This can be either the SSP or the USP depending on the mode of operation that is selected.

**Table 2-12**   The Mode and Register Fields Together

| Type | Form | Mode | Register |
|---|---|---|---|
| Data register | Dn | 000 | Data register number |
| Address register | An | 001 | Address register number |
| Address register indirect | (An) | 010 | Address register number |
| Address register indirect with postincrement | (An)+ | 011 | Address register number |
| Address register indirect with predecrement | −(An) | 100 | Address register number |
| Address register indirect with displacement | d16(An) | 101 | Address register number |
| Address register indirect with index | d8(An,Xn) | 110 | Address register number |
| Absolute short | XXX.W | 111 | 000 |
| Absolute long | XXX.L | 111 | 001 |
| Program counter with displacement | d16(PC) | 111 | 010 |
| Program counter with index | d8(PC,Xn) | 111 | 011 |
| Immediate | #XXX | 111 | 100 |

NOTE: With index addressing, the next word of memory contains both the 8-bit displacement and the Xn register number.

available to write programs. Machine language programming for a microprocessor as complex as the 68000 takes a tremendous amount of time and is error prone.

Appendix A shows that most instructions allow just about any addressing mode for the source operand, but not for the destination operand. In general, the destination operand cannot be immediate, nor can it use any of the program counter addressing modes. Program counter addressing is restrictive because it does not allow relative addressing for the destination.

### 2-2.2   Direct Addressed MOVE Instructions

To become proficient with machine language coding and the use of Appendices A and B, it is important to attempt a few examples of converting instructions into machine code. This portion of the text shows how to convert direct addressed instructions into machine language via a few examples.

Example 2-25 shows how to convert a simple instruction that addresses data registers directly into machine language. Notice that this instruction is one word in length because no other words are required for other information.

E  X  A  M  P  L  E     2 - 25

Example showing direct addressing.
```
001000   3602   MOVE.W   D2,D3
```

*MOVE.B  D1, -(SP)*  *same as  Push.B  D1*
*MOVE.W  D1, -(SP)*
*MOVE.B*
*MOVE.B  (SP)+, D1 → POP*

```
          dest    source
       ss reg  mode mode reg
Word one: 00 11 011 000  000  010 ($3602)
```

### 2-2.3  Indirect Addressed Instructions

Although the indirect mode is very similar to direct addressing, there can be complications. Example 2-26 illustrates the direct mode mixed with the indirect mode for a MOVE instruction, and Example 2-27 uses the indirect mode for postincrement and predecrement addressing.

**E X A M P L E    2 - 26**

Example illustrating postincrement addressing.
```
001000   241C   MOVE.L   (A4)+,D2
```

```
          dest    source
       ss reg  mode mode reg
Word one: 00 10 010 000  011  100 ($241C)
```

**E X A M P L E    2 - 27**

Example illustrating both postincrement and predecrement addressing.
```
001000   251B   MOVE.L   (A3)+,-(A2)
```
← *like stack*

```
          dest    source
       ss reg  mode mode reg
Word one: 00 10 010 100  011  011 ($251B)
```

### 2-2.4  Absolute Addressed Instructions

With absolute memory addressing, words are added to the instruction to hold the address referenced by the instruction. The number of words added depends on the instruction and the addressing modes used by the instruction. Examples 2-28 and 2-29 illustrate how absolute addressing is added to the instruction and how the machine language instruction is formed.

In Example 2-28 the instruction is two words long. The first word contains the opcode and the second word contains the short address $2000. This is a short address because it refers to a memory location within the first 32K bytes of the memory system.

**E X A M P L E    2 - 28**

Example illustrating the placement of a short absolute memory address.
```
001000   11C22000   MOVE.B   D2,$2000
```

                        dest      source
              ss  reg  mode  mode  reg
Word one: 00 01 000  111    000    010  ($11C2)

                  short address
Word two: 0010 0000 0000 0000        ($2000)

---

Example 2-29 illustrates a MOVE instruction that takes the contents of one location in the memory and transfers it to another. The addresses chosen are such that both are long memory addresses to illustrate that instructions in the 680XX can become rather lengthy. Notice that this instruction takes five words and that the source address follows the opcode.

E  X  A  M  P  L  E    2 - 9

---

Example illustrating the use of an absolute address for both the source and destination.

        001000       13F90003000000040000          MOVE.B      $300

                        dest      source
              ss  reg  mode  mode  reg
Word one: 00 01 001  111    111    001  ($13F9)

                  source long address
Word two:   0000 0000 0000 0011      ($0003)
                                                      ($00030000)
Word three: 0000 0000 0000 0000      ($0000)

                  destination long address
Word four:  0000 0000 0000 0100      ($0004)
                                                      ($00040000)
Word five:  0000 0000 0000 0000      ($0000)

---

## 2-2.5  Immediate Addressed Instructions

With immediate data, the data always follow the opcode in the memory system, as illustrated in the instruction of Example 2-30, where an immediate 100 decimal is moved into memory location $10000. This is a long instruction because the data requires a word of memory and the address requires two words.

E  X  A  M  P  L  E    2 - 30

---

Write an instruction that moves a 100 decimal into memory location $10000.
        001000       13FC006400010000        MOVE.B    #100,$10000

                        dest      source
              ss  reg  mode  mode  reg
Word one: 00 10 001  111    111    100  ($13FC)

                    immediate data
Word two:  0000 0000 0110 0100      ($0064)
                    long address
Word three: 0000 0000 0000 0001     ($0001)
                                               ($00010000)

Word four:  0000 0000 0000 0000     ($0000)

## 2-3  Other Data Transfer Instructions

The MOVE instruction comprises a great percentage of the data transfer instructions, but not all of them. This section details the operation of the remaining data transfer instructions, including a few MOVE instructions not presented before. Some of these instructions are optional if an assembler is used, but required for machine language programming.

### 2-3.1  The MOVEA Instruction

The MOVEA instruction is important to machine language programmers, but not to assembly language programmers. In most assembly language programs, the MOVE instruction is automatically converted to a MOVEA if it is warranted. The MOVEA instruction is used in machine language whenever the destination register is an address register. Appendix B lists the MOVEA instruction if you are writing your programs in machine language or if you are translating from machine language. MOVEA does not appear in Appendix A because this appendix is most often referenced by assembly language programmers, who don't normally use the MOVEA opcode.

Example 2-31 illustrates how the MOVEA.W #$2000,A2 instruction is converted to machine language. Note that the MOVEA instruction may have only a .W or .L extension to its opcode because address registers are never a byte wide. If the .W or word extension is used, the data moved into an address register are sign-extended as mentioned before.

E  X  A  M  P  L  E    2 - 31

Choose an instruction that will place a #2000 into the A2 register.
       001000   347C2000   MOVEA.W   #$2000,A2

                    dest     source
                 ss reg  mode mode reg
Word one: 00 11 010 001    111   100 ($347C)

                    immediate data
Word two: 0010 0000 0000 0000      ($2000)

## 2-3.2   The Move Quick Instruction (MOVEQ)

The move quick instruction (MOVEQ) is not normally found in assembly language because the assembler automatically uses it if a MOVE immediate instruction fits this form. The MOVEQ instruction is used to load small immediate numbers into a long-word–sized data register. It is called a quick move because it loads a 32-bit data register with a sign-extended 8-bit number using a single 2-byte instruction.

Suppose that you need to place a 1 into the 32-bit D2 register. This is accomplished in two ways: with a MOVEQ instruction or with a MOVE instruction. The difference (refer to Example 2-32) is that the MOVEQ instruction requires a single word of memory to store and the MOVE requires three.

E  X  A  M  P  L  E    2 - 32

---

Load D2 with a 32-bit number 1.

**(a)**
```
      001000   243C00000001   MOVE.L   #1,D2
```

```
                        dest     source
                  ss  reg  mode  mode reg
Word one:   00  10  010  000   111  100  ($243C)

Word two:   0000 0000 0000 0000      ($0000)
                                              ($00000001)
Word three: 0000 0000 0000 0001      ($0001)
```

**(b)**
```
      001000   7401   MOVEQ.L   #1,D2
```

```
                  reg  L  data
Word one:  0111 010 0 00000001      ($7401)
```

NOTE: MOVE.L is used for MOVEQ in the assembler.

---

## 2-3.3   The MOVEM Instruction

The MOVEM instruction is a very powerful instruction because it allows you to move multiple registers to or from the memory. If you want to save all the address and data registers or any combination of them with one instruction, MOVEM will accomplish this for you.

In machine language the MOVEM instruction is always a two-word instruction, with the first word containing the opcode and the second word containing the register mask. The register mask indicates to the MOVEM instruction which registers are to be transferred to or from the memory. The MOVEM instruction allows words or long-words to be transferred between the registers and the memory system.

The MOVEM instruction does not allow all the memory addressing modes for its operation. Refer to Appendix A for a description of which addressing modes are allowed with this instruction and Appendix B for the machine language coding of this instruction.

Figure 2-13 illustrates the bit pattern for the MOVEM instruction. Notice that the opcode contains a D and S field in addition to the mode and register field. The D bit is used to indicate the direction of the transfer (0 = register to memory and 1 = memory to register), and the S bit indicates the size of the transfer (0 = word and 1 = long-word). The second word appears as shown in Figure 2-31, depending on the type of transfer selected: one register list is used for predecrement and the other for postincrement addressing.

Example 2-33 illustrates an instruction that allows the contents of D2, D4–D6, and A0–A5 to be stored in the memory. The / is used to separate different groups of instructions that are to be transferred, and the - indicates ranges of registers to be stored in assembly language form. In this example long-words are stored in the memory at the location addressed by the stack pointer using the predecrement form of addressing. Using this mode of addressing effectively pushes the contents of these registers onto the stack. This is probably one of the more common forms of the MOVEM instruction when registers are to be stored in the memory temporarily.

E  X  A  M  P  L  E     2 - 33

Write an instruction that will store D2, D4, D5, D6, A0, A1, A2, A3, A4, and A5 into the memory location addressed by the stack pointer, using the predecrement mode of addressing.    *like a stack*

```
001000   48E72EFC   MOVEM.L   D2/D4-D6/A0-A5,-(SP)
```

```
                    D     S mode reg
Word one: 01001 0  001 1 100   111   ($48E7)

Word two: 0010 1110 1111 1100         ($2EFC)
```

Later in a program the contents of the register placed on the stack are normally removed from the stack and returned to the same registers. This is accomplished via the MOVEM instruction of Example 2-34. Here stack data are removed from the stack using the postincrement mode of addressing the stack with the stack pointer.

E  X  A  M  P  L  E     2 - 34

Restore the registers stored in Example 2-33.

```
001000   4CDF3F74   MOVEM.L   (SP)+,D2/D4-D6/A0-A5
```

```
                    D     S mode reg
Word one: 01001 1  001 1 011   111   ($4CDF)

Word two: 0011 1111 0111 0100         ($3F74)
```

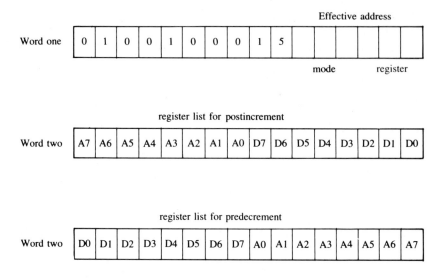

**Figure 2-13   The machine language bit pattern of the MOVEM instruction. Note that there are two versions of the second word of this instruction.**

### 2-3.4   Load Effective Address Instruction (LEA)

The LEA (load effective address) instruction is used to place a memory address into any address register. The MOVE instruction is also used to MOVE data or addresses into a register. Why would you ever want to move an address into an address register? Address registers are usually used to address memory data, and the most common way of loading an address into an address register is with either the MOVE immediate instruction or the LEA instruction. LEA is the first instruction presented that does not use an extension to the opcode because it is a long-word operation only.

Suppose that you are required to load address register A4 with memory address $10000. This is accomplished with either the LEA instruction or with the MOVE instruction. Often a MOVE immediate will accomplish the same thing that the LEA instruction accomplishes.

Example 2-35 illustrates both the LEA instruction and the MOVE instruction (assembled as MOVEA) with immediate data specified. These instructions look fairly similar. They are both the same length. So what is the difference? The LEA instruction calculates the effective address as the program executes, and the MOVE instruction's effective address is calculated as the assembler forms the machine language instruction. Both function as illustrated, but the MOVE instruction executes slightly faster. The MOVE instruction is often preferred over the LEA instruction unless you are writing relocatable software. This type of software is discussed in greater detail later in the text.

EXAMPLE 2 - 35

This example illustrates how to load address $1000 into address register A4.

**(a)**
```
001000   11F810002000   MOVE.B   $1000,$2000
```

              dest      source
           ss  reg     mode reg
Word one:  00  10 100  001  111  100   ($287C)

Word two:  0000 0000 0000 0001       ($0001)

                                           ($00010000)

Word three: 0000 0000 0000 0000      ($0000)

```
001006   49F900010000   LEA   $10000,A4
```

              dest      source
              reg      mode reg
Word one:  0100 100 111  111   001   ($49F9)

Word two:  0000 0000 0000 0001       ($0001)

                                           ($00010000)

Word three: 0000 0000 0000 0000      ($0000)

Suppose that you must write a short program that copies the byte contents of memory location $1000 to location $2000. This is accomplished in many different ways, as illustrated in Example 2-36. The first way uses one instruction with two short addresses to accomplish the data transfer. The second method uses three instructions to accomplish the same task. Notice that the first two instructions load A1 and A2 with the source and destination addresses $1000 and $2000. The third instruction moves the data from the location addressed by A1 to the location addressed by A2.

EXAMPLE 2 - 36

Copy the byte contents of memory location $1000 to memory location $2000.

**(a)**
```
001000   11F810002000   MOVE.B   $1000,$2000
```

**(b)**
```
001006   227C00001000   MOVE.L   #$1000,A1
00100C   247C00002000   MOVE.L   #$2000,A2
001012   1491           MOVE.B   (A1),(A2)
```

### 2-3.5   Exchange Instructions

The 680XX microprocessor has two exchange instructions. One exchanges the contents of any two 32-bit registers, and the other exchanges the word halves of any data register.

### The EXG Instruction

The EXG (exchange) instruction allows the programmer to exchange the contents of any two registers. These registers include any two data or address registers or any combination of data and address registers. Example 2-37 depicts an instruction that allows the contents of the D2 register to be exchanged with the contents of the A3 register. Notice that the instruction does not include an opcode extension to indicate byte, word, or long-word. This instruction is a long-word–only instruction that always exchanges all 32 bits of the registers.

**E  X  A  M  P  L  E     2 - 37**

---

Exchange D2 with A3.
```
001000   C58B   EXG   D2,A3
```

---

### The SWAP Instruction

The other type of exchange instruction is called SWAP. The SWAP instruction exchanges (swaps) the most and least significant words of any data register. For example, suppose that D2 contains a $20001000. If the SWAP D2 instruction is executed, D2 will contain a $10002000 after execution. Example 2-38 illustrates the assembly language form for the SWAP instruction. Again notice that no opcode extension is present because this instruction is of a fixed size.

**E  X  A  M  P  L  E     2 - 38**

---

Select the instruction that exchanges the most and least significant halves of D2.
```
001000   4842   SWAP   D2
```

---

### 2-3.6   Other Data Transfer Instructions

There are a few additional data transfer instructions that will be covered in later chapters where they apply; examples include MOVEP, MOVE to or from SR, MOVE to or from CCR, and MOVE to or from USP. Many of these instructions are used only for special purposes and a discussion at this point would prove futile. In addition, the 68020, 68030, and 68040 have additional data transfer instructions that are explained in Chapters 12 and 13, in connection with these more advanced microprocessors.

# Summary

1. The MOVE instruction transfers a byte (8 bits), word (16 bits), or long-word (32 bits) of data from a source operand to a destination operand. The type of move is specified with an extension to the opcode of .B (byte), .W (word), or .L (long-word).

2. The immediate addressing mode is used to load registers or memory with constants. This mode is designated with the # symbol followed by either a decimal or hexadecimal value, or a label in some cases. If the value is hexadecimal it must begin with a $. For example, $FF is FF hexadecimal. If the value is decimal, no $ is used.

3. Direct addressing is used to specify that a data register (D0–D7) or an address register (A0–A6 or SP) is either the source or destination operand. Data registers may be byte, word, or long-word, while address registers may be word or long-word only.

4. If a word is moved into an address register, the word is automatically sign-extended into the entire 32 bits of the address register. Because the numbers $0000–$7FFF are positive, the most significant word of the result is a $0000, and because the numbers $8000–$FFFF are negative, the most significant word of the result is $FFFF. This conforms to short absolute addressing, where the top and bottom 32K bytes of memory are accessible by a short (word) address.

5. Absolute memory addressing uses either a word or long-word memory address as an operand. With absolute memory addressing the data in memory or from memory are operated on by the instruction. Word absolute addresses allow the program to access memory locations $000000–$007FFF and $FF8000–$FFFFFF. This is sometimes called a scratchpad memory. The long-word absolute address allows access to any memory location in the system.

6. Address register indirect addressing uses an address register to point to a memory location that will be used with the instruction. For example, if A3 contains a $00001000 and the MOVE.B (A3),D1 instruction is executed, the byte contents of memory location $001000 are moved into register D1.

7. Indirect with postincrement addressing is used much like address register indirect addressing except that the address register is incremented after the instruction has been executed. A byte operation increments it by 1, a word operation by 2, and a long-word operation by 4.

8. Indirect with predecrement addressing is used in much the same way as address register indirect except that the address register is first decremented.

9. Indirect with displacement addressing is used whenever the address register is used to address an array of data and the exact array element number required is known. The displacement is the element number in bytes as long as the value doesn't exceed ±32K.

10. Indirect with index addressing allows the contents of an address register to be added to the contents of any other address register or data register to form the memory address of the data. This is useful if the address register contains the array address and the other register contains the element number. This form of addressing uses an 8-bit displacement.

11. Program counter addressing allows the data to be organized so that it is within a short distance of the program. Since the data are referenced through the address contained in the program counter, the entire program can be moved without changing the relative position of the data. This makes this type of software relocatable.

12. Machine language is the actual hexadecimal code that the microprocessor understands as instructions. We tend to more easily understand symbolic machine language instructions such as MOVE, while the machine understands hexadecimal values for these instructions.

13. The MOVEA instruction is used whenever data are moved into an address register; it does not often appear in programs because the assembler automatically converts a MOVE into a MOVEA if required.

14. The MOVEQ instruction, a special form of the MOVE immediate instruction, allows numbers up to 8 bits in width to be loaded into data registers with a single word instruction.

15. The EXG instruction allows the contents of any two registers (address or data) to be exchanged.

16. The SWAP instruction allows the two word halves of any data register to be exchanged.

17. The LEA (load effective address) instruction allows the operand to be loaded into any address register rather than having the operand address contents loaded as with a MOVE instruction.

18. The MOVEM instruction allows words or long-words of data to be transferred between memory and a register or registers. The registers transferred are specified by a register list. The - is used to specify a range of registers and the / to separate registers. The MOVEM.L D2/D4-D7,- (SP) instruction will move D2, D4, D5, D6, and D7 to the memory location addressed by the stack pointer. Note that this instruction uses the predecrement form of addressing the stack.

## Questions

1. The MOVE instruction copies data from the _____ operand to the _____ operand.

2. Explain the difference between the MOVE.B instruction and the MOVE.L instruction.

3. If one of the operands in a MOVE instruction contains a #, what type of operand is it?

4. Form symbolic MOVE instructions that will accomplish the following.
   (a) move a $FF into the byte portion of register D3
   (b) move a $88FF into the word portion of register A6
   (c) move a $56780000 into the long-word register D1
   (d) move a 300 decimal into the long-word register D0

5. Choose symbolic MOVE instructions to accomplish the following.
   (a) move the byte contents of D2 into D5
   (b) move the word contents of A3 into D4
   (c) move the long-word contents of D3 into D1

6. If D3 contains a $00008000 and a MOVE.W D3,A1 instruction is executed, what are the contents of A1 after execution?

7. Form symbolic MOVE instructions to perform the following tasks.
   (a) move the byte portion of D2 to memory location $2000
   (b) move the word contents of memory location $30000 into A4
   (c) move the long-word contents of memory location $3 into A2
   (d) move the long-word contents of the SP into memory location $12000
   (e) move the byte contents of memory location $3000 into memory location $2000

8. What portion of the memory is addressable by a short absolute memory address?

9. What portion of the memory is addressable by a long absolute memory address?

10. Sign-extend the following word addresses into 24-bit addresses for the 68000 microprocessor.
    (a) $2003    (b) $7AAA    (c) $8001    (d) $B333

11. What is the difference between a MOVE.B $8000,D1 instruction and a MOVE.B $008000,D1 instruction?

12. If parentheses surround an address register number, what type of memory addressing is indicated?

13. Select symbolic MOVE instructions that will perform the following tasks.
    (a) move the byte contents of the memory location addressed by address register A3 into the D2 register.
    (b) move the word contents of D4 into the memory location addressed by the SP.
    (c) move the long-word contents of the memory location addressed by A2 into the memory location addressed by A3.
    (d) move the byte contents of the memory location addressed by A3 into memory location $400F2.
    (e) move a $33 into the word memory location addressed by A6.

14. If a MOVE.L (A4)+,D2 instruction is executed, a _____ is added to A4 after the move operation.

15. Indicate what the following instructions accomplish.
    (a) MOVE.B #66,(A2)+
    (b) MOVE.W (A2)+,(A3)
    (c) MOVE.L (A1)+,(A2)+
    (d) MOVE.W $3000,(A2)+
    (e) MOVE.L (SP)+,D1

16. If a MOVE.W D2,−(A4) instruction is executed, _____ is subtracted from A4 before the MOVE operation.

17. Indicate what the following instructions accomplish.
    (a) MOVE.B −(A6),D2
    (b) MOVE.W −(A6),−(A5)
    (c) MOVE.L −(A4),(A3)+
    (d) MOVE.W #$88,−(SP)
    (e) MOVE.L $40000,−(A0)

18. Indicate what the following instructions accomplish.
    (a) MOVE.B 3(A3),D1
    (b) MOVE.L $4000(A3),(A4)+
    (c) MOVE.W $30000,$30(A2)
    (d) MOVE.L 3(A1),4(A1)

19. If A4 = $00003000 and a MOVE.L $8000(A4),D2 instruction is executed, what memory location is accessed?

20. If D2 = $00010000 and A2 = $00020000, what memory location is accessed by the MOVE.B (A2,D2.L),D5 instruction?

21. Why are programs written using program counter addressing considered relocatable?

22. When program counter addressing is used, the displacement contains the distance that the operand lies from the next instructions address.   (*true* or *false*)

23. Write a short program that will place a 3 into D1, a 2 into D2, and a 5 into D3. Assume that these are all long-word registers.

24. Write a program that will use indirect addressing to move the contents of memory locations $3000–$3004 to $4000–$4004.

25. Convert the following instructions into hexadecimal machine language.
    (a) MOVE.B D2,D3
    (b) MOVE.W D4,D5
    (c) MOVE.L D7,D0
    (d) MOVE.B D2,D7
    (e) MOVE.L D7,D6

26. Convert the following instructions into hexadecimal machine language.
    (a) MOVE.B #33,D2
    (b) MOVE.W #$3000,D4
    (c) MOVE.L #$2000,D0

27. Convert the following instructions into hexadecimal machine language.
    (a) MOVE.B (A1),$3000
    (b) MOVE.L $40000,$50000
    (c) MOVE.W #$1000,$34567
    (d) MOVE.L −(A3),(A5)+
    (e) MOVE.W 34(A3),$4000

28. What is the purpose of a MOVEA instruction?

29. What does the MOVEQ instruction accomplish?

30. Which registers are stored in memory with the MOVEM.L A2-A4,- (SP) instruction?

31. Form symbolic instructions that will do the following.
    (a) store the word contents of all the data registers in memory beginning at location $30000.
    (b) read all the long-word address registers from memory beginning at location $20000.
    (c) store the long-word D1, D3, D4, D5, and A6 registers into the memory location addressed by A3 using the predecrement mode of addressing.
    (d) load all the word registers beginning at memory location $30000.

32. Select an instruction that will exchange the long-word contents of D2 with D3.

33. Choose an instruction that will swap the most significant word of D3 with its least significant word.

34. Write an instruction that will load the A3 register with memory location $30000.

# 3

# *Arithmetic and Logic Instructions*

## OBJECTIVES

Upon completion of this chapter, you will be able to:

- Explain how the arithmetic instructions function and how they affect the condition code register.

- Write short programs that use arithmetic operations.

- Explain how each of the logic instructions functions, including the shift and rotate commands.

- Write short programs that use the arithmetic and logic operations.

- Explain the operation of the BCD addition, subtraction, and negation instructions.

- Detail the operation of multiplication and division and show how they are used in programs.

- Describe the operation of the binary bit manipulation instructions.

- Explain how CCR bits can be set, cleared, and complemented.

## KEY TERMS

| | | |
|---|---|---|
| effective address | inclusive or logically | logic inversion, one's- |
| signed | add | complement |
| unsigned | set | clear |
| underflow | comparator | compare |
| borrow | complement, invert | read/write/modify |
| two's-complement | | |
| negate | | |

THE 680XX microprocessor accomplishes a fairly wide range of arithmetic operations on byte-, word-, or long-word-sized data. The arithmetic operations include addition, subtraction, multiplication, and division. The basic logic functions are AND, OR, invert, and exclusive-OR. In addition to these basic logic functions, the 680XX can shift and rotate data.

The ability to accomplish binary bit manipulation allows the 680XX to set, clear, invert, or test any bit position of any data register or byte-sized memory location. This chapter explains the operation of each arithmetic and logic instruction. It also presents some simple examples of their usage.

## 3-1 Addition and Subtraction

We begin by detailing the operation of the binary and BCD (binary-coded decimal) addition, subtraction, and negation instructions. Binary addition and subtraction can be accomplished on a byte, word, or long-word. BCD addition and subtraction are functional only with packed bytes of BCD data (refer to Chapter 1 for packed BCD data). The binary and BCD negation instructions are used to change the arithmetic sign (two's complement) of signed binary data or signed BCD data (ten's complement).

### 3-1.1 Binary Addition

The ADD instruction is used to add two binary numbers. As with the MOVE instruction, ADD has an opcode extension of .B, .W, or .L that identifies the instruction as a byte, word, or long-word addition. The addressing modes that are allowed for addition are nearly as abundant as for the MOVE instruction. The main difference is that with the ADD instruction you may not add the contents of two memory locations. Memory-to-memory moves with two memory addresses are allowed with the MOVE instruction, but not with ADD.

Table 3-1 illustrates the operand forms that are allowed for the ADD instruction when an assembler is used for programming. The table lists each type of instruction, the extension to the opcode that is allowed for the instruction, and a brief description of the function of the instruction. In Table 3-1 you will notice that a new identifier (ea) is listed with each of the instructions. This identifier indicates the effective address. The *effective address* is almost any of the addressing modes discussed in Chapter 2. To determine exactly which addressing modes are allowed for a particular instruction, refer to Appendix A under the ADD instruction, where the allowable effective addresses are clearly identified for each of the instructions.

In general, with the ADD instruction, any addressing mode may be used as the

**Table 3-1**  ADD Instruction Forms

| Instruction | Size (e) | Comment |
| --- | --- | --- |
| ADD.e (ea),Dn | B,W,L | Adds the effective address to the data register. |
| ADD.e Dn,(ea) | B,W,L | Adds a data register to an effective address. |
| ADD.e (ea),An | W,L | Adds an effective address to an address register. |
| ADD.e #XXX,(ea) | B,W,L | Adds immediate data to any effective address. |

NOTES: e is the extension B, W, or L, the source (ea) may be any addressing mode, and the destination (ea) may be any mode except address register direct, immediate, or program counter addressing.

source effective address. Any addressing mode except address register direct, program counter addressing, and immediate addressing may be used as the destination effective address. Also note from Table 3-1 that each instruction is listed as an ADD.e. The e is a shorthand notation in the table that indicates the size of the data used by the instruction. The usage for the e is listed under the "Size (e)" column heading. For example, if the byte portion of D2 is added to the byte portion of D3, the ADD.B D2,D3 instruction is selected. From Table 3-1, this is either the ADD.B (ea),Dn or ADD.B Dn,(ea) instruction.

Suppose that a program is required to add the word contents of registers D1, D2, and D3 plus a constant value of $2000. The result is stored in register A4. Example 3-1 illustrates this program. Notice that the ADD.W instruction is used to accomplish the additions because they are all word-sized. After the additions, a MOVE.W is used to move the result into register A4 from D3. (Recall that this word MOVE to register A4 will sign-extend the result.) This program is readily accomplished with four instructions. This program will destroy the original contents of D2 and D3. Often this does not cause a problem.

If the values in all the registers need to be saved, the program listing of Example 3-2 is used. Example 3-2 is different because it forms the sum in register D0. This requires an extra instruction, so the listing is used only if the contents of D2 and D3 must be preserved.

E  X  A  M  P  L  E    3 - 1

```
001000 D441          ADD.W  D1,D2         ;sum D1 and D2
001002 D642          ADD.W  D2,D3         ;sum D2 and D3
001004 06432000      ADD.W  #$2000,D3     ;add $2000 to D3
001008 3843          MOVE.W D3,A4          ;move result to A4
```

E  X  A  M  P  L  E    3 - 2

```
001000 3001          MOVE.W D1,D0          ;move D1 to D0
001002 D042          ADD.W  D2,D0         ;add D2 to D0
001004 D043          ADD.W  D3,D0         ;add D3 to D0
001006 06402000      ADD.W  #$2000,D0     ;add $2000 to D0
00100A 3840          MOVE.W D0,A4          ;move result to A4
```

## Addition and the CCR

As with most instructions in the 680XX microprocessor instruction set, the condition code register bits will change when an instruction is executed. This also applies to most of the MOVE instructions explained in Chapter 2. For addition, all the CCR bits may change to reflect the condition of the sum. Refer to Appendix A for a complete listing of all of the 68000 instructions and the changes that occur in the CCR when they are executed.

E X A M P L E     3 - 3

```
001000 203C00120033     MOVE.L  #$120033,D0
001006 068000000011     ADD.L   #$11,D0
```

Example 3-3 illustrates a short program that adds two numbers. The result of $00120044 is left in the 32-bit D0 register and the CCR bits change as follows:

D0 = $00120044 (sum)

C = 0 (no carry)

N = 0 (positive)

V = 0 (no overflow)

X = 0 (no carry)

Z = 0 (not zero)

E X A M P L E     3 - 4

```
001000 7003     MOVE.L  #3,D0
001002 727F     MOVE.L  #$7F,D1
001004 D001     ADD.B   D1,D0
```

Example 3-4 illustrates another problem in which 8-bit data are added. In this example, the data are first loaded into registers D0 and D1 and then D1 is added to D0. The result and the condition of the CCR bits are indicated as follows:

D0 = $82 (sum)

C = 0 (no carry)

N = 1 (negative)

V = 1 (overflow)

X = 0 (no carry)

Z = 0 (not zero)

Notice that the V (overflow) condition code bit is set. This means that the addition of Example 3-4 caused an overflow. How is that possible? The numbers $7F (+127) and $03 (+3) were added to produce a $82 (−126). As you can see, the answer is not correct because the addition overflowed the capacity of the 8-bit result. Eight-bit *signed* numbers range in value from −128 ($80) to +127 $(7F). If the result is larger than +127 or less than −128, an overflow condition exists. Here we added a +3 and a +127, which causes a sum of +130. This is larger than +127 so an overflow occurred, indicating the result is incorrect. If the numbers are considered to be *unsigned* integers, the result is correct as an $82 or 130 and the overflow CCR bit is ignored. Overflows only apply to signed arithmetic operations and never to unsigned operations.

## Other Forms of ADD

In addition to the ADD instruction, used exclusively for binary addition of byte, word, or long-word data, Appendix B covers ADDA, ADDI, and ADDQ. These instructions are formed by the assembler if the operands fit a particular ADD instruction. In machine language programming, the programmer must use these forms where appropriate, so a discussion at this point is required.

The machine language ADDA instruction is used whenever data are added to an address register. The machine language ADDI instruction is used whenever immediate data are added to anything other than a data register. The machine language ADDQ instruction is unique, since it is used to add numbers between 1 and 8 to a byte, word, or long-word register or memory location.

A 3-bit field in the ADDQ opcode indicates the value of the number added. If this field contains a 000, an 8 is added; if it contains a 001, a 1 is added; if it contains a 010, a 2 is added, etc. The ADDQ instruction is invaluable because it requires only 2 bytes of memory to store. An equivalent ADD instruction using the same immediate data may take up to 6 bytes of memory. The ADDQ instruction, unlike the MOVEQ instruction, may be a byte, word, or long-word addition. The MOVEQ instruction is never anything but a long-word move immediate to a data register.

Again, if an assembler is used for programming, the assembler automatically chooses the correct form of the ADD instruction, which could be ADD, ADDA, ADDI, or ADDQ. This aids the programmer because only the ADD opcode is used for addition. Because most programs are written using an assembler, we rarely see these additional forms of the ADD instruction. If desired, you may use ADDA, ADDI, and ADDQ in an assembly language program.

## 3-1.2   Addition with Carry (ADDX)

In some instances, data that are wider than 32 bits must be added. To accomplish this, there is a method that allows a carry out of a 32-bit addition to be added. The method allows the carry to be added into another section of the numbers that are added. With the ADDX instruction, the carry from one section of an addition can be added or propagated into another, thus allowing the addition of very wide numbers.

Figure 3-1 shows the carry when two 64-bit numbers are added with two separate 32-bit additions. Notice that a carry may occur after the right-most two long-words are added with the ADD instruction. This carry is then added to the two left-most 32-bit numbers when they are added. The carry between these long-words is propagated through the (extend) X-CCR bit.

The ADDX instruction adds the two operands together plus the contents of the X-CCR bit. ADDX is a byte, word, or long-word operation that uses one of two distinct addressing modes. ADDX is used to add the contents of two data registers plus the X-CCR bit or to add the contents of two memory locations plus the X-CCR bit. When memory data are added, the ADDX instruction uses the predecrement

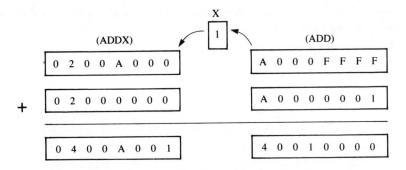

**Figure 3-1** In this addition of two 64-bit numbers, the X-CCR bit transfers the carry between the least significant long-word and the most significant long-word.

method of addressing memory data. If memory data are added, the ADDX instruction must be used because the ADD instruction cannot add memory data together. Table 3-2 illustrates the two allowable forms of the ADDX instruction.

Example 3-5 illustrates the instructions required to add the two 64-bit numbers stored in D0–D1 and D2–D3. D0 and D2 contain the most significant portions of the numbers, and D1 and D3 contain the least significant portions. The 64-bit result is stored in registers D2 and D3, erasing one of the original numbers.

Notice from this example that the least significant 32 bits are added with the ADD.L instruction. This instruction is used because there is never a carry into the right-hand edge of the addition. After the least significant long-words have been added, the most significant long-words are added with ADDX.L. This instruction is used because there may be a carry into the most significant part of the addition and ADDX.L adds the carry found in the X-CCR bit.

E X A M P L E     3 - 5

```
001000 D681    ADD.L   D1,D3
001002 D580    ADDX.L  D0,D2
```

Why is the only memory addressing mode available for the ADDX instruction the predecrement indirect mode? This mode allows the least significant portion of

**Table 3-2** Add with Extend (X) Instructions

| Instruction | Size (e) | Comment |
|---|---|---|
| ADDX.e Dx,Dy | B,W,L | Adds Dx to Dy with the extend bit. |
| ADDX.e -(Ax),-(Ay) | B,W,L | Decrements both Ax and Ay, then adds the contents of memory addressed by Ax to the contents of memory addressed by Ay plus X. |

the number to be addressed first because it is stored in the highest numbered memory location. As very long numbers are added, the more significant portions are in lower numbered memory locations. This requires that the memory address be decremented to reach each of these more significant values as numbers are added.

Example 3-6 shows how two 128-bit numbers from the memory are added using this mode of indirect memory addressing. Figure 3-2 illustrates how the numbers are stored in memory. One of the numbers is stored in 16 bytes of memory beginning at location $003000. The second number is stored in memory beginning at location $003010.

The short program of Example 3-6 adds these very long numbers together by using the ADDX instruction to add all four long-words of each number. For this sequence of instructions to function correctly, the X-CCR (extend) bit is first cleared to zero so that there is no carry with the first addition. To clear the X-CCR bit, the third instruction in the program adds a zero to the contents of the byte portion of D0. This does not change D0, but will always clear the X-CCR bit. The extend bit must be cleared for the first addition of the least significant long-words. After the program has been executed, the 128-bit result is stored over the number found in location $003000–$00300F. This erases these memory locations' contents and replaces them with the resultant sum.

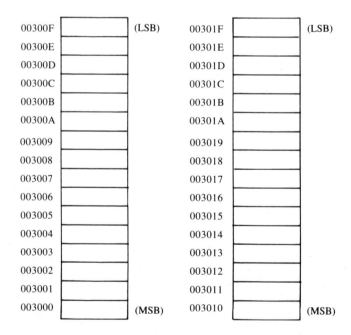

**Figure 3-2**   The memory locations used with Example 3-6 to add two 128-bit numbers. Locations $003000–$00300F contain one number and $003010–$00301F contain the other number. The result is stored on top of the number at location $003000–$00300F after the addition.

EXAMPLE   3-6

```
001000 227C00003020      MOVE.L  #$3020,A1      ;address data
001006 247C00003010      MOVE.L  #$3010,A2
00100C 06000000          ADD.B   #0,D0          ;clear X
001010 D589              ADDX.L  -(A1),-(A2)    ;sum data
001012 D589              ADDX.L  -(A1),-(A2)
001014 D589              ADDX.L  -(A1),-(A2)
001016 D589              ADDX.L  -(A1),-(A2)
```

### 3-1.3  Binary Subtraction

The 680XX subtracts binary data as bytes, words, and long-words using the SUB instruction. The addressing modes allowed for the SUB instruction are the same as indicated for the ADD instruction. Table 3-3 illustrates all the allowable forms of the SUB instruction.

The SUB instruction will subtract the contents of the source operand from the destination operand, and the result will be placed in the destination operand. A good way to remember this is to remember the subtract immediate instruction, namely, immediate data must always be placed in the source operand. This will help you remember which number is subtracted.

Suppose that you are required to subtract the byte-wide contents of register D2 from D1. This is accomplished with the SUB.B D2,D1 instruction. Now suppose that you are required to subtract the long-word contents of registers D2, D3, and D4 from D1, with the difference stored in register D5. This is accomplished by the short sequence of instruction of Example 3-7.

EXAMPLE   3-7

```
001000 9282      SUB.L  D2,D1
001002 9283      SUB.L  D3,D1
001004 9284      SUB.L  D4,D1
001006 2A01      MOVE.L D1,D5
```

**Table 3-3  Subtraction Instruction Forms**

| Instruction | Size (e) | Comment |
| --- | --- | --- |
| SUB.e (ea),Dn | B,W,L | Subtracts ⟨ea⟩ from Dn, with the difference placed in Dn. |
| SUB.e Dn,(ea) | B,W,L | Subtracts Dn from ⟨ea⟩, with the difference placed in ⟨ea⟩. |
| SUB.e (ea),An | W,L | Subtracts ⟨ea⟩ from An, with the difference placed in An. |
| SUB.e #XXX,(ea) | B,W,L | Subtracts #XXX from ⟨ea⟩, with the difference placed in ⟨ea⟩. |

NOTE: The source (ea) may be any addressing mode, and the destination (ea) may be any mode except address register direct, immediate, or program counter addressing.

Other forms of the subtraction instruction that appear only in machine language are SUBA, SUBI, and SUBQ. As with the additional forms of the ADD instruction, the additional forms of the subtraction instruction are not normally used in assembly language. The SUBA instruction is used to subtract data from an address register. The SUBI instruction is used to subtract immediate data from any effective address. The SUBQ instruction is used to subtract a 1–8 from any effective address. As with ADDQ, SUBQ uses a 3-bit binary field in the opcode to specify the numbers 1–8. Numbers 1–7 are stored as 001–111, and 8 is stored as 000.

## Subtraction and the CCR

As with addition, whenever data are subtracted, the contents of the CCR register are affected. When data are subtracted, all the CCR bits may change to delineate the difference.

E  X  A  M  P  L  E    3 - 8

```
001000 163C0045    MOVE.B  #$45,D3
001004 04030066    SUB.B   #$66,D3
```

Example 3-8 illustrates a simple subtraction, to show the changes in the CCR register. Here a $45 is loaded into register D3 and then a $66 is subtracted from it. The result from this subtraction is found in register D3. The register and CCR bits changed as follows:

D3 = $DF (difference)

C = 1 (borrow)

N = 1 (negative)

V = 0 (no overflow)

X = 1 (borrow)

Z = 0 (not zero)

Notice from the CCR bits that there is no overflow after this subtraction. When a $66 (+102) is subtracted from a $45 (+69), the result is a $DF (−33). A $DF is a valid 8-bit signed binary result. Because the contents of the register are not overflowed, the overflow CCR bit is cleared. (It is often customary to call an overflow an *underflow* after a subtraction.) Also notice that the carry and extend CCR bits contain *borrows* after a subtraction. These CCR bits will always contain borrows after a subtraction and carries after an addition. A borrow is represented as a logic one in the C and X condition code register bits.

## 3-1.4  Subtraction with Extend (SUBX)

The SUBX (subtract with extend) instruction allows data that are wider than 32 bits to be subtracted. It does so by subtracting the extend CCR bit, which holds the borrow, from the difference. This is similar to ADDX, which adds the extend CCR bit.

Table 3-4 illustrates the allowable forms of the SUBX instruction. The SUBX instruction allows data in two data registers to be subtracted minus the extend bit. It also allows the contents of two memory locations, using the predecrement form of indirect addressing, to be subtracted minus the extend bit.

Figure 3-3 illustrates how the extend bit is used to transfer the borrow from one half of a 64-bit subtraction to the other. The extend CCR bit propagates the borrow from the left to the right with SUBX, as the extend CCR bit propagates the carry from the right to the left with the ADDX instruction.

Suppose that you are required to develop a short sequence of instructions that will subtract the 128-bit number in D0, D1, D2, and D3 from the 128-bit number in D4, D5, D6, and D7. The difference is stored in memory locations $003000–$00300F. The program that accomplishes this wide subtraction is listed in Example 3-9. Notice how the difference is stored in the memory as the program executes. Also notice that the least significant long-words are subtracted with the SUB instruction. The remaining three long-word subtractions use the SUBX instruction, to ensure that the borrow can be taken into account.

E X A M P L E    3 - 9

```
001000 227C00003010    MOVE.L  #$3010,A1
001006 9E83            SUB.L   D3,D7
001008 2307            MOVE.L  D7,-(A1)
00100A 9D82            SUBX.L  D2,D6
00100C 2306            MOVE.L  D6,-(A1)
00100E 9B81            SUBX.L  D1,D5
001010 2305            MOVE.L  D5,-(A1)
001012 9980            SUBX.L  D0,D4
001014 2304            MOVE.L  D4,-(A1)
```

### 3-1.5  Changing the Arithmetic Sign of a Binary Number

To change the arithmetic sign of a signed binary number, the binary number is *two's-complemented*. To two's complement a number, the number is first one's-complemented, then a 1 is added to it. The 680XX microprocessor has a pair of

**Table 3-4   Subtract with Extend Instructions**

| Instruction | Size (e) | Comment |
|---|---|---|
| SUBX.e Dy,Dx | B,W,L | Subtracts Dy from Dx minus extend and leaves the difference in Dx. |
| SUBX.e -(Ay),-(Ax) | B,W,L | Decrements Ay and Ax and then subtracts the contents of memory addressed by Ay from the contents of memory addressed by Ax minus extend. The result is stored in the memory location addressed by Ax. |

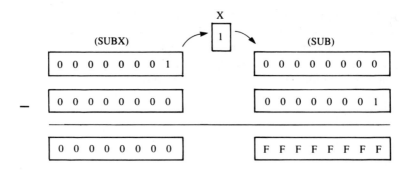

**Figure 3-3** Using the SUB and SUBX instructions to perform subtraction on numbers wider than 32 bits. Notice how the X-CCR bit is used to propagate the borrow.

instructions called *negate* instructions that are used to two's complement a number (change its sign).

One of these instructions, NEG, negates the operand, while the other, NEGX, negates the operand with the extend bit. NEGX is used to negate binary numbers that are wider than 32 bits, while NEG is used to negate bytes, words, or long-words. Table 3-5 illustrates the allowable forms of the negate and negate with extend instructions.

Suppose that you are required to change the sign of the 64-bit signed binary number in registers D0 and D1. Here D1 contains the least significant portion of the data. Example 3-10 illustrates how the NEG and the NEGX instructions are used to perform this sign change.

E  X  A  M  P  L  E    3 - 10

```
001000 4481    NEG.L   D1
001002 4080    NEGX.L  D0
```

## 3-1.6   BCD Addition and Subtraction

In some systems, data are found in binary-coded decimal form. BCD data are useful in systems that perform simple arithmetic. To allow BCD data to be added or subtracted, the 680XX has instructions that accomplish BCD addition and subtraction and also negation.

**Table 3-5   The Negation Instructions**

| Instruction | Size (e) | Comment |
|---|---|---|
| NEG.e (ea) | B,W,L | Negates the contents of the effective address. |
| NEGX.e (ea) | B,W,L | Negates with extend the contents of the effective address. |

NOTE: The effective address (ea) can be any addressing mode except address register direct, immediate, or program counter addressing.

**Table 3-6**  BCD Arithmetic Instructions

| Instruction | Comment |
|---|---|
| ABCD Dy,Dx | Adds the packed BCD byte in Dy to Dx plus extend. |
| ABCD -(Ay),-(Ax) | Decrements the contents of Ay and Ax, then adds the packed BCD byte at the memory location addressed by Ay to the contents of the memory location addressed by Ax with extend. The sum is stored in the memory location addressed by Ax. |
| SBCD Dy,Dx | Subtracts the packed BCD byte in Dy from Dx with extend. |
| SBCD -(Ay),-(Ax) | Decrements the contents of Ay and Ax; then subtracts the packed BCD contents of the memory location addressed by Ay from the contents of the memory location addressed by Ax with extend. The difference is placed into the memory location addressed by Ax. |
| NBCD (ea) | Ten's complements the packed BCD byte at the effective address with extend. |

NOTE: The effective address (ea) can be any addressing mode except address register direct, immediate, or program counter addressing.

Table 3-6 illustrates the instructions used to perform BCD arithmetic operations. Notice that all the BCD instructions are byte operations that operate on packed BCD numbers (two digits per byte). All the BCD instructions also use the extend CCR bit in their operation. ABCD will add two packed BCD numbers plus extend. SBCD will subtract two packed BCD numbers minus extend. NBCD will negate two packed BCD numbers with extend. Unlike the other instructions described thus far, none of the BCD instructions use the opcode extension in their symbolic form.

Suppose that memory contains a 4-byte area that is used to hold totals in a cash register. Figure 3-4 illustrates this section of the memory system with a 4004.55 stored. This number, as you can see, is stored in packed BCD form and represents four thousand four dollars and fifty-five cents. Because 4 bytes of memory are used to hold this number, the maximum capacity is $999999.99 dollars. This is a large enough section of the memory to store totals for most cash registers.

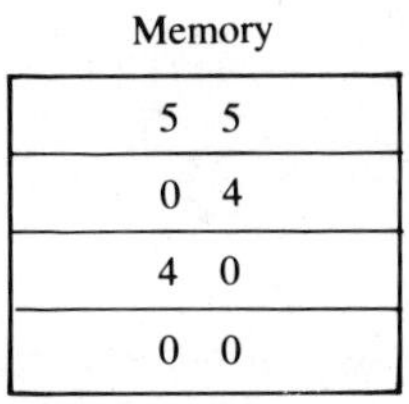

Memory

| | |
|---|---|
| 5 | 5 |
| 0 | 4 |
| 4 | 0 |
| 0 | 0 |

**Figure 3-4**  Four bytes of memory that hold the total in a cash register. In this case, these 4 bytes contain the packed BCD number that represents $4004.55.

Example 3-11 illustrates the instructions required to add the BCD number stored in memory locations $2000–$2003 to the total stored in memory locations $3000–$3003. Before the addition can begin, the extend CCR bit is cleared to zero. This is required because the ABCD instruction adds extend and there is no carry initially. In this example, the ADD.B #0,D0 instruction is used to clear the extend CCR bit without changing D0.

E X A M P L E    3 - 11

```
001000 207C00003004    MOVE.L  #$3004,A0
001006 227C00002004    MOVE.L  #$2004,A1
00100C 06000000        ADD.B   #0,D0
001010 C109            ABCD    -(A1),-(A0)
001012 C109            ABCD    -(A1),-(A0)
001014 C109            ABCD    -(A1),-(A0)
001016 C109            ABCD    -(A1),-(A0)
```

Example 3-11 can be changed to perform BCD subtraction by merely substituting the SBCD instruction for the ABCD instruction. It likewise can be used to perform BCD negation by changing the ABCD instruction to NBCD −(A0). Negative BCD numbers are stored in the ten's complement form. For example, a $45 is a +45, so the negation of this is a $55 or a −45 in the ten's complement form. To form the ten's complement, a number is subtracted from 99 and then 1 is added.

## 3-2   Multiplication and Division

Two operations used quite often in arithmetic are multiplication and division. The 680XX has two forms of the multiplication instruction and two forms of the division instruction. The MULU and DIVU instructions are used to perform multiplication and division on unsigned binary integers. The MULS and DIVS instructions are used to perform signed binary integer multiplication and division.

### 3-2.1   Multiplication

Table 3-7 illustrates the two forms allowed for the multiplication instruction. Both forms perform 16-bit multiplication on two 16-bit operands, and the result is a 32-bit product in the destination operand.

With all forms of multiplication, the carry and overflow CCR bits are always cleared and the X-CCR bit is unaffected. The N-CCR bit indicates that the result of the signed binary multiplication is negative. The N-CCR bit is set to a one if the most significant bit of the product of an unsigned binary multiplication is a one. The zero CCR bit indicates that the result of the multiplication is zero. The multiplication instructions do not use an opcode extension because they function only with word-sized operands that produce a long-word product. This means that no extension is required.

**Table 3-7** Multiplication Instructions

| Instruction | Comment |
|---|---|
| MULS (ea),Dn | Multiplies the signed word at the effective address times the signed word contents of Dn. The 32-bit signed product is found in Dn. |
| MULU (ea),Dn | Multiplies the unsigned word at the effective address times the unsigned contents of Dn. The 32-bit unsigned product is found in Dn. |

NOTE: The effective address (ea) can be any addressing mode except address register direct.

Example 3-12 illustrates how the unsigned contents of memory location $10000 are multiplied by the unsigned contents of memory location $20000. The unsigned result is stored in memory location $30000. This is accomplished using several instructions because the destination operand of the multiply instruction must be a data register.

E X A M P L E    3 - 12

```
001000 303900010000    MOVE.W  $10000,D0
001006 C0F900020000    MULU    $20000,D0
00100C 23C000030000    MOVE.L  D0,$30000
```

Suppose that the D0 register is loaded with the signed word $FFFE ($-2$) and that it is multiplied times the contents of register D4, which contains a $0004 ($+4$). The result will be a 32-bit $FFFFFFF8 ($-8$) found in the D0 register. The program to accomplish this signed multiplication is listed in Example 3-13.

E X A M P L E    3 - 13

```
001000 303CFFFE    MOVE.W  #$FFFE,D0
001004 383C0004    MOVE.W  #4,D4
001008 C1C4        MULS    D4,D0
```

### 3-2.2  Division

Division, like multiplication, can be performed on signed or unsigned binary numbers. The two divide instructions provided are DIVS for signed division and DIVU for unsigned division. The division instruction always divides the 32-bit number stored in the destination data register by the 16-bit number at the source effective address. The result, consisting of a quotient and remainder, is stored in the destination data register after the division. The right-most word of the destination data register will always contain the 16-bit quotient and the left-most word the remainder. Note that the remainder is always an integer. If a 10 is divided by a 3, then the quotient is a $0003 and the remainder is a $0001. Both are found in the destination register as a $00010003. Refer to Table 3-8 for the forms of the division instruction.

The X-CCR bit does not change for division, but the other CCR bits do change. The C-CCR bit is always cleared and the N, Z, and V bits change. The N-CCR bit indicates that the quotient is negative for a signed binary division or that the most significant bit of the unsigned quotient is set. The Z-CCR bit indicates that the quotient is zero. The V-CCR bit indicates that the quotient has overflowed the word capacity of the data register. An overflow will occur if the quotient is too large to be stored as a word. If an attempt is made to divide by zero, an interrupt (exception) occurs. Exceptions and interrupts are discussed in Chapter 5.

An interrupt or exception will cause the program to cease execution. Execution continues at another program (subroutine or procedure) that processes the divide by zero interrupt. In the case of divide by zero, the software stored in the 680XX system will most likely indicate an attempt to divide by zero. This is often shown by displaying some type of error message on the screen of the video monitor if one exists.

Example 3-14 illustrates the unsigned division of the contents of D2 by a $0010 (16). If D2 originally contained a $00000064 (100 decimal), the result in D2 would be a $00040006. The remainder, in the most significant word of D2, would be a $0004 and the quotient, in the least significant word, a $0006.

E  X  A  M  P  L  E      3 - 14

```
001000 343C0064    MOVE.W #100,D2
001004 84FC0010    DIVU   #16,D2
```

If signed binary division is used by the 680XX, the sign of the remainder will always be the same as the sign of the quotient unless the remainder is a $0000. Suppose that a $FFFFFFF8 ($-8$) is moved into register D0 and a $0005 ($+5$) is moved into register D1, whereupon D0 is divided by D1 using signed division. (See

**Table 3-8   Division Instructions**

| Instruction | Comment |
|---|---|
| DIVS (ea),Dn | Divides the signed contents of Dn by the signed contents of the effective address. The quotient is found in the least significant word of Dn and the remainder in the most significant word of Dn. |
| DIVU (ea),Dn | Divides the unsigned contents of Dn by the unsigned contents of the effective address. The quotient is found in the least significant word of Dn and the remainder in the most significant word of Dn. |

NOTE: The effective address (ea) may be any addressing mode except address register direct.

E X A M P L E 3 - 15

```
001000 70F8        MOVE.L  #FFFFFFF8,D0
001002 323C0005    MOVE.W  #5,D1
001006 81C1        DIVS    D1,D0
```

Example 3-15.) After the division, the contents of D0 will be $FFFDFFFF, where the remainder $FFFD ($-3$) and the quotient $FFFF ($-1$) are both found in D0.

### Fractions for Remainders

Suppose that instead of an integer remainder, you require a fractional remainder. How can the integer remainder be converted to a binary fraction? To convert an integer remainder (unsigned only) to a binary fraction, the remainder is divided in place (the most significant half of the data register) by the original divisor. In Example 3-16 a 100 decimal is divided by 8. The quotient of 12 is stored in word memory location $2000. The remainder is left in place, with the quotient (least significant half of the data register) cleared to zero, where it is again divided by the 8. This leaves the fractional remainder in the right-most word of data register D0. Here the integer remainder is 4 and the fractional portion, stored in word memory location $2002, is a 0.1 binary (0.5 decimal) stored as an $8000. For a binary fraction, the radix (binary point) is at the left end of the register or memory location.

E X A M P L E 3 - 16

```
001000 7064        MOVE.L  #100,D0
001002 80FC0008    DIVU    #8,D0
001006 31C02000    MOVE.W  D0,$2000      ;save quotient
00100A 303C0000    MOVE.W  #0,D0
00100E 80FC0008    DIVU    #8,D0         ;generate fraction
001012 31C02002    MOVE.W  D0,$2002      ;save remainder
```

### Converting Numbers from 16 Bits to 32 Bits for Division

At times, the dividend is not 32 bits wide and must be made this width before a division can occur. Because there are signed and unsigned numbers, there are two methods of converting a number from a byte or word into a long-word. When an unsigned number is converted from 16 to 32 bits, the most significant word is always cleared to a $0000. When a signed number is converted, it is sign-extended, with the result that the most significant word becomes a $0000 or a $FFFF.

Example 3-17 illustrates the sequence of instructions that are used to divide the unsigned word contents of memory location $2000 by the unsigned word contents of memory location $2002. The remainder is stored in word location $2000 and the quotient in word location $2002 after the division. Notice that a $0000 is moved into the most significant part of D0, to convert it to a 32-bit unsigned integer, before the division.

E  X   A   M   P   L   E      3 - 17

```
001000 7000          MOVE.L  #0,D0
001002 30382000      MOVE.W  $2000,D0
001006 80F82002      DIVU    $2002,D0
00100A 21C02000      MOVE.L  D0,$2000
```

To convert signed words into long-words before division, the sign-extend instruction (EXT) is used. This instruction can convert (sign-extend) the byte in a data register into a word (EXT.W Dn) or the word in a data register into a long-word (EXT.L Dn). Example 3-18 illustrates how the signed byte at memory location $2000 is divided by the signed byte at memory location $2001. The result after this division is found in D0, and no attempt is made to save it in the memory. Notice that the contents of $2000 are sign-extended into a long-word before division. Also notice that the contents of $2001 are sign-extended into a word.

E  X   A   M   P   L   E      3 - 18

```
001000 10382000      MOVE.B  $2000,D0
001004 4880          EXT.W   D0
001006 48C0          EXT.L   D0
001008 12382001      MOVE.B  $2001,D1
00100C 4881          EXT.W   D1
00100E 81C1          DIVS    D1,D0
```

## 3-3  Logic Operations

The 680XX microprocessor can perform four basic logic functions: AND, OR, exclusive-OR, and NOT (inversion). Logic functions are often used to replace hardware logic circuitry at a significant cost savings. For example a 7408 two-input AND gate integrated circuit costs about 25¢. Each 7408 contains four of these two-input AND gates. If an AND instruction is executed on a byte of data, eight two-input AND gates are simulated. This means that one of the AND instructions can replace up to two 7408 integrated circuits. How much does it cost to store the AND instruction? If it is a 6-byte-long AND instruction, it would cost less than a tenth of a penny to store it in the memory. That means that you can save more than 49¢ each time the AND instruction is used to replace an AND logic gate integrated circuit.

Also described in this section are the bit control (manipulation) instructions BCHG, BCLR, BSET, and BTST. These instructions allow selected bits to be inverted, cleared, set, and tested, respectively. Actually all four operations test the designated bit, but only BCHG, BCLR, and BSET will change it.

### 3-3.1  The AND Instruction

Table 3-9 illustrates the AND instructions that are valid with the 680XX microprocessor. The AND operation performs logical multiplication on two numbers that

**Table 3-9   The AND Instructions**

| Instruction | Size (e) | Comment |
|---|---|---|
| AND.e (ea),Dn | B,W,L | ANDs the effective address with the contents Dn. |
| AND.e Dn,(ea) | B,W,L | ANDs the contents of Dn with the effective address. |
| AND.e #XXX,(ea) | B,W,L | ANDs the immediate data with the effective address. |

NOTE: If the effective address is the source operand, any addressing mode except address register direct may be used. If the effective address is the destination, any addressing mode except address register direct, immediate, and program counter addressing may be used.

are a byte, word, or long-word in width. The truth table, in Figure 3-5, illustrates how the AND function operates. Notice that the result from the AND operation is a logic one only when both the input bits are a logic one. Otherwise, the output of the AND gate is a logic zero if any input is a logic zero.

The AND operation is often used to mask off (hide or erase) a portion of a number. The term "mask" means to clear or turn off selected bits of a number to zero without affecting any other bits.

The AND operation is illustrated in Example 3-19, where an unknown number (XXXX XXXX) is ANDed with the binary bit pattern 0000 1111. Notice that the result has its left-most 4 bits cleared to zero and the right-most 4 bits remain unchanged. The AND operation is used to selectively clear bits to zero. Thus it is used to turn bits off. This feature is useful in control systems in which bits of a number are used to control external machines. If you use the AND instruction, you can selectively turn off one or more of these machines.

**E X A M P L E   3 - 19**

```
        XXXX  XXXX
   AND  0000  1111
        0000  XXXX
```

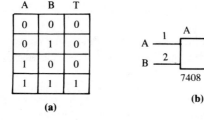

(a)

(b)

**Figure 3-5   The AND instruction: (a) the truth table of the AND function and (b) the logic symbol used for the AND gate.**

## The CCR Bits and the AND Instruction

All the CCR bits are affected by the AND instruction except the X-CCR bit, which remains unchanged. Both the carry and overflow CCR bits are always cleared by the AND, and the N and Z bits reflect whether the result is zero or negative. This instruction can be used to clear carry if needed.

Example 3-20 illustrates a program that takes the byte contents of memory location $30000 and ANDs it with D1 and D2. The logical product is then stored in memory at location $30001.

E  X  A  M  P  L  E    3 - 20

```
001000  C23900030000    AND.B   $30000,D1
001006  C401            AND.B   D1,D2
001008  13C200030001    MOVE.B  D2,$30001
```

## Other Forms of the AND Instruction

In machine language, the AND instruction has one additional form that is not used with assembly language programming. The ANDI instruction is used whenever immediate data are ANDed to any effective address except a data register, an address register, immediate data, or any memory location using the program counter form of indirect addressing. In addition, the ANDI instruction is used to AND data with the CCR. This feature is explained later in Section 3-6.

### 3-3.2    The OR Instruction

Table 3-10 illustrates all of the possible versions of the OR instruction. The OR instruction performs logical addition and is at times called the *inclusive OR* function. Notice that OR has the same addressing forms as the AND instruction. The OR instruction is used to *logically add* bytes, words, or long-words. Figure 3-6 illustrates how the OR function operates. Notice from the truth table (Figure 3-6a) that the result is a one if either or both the inputs are one. The result is a zero only if both inputs are zero.

The OR instruction is used to selectively *set* any bit or bits in any byte, word, or long-word. Example 3-21 illustrates what occurs when a 0000 1111 is ORed with

**Table 3-10    The OR Instructions**

| Instruction | Size (e) | Comment |
|---|---|---|
| OR.e (ea),Dn | B,W,L | ORs the effective address with Dn. |
| OR.e Dn,(ea) | B,W,L | ORs Dn with the effective address. |
| OR.e #XXX,(ea) | B,W,L | ORs immediate data with the effective address. |

NOTES: If the effective address is the source operand, any addressing mode may be used except address register direct. If the effective address is the destination operand, any addressing mode may be used except address register direct, immediate, or program counter addressing.

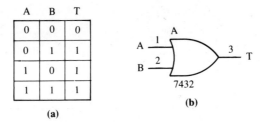

| A | B | T |
|---|---|---|
| 0 | 0 | 0 |
| 0 | 1 | 1 |
| 1 | 0 | 1 |
| 1 | 1 | 1 |

(a)

(b)

**Figure 3-6** (a) The truth table and (b) the logic symbol of the inclusive-OR function.

the number XXXX XXXX. Notice that when a one is ORed with the unknown number, the result is a one, and when a zero is ORed, the result is X–the unknown number. The OR instruction is often used in control systems to set bits to logic ones. When a bit is set, it is often called on. So far, we can turn bits off with the AND instruction and turn bits on with the OR instruction. Imagine a byte of data containing control information for eight external on/off devices. Think how much power can be wielded in a control system by a single byte of data!

E X A M P L E   3 - 21

```
     XXXX  XXXX
OR   0000  1111

     XXXX  1111
```

### The CCR and the OR Instruction

As with the AND instruction, all the CCR bits are affected by the OR instruction except the X-CCR bit. Both the carry and the overflow CCR bits are cleared by the OR operation, and the Z and N bits reflect whether the result was zero or negative. The OR instruction can be used to clear the carry flag, as could the AND instruction.

### Other Forms of the OR Instruction

The OR instruction has one other form, ORI, which normally appears only in machine language. ORI is used to OR immediate data with any effective address except address register, immediate, or any program counter addressing mode. In addition, the ORI instruction can be used to OR data with the CCR. This is described in Section 3.5.

### 3-3.3 The Exclusive-OR Instruction (EOR)

The exclusive-OR instruction (EOR) and its valid forms appear in Table 3-11. Notice that there are only two forms, compared to three forms for the AND and OR operations. The exclusive-OR operation can be used to exclusive-OR bytes, words,

**Table 3-11    The Exclusive-OR Instructions**

| Instruction | Size (e) | Comment |
|---|---|---|
| EOR.e Dn,(ea) | B,W,L | Exclusive-ORs Dn with the effective address. |
| EOR.e #XXX,(ea) | B,W,L | Exclusive-ORs immediate data with the effective address. |

NOTES: If the effective address is the source operand, any addressing mode may be used except address register direct. If the effective address is the destination operand, any addressing mode may be used except address register direct, immediate, or program counter addressing.

or long-words together. Figure 3-7 illustrates how the exclusive-OR function operates. Notice that if the two inputs are the same, the output is a zero. Also notice that if the two inputs are different, the output is a logic one. This function is sometimes called a *comparator* because of its ability to determine whether two bits are equal.

The exclusive-OR operation is used to selectively *invert* or *complement* bits in bytes, words, or long-words. This is illustrated in Example 3-22. Notice that the unknown number (XXXX XXXX) is exclusive-ORed with a 0000 1111. The result clearly shows that a part of the number is inverted, and a part remains unchanged by this operation. At this point, you have complete control over each bit in the 680XX. The AND operation is used to turn bits off, the OR operation is used to turn bits on, and now the exclusive-OR operation is used to invert bits. When a bit is inverted, it is used to toggle a device from on to off or from off to on in a control system.

E  X  A  M  P  L  E    3 - 22

```
                      XXXX    XXXX
   (Exclusive-OR)     0000    1111
                      ----    ----
                      XXXX    X X X X
```

### The CCR Bits and the Exclusive-OR Operation

As with AND and OR, the exclusive-OR operation affects the CCR bits except for the X-CCR bit. The carry and overflow CCR bits are always cleared by the exclusive-OR operation just as they were by AND and OR. Both the N- and Z-CCR

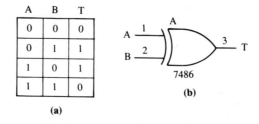

Figure 3-7    (a) The truth table and (b) the logic symbol of the exclusive-OR function.

bits are changed to indicate whether the result after an exclusive-OR is negative or zero.

## Other Forms of the EOR Instruction

In addition to EOR, the EORI instruction is often found in machine language. EORI is used to exclusive-OR immediate data with the contents of any effective address except immediate, address register, or programmer counter indirect address. EORI is also used to exclusive-OR immediate data with the CCR and SR, as discussed later in this text.

### 3-3.4   The NOT Instruction

The last logic instruction to be discussed in this section is the NOT or invert instruction. NOT is called *logic inversion*. When a number is inverted, all its bits are changed from zeros to ones or from ones to zeros. This function is often called the *one's complement*. The NOT instruction is used to invert bytes, words, or long-words of data. Any addressing mode is allowed except address register direct, immediate, or program counter addressing. The NOT instruction, like many of the other instructions in the 680XX, uses the opcode extension .B, .W, or .L to indicate byte, word, or long-word operations. Example 3-23 illustrates how the contents of data registers D0, D1, and D2 are inverted with the NOT instruction.

E  X  A  M  P  L  E      3 - 23

```
001000 4680    NOT.L D0
001002 4681    NOT.L D1
001004 4682    NOT.L D2
```

## The NOT Instruction and the CCR

All the CCR bits are affected by NOT except the X-CCR bit, which does not change after this instruction is executed. Overflow and carry are always cleared, while the N and Z bits are changed to indicate the result of the NOT instruction.

### 3-3.5   Binary Bit Manipulation Instructions

The 680XX microprocessor has four instructions that allow binary bit manipulation. BCHG (bit change) allows a single bit to be inverted or changed. BCLR (bit clear) allows a single bit to be cleared to zero. BSET (bit set) allows a single bit to be set to one. BTST (bit test) allows a single bit to be tested for a logic one or zero. These instructions are used in control systems to control individual bits just as the AND, OR, and exclusive-OR instructions are used to clear, set, or invert single or *multiple* bits.

The BCHG, BCLR, BSET, and BTST instructions all function in a similar manner. All four instructions first test the selected bit to determine whether it is a logic one or a logic zero. This test causes the contents of the Z-CCR bit to be set if the bit under test is a zero and cleared if the bit under test is a one. This means that if the bit tested is a zero, the Z-CCR bit will indicate a zero result. The remaining CCR bits will be unaffected by the bit manipulation instructions.

All four bit manipulation instructions allow a bit in either a byte or long-word to be changed, cleared, set, or tested. If the destination operand is a data register, the bit manipulation function is performed on a long-word. If the destination operand is a memory location, the bit manipulation is performed only on a byte. No extension size is required with any of these instructions.

All four instructions allow two instruction forms: one that uses the bit position number, placed in a data register, to select the bit to be changed, cleared, set, or tested, and a second, in which an immediate number is used to select the bit. In all cases bit position zero is the right-most binary bit position. Refer to Table 3-12 for the bit manipulation instructions and all forms of usage.

Suppose that you need to set bit position 0, the right-most bit of D0, bit position 1 of D1, and bit position 2 of D2. This can be accomplished in two ways. Example 3-24a shows how this is accomplished using data register D5 to specify the bit position to be set, and Example 3-24b shows how this is accomplished using the immediate form. Note that if a data register is used to indicate the bit position, the value is specified by the right-most 5 bits. This means that the bit position to be changed, cleared, set, or tested is indicated by the byte-sized data register.

E  X  A  M  P  L  E     3 - 24

**(a)**
```
001000  1A3C0000      MOVE.B   #0,D5
001004  0BC0          BSET     D5,D0
001006  5205          ADD.B    #1,D5
001008  0BC1          BSET     D5,D1
00100A  5205          ADD.B    #1,D5
00100C  0BC2          BSET     D5,D2
```

**(b)**
```
001000  08C00000      BSET     #0,D0
001004  08C10001      BSET     #1,D1
001008  08C20002      BSET     #2,D2
```

## 3-4   Shift and Rotate Instructions

The shift and rotate instructions allow data to be positioned in a register or a memory location. Bits are shifted to the right or left using the shift instructions and rotated right or left using the rotate instructions. In some cases multiplication and division are accomplished using the shift instructions. This is especially true if the number is small and high speed is required. The shift instructions function more quickly than the multiplication or division instructions in certain cases.

### 3-4.1   The Shift Instructions

There are two main types of shift. The logical shift is used to shift unsigned numbers, and the arithmetic shift is used with signed numbers. Shift operations of both types are available for byte, word, or long-word data.

**Table 3-12   Binary Bit Manipulation Instructions**

| Instruction | Comment |
|---|---|
| BCHG Dn,(ea) | Tests the bit position indicated by Dn and then inverts it. |
| BCHG #XXX,(ea) | Tests the bit position indicated by the immediate number and then inverts it. |
| BCLR Dn,(ea) | Tests the bit position indicated by Dn and then clears it to zero. |
| BCLR #XXX,(ea) | Tests the bit position indicated by the immediate number and then clears it to zero. |
| BSET Dn,(ea) | Tests the bit position indicated by Dn and then sets it to one. |
| BSET #XXX,(ea) | Tests the bit position indicated by the immediate number and then sets it to one. |
| BTST Dn,(ea) | Tests the bit position indicated by Dn. |
| BTST #XXX,(ea) | Tests the bit position indicated by the immediate number. |

NOTE: The effective address can be any addressing mode except address register direct, immediate, or program counter indirect.

## Logical Shift Instructions

Figure 3-8 illustrates the two logical shift instructions and their operation. Notice that both instructions shift the number in the target register or memory location, both shift a zero into the input end of the target, and both steer the data from the output end of the target into both the carry and extend CCR bits. The LSL instruction is used to shift data to the left and the LSR instruction is used to shift it to the right.

Table 3-13 depicts the logical shift instructions, showing all the applicable forms. Notice the three basic forms to each of these instructions: two data register operands, an immediate and a data register operand, and an effective address. The first two forms allow data to be shifted more than one bit position, while the third

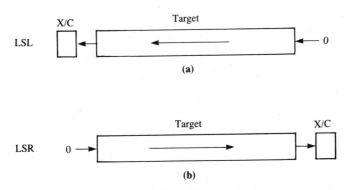

**Figure 3-8   The operation of (a) the logical shift left (LSL) and (b) the logical shift right (LSR) instructions.**

**Table 3-13   The Logical Shift Instructions**

| Instruction | Size (e) | Comment |
|---|---|---|
| LSL.e Dx,Dy | B,W,L | Shifts Dy left Dx number of places. |
| LSL.e #XXX,Dy | B,W,L | Shifts Dy left the immediate number of places. |
| LSL (ea) | word | Shifts the effective address left one place. |
| LSR.e Dx,Dy | B,W,L | Shifts Dy right Dx number of places. |
| LSR.e #XXX,Dy | B,W,L | Shifts Dy right the immediate number of places. |
| LSR (ea) | word | Shifts the effective address right one place. |

NOTE: The effective address may be a memory addressing mode only except for data register, address register direct, immediate, or program counter addressing, and the data must be a word. #XXX may be any number, 1–8.

form allows operand data to be shifted just one place. The first two forms can be of any size, while the third form works with only word-sized data.

The first form of addressing uses register Dx to indicate how many bits in register Dy are to be shifted. For example, if you wished to shift register Dy left 5 places, place a 5 into Dx before executing the shift instruction. The second form of addressing uses an immediate shift count instead of a count in register Dx. The application of this form is limited because the immediate shift count can be only the numbers 1–8, but that is the only drawback. The final form uses an effective address and shifts the word data specified by the operand only one bit position in the memory.

Suppose that you need to multiply the number in the word-sized data register D5 by a 32. This is accomplished using the multiply instruction or by shifting the number to the left 5 places. (See Example 3-25.) Each time a number is shifted left one place, it is multiplied by 2. So if a number is shifted left 5 binary places, you multiply it by 32 (= $2 \times 2 \times 2 \times 2 \times 2$). This shift instruction requires about 2.625 microseconds ($\mu$s) to execute in the 680XX microprocessor while the multiply instruction requires about 5.5 $\mu$s. (Both times assume an 8 MHz system clock.)

E  X  A  M  P  L  E    3 - 25

**(a)**

        001000 EB4D        LSL.W #5,D5

**(b)**

        001002 CAFC0020    MULU  #32,D5

If a number is shifted to the right, it is divided by a factor of 2 for each bit position it is shifted. Suppose that you need to divide the long-word contents of D3 by a factor of 16. This can be accomplished by shifting it to the right 4 places. The speed advantage over the divide instruction is as dramatic as it is with multiplication. Example 3-26 illustrates the instruction used for this division.

E  X  A  M  P  L  E      3 - 26

001000 E88B     LSR.L #4,D3

## Arithmetic Shift Instructions

Arithmetic shift instructions are used to divide or multiply signed numbers by factors of 2. Signed right shifts are different from logical right shifts because the sign-bit is preserved as the signed number in shifted right. For example, if an 8-bit signed number has a value of 1111 1100 ($-4$), and it is shifted right one place to divide it by 2, it becomes a 1111 1110 ($-2$). Notice that the sign-bit is preserved. If the sign-bit is not preserved, it becomes a 0111 1110 ($+126$), which is not $-4$ divided by 2. The arithmetic shift left is identical to the logical shift left but is provided to identify its use with signed numbers as compared to unsigned numbers, which use logical shifts. Refer to Figure 3-9 for the operation of the arithmetic left and right shifts.

Table 3-14 illustrates all the possible combinations available to the arithmetic shift right and left instructions. Notice that they have the same addressing options used with the logical shift instructions.

### 3-4.2   Rotate Instructions

The rotate instruction allows a number to be rotated through a data register or a memory location. Rotates are available in two forms. One form rotates the number through the register or memory location and the other through the memory or register and the extend (X-CCR) bit. Figure 3-10 illustrates the four rotate instructions and their operation. With all four instructions, the carry CCR bit receives a copy of the last bit rotated through the register or memory location. The X-CCR bit

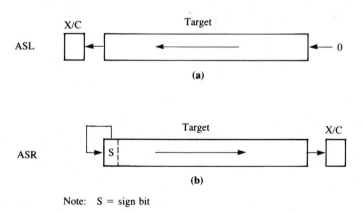

Note:   S = sign bit

**Figure 3-9   The two arithmetic shift instructions: (a) arithmetic shift left (ASL) and (b) arithmetic shift right (ASR).**

**Table 3-14**   Arithmetic Shift Instructions

| Instruction | Size (e) | Comment |
| --- | --- | --- |
| ASL.e Dx,Dy | B,W,L | Shifts Dy left Dx number of places. |
| ASL.e #XXX,Dy | B,W,L | Shifts Dy left the immediate number of places. |
| ASL (ea) | word | Shifts the effective address left one place. |
| ASR.e Dx,Dy | B,W,L | Shifts Dy right Dx number of places. |
| ASR.e #XXX,Dy | B,W,L | Shifts Dy right the immediate number of places. |
| ASR (ea) | word | Shifts the effective address right one place. |

NOTE: The effective address may be a memory addressing mode only except for program counter addressing, and the data must be a word. #XXX is a number between 1 and 8.

is used with the ROXL and ROXR instructions to hold the bit that is rotated through the register or memory location.

Table 3-15 illustrates the rotate instructions and shows the allowable forms used with symbolic coding. Notice that each of these instructions has three forms. The first, as with the shift instructions, allows register Dy to be rotated Dx number of

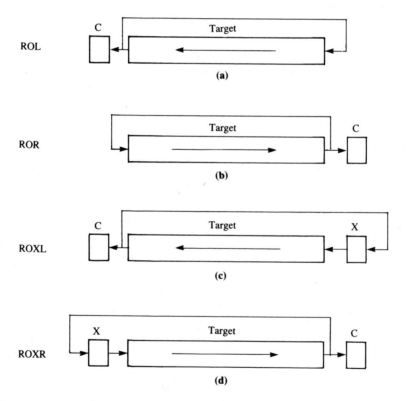

**Figure 3-10**   The four forms of the rotate instruction: (a) rotate left (ROL), (b) rotate right (ROR), (c) rotate left through extend (ROXL), and (d) rotate right through extend (ROXR).

**Table 3-15** The Rotate Instructions

| Instruction | Size (e) | Comment |
|---|---|---|
| ROL.e Dx,Dy | B,W,L | Rotates Dy left Dx places. |
| ROL.e #XXX,Dy | B,W,L | Rotates Dy left the immediate number of places. |
| ROL (ea) | word | Rotates the memory location addressed as the effective address left one place. |
| ROR.e Dx,Dy | B,W,L | Rotates Dy right Dx places. |
| ROR.e #XXX,Dy | B,W,L | Rotates Dy right the immediate number of places. |
| ROR (ea) | word | Rotates the memory location addressed as the effective address right one place. |
| ROXL.e Dx,Dy | B,W,L | Rotates Dy with X left Dx places. |
| ROXL.e #XXX,Dy | B,W,L | Rotates Dy with X left the immediate number of places. |
| ROXL (ea) | word | Rotates the memory location addressed by the effective address with X left one place. |
| ROXR.e Dx,Dy | B,W,L | Rotates Dy right with X Dx places. |
| ROXR.e #XXX,Dy | B,W,L | Rotates Dy right with X the immediate number of places. |
| ROXR (ea) | word | Rotates the memory location addressed by the effective address with X right one place. |

NOTE: The effective address is any memory addressing mode except program counter addressing. #XXX is a number between 1 and 8.

places. The second allows register Dy to be rotated an immediate number of places. The final form allows the contents of memory to be rotated one binary place.

The rotate instructions are used to position data in a data register or a memory location. For example, suppose that you need to exchange or reposition the bytes in the long-word data register so each byte is shifted left, with the most significant byte moved to the right-most byte. Assume that the data register contains a $00123466. If this number is repositioned as described, it would be $12346600. Notice how the bytes have moved left with the left-most placed at the right. Example 3-27 illustrates the sequence of instructions required to do this to D2 and store each of the four bytes in separate data registers D4, D5, D6, and D7.

E X A M P L E    3 - 27

```
001000 E19A      ROL.L   #8,D2
001002 1802      MOVE.B  D2,D4
001004 E19A      ROL.L   #8,D2
001006 1A02      MOVE.B  D2,D5
001008 E19A      ROL.L   #8,D2
00100A 1C02      MOVE.B  D2,D6
00100C E19A      ROL.L   #8,D2
00100E 1E02      MOVE.B  D2,D7
```

## 3-5   Miscellaneous Arithmetic and Logic Instructions

Now we describe the remaining arithmetic and logic instructions: clear (CLR), compare (CMP), test and set (TAS), and test (TST). Also shown are the instructions used to change the contents of the status register (SR) and the condition code register (CCR). These instructions are reserved for the final section of the chapter because they are not used as often as the commands covered earlier.

### 3-5.1   The Clear Instruction (CLR)

The CLR instruction is a special move instruction that is used to *clear* the contents of any data register or any memory location using any effective addressing mode except program counter addressing. The clear instruction allows bytes, words, or long-words to be cleared to zero. The clear instruction and its valid addressing modes are illustrated in Table 3-16. Notice that there is only one form of CLR and one operand. The CLR instruction never changes the contents of the X-CCR bit, but it does change the other CCR bits. The C-, V-, and N-CCR bits are always cleared to zero, and Z is always set by the CLR instruction. This instruction is used to clear the extend and carry bits if another register or memory location must also be cleared.

Suppose that you are required to clear the contents of the long-word data registers D1, D2, and D3 and the word contents of memory location $20000. Example 3-28 illustrates the program that is used to clear these registers and memory. An alternate to the clear instruction is the MOVE instruction with an immediate data of zero. The CLR instruction requires 2 bytes of memory to store, plus any additional bytes for the effective address. The MOVE requires at least 4 and up to 6 bytes, plus any additional for the effective address. CLR is the much more efficient choice.

E  X  A  M  P  L  E     3 - 28

```
001000 4281          CLR.L  D1
001002 4282          CLR.L  D2
001004 4283          CLR.L  D3
001006 427900020000  CLR.W  $20000
```

### 3-5.2   The Compare Instruction (CMP)

The compare instruction is used whenever two numbers are compared. *Compare* actually performs a subtraction, but the difference is not placed into the destination operand, as with subtraction. Instead, the compare instruction indicates the difference by changing the contents of the CCR bits to delineate the difference. This is useful whenever a number is to be tested for several different values, because the number under test does not change. Compare is the foundation of artificial intelligence.

Compare is available in several different forms, denoted in Table 3-17. As with certain other instructions that are written with assembly language, some forms of

**Table 3-16  The Clear Instruction**

| Instruction | Size (e) | Comment |
|---|---|---|
| CLR.e (ea) | B,W,L | Places a logic zero in the effective address. |

NOTE: The effective address is any addressing mode except address register direct and program counter addressing.

CMP that do not appear in this table are found in machine language. CMP in machine language may take the forms of CMPI (for a compare immediate), CMPA (to compare an address register), and CMPM (to compare the contents of memory data). Again these forms do not normally appear in programs written in assembly language, but only in machine language form.

Suppose that the byte portion of data register D2 contains an ASCII character and you need to determine whether the letter Y is present. This can be accomplished by comparing the portion in question with the ASCII code for the letter Y ($59). Example 3-29 illustrates the compare instruction used for this purpose. Normally the compare is followed by a conditional branch instruction to determine whether an equal condition exists. The instructions used for branching are discussed in the next chapter, along with many examples of their usage. The zero CCR bit is used to indicate whether D2 contains a $59. If the result of the comparison is zero, then D2 contained a $59; if the result was not zero, D2 did not contain a $59.

E X A M P L E   3 - 29

```
    001000 0C020059    CMP.B #$59,D2
```

**Table 3-17  The Compare Instructions**

| Instruction | Size (e) | Comment |
|---|---|---|
| CMP.e (ea),Dn | B,W,L | Subtracts the effective address from Dn; only the CCR bits change. |
| CMP.e (ea),An | W,L | Subtracts the effective address from An; only the CCR bits change. |
| CMP.e #XXX,(ea) | B,W,L | Subtracts the immediate data from the effective address; only the CCR bits change. |
| CMP.e (Ay)+,(Ax)+ | B,W,L | Subtracts the contents of the memory locations addressed by Ay and Ax; and only the CCR bits change. Next, the contents of both Ay and Ax are incremented without affecting the CCR. |

NOTE: If the effective address is the source operand, any addressing mode may be used; if it is the destination operand, any addressing mode may be used except address register direct, immediate, or program counter addressing.

### 3-5.3   The Test and Set Instruction (TAS)

Test and set (TAS) is an instruction that will test the byte contents of the operand address and change CCR bits N and Z to indicate the outcome of the test. After the test, TAS will set the most significant bit position of the byte under test. This instruction is unique because it reads the data from memory and tests and rewrites everything in one indivisible operation called a *read/write/modify* memory cycle. This means that no other microprocessor in a shared system can interfere with this operation as it executes. This unique instruction and its application are discussed in more detail in later chapters devoted to hardware.

The TAS instruction appears in the form TAS (ea), where the effective address is any byte located in a data register or any memory location. This instruction allows all memory addressing modes except program counter addressing.

### 3-5.4   The Test Instruction (TST)

The test instruction is used to test the byte, word, or long-word addressed as the operand. The operand can address any data register or any memory location using any of the memory addressing modes except program counter addressing. TST evaluates the number under test and then adjusts the contents of the CCR bits Z and N, the condition code register bits that indicate whether the number is zero or negative. The number being measured is never changed by this instruction. This instruction actually performs a compare immediate, using the number zero as the test data. A zero is subtracted from the operand and the CCR bits change to indicate the difference. The TST instruction appears as a TST.B (ea), TST.W (ea), or TST.L (ea) in a program, and the effective address can be anything except an address register, immediate data, or program counter addressing.

### 3-5.5   Modifying the CCR Register

At times, the CCR register must be modified by a program. For example, it is sometimes desired to clear or set the carry CCR bit. The 680XX does not have an instruction to do this directly, but it can be done using the CCR as an operand with the AND, OR, exclusive-OR, and MOVE instructions. Note that any AND, OR, or exclusive-OR instruction will also clear the carry CCR bit. Table 3-18 illustrates the instructions that may use the CCR register as an operand.

Suppose that you are required to clear the extend CCR bit, as is often done before an addition with extend (ADDX). This is accomplished by using the AND #$EF,CCR instruction. This instruction leaves all the bits of the CCR unaffected except the X-CCR bit, which is cleared to zero. The X-CCR bit is set if the OR #$10,CCR instruction is executed and complemented if the EOR #$10,CCR instruction is used. The remaining CCR bits can be cleared, set, or complemented in like manner using the correct immediate data.

The MOVE to or from the CCR can be used to save the contents of the CCR in memory or a data register. Later in a program, CCR can be loaded with a MOVE instruction. This can become a useful feature for saving the condition code bits at the point at which they change, in some programs.

**Table 3-18    Instructions That Use CCR as an Operand**

| Instruction | Size | Comment |
|---|---|---|
| AND #XXX,CCR | byte | ANDs immediate data with the CCR to clear bits. |
| EOR #XXX,CCR | byte | Exclusive-ORs immediate data with the CCR to invert bits. |
| MOVE (ea),CCR | byte | Moves byte from the effective address into the CCR. |
| MOVE CCR,(ea) | word | Transfers the CCR to the effective address, with the left-most 8-bits of the effective address cleared to zero. |
| OR #XXX,CCR | byte | OR immediates data, with the CCR to set bits. |

NOTE: If the effective address is the source operand, any addressing mode may be used except address register direct; if it is the destination operand, any addressing mode may be used except immediate, address register direct, and program counter addressing.

### 3-5.6    Modifying the Status Register (SR)

Although the status register is not normally changed and, in fact, cannot be changed from user programs, it is often changed in system software operating in the supervisor mode. If the SR is changed while operating in the user mode, the microprocessor will execute a privilege violation exception. This prohibits the use of SR modifying instructions in the user mode. More information about privileged instructions is provided in Chapter 9, which details interrupts and exceptions. Table 3-19 illustrates the instructions that are used to manipulate the contents of the SR.

## Summary

1. Binary addition is accomplished with the ADD instruction. Bytes, words, and long-words are added using data registers, immediate data, address registers, or any memory location. About the only addition that cannot be accomplished is memory-to-memory addition. As data are added, the contents of the CCR are affected to disclose condition of the sum.

**Table 3-19    Modifying the Status Register (SR)**

| Instruction | Size | Comment |
|---|---|---|
| AND #XXX,SR | word | AND immediates data with SR to clear bits to zero. |
| EOR #XXX,SR | word | Exclusive-OR immediates data with the SR to invert bits. |
| MOVE (ea),SR | word | Moves the contents of the effective address to the SR. |
| MOVE SR,(ea) | word | Moves the SR to the effective address. |
| OR #XXX,SR | word | OR immediates data with SR to set bits. |

NOTE: If the effective address is the source operand, any addressing mode may be used except address register direct. If it is the destination operand, any addressing mode may be used except immediate, address register direct, and program counter addressing.

2. Other forms of addition that normally appear only in machine language are ADDI (add immediate), ADDQ (add quick), and ADDA (add an address register). These opcodes are available with the assembler, but are seldom found. Luckily only the ADD instruction ever need appear in an assembly language program, which requires the programmer only to remember that any addition is ADD.

3. The ADDX instruction allows byte, word, or long-word data to be added plus the contents of the extend (X-CCR) bit. This operation is important if numbers wider than 32 bits are to be added. Two forms are available for this instruction: a data register may be added plus X, and the contents of two memory locations may be added plus X using only the predecrement mode of indirect memory addressing.

4. Subtraction occurs on bytes, words, or long-words using the SUB instruction. This instruction uses almost any addressing mode. About the only subtraction that cannot be performed is a memory-to-memory subtraction. The CCR bits are affected by the subtraction instruction to indicate the condition of the difference. There are other forms of subtract that normally appear only in machine language, such as SUBI (subtract immediate), SUBA (subtract an address register), and SUBQ (subtract quick).

5. Subtraction with the extend CCR bit is accomplished by using the SUBX instruction. This instruction is normally used whenever two numbers wider than 32 bits are to be subtracted. This instruction allows the contents of two byte, word, or long-word data registers to be subtracted with X and also the contents of two memory locations using the predecrement mode of addressing.

6. The NEG and NEGX instructions are used to two's-complement a byte, word, or long-word and also, using NEGX, to two's-complement a number of any size that is wider than 32 bits. When a signed integer is two's-complemented, its arithmetic sign is changed without affecting its magnitude.

7. Binary-coded decimal (BCD) operations are performed directly on packed bytes of data using the ABCD (addition), SBCD (subtraction), or NBCD (negation) instructions. In all cases the X-CCR bit is added or subtracted as part of the operation.

8. Multiplication and division are performed on signed and unsigned numbers using the MULU, MULS, DIVU, and DIVS instructions. In multiplication, two 16-bit numbers are multiplied and the product is 32 bits wide. With division, a 32-bit number is divided by a 16-bit number to produce a 16-bit quotient and 16-bit remainder. There are two types of division error: divide by zero and divide overflow. The divide overflow causes the overflow CCR bit to be set, and the divide by zero causes an interrupt to occur.

9. The EXT instruction is used to convert signed bytes to words or signed words to signed long-words by sign-extending them. This instruction is most often used before a division to make an 8- or 16-bit number into a 32-bit number for the dividend.

10. The four logic instructions available are AND, OR, exclusive-OR, and NOT (invert). The AND instruction is often used to turn bits off, and the OR instruction turns bits on; the exclusive-OR and NOT instructions both inverts bits.

11. BTST, BSET, BCLR, and BCHG are used to test a binary bit and then set, clear, or change it.

12. Shift instructions occur in logical and arithmetic forms. The logical shift instructions are often used to multiply or divide unsigned numbers by powers of 2 and the arithmetic shifts are used with signed numbers.

13. Rotate instructions are available to rotate a byte, word, or long-word right or left. Two options of the right and left rotate are available: rotate without X and rotate with X. ROL and ROR rotate without X and ROXL and ROXR rotate with X.

14. The CLR (clear) instruction is used to clear the contents of data registers or memory locations to zero.

15. Compare (CMP) is used to compare two numbers to determine whether they are equal or to test their relative sizes. A compare is a subtraction, but the difference is not placed into the destination operand; instead, only the CCR bits change to indicate the characteristics of the difference.

16. The contents of the CCR register are changed by using the AND, OR, or EOR instructions. The CCR may also be transferred between itself and an operand using the MOVE instruction.

17. The status register (SR) may be set, cleared, or changed with the AND, OR, and EOR instructions, as well as MOVE.

18. The TST instruction is used to test an operand for a zero or negative condition. Test is performed by subtracting the operand from a zero.

19. The test and set instruction TAS is used to test a byte and change the Z-CCR and N-CCR bits to indicate the sign and whether the number under test is a zero. After the test, the most significant bit of the byte under test is set to a logic one.

## Questions

1. The ADD instruction can add _____, _____, or _____-_____.

2. Write the assembly language instruction to perform each of the following tasks.
   (a) Add the byte in register D2 to register D3 and store the result in D3.
   (b) Add a $1234 to the word in register D6.
   (c) Add the long-word contents of the memory location addressed by A4 to D2 and store the result in D2.
   (d) Add the long-word in A3 to A4 and store the result in A4.
   (e) Add the byte contents of D3 to memory location $3000 and store the result in memory location $3000.

3. Explain what each of the following instructions accomplishes.
   (a) ADD.L  D3,D4
   (b) ADD.W  $2300,D3
   (c) ADD.B  #250,D5
   (d) ADD.L  D3,(A3)+
   (e) ADD.B  A3,A6

4. Develop a short program that will add the contents of all the byte-sized data registers together and store the result in memory location $2000.

5. Write a short sequence of instructions that adds the contents of word memory locations $1000, $1002, and $1004 together and stores the sum at word memory location $1006.

6. What two addressing modes are allowed when using the ADDX instruction?

7. Develop the sequence of instructions required to add the two 64-bit numbers stored in locations $1000–$1007 and $1008–$100F together. Store the 64-bit result in memory locations $1010–$1017.

8. Write an assembly language instruction to perform each of the following tasks.
   (a) Subtract the byte D2 register from D3.
   (b) Subtract a $1000 from the word contents of memory location $23000.
   (c) Subtract the long-word contents of the memory location addressed by A3 from D3.
   (d) Subtract long-word A3 for A4.
   (e) Subtract the byte in D2 from the memory location addressed by A3 and after subtracting, increment A3.

9. Explain what each of the following instructions accomplishes.
   (a) SUB.B  D2,D7
   (b) SUB.L  -(A6),D1
   (c) SUB.B  #3,(A4,D2.W)
   (d) SUB.L  #$44FF,$20000
   (e) SUB.W  A6,SP

10. Write the sequence of instructions required to subtract the byte contents of memory location $3000 from $3001 and store the result in $3002.

11. Develop a short program that will subtract the word contents of D2 from each of the following memory locations: $2000, $2002, and $2004. Store the three differences in these three memory locations.

12. What does a SUBX.B D2,D3 instruction accomplish?

13. Write a program that will subtract the 64-bit number in memory locations $1000–$1007 from the 64-bit number in $1008–$100F and store the difference at locations $1010–$1017.

14. What is an underflow and when does it occur?

15. What is the difference between a MULU and an MULS?

16. The MULU D2,D3 instruction will multiply the _____-bit number in D2 times the _____-bit number in D3 and store the _____-bit product in D3.

17. The DIVU D2,D3 instruction will divide the _____-bit number in D3 by the _____-bit number in D2.

18. Develop a short program that will find the average of the five byte-wide numbers stored in memory locations $3000-$3004 and store the average in $3005.

19. Write a short program that will multiply the byte at memory location $3000 times the byte at location $3001 and store the word product at location $3002.

20. The AND operation will produce a logic one when what condition exists?

21. The OR operation will produce a logic zero when what condition exists?

22. The exclusive-OR operation will produce a logic one for what conditions?

23. Write a short sequence of instructions that will set bits 7 and 6 of D2, clear bits 10 and 11 of D2, and then invert bits 31 and 24 of D2.

24. Develop a short sequence of instructions that will set bits 7 through 4 of the byte memory location $2000 and clear bit 0 of the same location.

25. Use the BSET and BCLR instructions to accomplish question 24.

26. Develop the sequence of instructions required to logically shift the byte contents of memory location $3000 three places to the right.

27. Explain the difference between the logical and arithmetic right shift.

28. Which rotate instruction will rotate data to the right through the X-CCR bit?

29. Develop a short program that will logically shift the 64-bit number in memory locations $3000–$3007 one place to the right.

30. Select an instruction that will set the X-CCR bit.

31. Choose an instruction that will clear the word contents of data register D4 to a zero.

32. Write a short program that will clear the contents of memory locations $3000-$3007 to zero.

33. Choose an instruction that will clear the carry CCR bit.

34. Select an instruction that will invert the contents of the zero CCR bit.

35. What instruction is used to store the contents of the CCR into memory location $3000?

# 4

# *Program Control Instructions*

**OBJECTIVES**

Upon completion of this chapter, you will be able to:

- Explain what each conditional branch instruction tests and how such instructions are used in short example programs.

- Describe how the unconditional branch instructions function.

- Detail the difference between a jump and a branch.

- Define the purpose of a subroutine or procedure.

- Explain how the branch-to-subroutine or jump-to-subroutine instruction uses the system stack to store the return address.

- Explain how a user LIFO and FIFO stack is created in the memory system.

- Explain the function and operation of the LINK and UNLK instructions.

**KEY TERMS**

| | | |
|---|---|---|
| displacement | subroutine | queue |
| relocatable | nesting | silo-mode |
| indirect jump | local subroutines | storage, spooler, or |
| conditional branch | system subroutines | pipeline |
| instructions | local system, global | software fix |
| repeat-until | subroutines | |
| operation | | |

THE program control instructions, the last group of instructions described, are by no means the least used or the least important instruction type. On the contrary, program control instructions have made the computer the powerful and useful system that it is today.

Modern computing machines appear to think because of the program control instruction's ability to make decisions. Without this type of instruction, and the computer's ability to make a decision, the computer would be no more powerful than the nonprogrammable hand-held calculator.

## 4-1 Branch and Jump Instructions

We begin with the branch and jump program control instructions, which allow the program flow to be altered whenever the program is executed by the microprocessor. Branch instructions are either unconditional or conditional, while the jump instruction is always unconditional. The unconditional branch and unconditional jump instructions allow the program to branch or jump to another memory location to continue executing the program. This alters the flow of the program.

### 4-1.1 Unconditional Branch

The unconditional branch instruction allows the microprocessor to branch to any point in the program. This operation is fundamentally the same as performed by the GOTO instruction in a BASIC language program. Branch allows the program to GOTO another step in the program. The branch is unconditional because no restriction is placed on it. The branch instruction will always branch if placed in a program. In keeping with structured programming concepts, the unconditional branch instruction should be used sparingly in a program.

The unconditional branch is available in two forms in the 680XX microprocessor: (1) a short branch that allows a branch within +129 or −126 bytes from the branch instruction's memory location and (2) a long branch that allows a branch to occur within +32,769 or −32,766 bytes from the location of the branch instruction. The symbolic opcode used for a branch instruction is BRA. If an assembler is used, the operand for the BRA instruction is usually a symbolic memory location or label.

Table 4-1 illustrates the forms allowed for the BRA instruction using an assembler. The first two instructions in the table are examples that use a numeric displacement as the operand. A *displacement* is a distance. In the 680XX microprocessor the value of the displacement is sign-extended to 32 bits. This sign-extended displacement is added to the address where the branch instruction is stored plus 2 bytes to form the address of the next instruction. The location plus 2 bytes is the value contained in the program counter for the branch instruction. As mentioned, the distance that is allowed for the branch ranges between +129 and −126 bytes for a short branch and between +32,769 and −32,766 bytes for a long branch.

Be forewarned that the BRA instruction with a numeric displacement is not

**Table 4-1** The Unconditional Branch Instruction

| Instruction | Comment |
|---|---|
| BRA *+$30 | Branches to the location that is $32 bytes past the BRA instruction. |
| BRA *+$1000 | Branches to the location that is $1002 bytes past the branch instruction. |
| BRA NEXT | Branches to memory location NEXT. |

NOTE: The * + displacement is used to indicate the displacement to many assemblers, and the last form is normally used with the assembler.

coded the same in all assembler programs. If you have a doubt, refer to the manual that accompanies your version of the assembler. Also note that some assemblers always use the 2-byte displacement for a branch. Some use the 2-byte form for all forward references and the 1-byte form for reverse references if possible. Still other assembler programs use the best possible form for the distance to be traversed. This last form is the ideal version of the assembler because it is the most efficient code generator.

The short BRA instruction uses an 8-bit signed displacement that is sign-extended to 32 bits and added to the location of the branch instruction plus 2 bytes (the program counter contents) when the branch occurs. This addition creates the address of the location branched to by the BRA instruction. Short branch instructions are always 2 bytes in length with an opcode of $60 followed by an 8-bit signed displacement. Figure 4-1 illustrates the effect of a BRA $4 instruction. Here the 4 is added to the contents of the program counter plus 2 bytes to jump to the memory location illustrated. The BRA branches over 4 bytes of memory with a displacement of $04. Note that the program counter address for a BRA is the address of the branch instruction plus 2 bytes.

The long branch instruction uses a 16-bit signed displacement. The displacement is sign-extended to 32 bits and added to the program counter when the branch occurs. This is the same as the short branch instruction except the displacement is initially 16 bits instead of 8. The long branch instruction always occupies 4 bytes of memory with the first 2 bytes equal to a $6000 followed by the 16-bit signed displacement.

The main difference between short and long branches is that the short branch allows a branch within +129 and −126 bytes from the BRA instruction address, while the long branch allows a branch within +32,769 and −32,766 bytes—a much greater range. Note that a short branch may not use a displacement value of $00 because the 680XX interprets this as a long branch instruction. A displacement of $00 branched to the next instruction serves no useful purpose.

Figure 4-2 illustrates the long branch instruction using a displacement of $1000. Here the instruction occupies 4 bytes of memory and branches $1002 bytes

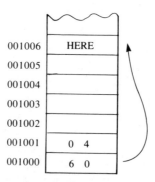

**Figure 4-1**   The short BRA instruction placed at memory location $001000 branches to location $001006 because the displacement in this example is $04.

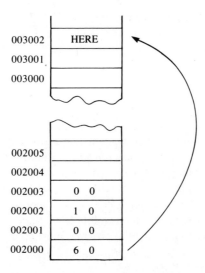

**Figure 4-2** The long BRA instruction uses a 16-bit signed displacement to create the branch address. The branch address is $1002 bytes forward in the memory in this example because the displacement is a $1000.

ahead in the memory from the location of the branch instruction. As with the short branch, the displacement is added to the program counter plus 2 bytes.

In most cases the form of the branch instruction most often used with assembly language programming is the BRA instruction with the symbolic memory address as an operand. When the assembler encounters a symbolic label (memory address), it calculates the displacement value and stores the BRA as either a short or a long branch instruction. (Some assemblers will always store the long form of the BRA instruction.)

Example 4-1 shows how the BRA instruction is used to branch to other parts of the program. Notice that some of these branches are short and require 2 bytes for storage and some are long, calling for 4 bytes for storage. The first BRA adds a $00000006 to the address $001002 (the address of the BRA instruction plus 2 bytes) to branch to memory location $001008. The second branch adds a $00001000 to the branch instruction address plus 2 ($00100A) to branch to memory location $00200A. The last branch instruction repeats this process continuously because it adds an $FFFFEFF4 (a sign-extended $EFF4) to the branch instruction address plus 2 ($00200C) to branch back to location $001000.

E X A M P L E   4 - 1

```
001000  6008        BRA     *+$08       ;branch to location 001008
              .          .
              .          .
              .          .
```

```
001008 60001000      BRA     *+$1000      ;branch to location 00200A
                       .       .
                       .       .
                       .       .
00200A 6000EFF4      BRA     *+$EFF4      ;branch to location 001000
```

## Why Is a Displacement Used with a BRA?

The BRA instruction uses a displacement instead of an actual absolute branch address to ensure that it can be easily relocated. Because the displacement stored with the BRA is a distance, it is very easy to move this instruction and any other instruction that uses displacement addressing. The reason is that the distance between the BRA and the location being branched to does not change if a program is moved or relocated. Programs written in this fashion are called *relocatable*. Note that to qualify as relocatable, an entire program must be moved together as a unit.

### 4-1.2   Unconditional Jump

The unconditional jump instruction (JMP) performs the same basic operation as a branch. The difference between the BRA and JMP is that a BRA stores a displacement with the opcode and a JMP stores the absolute memory address of the next instruction. The absolute memory address is stored following the opcode. JMP may also use some of the indirect forms of addressing memory. For this reason, the JMP instruction is not easily relocated because an absolute address is stored as an operand. Relocatable software does not normally use the JMP instruction.

Suppose that Example 4-1 is rewritten so that it uses the JMP instruction in place of the BRA instruction. Notice that the address is stored after the opcode in Example 4-2 instead of a displacement. In this example, all the JMP instructions use the word absolute memory address as an operand. A long-word address is found with JMP if the location that is jumped to warrants it.

**E X A M P L E   4 - 2**

```
001000 4EF81008      JMP     $1008      ;jump to location 001008
                      .        .
                      .        .
                      .        .
001008 4EF8200A      JMP     $200A      ;jump to location 00200A
                      .        .
                      .        .
                      .        .
00200A 4EF81000      JMP     $1000      ;jump to location 001000
```

## Addressing Modes for JMP

The jump instruction allows an operand addressing mode of anything except immediate, data or address register direct, or address register indirect, using either the predecrement or postincrement modes. Table 4-2 illustrates the JMP instruction

Table 4-2 The JMP Instruction Addressing Modes

| Instruction | Comment |
|---|---|
| JMP (An) | Jumps to the address held in An. |
| JMP d(An) | Jumps to the address held in An plus d. |
| JMP d(An,Rn) | Jumps to the address held in An plus d plus Rn. |
| JMP $8000 | Jumps to address $FF8000 (word address). |
| JMP $008000 | Jumps to address $008000 (long-word address). |
| JMP d(PC) | Jumps to address held in PC plus d. |
| JMP d(PC,Rn) | Jumps to address held in PC plus d plus Rn. |

NOTE: d = displacement and Rn = any data or address register.

with each valid addressing mode. Remember that the most common form of addressing for the JMP instruction is the word or long-word absolute form.

Suppose that A3 contains a $00004000 and the JMP (A3) instruction is executed. The program will jump to memory location $004000 for its next instruction because A3 contains the address that is jumped to by this instruction. This type of jump is often called an *indirect jump*. If a displacement is added, then the value of the displacement is added to the number in the address register to form the address. Suppose that A3 still contains a $00004000 and the JMP 3(A3) instruction is executed. Now the next instruction after the JMP 3(A3) instruction will be at memory location $004003, which is $00004000 plus the displacement of 3.

### 4-1.3 Conditional Branches

The *conditional branch instructions* allow the 680XX to make decisions based on the state of the machine as reflected by the CCR bits. Table 4-3 illustrates all the configurations available for the conditional branch instructions. Notice from the table that each branch is listed with the first byte of its opcode and also the condition tested. Each conditional branch instruction is followed by either an 8- or a 16-bit displacement that dictates the distance or displacement of the branch.

A conditional branch instruction branches only if the condition under test is true. If the condition is false, the microprocessor continues execution of the next sequential instruction in the program. Note that this is identical to the syntax of the IF statement in a BASIC language program (If – true then branch).

If a BCC (branch if carry is cleared) instruction is used in a program, and the place to be branched to is 4 bytes from the location of the BCC instruction, then the displacement value is a 02. If the instruction is stored as a $6402, the branch if carry is cleared instruction will branch 4 bytes beyond itself if the carry CCR bit is a zero. If a BCC is used and the place branched to is $200 bytes from the location of the BCC instruction, the displacement is a $1FE. The instruction is stored as a $640001FE. Notice that the byte following the opcode of $64 is a zero, and next two bytes contain the displacement value of $1FE stored as $01FE. Recall that if the second byte of a branch instruction is a zero, the branch is a long branch.

**Table 4-3**   The Conditional Branch Instructions

| Opcode | Instruction | CCR bit(s) tested | Command |
|--------|-------------|-------------------|---------|
| 64 | BCC disp | C | branch if carry is cleared (0) |
| 65 | BCS disp | C | branch if carry is set (1) |
| 67 | BEQ disp | Z | branch if equal (zero) |
| 6C | BGE disp | N,V | branch if greater than or equal |
| 6E | BGT disp | N,V,Z | branch if greater than |
| 62 | BHI disp | C,Z | branch if higher |
| 6F | BLE disp | N,V,Z | branch if less than or equal |
| 63 | BLS disp | C,Z | branch if lower or the same |
| 6D | BLT disp | N,V | branch if less than |
| 6B | BMI disp | N | branch if minus |
| 66 | BNE disp | Z | branch if not equal (not zero) |
| 6A | BPL disp | N | branch if plus |
| 68 | BVC disp | V | branch if overflow cleared (0) |
| 69 | BVS disp | V | branch if overflow set (1) |

NOTE: disp is an 8- or 16-bit displacement, and the opcode is always follwed by an 8-bit displacement or a $00, then a 16-bit displacement.

Probably the most commonly used conditional branch instruction is the BEQ or the BNE. In many cases, in most programs that use conditional branch instructions, we are searching for an equal or not equal condition. The BEQ instruction also is used to branch if a value is zero, and the BNE instruction is also used to branch on a not-zero value.

For example, suppose that you need to develop a sequence of instructions to test the byte portion of D2 for a value of $0D, $1A, or $20. If the $0D is present, you wish to jump to memory location $001020; if the $1A is present, to location $001030; and if the $20 is present, to $001040. Refer to Example 4-3 for this program. The program illustrated uses compare instructions to test D2, then a conditional branch to make each decision.

E  X  A  M  P  L  E     4 - 3

```
001000 B038000D        CMP.B  $0D,D0
001004 671A            BEQ    *+$1C       ;if $0D branch to $1020
001006 B038001A        CMP.B  $1A,D0
00100A 6724            BEQ    *+$26       ;if $1A branch to $1030
00100C B0380020        CMP.B  $20,D0
001010 672E            BEQ.B  *+$30       ;if $20 branch to $1040
```

## Testing Relative Magnitudes

Using the conditional branch instructions for testing relative magnitudes of numbers is accomplished on signed numbers by using the BEQ, BNE, BGT, BGE, BLT, or BLE instructions. If the relative magnitudes of unsigned numbers are tested, the

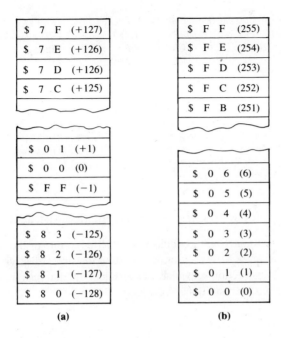

**Figure 4-3** The pattern followed by signed (a) and unsigned (b) numbers.

BEQ, BNE, BHI, or BLS instructions are used in a program. The terms "higher than," "lower than," and "the same" refer to unsigned numbers. The terms "greater than" and "less than" refer to signed numbers.

Two sets of magnitude tests are included in the instruction set because signed and unsigned numbers do not follow the same binary order. Figure 4-3 shows how signed and unsigned numbers are ordered. Notice that the $00 is at the bottom of the list of unsigned numbers, but in the middle of the list of signed numbers. Because of the difference in the ordering, two sets of relational comparison instructions for decisions (conditional branches) are needed.

Example 4-4 illustrates a program that tests the signed bytes of memory between $002000 and $002030. These numbers are tested to see whether they are above or below a +10. Each time a byte that is above +10 is encountered, it is counted, and each byte below +10 is counted. If the value is equal to a +10, it is not counted. After the program has been executed, the contents of memory location $002031 contain the count of the numbers above a +10 and location $002032 contains a count of the numbers below a +10.

E X A M P L E   4 - 4

```
001000 207C00002000    MOVE.L #$2000,A0    ;address data
001006 103C0031        MOVE.B #$31,D0      ;load count
00100A 4201            CLR.B  D1           ;clear counters
00100C 4202            CLR.B  D2
```

```
00100E  0C18000A     LOOP  CMP.B   #10,(A0)+   ;compare numbers
001012  6700000E           BEQ     NEXT        ;if a + 10
001016  6E000008           BGT     UP          ;if greater than + 10
00101A  5201         ·     ADD.B   #1,D1       ;if less than + 10
00101C  60000004           BRA     NEXT
001020  5202         UP    ADD.B   #1,D2
001022  5300         NEXT  SUB.B   #1,D0
001024  66E8               BNE     LOOP

001026  11C12032           MOVE.B  D1,$2032    ;save less than count
00102A  11C22031           MOVE.B  D2,$2031    ;greater than count
00102E  60FE         ENDP  BRA     ENDP
```

## 4-1.4   The Decrement and Branch Until Condition Instruction

The decrement and branch until condition instruction is one of the more powerful instructions in the 680XX instruction set and one that is used in virtually all programs. The DBcc instruction is available as an unconditional instruction and also as 14 different versions of conditional instructions.

### The DBRA Instruction

The DBRA instruction is in the form of DBRA Dn,LABEL, where Dn is a word-sized counter and LABEL is the address of the branch. DBRA is a conditional instruction in the sense that it decrements the word-sized data register Dn and branches to the LABEL if the value of Dn is not equal to a $-1$ after the decrement. The DBRA instruction is a decrement and branch until Dn is a $-1$. As shown later, the DBRA instruction is not considered to be a conditional instruction because it does not test any condition other than the value of Dn. The other 14 DBcc instructions apply to conditions in addition to the testing of the value of the loop counter for a $-1$.

The DBRA form of the decrement and branch instruction is useful in Example 4-4 as a loop counter. Example 4-5 shows how DBRA is used when Example 4-4 is rewritten using this instruction to form a loop. Notice that D0 is still used for the loop counter, but it is initialized to one less than the number of iterations required. This occurs because the DBRA instruction terminates the loop on a count of $-1$ rather than zero as in Example 4-4. Also notice that if the count is small, such as $31, the DBRA instruction requires extra register space because a word counter is required. In cases of a small count, it may be advantageous in certain instances to use the technique illustrated in Example 4-4 rather than Example 4-5.

E  X  A  M  P  L  E      4 - 5

```
001000  207C00002000       MOVE.L  #$2000,A0   ;address data
001006  303C0030           MOVE.W  #$30,D0     ;load count
00100A  4201               CLR.B   D1          ;clear counters
00100C  4202               CLR.B   D2
```

```
00100E  0C18000A    LOOP  CMP.B  #10,(A0)+    ;compare numbers
001012  6700000E          BEQ    NEXT         ;if +10
001016  6E000008          BGT    UP           ;if greater than +10
00101A  5201              ADD.B  #1,D1        ;if less than +10
00101C  60000004          BRA    NEXT
001020  5202        UP    ADD.B  #1,D2
001022  51C8FFEA    NEXT  DBRA   D0,LOOP

001026  11C12032          MOVE.B  D1,$2032    ;save less than count
00102A  11C22031          MOVE.B  D2,$2031    ;greater than count
00102E  60FE        ENDP  BRA    ENDP
```

The DBRA instruction follows the structured programming concept *repeat-until*. Figure 4-4 illustrates this construct using the DBRA instruction to repeat an *operation* until the count in Dn hits a value of $-1$. Again note that the count is a 16-bit count and the branch displacement is a 16-bit sign-extended displacement.

Suppose that you are required to copy the contents of a block of memory beginning at location $3000 into a block of memory beginning at location $4000. In this example you are to transfer all the bytes of memory from $3000–$3FFF into locations $4000–$4FFF.

Example 4-6 illustrates this task using the DBRA instruction for the repeat-until construct. The first three instructions are used to initialize the two address registers and also the count, which is $0FFF in this example. The instruction at address LOOP moves the byte data from the first block of memory into the second block and then increments both address registers. Finally, the DBRA instruction causes the MOVE.B $(A0)+,(A1)+$ instruction to be repeated $1000 times because the count is $FFF.

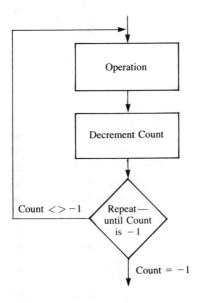

**Figure 4-4** The repeat-until construct followed by the DBRA instruction.

```
001000 307C3000        MOVE.W #$3000,A0     ;address source
001004 327C4000        MOVE.W #$4000,A1     ;address destination
001008 303C0FFF        MOVE.W #$FFF,D0      ;load count

00100C 12D8     LOOP   MOVE.B (A0)+,(A1)+   ;move byte
00100E 51C8FFFC        DBRA   D0,LOOP       ;repeat $1000 times

001012 60FE     ENDP   BRA    ENDP          ;end program
```

## The Conditional DBCC Instructions

In addition to unconditional DBRA, there are conditional forms of the decrement and branch instruction. These conditional forms test all the conditions that the branch instructions are able to test. Table 4-4 lists all the variations of the DBCC instruction, including DBRA, along with the first byte of each of these 4-byte-long instructions. The second byte contains the data register number so it is not listed here. Refer to Appendix B for binary placement of the data register number in this second byte. The third and fourth bytes of the DBCC instruction contain a signed 16-bit displacement for the branch.

The conditional decrement and branch instructions basically perform the DBRA operation if the condition tested is false. For example, if the DBCC instruction is used in a program, the carry CCR bit is tested. If carry is set, DBCC will decrement Dn and branch if Dn is not equal to a $-1$. If the carry CCR bit is cleared, the next instruction following the DBCC instruction is executed without changing Dn.

You might try to remember the function of these instructions by stating that DBCC means "decrement and branch until carry is cleared." The key word here is until (repeat-until carry is cleared). The branch occurs as long as the carry CCR bit is set and Dn does not reach $-1$.

Although it is not possible to show an example of each of the DBCC instructions, a few are given. Suppose that it is required to search through a list of word data stored at locations $3000–$4FFF for a value of $340F. This is accomplished by using the DBEQ instruction as illustrated in Example 4-7.

```
001000 307C3000        MOVE.W #$3000,A0     ;address data
001004 303C0FFF        MOVE.W #$FFF,D0      ;load count
001008 323C340F        MOVE.W #$340F,D1     ;load number

00100C B258     LOOP   CMP.W  (A0)+,D1      ;compare data
00100E 57C8FFFC        DBEQ   D0,LOOP       ;repeat until found

001012 0C40FFFF        CMP.W  #$FFFF,D0     ;test D0 for -1
001016 67XX            BEQ    NOTFOUND      ;if not found
```

**Table 4-4** The Decrement and Branch Until Instructions

| Opcode | Instruction | Comment |
|---|---|---|
| 54 | DBCC Dn ,LABEL | If carry is a 1, decrements Dn and branches if Dn ⟨⟩ −1. |
| 55 | DBCS Dn ,LABEL | If carry is a 0, decrements Dn and branches if Dn ⟨⟩ −1. |
| 57 | DBEQ Dn ,LABEL | If not equal, decrements Dn and branches if Dn ⟨⟩ −1. |
| 51 | DBRA Dn ,LABEL | Decrements Dn and branches if Dn ⟨⟩ −1. |
| 5C | DBGE Dn ,LABEL | If less than, decrements Dn and branches if Dn ⟨⟩ −1. |
| 5E | DBGT Dn ,LABEL | If less than or equal, decrements Dn and branches if Dn ⟨⟩ −1. |
| 52 | DBHI Dn ,LABEL | If lower or the same, decrements Dn and branches if Dn ⟨⟩ −1. |
| 5F | DBLE Dn ,LABEL | If greater, decrements Dn and branches if Dn is ⟨⟩ −1. |
| 53 | DBLS Dn ,LABEL | If higher, decrements Dn and branches if Dn is ⟨⟩ −1. |
| 5D | DBLT Dn ,LABEL | If greater or equal, decrements Dn and branches if Dn ⟨⟩ −1. |
| 5B | DBMI Dn ,LABEL | If positive, decrements Dn and branches if Dn ⟨⟩ −1. |
| 56 | DBNE Dn ,LABEL | If equal, decrements Dn and branches if Dn ⟨⟩ −1. |
| 5A | DBPL Dn ,LABEL | If negative, decrements Dn and branches if Dn ⟨⟩ −1. |
| 50 | DBT Dn ,LABEL | No operation performed. |
| 58 | DBVC Dn ,LABEL | If overflow, decrements Dn and branches if Dn ⟨⟩ −1. |
| 59 | DBVS Dn ,LABEL | If no overflow, decrements Dn and branches if Dn ⟨⟩ −1. |

NOTE: If the condition is false, the Dn is decremented and tested for a −1.

In this example the address register is loaded with the starting address of the data, the count of $1000 words is loaded into D0 as a $FFF, and the number being searched for is placed into D1. The program then searches through the data in memory until either a $340F is located or the program has searched through all the data. To determine whether the data have been found, the value of D0 is tested following the repeat-until loop: if the value in D0 is a −1, the data did not exist; if the value in Dn is other than a −1, the data did exist. Alternately, the condition of the zero CCR bit is tested. If the data are found, the condition upon exit from the DBEQ instruction will be equal.

The condition tested is never the condition of Dn for a DBCC instruction because when Dn is decremented, the CCR bits never change. The CCR bits are changed by the instruction prior to the DBcc instruction, which then tests the CCR bits.

Suppose that a file of byte data, beginning at memory location $3000 and extending to location $3063, is to be searched for the first number that is not a $20. This is accomplished by using the DBNE instruction (decrement and branch until not equal) to scan through the data until the first number that is not equal to a $20 is located. See Example 4-8 for this sequence of instructions.

E X A M P L E    4 - 8

```
001000 307C3000            MOVE.W #$3000,A0    ;address data
001004 303C0063            MOVE.W #$63,D0      ;load count
001008 123C0020            MOVE.B #$20,D1      ;load number

00100C B218         LOOP   CMP.B  (A0)+,D1     ;test for $20
00100E 56C8FFFC            DBNE   D0,LOOP      ;repeat-until

001012 5388               SUB.L  #1,A0        ;adjust address
```

## 4-2   Subroutines and the Stack

An integral portion of programming is a structure or procedure called a subroutine. A *subroutine* is a group of instructions that are stored in the memory once. The subroutine is used from many points in a program merely by branching or jumping to the subroutine with a special instruction designed for this purpose. In most cases subroutines perform one task and make it much easier to develop modular programs. They also reduce the length of a program because they are stored once and used as often as desired from any point in the program.

In the 680XX microprocessor, a subroutine is linked to by using the BSR (branch to subroutine) or JSR (jump to subroutine) instruction. The return from a subroutine is made with the RTS instruction. These instructions are similar to the BASIC language instructions GOSUB (which is equivalent to BSR or JSR) and RETURN (which is equivalent to RTS).

### 4-2.1   Branch to Subroutine (BSR)

The BSR instruction is similar to a branch instruction except that before the branch occurs, a copy of the program counter is placed onto the stack. Recall that the program counter contains the address of the next instruction in a program. This is the instruction after the BSR instruction. The address placed on the stack is used so that the step after the BSR instruction can be returned to at the end of the subroutine. The return from the subroutine is accomplished by the RTS (return from subroutine) instruction at the end of the subroutine. RTS removes data from the stack and places it into the program counter; this ensures that the next instruction that is executed is the one following the BSR instruction.

Figure 4-5 illustrates how a subroutine is linked to with the BSR instruction and how the return instruction (RTS) returns control to the instruction following the BSR. The subroutine in this illustration multiplies the contents of D0 times a 16 by using a shift instruction. After this multiplication, an RTS occurs, returning control to the instruction that follows the most recent branch to the subroutine. Note that this process may be repeated from many places in a program.

### How Is the Stack Used with a BSR?

The stack is an integral part of subroutine, and it is the mechanism used by the BSR and RTS instructions to link to and return from the subroutine. The stack is important because the return address for the BSR is stored on the stack.

In the 680XX microprocessor, the stack is an area of memory that is assigned by the program and located by the microprocessor through the stack pointer register (SP). There are two stack pointers in the 680XX. One, the user stack pointer (USP), addresses the stack for all user programs; the other, the supervisor stack pointer (SSP), addresses another stack area of memory for all supervisor programs. In either case, the stack pointer is referred to as SP with instruction set and is address register A7 for the user mode and A7' for the supervisor mode.

When a BSR instruction is executed, the following sequence of events occurs.

**1.** The stack pointer is decremented by 4.

**2.** The contents of the program counter (all 32 bits) are stored in the memory location addressed by the stack pointer. This stores the return address on the stack.

**3.** A branch occurs to the address indicated by the displacement stored with the BSR instruction plus 2 bytes.

When the return instruction is executed, the following sequence occurs.

**1.** The long-word data from the stack are placed into the program counter. This removes the return address from the stack, so a return is made to the instruction after the most recent BSR or JSR instruction.

**2.** The stack pointer is incremented by 4.

```
PROG  MOVE.L  #1,D0    ;load D0 with 1

      BSR     MULT     ;multiply D0 times 16 ──────▶
                                              MULT   LSL.L  #4,D0    ;multiply D0 times 16
      BSR     MULT     ;multiply D0 times 16 ◀┄┄
                                              └──── RTS             ;return from subroutine
END   BRA     END      ;end program ◀─ ─ ─ ─ ─ ─┘
```

**Figure 4-5   A program that branches to a subroutine at different points, indicated with a solid line and a dotted line. The returns are to different locations because the RTS instruction always returns to the instruction following the most recent BSR.**

Suppose that memory location $1000 contains the BSR instruction 6104. First the contents of the program counter ($00001002) are placed into the memory location addressed by the stack pointer after it has been decremented by 4. Next a branch occurs to memory location $1006, which is the displacement of 4 plus 2. When the RTS instruction is encountered in the subroutine, the data placed on the stack ($00001002) are retrieved from the stack and placed into the program counter. This causes the instruction, after the BSR (at memory location $1002), to be executed.

Each time the BSR instruction is executed, the PC is placed on the stack and a branch occurs. Each time the RTS instruction is executed, long-word data are removed from the stack and placed back into the PC. When data are removed from the stack, the stack pointer is automatically incremented by a factor of 4. When the data are placed onto the stack, the stack pointer is automatically decremented by 4. This process allows nesting of subroutines. *Nesting* occurs when a subroutine is branched to within a subroutine.

Suppose the program in Example 4-9 is executed. Here a subroutine is called twice by the main program. Each time the subroutine is called, the program counter is placed on the stack, and each time the return is executed, it is removed from the stack.

E  X  A  M  P  L  E      4 - 9

```
001000 103C0002          MOVE.B  #2,D0
001004 6100000C          BSR     SUBR
001008 1400              MOVE.B  D0,D2
00100A 61000006          BSR     SUBR
00100E 1600              MOVE.B  D0,D3
001010 60FE       ENDP   BRA     ENDP

001012 E308       SUBR   LSL.B   #1,D0
001014 1200              MOVE.B  D0,D1
001016 E508              LSL.B   #2,D0
001018 D001              ADD.B   D1,D0
00101A 4E75              RTS
```

In this example, D0 is loaded with a 2. The subroutine is called and the 2 in D0 is multiplied by a factor of 10 so that, at the RTS instruction, D0 equals a 20. D0 is stored in D2 after the return. Again the subroutine is called. This time the 20 is multiplied by 10 to become 200, which is stored in D3 after the return. When the first BSR is encountered, the program counter contains a $00001004, which is pushed on the stack. The RTS instruction returns to location $00001004 after the first use of the subroutine. The second BSR stores a $00001008 on the stack, so that the second time the subroutine is executed, a return to this location occurs. Notice how the same area of the stack memory is used to store both return addresses. This tends to conserve memory space on the stack.

### 4-2.2  Jump to Subroutine (JSR)

As with the JMP instruction, the JSR instruction allows a subroutine to be used from any location in the memory. The JSR instruction also allows the same addressing modes as did the JMP instruction. Additional addressing modes allow subroutines to be called indirectly. The BSR instruction allows an 8- or 16-bit displacement, which gives it a maximum range of approximately ±32K, while the JSR instruction allows a subroutine to be called from any location in the memory. *Local subroutines* are normally called with the BSR instruction, while *system subroutines,* which tend to be anywhere in the memory, are often called with the JSR instruction. System subroutines are also called *global subroutines.* As with the BRA instruction, the BSR instruction is relocatable, while the JSR instruction is not.

*Other Return Instructions*

Table 4-5 lists all the return instructions that are used with the 68000 and 68008 microprocessors. Notice that there are three different return instructions: RTS, RTR, and RTE. The first two are used with subroutines, while the third is used with supervisory interrupt and exception service subroutines (discussed in Chapter 9).

The RTS instruction pops 4 bytes of data from the stack (PC), the RTR instruction pops 6 bytes from the stack (CCR and PC), and the RTE instruction pops 6 bytes from the stack (SR and PC). Note that RTR does remove 6 bytes from the stack, but the most significant part of the word popped into the CCR register is lost. In most cases the RTS instruction is used to return from a subroutine. If the contents of the CCR are saved inside of the subroutine, however, the RTR instruction is used to return from the subroutine.

Example 4-10 shows a case of RTR being used to return from a subroutine. The first instruction inside the subroutine places the contents of the SR on the stack, using the predecrement mode of addressing memory with the stack pointer. To place the SR on the stack after the program counter, this type of SP addressing must be used. When the RTR instruction is encountered at the end of the subroutine, it pops the most recent word from the stack into the CCR, followed by a pop to the PC. In this manner, RTR restores both the CCR and the program counter. Note that a word is popped off the stack representing the entire status register. Only the CCR register changes with the RTR instruction, and the most significant byte of the word is lost.

**Table 4-5  Return Instructions**

| Opcode | Instruction | Comment |
|--------|-------------|---------|
| 4E75 | RTS | Return from subroutine: removes stack data to the PC. |
| 4E77 | RTR | Return and restore: removes a word from the stack and places it in CCR, then removes the PC from the stack. |
| 4E73 | RTE | Return from exception: removes a word from the stack and places it into the status register, then removes the PC from the stack. |

E X A M P L E     4 - 10

```
001000 40E7     SUBR     MOVE.W SR,-(SP)
                  .        .       .
                  .        .       .
                  .        .       .
001032 4E77              RTR
```

The RTE instruction is a privileged instruction that may be executed only in the supervisor mode of operation. If RTE is executed in the user mode, the 680XX will start a privilege violation exception. RTE is used only to end special subroutines that service interrupts and exceptions. These special subroutines are found executed in the supervisor mode, never in the user mode.

### 4-2.3   Using the Stack to Store Data

In addition to storing return addresses on the stack, the stack is used to store data temporarily without regard to a memory address. The address isn't that important, because the stack pointer automatically keeps track of the stack and its address for the programmer. Once the stack pointer has been loaded with the top boundary of the stack, the programmer need worry only about the stack becoming too large. If the stack grows too large, a program or data may be erased.

The most common instructions used to place data on the stack are MOVE and MOVEM. Example 4-11 illustrates how the MOVE instruction is used to place the contents of D0 and D1 on the stack inside a subroutine. Notice that the −(SP) mode of addressing is used as a destination when the registers are stored on the stack. The (SP)+ mode is used when registers are removed from the stack. Also notice that D0 is placed on the stack before D1, but D1 is removed from the stack first. This must be done because the stack memory is a LIFO (last-in, first-out) stack. For the last information placed on the stack to be the first out, the D1 register must be removed first, because it was the last information placed on the stack.

E X A M P L E     4 - 11

```
001000 2F00     SUBR     MOVE.L D0,-(SP)      ;Push D0
001002 2F01              MOVE.L D1,-(SP)      ;Push D1
                  .        .
                  .        .
                  .        .
001034 221F              MOVE.L (SP)+,D1      ;Pop D1
001036 201F              MOVE.L (SP)+,D0      ;Pop D0
001038 4E75              RTS
```

Example 4-12 illustrates how the MOVEM instruction is used to accomplish the same thing that was accomplished in Example 4-11 with the MOVE instructions. Notice how the register masks (see Appendix B) are reversed between the MOVEM to memory and the MOVEM from memory instructions.

E  X  A  M  P  L  E     4 - 12

```
001000 48E7C000     SUBR     MOVEM.L D0/D1,-(SP)
                              •        •
                              •        •
                              •        •
001044 4CDF0003              MOVEM.L (SP)+,D0/D1
001048 4E75                  RTS
```

### 4-2.4  Creating Your Own LIFO Stack Area Using Other Address Registers

You can create your own stack memory areas using any of the address registers. Suppose that you wish to create a separate stack area for storing data registers. This is accomplished by initializing an address register to the top location of an area of memory, plus one byte, which you wish to designate as your stack.

Suppose that you are going to use memory locations $20000–$21FFF for a stack to be addressed by register A6. This is accomplished by loading A6 with address $22000, the top location of the stack plus one byte. After loading A6, you may choose the MOVE or MOVEM instruction to store and remove data from the stack, using the −(A6) and (A6)+ addressing modes.

As you use this stack, you never need worry about the value of the address in A6. The MOVEs or MOVEMs will handle the tracking of the stack. This is true as long as you make sure that, if you place data on the stack, you remove it. Also make sure that you have reserved enough memory space for the stack. If you plan to place up to six long-word registers on the stack at a time, reserve 24 bytes of memory for the stack.

### 4-2.5  Creating a FIFO Stack Memory

A FIFO (first-in, first-out) memory stores data so that the first information into the stack is the first information out. This type of memory is very useful as a buffer between systems that operate at different speeds. FIFO memory is often called a *queue, silo-mode storage, spooler,* or *pipeline.*

Suppose that you wish to buffer data using two subroutines. The first stores data into the FIFO and is called SAVE. The second removes data from the FIFO and is called RESTORE.

To set up a FIFO in the memory, two pointers are required: one to point to the entry address and one to point to the exit address. The entry pointer locates the memory location at which data are stored in the FIFO. The exit pointer locates the data as removal from the FIFO takes place. These pointers are used to store and remove data from the FIFO stack.

In this example, a FIFO is set up using address registers A0 as the entry pointer and A1 as the exit pointer. The FIFO occupies memory locations $10000–$10FFF or 4K bytes of the memory system. Before the FIFO is used in a program, both pointers are initialized to location $10000.

Before the SAVE and RESTORE subroutines are written, some conventions about the pointers must be understood. If the FIFO is empty, both memory pointers are equal. This is why they are initialized to the same value. If the FIFO is full, the exit pointer is one memory location below the entry pointer. With both pointers, one location above $10FFF must be $10000. The reason for this is that the FIFO is cyclic and must reuse the same area of memory continuously—otherwise, you will eventually run out of memory. Recall that the LIFO stack also reused the same area of memory.

Example 4-13 lists SAVE, the subroutine that is used to store data in the FIFO. In both the SAVE and RESTORE subroutines, the byte data are transferred through the D0 register to or from the FIFO. The SAVE subroutine first tests to see whether the FIFO is full. If it is not full, the data from D0 are stored in the location addressed by the entry pointer. If the FIFO is full, the SAVE subroutine waits until a byte is removed with the RESTORE subroutine.

E  X  A  M  P  L  E     4 - 13

```
001000 2F01        SAVE    MOVE.L   D1,-(SP)     ;push D1

001002 2209        SAVE1   MOVE.L   A1,D1        ;increment A1
001004 61000014            BSR      INC
001008 B288               CMP.L    A0,D1        ;FIFO full?
00100A 67F6               BEQ      SAVE1

00100C 1080               MOVE.B   D0,(A0)      ;save byte
00100E 2208               MOVE.L   A0,D1        ;increment A0
001010 61000008           BSR      INC
001014 2041               MOVE.L   D1,A0
001016 221F               MOVE.L   (SP)+,D1
001018 4E75               RTS                   ;pop D1

00101A 5281        INC     ADD.L    #1,D1
00101C 02410FFF           AND.W    #$FFF,D1
001020 4E75               RTS
```

The RESTORE subroutine is normally called via an interrupt, as explained in later chapters. When an interrupt occurs it will interrupt the section of SAVE that tests for the full condition. RESTORE then removes a byte from the FIFO, whereupon it is no longer full. A return from RESTORE to the section of SAVE that tests for full condition will then indicate a "not full" condition. This is because RESTORE has removed a byte from the FIFO. Notice how the INC subroutine is used to add a 1 to D1 and then make sure that it stays within the $00100000–$00010FFF range. This is accomplished with the AND instruction.

Example 4-14 uses the INC subroutine to increment the exit pointer A0. The first thing RESTORE does is test to see whether the FIFO is empty. If it is empty, a return is made with the carry CCR bit cleared. If it isn't empty, the carry CCR bit is set and a return occurs with the data removed from the FIFO in D0. The calling program would test the carry CCR bit to determine whether the FIFO is empty or data are present.

E  X  A  M  P  L  E    4 - 14

```
001030 2F01    RESTORE    MOVE.L  D1,-(SP)    ;push D1
001032 B3C8               CMP.L   A0,A1       ;test for empty
001034 66000006          BNE     NEXT        ;if not empty
001038 221F              MOVE.L  (SP)+,D1    ;pop D1
00103A 4E75              RTS

00103C 1011    NEXT       MOVE.B  (A1),D0     ;get data
00103E 2209               MOVE.L  A1,D1       ;increment A1
001040 61D8               BSR     INC
001042 2241               MOVE.L  D1,A1
001044 221F               MOVE.L  (SP)+,D1    ;pop D1
001046 007C0001           OR      #1,CCR      ;set carry
00104A 4E75               RTS
```

## 4-3  Miscellaneous Program Control Instructions

Now we have discussed virtually all the 680XX instructions except for a few that are important but didn't really fit into any of the other categories or chapters thus far. These miscellaneous instructions include PEA (push effective address), RESET, LINK, UNLK, Scc (set according to condition), STOP, TRAP, and TRAPV.

### 4-3.1  The Push Effective Address Instruction (PEA)

The push effective address instruction (PEA) is similar to the LEA instruction explained in Chapter 2, which covered data transfer instructions. The difference is that PEA pushes the effective address on the stack, whereas LEA loads the effective address into one of the address registers.

The LEA instruction is used in a program to allow the microprocessor to calculate the effective address as the program executes, then loads the address into an address register. The PEA instruction also calculates the effective address as a program executes, but it then pushes the address onto the stack. This instruction is useful for loading different return addresses on the stack from within subroutines. By changing the return address, you can return to a different location in the program. Note that the stack pointer must be adjusted so that the old return address is removed from the stack before the PEA instruction places a new return address on the stack. The adjustment is normally accomplished by adding a 4 to the stack pointer.

Suppose that you are to write a subroutine that will translate the value in byte register D0 to one of many possible return addresses. In this example the values found in D0 range in value from 0 to 3, and the long-word addresses exist in a table that is addressed by the A0 register. This technique is often used in menu-driven software, which asks the user to type a number or even a letter in response to a question. Example 4-15 illustrates the calling sequence for this subroutine and also the table data used by the subroutine. Locations $002010–$00201F contain four long-word addresses that are used for the four numbers 0–3.

E X A M P L E    4 - 15

```
001000 207C00002010        MOVE.L  #TABLE,A0   ;address table
001006 4EB900300000        JSR     JTABLE      ;go to table address

002010 00003000     TABLE  DC.L    $3000       ;entry 0
002014 00004000            DC.L    $4000       ;entry 1
002018 00005000            DC.L    $5000       ;entry 2
00201C 00006000            DC.L    $6000       ;entry 3
```

The subroutine JTABLE, which appears in Example 4-16, references the table listed in Example 4-15. JTABLE will look up the address that corresponds to the numeric value of the byte portion of D0 and then push that address onto the stack. When the return occurs from JTABLE, it will return to the address indicated in the table and referenced by D0. A second return will send program control back to the location following the JSR JTABLE instruction. This is very similar to the computed GOSUB, common in BASIC language programs.

The first instruction in JTABLE clears all the bits of D0 except the right-most 8. This converts the byte in D0 into a 32-bit number. Next the number in D0 is shifted to the left two places, which multiplies it by a factor of 4. To locate the address in the table, this value is added to the contents of address register A0, which addresses the first location in the table. Finally the address at the location addressed by the modified contents of A0 is loaded into address register A1 so that it can be pushed onto the stack with the PEA instruction. When the RTS instruction in JTABLE is encountered, the address placed on the stack is the return address for the RTS instruction. This subroutine calls the subroutine whose address is in the table referenced by A0. When the return is made from the second subroutine, it will return to the address following the original JSR.

E X A M P L E    4 - 16

```
300000 0280000000FF  JTABLE  AND.L   #$FF,D0    ;form 32-bit number
300006 E588                  LSL.L   #2,D0      ;multiply by 4
300008 D1C0                  ADD.L   D0,A0      ;form table address
30000A 2250                  MOVE.L  (A0),A1    ;get address
30000C 4851                  PEA     (A1)       ;push address
30000E 4E75                  RTS                ;return new address
```

## 4-3.2 The RESET Instruction

RESET is a special instruction, one of the privileged instructions that are executable only from the supervisor mode of operation. If executed in the user mode, the machine causes an interrupt (privilege violation exception) to occur so that processing is terminated and control returns to the supervisor program. A much more thorough discussion of privileged instructions and supervisory mode is offered in connection with hardware interrupts and exception processing in Chapter 9.

If in the supervisor mode, the RESET instruction will cause the $\overline{\text{RESET}}$ pin on the 680XX to become active (logic 0) for 124 clocking periods. If the 680XX is operating with an 8 MHz clock, the $\overline{\text{RESET}}$ pin will become active for 15.5 µs. The $\overline{\text{RESET}}$ pin is used to initialize peripheral components in the system. It does not reset the microprocessor.

### 4-3.3   The Set According to Condition Instruction (Scc)

The set according to condition instruction (Scc) is a conditional instruction that addresses a byte of data. Scc may use any of the memory addressing modes except program counter addressing or address register direct addressing.

If the condition tested is true, a $FF is moved to the effective address; if the condition tested is false, a $00 is moved to the effective address. Table 4-6 illustrates all the valid Scc instructions and the first byte of their respective opcodes.

The Scc instruction is useful for setting or clearing memory. A memory location often represents register flags that indicate conditions. For example, suppose that later in a program you will need to know whether the CCR indicates a carry. You can accommodate this requirement by using one of the byte data registers or a memory location as a flag. If the SCC FLAG instruction is executed, the value found in the byte memory location FLAG will be $FF if carry is cleared and $00 if carry is set. This value can be tested later in the program to determine the status of the carry flag at the time the Scc instruction was executed.

**Table 4-6   The Set According to Condition Instructions (Scc)**

| Opcode | Instruction | Comment |
|--------|-------------|---------|
| 54 | SCC (ea) | Sets (ea) if carry cleared. |
| 55 | SCS (ea) | Sets (ea) if carry set. |
| 57 | SEQ (ea) | Sets (ea) if equal. |
| 51 | SF  (ea) | Always clears (ea). |
| 5C | SGE (ea) | Sets (ea) if greater than or equal. |
| 5E | SGT (ea) | Sets (ea) if greater than. |
| 52 | SHI (ea) | Sets (ea) if higher than. |
| 5F | SLE (ea) | Sets (ea) if less than or equal. |
| 53 | SLS (ea) | Sets (ea) if lower than or the same. |
| 5D | SLT (ea) | Sets (ea) if less than. |
| 5B | SMI (ea) | Sets (ea) if minus. |
| 56 | SNE (ea) | Sets (ea) if not equal. |
| 5A | SPL (ea) | Sets (ea) if plus. |
| 50 | ST  (ea) | Always sets (ea). |
| 58 | SVC (ea) | Sets (ea) if overflow cleared. |
| 59 | SVS (ea) | Sets (ea) if overflow set. |

### 4-3.4   The STOP Instruction

The STOP instruction, like RESET, is a supervisor mode instruction. If STOP, a privileged instruction, is executed in the user mode, the 680XX will suspend execution of the program and a privilege violation exception will occur. The exception will return control to the supervisor program for processing.

   The STOP instruction is in the form of STOP #XXX, where #XXX is an immediate 16-bit value that is used to indicate which STOP instruction is executed. When the STOP instruction is encountered in a program operating in the supervisor mode, the value of the immediate data is transferred to the status register (SR) and all program execution ceases. Program execution cannot restart until a trace, interrupt, or reset has occurred. This instruction can be useful in debugging a system program. The user can determine which STOP instruction was executed by interrogating the SR with a trace or interrupt, after execution has been restarted. STOP can also be used as an error trap instruction because the SR can be examined to determine which error occurred.

### 4-3.5   Software Interrupt Instructions

The TRAP instructions (TRAP and TRAPV) are used to cause software exceptions. Although much more is explained about interrupts and exceptions in Chapter 9, these instructions are introduced here. TRAP and TRAPV instructions may be used in either the supervisor or user mode and are often used to call system level subroutines.

   The TRAP #XX instruction, where #XX has a value of 0–15 decimal or $0–$F hexadecimal, will call a software exception service subroutine at one of 16 different locations in the memory. When a TRAP is executed, control is passed to the supervisory program through an exception. There are only two ways to get into the supervisory program: (1) through an interrupt or exception or (2) through a system reset.

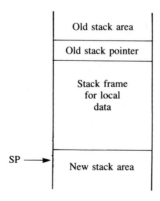

**Figure 4-6   The stack area whenever a LINK instruction is executed. Notice that a stack area is created for local variables between the old and new stack areas.**

The TRAPV instruction is a conditional software interrupt that will interrupt the program only if the overflow CCR bit is set. If the overflow CCR bit is cleared, this instruction performs no operation. The TRAPV instruction, which often follows signed arithmetic operations, permits an overflow to be detected so that the supervisor can take appropriate action. This action often informs the user that an overflow condition has been detected.

With both the TRAP and TRAPV instructions, the program counter is pushed onto the stack, after which the contents of the status register are placed onto the stack. Next, the instruction jumps to a location addressed by a vector stored in the exception/interrupt vector table in the first kilobyte of memory. To return from the software exception, the RTE instruction is executed. RTE restores the contents of both the SR and PC from the stack and returns from the exception service subroutine.

### 4-3.6 Link and Unlink Instructions (LINK and UNLK)

The LINK and UNLK instructions are used to obtain local memory storage for users in a multiuser environment. The LINK instruction pushes an address register (An) onto the stack, copies the SP (stack pointer) to the address register (An), and then adds a signed 16-bit displacement to the stack pointer. This allows access to an area of memory between the two stacks for local variable storage. This local area plus the new area for the stack is often called a *stack frame*. Figure 4-6 illustrates the stack frame created for this local data storage.

If the LINK A0,#−16 instruction is executed, the value in A0 is saved on the stack, the old SP is moved into A0, and the stack pointer is decremented by 16, allowing a 16-byte-long local variable area addressed by A0. LINK should be the first instruction executed in a multiuser environment subroutine when a new user gains access to the system. Local data storage prevents any user from erasing any other user's data.

The UNLK instruction disconnects from the local variable area by moving the value in An back into the SP followed by a pop SP to retrieve the old value of An. UNLK should be the last instruction executed by the user subroutine before returning.

Example 4-17 illustrates the LINK and UNLK instructions utilized within a user software module. It also shows how data are stored in the local memory area using the displacement mode of addressing data. (Review Figure 4-5, which shows the placement of the local variables from D0 and D1 and also the placement of the stored value of A0.)

E  X  A  M  P  L  E    4 - 17
_____

```
002000 4E50FFF0     LINK    A0,#-16        ;set up link frame
                      '       '
                      '       '
                      '       '
002024 2140FFFC     MOVE.L  D0,-4(A0)      ;save D0 in local
```

```
002028 2141FFF8        MOVE.L  D1,-8(A0)         ;save D1 in local
                         .         .
                         .         .
                         .         .
00204C 2228FFF8        MOVE.L  -8(A0),D1         ;restore D1
002040 2028FFFC        MOVE.L  -4(A0),D0         ;restore D0
                         .         .
                         .         .
                         .         .
002064 4E58            UNLK    A0                ;unlink from frame
002066 4E75            RTS
```

### 4-3.7  The NOP Instruction

The no operation (NOP) instruction performs no operation. All that happens when a NOP is executed is that the instruction is fetched from the memory and the program counter is advanced by two to the next instruction. The only thing the NOP instruction does is waste a small amount of time, because it takes a few clock cycles to fetch and determine that the instruction is indeed a NOP.

NOP instructions are traditionally placed in machine language programs every hundred or so bytes so that a patch or *software fix* can be added at a later date. Today, because most programs are generated by assemblers, the patching area is no longer needed. Another use for the NOP instruction is found in time delay software, where the NOP is used to produce a predictable time delay.

## Summary

1. The branch and jump instructions allow the program to branch or jump to another instruction in the program. This is similar to the GOTO operation in a BASIC language program. As with GOTO, the branch and jump instructions should not normally be used in a program unless there is an exceptional case.

2. The unconditional branch instruction (BRA) allows the program to continue at another location, provided it isn't too far from the branch instruction. Branch is available as a short (within $+129$ to $-126$ bytes from the branch instruction) branch or a long (within $+32,769$ to $-32,766$ bytes from the branch instruction) branch. The distance, which is stored as a signed 8- or 16-bit displacement following the opcode, specifies how far the branch instruction branches.

3. The unconditional jump instruction (JMP) allows the program to continue at another location, which can be anywhere in the memory system. The jump instruction uses any memory addressing mode except predecrement or post-increment modes to jump to the next step in a program. Indirect jump instructions are useful for performing such BASIC commands as computed GOTO.

4. The conditional branch instructions allow a branch using a signed 8- or 16-bit displacement. Conditional branch instructions are available to test each of the

CCR bits except extend and also some combinations of these bits. BCC and BCS test carry, BEQ and BNE test zero, BMI and BPL test negative, and BVC and BVS test the overflow CCR bit. Multiple CCR bits are tested using the BGE, BGT, BLE, and BLT conditional branch instructions to test the relative magnitudes of signed numbers. The BLS and BHI are used to test for the relative magnitudes of unsigned numbers.

5. The decrement and branch until instruction (DBRA) is extremely powerful because it allows a word counter to be decremented and then checked to see whether it has reached a terminal value of $-1$. If the terminal value has not been reached, a branch occurs; if it has, the next sequential instruction is executed. The branch uses a signed 16-bit displacement. Recall that the count loaded into the data register counter must be a word wide and is always one less than the number of iterations.

6. The conditional decrement and branch instructions are similar to DBRA except that in addition to decrementing a count, a condition is checked. As with conditional branches, conditional decrement and branches are available to test each of the CCR bits except extend. In all cases, the condition is tested and if it is true, the next sequential instruction is executed. If the condition is false, the contents of the data register are decremented, and if they reach a $-1$, the next sequential instruction is executed. If they do not reach a $-1$, the branch occurs. For example, the DBEQ D2,LOOP instruction will test for an equal condition. If equality is not found, D2 will be decremented, and if D2 does not reach a $-1$, a branch will occur. DBEQ means "decrement D2 and branch until equal or D2 hits a $-1$."

7. A subroutine is a group of instructions that are stored in the memory once but can be used many times from different points in a program. The BSR (JSR) instruction is used to branch (jump) to a subroutine. The RTS instruction is most often used to return from a subroutine.

8. The BSR or JSR instruction will always push the contents of the program counter on the stack and then branch or jump to the subroutine. The program counter contents placed on the stack always address the next sequential instruction in the program. The number pushed on the stack is called the return address. The RTS instruction will pop data from the stack and place it into the program counter. If the data consist of the return address, the next instruction executed will be at the step after the most recent BSR or JSR instruction.

9. Two returns are provided in addition to the RTS instruction: RTR and RTE. The RTS instruction pops data from the stack into the program counter, RTR pops word data to the CCR and then to the PC, and RTE pops data to the SR and then to the PC. The RTS and RTR instructions are used with subroutines, and RTE is used with interrupt service subroutines or exceptions. Note that the most significant byte popped from the stack into the CCR for an RTR instruction is lost.

10. The LIFO stack memory is used to store return addresses with subroutines and also to temporarily store data. The MOVE or MOVEM instruction is used to

transfer data to and from the stack. For example, if the long-word D2 register is stored on the stack, the MOVE.L D2,−(SP) instruction is used. To remove D2 from the stack, the MOVE.L (SP)+,D2 instruction is used. Any address register may act as a stack pointer, but the normal stack is addressed by SP (A7).

**11.** A FIFO stack memory is created by using one address register as an entry pointer and another as an exit pointer. Because FIFO stack memory is cyclic, both pointers must be set back to their start when an upper limit is reached. The empty condition is indicated when the pointers are equal, and the full condition is indicated when the exit pointer is one less than the entry pointer.

**12.** The push effective address instruction PEA is used to place the effective address on the stack. This instruction is most often used to place a new return address on the stack.

**13.** The RESET instruction is used to cause the $\overline{\text{RESET}}$ pin of the 680XX to become a logic zero for 124 clocks each time it is executed. The RESET instruction is privileged because it may be executed only in the supervisor mode of operation.

**14.** The set according to condition instruction Scc is a conditional instruction that places a $00 or a $FF into a byte register or memory location. If the condition is true, the effective address is set to $FF; if the condition is false, the effective address is cleared to $00. This instruction is used to indicate the condition of the CCR bits by storing a $FF or a $00 for later interrogation.

**15.** The STOP instruction is a privileged instruction that will cause all program execution to halt when it is executed. When stopped, the 680XX will place the 16-bit operand of the STOP instruction into the status register. The only way to restart the program is via an interrupt or a reset.

**16.** The software interrupt instructions allow an interrupt when executed. The 16 software interrupts (TRAP 0–TRAP 15) allow 16 different interrupt service subroutines to be called. There is also a TRAPV instruction, which will interrupt only if the overflow CCR bit is set.

**17.** The LINK and UNLK instructions are used in multiuser environments to obtain local storage and also a local stack. This is accomplished by the LINK instruction that stores an address register on the stack, copies the SP register to the address register, and adds a signed 16-bit displacement to the stack pointer register. The UNLK command unlinks from this local storage by moving the address register to the stack pointer and popping the stack into the address register.

**18.** The NOP instruction performs no operation.

## Questions

1. Which BRA instruction is used (short or long) to branch to a location that is −100 bytes from the BRA instruction?

2. Which BRA instruction is used (short or long) to branch to a location that is +1000 bytes from the BRA instruction?

3. Form the correct type of branch instruction in hexadecimal machine language to branch the following distances from the BRA instruction:
   (a) $-20$    (b) $+130$    (c) $-4000$    (d) $+212$    (e) $-2$

4. List all the addressing modes that are allowed by the JMP instruction.

5. The conditional branch instructions will branch to the address indicated by the displacement if the condition under test is _____.

6. Choose the correct conditional branch instruction to test the following conditions.
   (a) Branch if the carry CCR bit is zero.
   (b) Branch if an equal condition exists.
   (c) Branch if the sign of a number is negative.
   (d) Branch if there is no overflow.
   (e) Branch if the number is greater than or equal.

7. If the CMP.L D0,D1 instruction is executed, which conditional branch instruction will follow if the numbers compared are signed numbers and a branch is to occur if D0 is less than D1?

8. What two conditional branch instructions, other than BEQ or BNE, are used to test the relative magnitudes of unsigned numbers?

9. Write a short program that will invert the long-word contents of register D1 if register D0 is zero, add one to register D1 if register D0 is positive, and subtract one from register D1 if register D0 is negative.

10. If a DBRA D2,LOOP instruction is executed, a branch will occur if the contents of D2 become a _____.

11. Form a short sequence of instructions that use DBRA to place a logic $00 into the byte memory locations $2000–$27FF.

12. Form a short sequence of instructions that use DBRA to shift the word memory locations $3000–$3234 left two places.

13. What instruction performs the repeat until equal construct?

14. Develop a short sequence of instructions that will locate the first negative number in a block of memory long-words at locations $2000–$2120.

15. When a DBLS D0,LOOP instruction is executed, what condition must exist for the branch to occur?

16. The displacement for a decrement and branch instruction is always a signed _____-bit displacement.

17. Define the term "subroutine."

18. Where is the subroutine return address stored whenever a subroutine is called?

**19.** Explain what a BSR instruction accomplishes.

**20.** What is the difference between a BSR and a JSR instruction?

**21.** Explain what the RTS instruction does and how it accomplishes a return from a subroutine.

**22.** Write a short subroutine that will copy the contents of byte memory locations $2000–$20FF to locations $2100–$21FF.

**23.** Write a short subroutine that will exchange the contents of registers D0–D3 with D4–D7.

**24.** Develop a short subroutine that will add the byte contents of memory locations $2000–$20FF to byte memory locations $2100–$21FF and store the byte sums at locations $2200–$22FF.

**25.** Explain the difference between the RTS, RTR, and RTE instructions.

**26.** Select symbolic instructions that perform the following stack operations.
   **(a)** Return from a subroutine and pop CCR.
   **(b)** Pop the word-sized data from the stack to D3.
   **(c)** Push the byte-sized data from register D4 onto the stack.
   **(d)** Push the long-word contents of registers D0–D5 and A4 onto the stack.
   **(e)** Pop the word data from the stack into D3 and D5.

**27.** If a LIFO stack memory is to be located in the memory at memory locations $30000–$300FF and address register A6 is used as a stack pointer, select an instruction to load this address register to act as a stack pointer.

**28.** If memory area $20000–$20100 is used as a FIFO stack, what location is used to initialize both the entry and exit pointers?

**29.** With respect to the entry and exit pointers, a FIFO stack is empty whenever _____.

**30.** If a PEA (A1) instruction is executed, what is placed on the stack?

**31.** If a PEA (A0,D1.L) instruction is executed, what is placed on the stack?

**32.** The RESET instruction causes the 680XX RESET pin to become a logic one for _____ clocking periods.

**33.** The SEQ D2 instruction will place a _____ in D2 if the condition is not equal.

**34.** What is placed in the status register by the STOP instruction?

**35.** The TRAPV instruction will interrupt for what CCR bit condition?

**36.** How many different TRAP instructions are found in the 680XX instruction set?

**37.** A LINK A2,#−32 instruction will do what?

**38.** What does the UNLK A2 instruction accomplish?

**39.** If a LINK A0,#−32 instruction is executed, how much room is available for local data storage?

**40.** If address register A6 is used as the LINK register, how are data addressed through A6 in the local data storage area?

**41.** What is accomplished by the NOP instruction?

# 5

# *Assembly Language Programming*

**OBJECTIVES**

Upon completion of this chapter, you will be able to:

- Explain how the assembler program assembles a source program into an object program.

- Explain the purpose of each field of an assembly language statement and give examples of their contents.

- Use the pseudo opcodes in short assembly language programs.

- Develop software that will transfer blocks of data, exchange blocks of data, and transfer character strings.

- Write programs that will convert data between ASCII, binary, BCD, hexadecimal, and decimal.

- Develop programs that will test the system RAM and ROM.

- Write a program that will sort data.

**KEY TERMS**

| | | |
|---|---|---|
| assembler | directives | connector symbol |
| object program | delimited | input/output symbol |
| source program | ASCII-Z string | computed jump |
| symbolic memory addresses | default | static, dynamic memory errors |
| listing, object, and print files | linear programming control flow | walking bit test |
| statement | terminal, process symbols | checksum |
| peusdo opcodes or assembler language | predefined process | bubble sort |

THIS chapter explains what the assembler program accomplishes and how it converts assembly language programs into machine language programs. It also explains standard 680XX assembly language programming syntax, including the pseudo operations that are used to form a machine language program with the assembler.

After the assembler and assembly language programming have been covered, some common programming techniques are presented so that the applications provided in later chapters can be properly understood. These programming techniques include data conversions, table lookup, diagnostic testing of the memory system, and sorting data.

## 5-1   The Assembler Program

The *assembler* is a program that processes the source program, written in symbolic assembly language, and converts it into an object program, written in hexadecimal machine language. In many cases the assembler converts the source program, located in a disk file, to an object program, also located in a disk file.

The task of converting a program into machine language requires that the assembler program read or pass through the source program two times. On the first pass, a label table is created so that the assembler is able to locate labels in the program. On the second pass the assembler generates the actual hexadecimal version of the program, which is called the *object program*. The program written with symbolic instructions (MOVE, ADD, etc.) is called a *source program*.

### 5-1.1   Assembler Pass One

During the first pass of the assembler, the source program is examined for each label. These labels are assembled into a label table, which is created and stored in the memory. Labels are used in the assembly language process as *symbolic memory addresses*. The label table contains these symbolic addresses along with the actual machine language hexadecimal addresses.

E X A M P L E   5 - 1

```
START   MOVE.L  #DATA,A1        ;address data
        MOVE.L  #LISTX,A2
        MOVE.W  #99,D0          ;load count

LOOP    MOVE.B  (A1)+,(A2)+     ;move bytes
        DBRA    D0,LOOP         ;repeat

ENDP    BRA     ENDP

DATA    DS.B    100
LISTX   DS.B    100

        END
```

Suppose that the sample source program listed in Example 5-1 is passed through the assembler. During the first pass, the label table of Table 5-1 is constructed and stored in the memory in preparation for the second pass. Notice that each label appears in the table along with its equivalent hexadecimal machine

**Table 5-1   Label Table for Program of Example 5-1**

| Label | Address |
|-------|---------|
| START | $000000 |
| LOOP  | $000010 |
| ENDP  | $000016 |
| DATA  | $000018 |
| LISTX | $00007C |

language address. Because the label is a symbolic address, the label table informs the assembler, during the second pass, where each symbolic address is actually located in the memory.

If the assembler did not contain this first pass, labels could reference past or prior memory locations (reverse references) only. Forward references would not be allowed. Early assembler programs, written and used in 1950s, were one-pass assemblers that allowed only reverse references. These references were to labels that were located prior to the instruction using the label. This proved too cumbersome, so two-pass assemblers were developed that allow forward references.

In addition to forming the label table during the first pass, most assemblers test each opcode to make certain that it is valid. If an opcode is not valid, the assembler will store in its place a dummy instruction that performs no operation so that the assembled object program can still partially function.

In the 680XX microprocessor, the dummy instruction that is often stored is the NOP instruction (no operation). This instruction has an opcode of $4E71 in machine language. This of course is not true of all assembly language programs, so consult the manual for the operation of your assembler program.

### 5-1.2   Assembler Pass Two

During pass two of the assembly process, the label table and the contents of the source program are once again examined to produce the final assembled object program listing. An example output of the assembler is listed in Example 5-2. Notice that not only is the source program listed, but the object program is also listed to the left of the source program. This type of presentation is often called a *listing file* or a *print file*. In addition to the listing or print file, most assembler programs generate a hexadecimal file, which contains only hexadecimal machine language. This hexadecimal file is often called the *object file*.

### E X A M P L E   5 - 2

| Object Program | | Source Program | | | |
|---|---|---|---|---|---|
| Addr | Code | Label | Opcode | Operand | Comment |
| 000000 | 227C00000018 | START | MOVE.L | #DATA,A1 | ;address data |
| 000006 | 247C0000007C |  | MOVE.L | #LISTX,A2 |  |

```
00000C    303C0063              MOVE.W    #99,D0        ;load count

000010    14D9          LOOP    MOVE.B    (A1)+,(A2)+    ;move bytes
000012    51C8FFFC              DBRA      D0,LOOP        ;repeat

000016    60FE          ENDP    BRA       ENDP

000018                  DATA    DS.B      100
00007C                  LISTX   DS.B      100

                                END
```

The object program is composed of two parts: the address and the code. These parts are always listed in hexadecimal form as shown in this illustration. The source listing mimics the original source listing. This is clearly visible if Example 5-1 is compared with Example 5-2.

Note that the headings applied to the example are not normally printed as the output of the assembler in the listing or print file. They are listed here only to clarify the example. Some assemblers will add a decimal line number, as a reference, to the left of the machine language object program. Line numbers, which are optionally generated by the assembler, are not shown in this text.

### 5-1.3 The Assembly Language Statement

Each line of the source program is called a *statement*. A statement is composed of four distinct fields of information: the label, the opcode, the operand, and the comment. Although no field of information need be placed in any particular column to function properly, each field must be separated from its neighbor(s) by at least one blank space. Also not all fields are required for each assembly language statement.

Example 5-3 illustrates a typical source program statement with each of the four fields identified. Notice that the label in this example is START, the opcode is a MOVE.L, the operand is #ADDRESS,A1, and the comment is load address to A1.

### E X A M P L E   5 - 3

| Label | Opcode | Operand | Comment |
|-------|--------|---------|---------|
| START | MOVE.L | #ADDRESS,A1 | ;load address to A1 |

### Label Field

The label field contains a label that represents a symbolic memory address. As described earlier, the assembler converts labels to actual hexadecimal addresses during the first pass of the assembly process. In most assemblers, the first character of a label must be a letter of the alphabet (A–Z) and may be followed by letters or numbers. Special characters generally do not appear in a label. If a label is not used in a statement, the very first character position of the line must be a blank space. If a label does exist, the first character of the label must be placed in the first column of the line. This is not always true, but in general applies to most assemblers.

In addition to letters and numbers, some assemblers allow the __ (underscore) as a character in the label and some do not. If the underscore is allowed, labels are often chosen that are much more descriptive. For example, the label RETURN __ TO __ HERE is much more descriptive than a simple RETURN or HERE. Most assemblers allow the label to be of any length up to 35 characters. If a label is longer than this, the remaining characters are ignored by the assembler.

Many labels are listed in Table 5-2, along with the reason why each is valid or invalid. Remember to always use labels that describe, as much as possible, the statement or portion of the program where the label appears. Don't place a label on every statement. Labels are only used if a statement is referenced by a branch, jump, branch to subroutine, or jump to subroutine, or as data, and normally should appear only on these statements.

### Opcode Field

The opcode field contains any valid 680XX opcode as described in Chapters 1–4. The opcode must include the .B, .W, or .L opcode extension when required. The extension must come immediately after the opcode with no intervening spaces. An example opcode is the MOVE.L instruction, which moves a long-word of data.

The opcode must always be separated from the label by one or more spaces. If no label is present, at least one blank space must precede the opcode. In most cases it is advantageous to set up tab stops on the computer or video terminal. Tab stops allow all the fields to be lined up, one beneath the other. This makes the source listing much more readable than an arrangement of randomly aligned fields.

In addition to the opcodes described in the first portion of the text, there are also special directives to the assembler program called pseudo opcodes or directives. Pseudo opcodes also appear in the opcode field just as any other valid 680XX opcode. Pseudo opcodes direct the assembly process and are discussed in detail in Section 5-3.

**Table 5-2    Valid and Invalid Assembly Language Labels**

| Label | Reason |
|---|---|
| TEST | Valid because it contains only alphabetic characters. |
| TEST52 | Valid because it starts with a letter and contains only letters and numbers. |
| TEST5.2 | Invalid because it contains the special character (.). |
| 4LONG | Invalid because it starts with a numeric character. |
| THIS__PLACE | Valid in most assemblers because it is only alphabetic and contains the underscore ( __ ). |

## Operand Field

The operand field follows the opcode and is separated from it by at least one blank space. The operand may contain nothing, one operand, or two operands; a pseudo opcode may contain many operands. The number and type of operands depend on the instruction that appears in the opcode field of the statement.

For example, the RESET instruction requires no operand. The CLR.B D0 instruction uses one operand (D0). The MOVE.L D2,D6 instruction uses two operands (D2 and D6). Operands may also be instruction references, as described in Chapters 1–4 and listed in Table 5-3.

Sometimes the operand contains immediate data that take many different forms. It may also contain an arithmetic operator such as addition, subtraction, multiplication, or division with immediate data or with a symbolic memory address. These modifications to operands and some examples of their usage appear in Table 5-4.

## Comment Field

The right-most field of the source statement is reserved for comments that explain the purpose of the statement or, at times, the purpose of a group of statements. This portion of the statement is not assembled by the assembler and exists only as a convenience to the programmer for documentation. Comments are present merely so that personal notes may be added to the assembly language program. Comments are very important when a program is documented because they make it easier to interpret the program at some future time. Without comments, a program is very difficult to decipher.

Most assemblers require a space after the operand if the remainder of the line is to be considered a comment. Some assemblers require that the comment begin with a semicolon (;). This book uses the convention that a comment field is separated from the operand by a semicolon.

In addition to the comment field, comments may be placed in a program if the very first character of the line (first character in the label field) is an asterisk (*) or a semicolon. This feature is important because the asterisks or semicolons allow portions of the program to be set off as banners so that they are more readable.

Example 5-4 illustrates a short program that uses comments to set off each portion of the program. Comments are also used to indicate what certain lines of the

**Table 5-3  Instructions References Using Operands of Different Types**

| Operand | Example | Reference |
|---------|---------|-----------|
| none | RESET | causes an external reset |
| implied | RTS | return from subroutine |
| immediate | MOVE.B #100,D0 | immediate data |
| single | CLR.B D0 | register or address |
| double | MOVE.L D1,D7 | registers, immediate data, or addresses |

Table 5-4   Various Forms of Immediate and Address Operands

| Example | Description |
| --- | --- |
| MOVE.B $1000,D0 | The $ is used to indicate that a hexadecimal expression follows. |
| MOVE.B #30,D0 | The # is used to indicate immediate data: in this example, decimal data, because no $ appears. |
| MOVE.B #'A',D0 | An ASCII character is indicated by an apostrophe on either side; in this example, an ASCII A is moved to D0. |
| MOVE.B #3+4,D0 | A + is used for addition in immediate data or to a symbolic address. |
| MOVE.B DATA-2,D0- | A − is used for subtraction in immediate data or to a symbolic address. DATA−2 means address DATA minus two bytes. |
| MOVE.B #2*3,D0 | An asterisk (*) is used for multiplication. |
| MOVE.B #7/2,D0 | A solidus (/) is used for division. Note that the result here is a 3. The remainder is dropped by the assembler. |

program accomplish, making the program simpler to understand than if it contained no such explanations.

E X A M P L E     5 - 4

```
                        ;
                        ;See how comments can set off parts of a
                        ;program!
                        ;
000000 207C00000012  START    MOVE.L  #ADDRESS,A0   ;address data
000006 303C0063                       #99,D0        ;load count
00000A 4218          LOOP     MOVE.W  (A0)+         ;clear byte
00000C 51C8FFFC                CLR.B   D0,LOOP       ;repeat 100
000010 60FE          ENDP     DBRA    ENDP          times
                        ;        BRA
                        ;Data
                        definition
                        ;
000012               ADDRESS  DS.B    100           ;reserve bytes
                        ;
                                 END
```

## 5-2   Assembler Pseudo Opcodes

For the assembler to function properly with a source program, certain extra instructions (opcodes) called *pseudo opcodes* must be added to the list of valid 680XX opcodes. These pseudo opcodes, also at times called *assembler language directives,*

**Table 5-5  Common 680XX Assembly Language Pseudo Opcodes**

| Opcode | Function |
|--------|----------|
| DC.e | Defines a constant where .e is a byte, word, or long-word constant. |
| DS.e | Reserves memory space where .e is a byte, word, or long-word. |
| END | Indicates the end of the program listing to the assembler. |
| ENDM | Indicates the end of a macro definition. |
| EQU | Allows labels to be equated to values or other labels. |
| LLEN X | Indicates to the assembler the length (X) of each line. |
| LIST | Lists the statements that follow. |
| MACRO | Defines a new assembler language opcode. |
| NOLIST | Tells the assembler not to list the statements that follow. |
| ORG | Specifies the hexadecimal address of the instructions that follow it. |
| PAGE | Causes the listing to proceed on the next page. |
| SPC X | Indicates to the assembler how many (X) blank lines are to appear here. |

direct the operation of the assembler and also control how the program is listed as it is assembled. Some directives are also used to store data in the memory or to reserve memory space for future data.

Table 5-5 lists the pseudo opcodes that are commonly available in many 680XX assembly language programs. The END pseudo opcode, which indicates to the assembler that the end of the listing has been reached, makes it possible to locate the end of the first and second passes. END must be used as the last statement in all programs.

## 5-2.1  Origin (ORG)

The origin (ORG) pseudo opcode tells the assembler where to store the instructions or data that follow it. This is an important statement because, if it is not used in the program, the assembler automatically begins storing the instructions and data beginning at memory location $000000. In most 680XX-based systems, starting a program at memory location $000000 is undesirable. This is because the bottom part of the memory is normally reserved for a vector table, which is used with interrupts and exceptions.

Example 5-5 illustrates a program that uses the origin statement in two places. The first ORG sets up the program so that it is stored beginning at memory location $001000. The second ORG places the data associated with the program at memory location $003000.

E X A M P L E   5 - 5

```
                         ORG     $1000
001000 207C00003000   START   MOVE.L #DATA1,A0    ;set up A0
001006 227C0000312C           MOVE.L #DATA2,A1    ;set up A1
00100C 303C012B               MOVE.W #299,D0      ;set up counter
```

```
001010 1218          LOOP    MOVE.B  (A0)+,D1    ;add data
001012 D319                  ADD.B   D1,(A1)+
001014 51C8FFFA              DBRA    D0,LOOP     ;repeat 300 times

001018 60FE          ENDP    BRA     ENDP

003000                       ORG     $3000

003000               DATA1   DS.B    300
00312C               DATA2   DS.B    300

                             END
```

The ORG statement may appear in a program as many times as necessary and may include a hexadecimal address, a decimal address, or a symbolic address. If the address is symbolic, it is usually set up with another pseudo opcode called equate (EQU) prior to the point at which the ORG statement is located.

## 5-2.2   Equate (EQU)

The equate (EQU) pseudo opcode equates a label to either a value or another label. Equate is used to make a program more readable by setting labels equal to values. Suppose that you are required to write a subroutine that searches through a block of memory for an ASCII space code ($20). Instead of comparing for a $20, which is not very readable, the equate statement can be used to equate the label SPACE to the ASCII coded space ($20).

Example 5-6 illustrates a subroutine that scans through a part of the memory in search of an ASCII space. Notice that the EQU statement is used to set SPACE equal to a $20. The EQU statement may appear at any point in the program, but it is more desirable, for documentation purposes and readability, to locate equates before the start of the program. This follows structured programming concepts.

The program itself uses DBEQ (decrement and branch until equal) to search through the memory beginning at location $002000 until a $20 or SPACE is found. The count (register D0) used in this example is as large as possible, to prevent it from affecting the search.

### E X A M P L E    5 - 6

```
001000                       ORG     $1000

001000 20            SPACE   EQU     32

001000 207C00002000  FIND    MOVE.L  #DATA,A0    ;address data
001006 303CFFFF              MOVE.W  #$FFFF,D0   ;load counter
00100A 123C0020              MOVE.B  #SPACE,D1   ;load space

00100E B218          LOOP    CMP.B   (A0)+,D1    ;search for space
001010 57C8FFFC              DBEQ    D0,LOOP     ;repeat until
001014 4E75                  RTS

002000                       ORG     $2000

002000               DATA:   DS.B    128

                             END
```

### 5-2.3   Define Constant (DC)

The define constant (DC) pseudo opcode is used whenever data are stored in the memory. Because three types of datum are stored in the memory, the DC pseudo opcode has an opcode extension of .B, .W, or .L to indicate byte, word, or long-word constants. The DC directive is used to place one of these data types into the memory. It also sets aside a byte, word, or long-word of memory for the constant.

Example 5-7 illustrates how the DC directive is used to store constant data in the memory. Note that the data may be decimal, hexadecimal, or ASCII data and that more than one constant may be stored with a DC. If multiple data are stored, the data are separated (*delimited*) with commas. This example subroutine transfers the contents of memory block DATA to memory block LISTX. The transfer continues until it finds the CR (carriage return). When CR ($0D) is located, it stores a null ($00) in its place in LISTX. The line feed (LF) is ignored.

Essentially this subroutine converts the ASCII character string terminated with a CR ($0D), LF ($0A) into an *ASCII-Z string* terminated by a null code ($00). The ASCII-Z string is popular because it requires less storage space than the traditional character string terminated with a carriage return followed by a line feed.

**E  X  A  M  P  L  E     5 - 7**

```
00100                           ORG     $1000

001000 0000000D     CR          EQU     13
001000 0000000A     LF          EQU     10
001000 00000100     LENGTH      EQU     256
001000 00000000     NULL        EQU     0

001000 207C00003000 TRANSFER    MOVE.L  #DATA,A0        ;address
001006 227C00003009             MOVE.L  #LISTX,A1
00100C 303C0100                 MOVE.W  #LENGTH,D0      ;counter
001010 123C000D                 MOVE.B  #CR,D1          ;load CR
001014 12D8         LOOP        MOVE.B  (A0)+,(A1)+     ;move
001016 B229FFFF                 CMP.B   -1(A1),D1       data
00101A 57C8FFF8                 DBEQ    D0,LOOP         ;test CR
                                                        ;repeat

00101E 137C0000FFFF             MOVE.B  #NULL,-1(A1)    ;null
001024 4E75                     RTS

                                ORG     $3000
0003000

003000 4D6573736167650D DATA    DC.B    'Message',CR,LF
003008 0A
                        LISTX    DS.B    100
003009

00306D 101620       DATA1       DC.B    16,$16,32       ;dummy
003070 000300040005 DATA2       DC.W    3,4,5           ;dummy

                                END
```

### 5-2.4   Define Storage (DS)

The define storage (DS) pseudo opcode allows an area of memory to be set aside for future use as bytes, words, or long-words. As with DC, DS also requires the size extension to the opcode. The size extension allows the assembler to set aside bytes, words, or long-words of memory for data storage.

To set aside bytes of memory, use the DS.B pseudo opcode. The operand portion of the DS pseudo opcode tells the assembler how many bytes, words, or long-words to set aside. Example 5-7 used this pseudo opcode to set aside 100 bytes (decimal) of memory for label LISTX. The locations set aside by the assembler for LISTX do not contain any specific values. Rather, they contain whatever data happen to be in that area of memory at the time the program is executed.

Suppose that you designate an area of the memory as a word buffer of 256 words for some future list of data. For this section of memory to be useful, you need to store a $0000 in each location. Example 5-8 illustrates a subroutine that clears these word memory locations to $0000.

E   X   A   M   P   L   E        5 - 8

```
001000                                    ORG      $1000

001000 00000100          LENGTH           EQU      256

001000 48E78080          CLEAR            MOVEM.L D0/A0,-(SP)
001004 207C0000101A                       MOVE.L  #BUFFER,A0
00100A 303C0100                           MOVE.W  #LENGTH,D0

00100E 4258              LOOP             CLR.W   (A0)+
001010 51C8FFFC                           DBRA    D0,LOOP

001014 4CDF0101                           MOVEM.L (SP)+,D0/A0
001018 4E75                               RTS

00101A                   BUFFER           DS.W    256

                                          END
```

### 5-2.5   LIST/NOLIST Directives

The LIST directive causes the program to be listed as it is assembled by the assembler. Listing takes place on either a printer or the VDT (video display terminal). The assembler uses LIST as its *default* option and will always list the program unless told to do otherwise. In other words, the assembler will normally list the program unless directed not to do so by the NOLIST directive.

LIST and NOLIST are used to list only certain parts of a program. These directives tend to be used sparingly or not at all because all portions of a program are important for proper program documentation.

### 5-2.6   LLEN Directive

The LLEN (line length) directive indicates how many characters are to be printed on each line. LLEN is used to customize the output of the assembler to fit your VDT screen or printer. The normal number of characters varies from as few as 40 to as wide as 132.

To set the output of the assembler so that it generates 72 characters on each line, use LLEN 72. The exact number of characters specified should match either the paper width of the printer or VDT screen. Default for LLEN is 72 in most assemblers because this is considered to be the standard line width. This means that if no LLEN directive is used, the line length will be 72 characters.

### 5-2.7  PAGE and SPC Directives

The PAGE directive tells the assembler to cause the listing to continue on the next printed page. This feature causes the form-feed (FF) ASCII character to be sent to the printer. The form-feed character causes the printer to feed the paper to the top of the next new page. On most video display screens, it causes the screen to be cleared and a new page of information to be displayed.

The space directive (SPC) is used to place blank lines between parts of your program listing. Associated with SPC is an operand that indicates how many spaces are to be placed between data. The SPC command itself is never printed, and neither is the PAGE directive. An SPC 4 will leave four blank lines of paper in place of the command itself when the program is assembled and listed. Some assemblers don't use the SPC directive. Instead, they allow a space between lines if a blank line appears in the source program.

### 5-2.8  Macro Definitions

A macro allows programmers to generate their own assembly language opcode by using the MACRO and ENDM directives. The MACRO statement is used to define the name of the new opcode along with any parameters associated with it. The ENDM statement indicates the end of the macro sequence, as well as the name of the macro. In other words, a MACRO allows you to generate your own specialized opcodes for a program.

A macro is similar to a subroutine, yet different. The macro may perform the same task as a subroutine, but it is handled differently by the assembler. A subroutine is stored once in the memory and used as many times as necessary by calling it with a BSR or JSR instruction. The macro also may be used many times, but each time it is used, the assembler stores the instructions of the macro in the flow of the program. A subroutine also uses the stack to store a return address, while the macro does not because the macro is not a subroutine.

Macros are used in software that requires extremely high speed execution. When macros are used instead of subroutines, the programming technique is often called *linear programming*. A linear program is a program that starts at one location in memory and proceeds directly through memory without using a BSR or a JSR instruction. Because the linkage (return address) through the stack requires time to execute with BSR and JSR, linear programs tend to execute faster. They also consume a much greater part of the memory because each time a macro is invoked, all the instructions of the macro are stored in the flow of the program.

Suppose that there is a requirement to add the 64-bit contents of D1 and D0 to the 64-bit contents of D3 and D2. It may make software development easier and more efficient if this DADD sequence is defined as a macro. Example 5-9 illustrates the statements required to define this macro sequence. Once the macro has been defined, it is used at any time in a program to perform the indicated task. This macro actually creates a new opcode called DADD.

E  X  A  M  P  L  E     5 - 9

```
MACRO       DADD

ADD.L       D1,D3
ADDX.L      D0,D2

ENDM        DADD
```

The macro defined in Example 5-9 is used in Example 5-10 to add some 64-bit numbers. Each time the DADD opcode is used, the assembler inserts the code defined for the macro DADD in the program. This program adds a set of numbers using a DADD opcode.

Note that the program appears twice in the example. The first time (Example 5-10a) it appears exactly as typed. The second appearance (Example 5-10b) is the output of the assembler with expansion. Each time the DADD instruction appears, so do the instructions that comprise this macro, with one difference: each expanded instruction includes a plus sign to indicate that it is an expanded macro instruction.

E  X  A  M  P  L  E     5 - 10

(a)
```
001000 22382004      MOVE.L   $2004,D1
001004 20382000      MOVE.L   $2000,D0
001008 2638200C      MOVE.L   $200C,D3
00100C 24382008      MOVE.L   $2008,D2

                     DADD

001014 21C32014      MOVE.L   D3,$2014
001018 21C22010      MOVE.L   D2,$2010

                     END
```

(b)
```
001000 22382004      MOVE.L   $2004,D1
001004 20382000      MOVE.L   $2000,D0
001008 2638200C      MOVE.L   $200C,D3
00100C 24382008      MOVE.L   $2008,D2

                     DADD

001010 D681          +ADD.L   D1,D3
001012 D580          +ADDX.L  D0,D2
```

```
001014 21C32014      MOVE.L   D3,$2014
001018 21C22010      MOVE.L   D2,$2010

                     END
```

## Macros with Parameters

Besides defining new opcodes, macros may carry parameters to form complex macros. Example 5-11 illustrates a macro that is used to add the contents of two long-word memory locations together and store the result in a third long-word memory location. The opcode defined by the macro, MADD, carries three parameters with it: the two source long-word memory locations, and the destination long-word memory location. Notice in the example that each parameter begins with an ampersand (&), which indicates that the label is a parameter for the macro. This allows the assembler to dynamically insert any label in place of one that starts with an ampersand.

**E X A M P L E    5 - 11**

```
                     MACRO      MADD(&FIRST,&SECOND,$THIRD)

                     MOVE.L     D0,-(SP)
                     MOVE.L     &FIRST,D0
                     ADD.L      &SECOND,D0
                     MOVE.L     D0,$THIRD
                     MOVE.L     (SP)+,D0

                     ENDM       MADD

           START     MADD       $2000,$2004,$2008

001000 2E80          +MOVE.L    D0,(SP)-
001002 20382000      +MOVE.L    $2000,D0
001006 D0B82004      +ADD.L     $2004,D0
00100A 21C02008      +MOVE.L    D0,$2008
00100E 201F          +MOVE.L    (SP)+,D0

                     MADD       $3000,$3004,$3008

001010 2E80          +MOVE.L    D0,(SP)-
001012 20383000      +MOVE.L    $3000,D0
001016 D0B83004      +ADD.L     $3004,D0
00101A 21C03008      +MOVE.L    D0,$3008
00101E 201F          +MOVE.L    (SP)+,D0

                     END
```

After the macro has been defined, it is invoked two times in Example 5-11. Note that the entire program listed consists of the macro definition and two MADD instructions.

Before using the macro sequences in programs, refer to your assembly language manual to make sure that your assembler supports macro sequences. Also make sure that the MACRO and ENDM statements are used to define the start and end of a macro.

## 5-3    Common Programming Techniques

This section illustrates many common programming techniques or building blocks of software development. The concepts explained are all illustrated as subroutines so that they may be incorporated into software that is developed. Many times building blocks (subroutines) are used as modules to construct a program. Some of the techniques explained are data transfers, data exchanges, conversions, table lookup, memory testing, sorting, and parsing.

### 5-3.1    Flowcharts

Before a program of any complexity or length is written, flowcharting must be understood and applied to explain the flow of a program. We do not normally generate a flowchart, for a short program, but with complex control structures, flowcharting becomes very important.

The flowchart not only explains what the program accomplishes in simple terms, but it also shows the decision-making paths, the so-called *control flow* of the program. A flowchart is much like a road map in that it allows the program to be written with less effort, just as a road map allows a new city or town to be navigated with less difficulty.

Typically only five or six flowcharting symbols are used to develop the control flow of a program. All six of these symbols are listed in Figure 5-1.

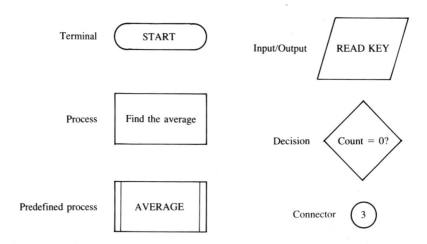

**Figure 5-1    The common flowcharting symbols: terminal, process, predefined process, input/output, decision, and connector.**

### The Terminal Symbol

The *terminal* symbol is used to indicate the START or END of a program and also the start and end of subroutines. When the terminal symbol is applied to subroutines, the starting terminal symbol should contain the name of the subroutine. The last step in the flowchart of a subroutine should be the terminal flowcharting symbol with the word RETURN in it. This identifies the subroutine for the reader and also makes it easy to find the ending (return) point. For a program, the initial terminal symbol should contain the word START and the ending terminal symbol should contain the word END. On occasion, the terminal symbol may also include the word STOP, PAUSE or HALT, but this is uncommon.

### The Process Symbol

The *process* flowchart symbol is used to indicate any process that appears in a program. It is important that the process be written in the boxlike symbol in English. Never write machine or assembly language statements in a flowcharting symbol. Remember that the flowchart is an aid to writing and understanding a program. It is not written for the sole benefit of the person developing the software. The flowchart is not directly a program; rather, it shows the flow of the program. Thus you should never use instructions in flowchart symbols.

For example, if a part of a program is used to find the average of a set of numbers, write "average numbers" or "find average" in the process block. Don't write a list of steps that find the average in several process flowchart symbols. This confuses the issue and makes the flowchart virtually worthless. Remember, you want the flowchart to serve to indicate the flow of the program.

### The Predefined Process Symbol

The predefined process symbol is used in a flowchart whenever a subroutine (*predefined process*) is used. It is important always to use this symbol when writing flowcharts that incorporate subroutines. Always write the name of the subroutine in this box. Always use the same name in the terminal symbol used to start the flowchart of the subroutine. This convention makes flowcharts very readable. Finally, be sure the name that is used for the subroutine is as descriptive as possible.

### The Input/Output Symbol

The *input/output* flowcharting symbol is used whenever the flowchart of a program inputs or outputs data. Normally the I/O symbol contains the type of input or output and also the word "read" (for input) or "write" (for output).

For example, use "read keyboard" to read data from the keyboard in a program or "write printer" to print data. This symbol is also used for I/O that controls devices such as a motor in a control system. In a control system flowchart one might find "motor two on" or "read sensor six."

## The Decision Symbol

Decision flowcharting symbols are used to ask a question in a flowchart. In almost all cases, the decision flowchart symbol should contain a short question. As a result of the question, there are either two or three outcomes. If two outcomes are required, they are usually combinations of yes–no, true–false, positive–negative, and carry–no carry. If three outcomes are required, they are always positive, negative, and zero.

For example, suppose that a counter is used in a program and you wish to test the counter for a value of zero. This is accomplished by writing the question "counter zero?" in the decision block. The two lines that leave the decision box should have "YES" on one and "NO" on the other as answers to the question. These answers determine and clearly illustrate the flow of the program.

## The Connector Symbol

The *connector* is used to link sections of the flowchart and flowcharting symbols. Connectors usually contain numbers or letters and always appear in pairs. One of the connectors in the pair has an arrow flowing from it and the other has an arrow flowing into it. Example connecters might use a number to indicate that the flowchart continues on the same page and a number and letter combination to indicate that it appears on another page. The convention selected is arbitrary. The key to good flowcharting is consistency. It is also important that the flowchart be as short and as clear as possible. These are the keys to good flowcharting.

In all cases, arrows are drawn from one flowchart symbol to the next to indicate the flow of the program. To prevent a confusing maze of crossed flowcharting lines, programmers rely on the connector symbol, which allows the flowchart to continue at another point without having crossed flow lines on the chart.

### 5-3.2  Data Transfers

One of the more common software building blocks is the data transfer. Data transfers are used to move data into and out of different areas of the memory for various reasons. Figure 5-2 illustrates the flowchart of a data transfer subroutine that moves bytes of memory data. With this subroutine, data are moved from the address contained in A0 to the address contained in A1. The number (count) of the data transferred is held in word register D0 when the subroutine is called. This flowchart is rather short, as are the subroutines to transfer bytes, words, or long-words that follow.

Example 5-12 illustrates the subroutine that transfers bytes, words, or long-words of data. Notice that this subroutine is really three separate subroutines listed as one. If a BSR or JSR instruction is used to branch to subroutine address MOVEBYTE, bytes are transferred from the location addressed by A0 to the location addressed by A1. Likewise words are transferred by using address MOVEWORD and long-words with MOVELONG.

The number of bytes, words, or long-words that are transferred is loaded into word register D0 before a branch to the subroutine. Note that the count in D0 is the

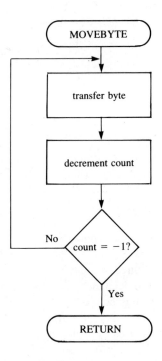

**Figure 5-2**  The flowchart for a subroutine that moves bytes of data; the same flowchart applies to the movement of words or long-words.

number of data to be transferred −1. For example, if 100 bytes are transferred, the count is a 99. In all three subroutines, the DBRA instruction is used to repeat a MOVE instruction. The MOVE uses the postincrement form of addressing to accomplish the data transfer.

E X A M P L E    5 - 12

```
                              ORG       $1000
                    ;
                    ;Subroutines what transfer data
                    ;addressed by A0 to memory ad-
                    ;dressed by A1. The number of bytes,
                    ;words, or long-words transferred
                    ;minus 1 is in D0.W.
                    ;
001000 12D8         MOVEBYTE    MOVE.B   (A0)+,(A1)+
001002 51C8FFFC                 DBRA     D0,MOVEBYTE
001006 4E75                     RTS

001008 32D8         MOVEWORD    MOVE.W   (A0)+,(A1)+
00100A 51C8FFFC                 DBRA     D0,MOVEWORD
00100E 4E75                     RTS

001010 22D8         MOVELONG    MOVE.L   (A0)+,(A1)+
```

```
001012 51C8FFFC                          DBRA      D0,MOVELONG
001016 4E75                              RTS

                                         END
```

### 5-3.3   Data Exchanges

In another common data transfer operation, the contents of two blocks of memory data are exchanged. As with the data transfer subroutines of Example 5-12, the A0 register is preloaded with the source address, the A1 register is preloaded with the destination address, and the word-sized D0 register contains the number of data to be exchanged minus a 1. Here the same registers are used for the data exchange. The flowchart of Figure 5-3 is remarkably similar to the flowchart of Figure 5-2. In fact, the only difference is the operation. The flowchart in Figure 5-2 transfers data, while the flowchart in Figure 5-3 exchanges data. This basic flowchart is a template for many other forms of software.

Example 5-13 illustrates three subroutines that exchange bytes, words, and long-words of memory data. Notice that to exchange memory data, one number is removed from memory completely before a number is transferred back into memory. Afterward, data from the other memory location are transferred and the number pulled out of memory is transferred back into the opposite memory location.

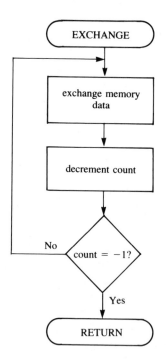

**Figure 5-3    The flowchart used to exchange memory data.**

E X A M P L E   5 - 13

```
001000                         ORG     $1000
                        ;
                        ;Subroutines that exchange
                        ;data addressed by A0 with
                        ;memory data addressed by A1.
                        ;The number of bytes, words,
                        ;or long-words exchanged
                        ;minus 1 is in D0.W.
                        ;
001000 1F01     EXGBYTE   MOVE.B D1,-(SP)
001002 1210     BYTELOOP  MOVE.B (A0),D1        ;exchange bytes
001004 10D1               MOVE.B (A1),(A0)+
001006 12C1               MOVE.B D1,(A1)+
001008 51C8FFF8           DBRA   D0,BYTELOOP    ;repeat
00100C 121F               MOVE.B (SP)+,D1
00100E 4E75               RTS
001010 3F01     EXGWORD   MOVE.W D1,-(SP)
001012 3210     WORDLOOP  MOVE.W (A0),D1        ;exchange words
001014 30D1               MOVE.W (A1),(A0)+
001016 32C1               MOVE.W D1,(A1)+
001018 51C8FFF8           DBRA   D0,WORDLOOP
00101C 321F               MOVE.W (SP)+,D1
00101E 4E75               RTS
001020 2F01     EXGLONG   MOVE.L D1,-(SP)
001022 2210     LONGLOOP  MOVE.L (A0),D1        ;exchange long words
001024 20D1               MOVE.L (A1),(A0)+
001026 22C1               MOVE.L D1,(A1)+
001028 51C8FFF8           DBRA   D0,LONGLOOP
00102C 221F               MOVE.L (SP)+,D1
00102E 4E75               RTS
                          END
```

### 5-3.4   Summing Memory Data

Often, memory data must be summed to form averages and for other types of statistical application. In the 680XX microprocessor, this is a simple task because of the diversity of the memory addressing modes that are available. Figure 5-4 depicts a flowchart for a subroutine that sums the long-word data in the block of memory addressed by address register A0. The first word of the block of memory contains the count of the number of long-words to be summed. The result of this subroutine is returned as a 64-bit sum located in registers D0 and D1, with D1 containing the most significant portion of the sum and D0 in the least significant. The flowchart

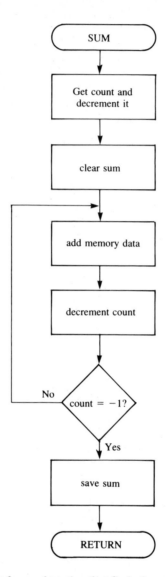

**Figure 5-4    The flowchart for a subroutine that finds the sum of a list of memory data.**

shows that the data are saved. This allows the flowchart to be used if the data must be saved in the memory for later reference.

Example 5-14 lists the subroutine required to perform this addition. Note that the contents of register D2 are placed on the stack so that the subroutine can use D2 as a counter without changing it for the program that called the subroutine. Also notice that D0 and D1 are cleared before any addition takes place because the sum is initially a zero.

E X A M P L E    5 - 14

```
001000                              ORG      $1000
                            ;
                            ;Subroutine to sum long-word
                            ;data addressed by AO. The
                            ;count is initially in the
                            ;first word of the block of
                            ;memory addressed by AO. The
                            ;result is found in D1 and DO
                            ;with D1 containing the most
                            ;significant portion.
                            ;
001000 2F02       SUM       MOVE.L  D2,-(SP)
001002 3418                 MOVE.W  (AO)+,D2        ;get count
001004 5342                 SUB.W   #1,D2
001006 4280                 CLR.L   DO
001008 4281                 CLR.L   D1

00100A D098       SUMLOOP   ADD.L   (AO)+,DO        ;form sum
00100C 64000004             BCC     SUMUP
001010 5281                 ADD.L   #1,D1
001012 51CAFFF6   SUMUP     DBRA    D2,SUMLOOP      ;repeat

001016 241F                 MOVE.L  (SP)+,D2
001018 4E75                 RTS
                            END
```

## 5-3.5   The Difference of Two Lists of Numbers

At times differences must be formed. The subroutine presented in this section takes the difference of two blocks of memory data and stores the result in a third block of memory. The word contents of the block of memory addressed by A1 are subtracted from the word contents of memory addressed by A0. The difference is then stored in the word memory location addressed by A2. Before using this subroutine, registers A0, A1, and A2 are loaded with these addresses and the count minus 1 of the number of subtractions performed is placed in the word-sized D0 register.

Figure 5-5 illustrates the flowchart required to perform this difference. Notice that like most of the flowcharts thus far, this flowchart is very simple. The steps required to do the subtraction are just a few and appear in the flowchart as one block. Example 5-15 illustrates the subroutine that performs this subtraction.

E X A M P L E    5 - 15

```
001000                              ORG      $1000
                            ;
                            ;Subroutine that subtracts
                            ;the block of words addressed
                            ;by A1 from the block of words
```

```
                              ;addressed by A0. The differ-
                              ;ence is placed in the block
                              ;addressed by A2. The count -
                              ;1 is in word register D0.
001000 2F01    SUBTRACT MOVE.L D1,-(SP)

001002 3218    LOOP1    MOVE.W (A0)+,D1        ;difference
001004 9259             SUB.W  (A1)+,D1
001006 34C1             MOVE.W D1,(A2)+
001008 51C8FFF8         DBRA   D0,LOOP1        ;repeat

00100C 221F             MOVE.L (SP)+,D1
00100E 4E75             RTS

                        END
```

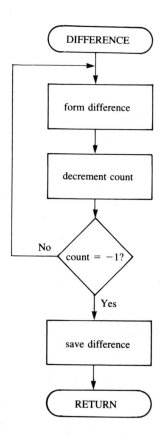

**Figure 5-5**   **The flowchart of a subroutine that takes the difference of two blocks of memory data.**

### 5-3.6    Multiplication by a Constant

Because the multiply instruction (MULU) often requires more time than is called for here, this technique finds application if speed is critical and the value of the multiplier is small and fixed. Multiplication by a constant shifts a number to the left to multiply it by a factor of 2. It then adds selected powers of 2 to form the product. For example, to multiply by a constant of 10 decimal, the numbers 2 times and 8 times the original value are added to form the product. Example 5-16 illustrates how this occurs.

E  X  A  M  P  L  E        5 - 16

_____

$$10X = 2X + 8X$$

Multiplication by any constant is formed in a likewise manner by using the following steps.

**1.** Convert the decimal multiplier to a binary number.

**2.** Determine the numeric weights of each logic one in the binary result. The logic one weights are the powers of 2 that are added to form the product.

_____

Suppose that you need to multiply the contents of D0 by a constant value of 20 decimal. This is accomplished by first converting the 20 to binary ($10100_2$). Once the binary value has been obtained, determine the weights of each logic one in the result. For a 20 decimal, these weights are 16 and 4. This means that to form the product of D0 times 20, all that is needed is to find 4 times the number in D0 and 16 times the number in D0 and add them together.

This technique is faster than using the multiply instruction if the multiplier has only a few ones. See Example 5-17 for a few example subroutines that multiply the word contents of D0 to produce a long-word product in D0. Here subroutines that multiply by 10, 20, and 100 times are illustrated.

E  X  A  M  P  L  E        5 - 17

```
001000                           ORG     $1000

001000 02800000FFFF   MULT10     AND.L   #$FFFF,D0    ;clear
001006 E388                      LSL.L   #1,D0        ;X2
001008 2200                      MOVE.L  D0,D1        ;save X2
00100A E588                      LSL.L   #2,D0        ;X8
00100C D081                      ADD.L   D1,D0        ;X2 + X8
00100E 4E75                      RTS

001010 02800000FFFF   MULT20     AND.L   #$FFFF,D0    ;clear
001016 E588                      LSL.L   #2,D0        ;X4
001018 2200                      MOVE.L  D0,D1        ;save X4
00101A E588                      LSL.L   #2,D0        ;X16
00101C D081                      ADD.L   D1,D0        ;X4 + X16
00101E 4E75                      RTS
```

```
001020 02800000FFFF    MULT100    AND.L    #$FFFF,D0    ;clear
001026 E588                       LSL.L    #2,D0        ;X4
001028 2200                       MOVE.L   D0,D1        ;save X4
00102A E788                       LSL.L    #3,D0        ;X32
00102C D280                       ADD.L    D0,D1        ;save X32 + X4
00102E E388                       LSL.L    #1,D0        ;X64
001030 D081                       ADD.L    D1,D0        ;X64 + X32 + X4
001032 4E75                       RTS

                                  END
```

### 5-3.7   Lookup Tables

Lookup tables are used to convert data from one form to another. Both the original and final forms of the data may be any code or value. The lookup table holds the data that are coded in the final form. Table lookup conversion is most often performed when no arithmetic method is available for the data conversion operation.

A code like excess-three, which is a 3 added to a BCD number, does not require a lookup table. Conversion is accomplished by adding a 3 to convert to excess-three code. Conversion from excess-three code is accomplished by subtracting a 3.

Some codes—for example, converting from BCD code to the 7-segment code for numeric display devices—do not lend themselves to arithmetic conversion. There is no simple or complex method of adding, subtracting, or any other arithmetic operation that converts BCD code to 7-segment code. Instead a lookup table is normally employed for the conversion process.

Example 5-18 illustrates a subroutine that converts the BCD unpacked byte portion of D0 into a 7-segment code. The conversion process uses the lookup table that follows the subroutine in the memory.

#### E X A M P L E    5 - 18

```
001000                             ORG      $1000

001000 2F08            LOOKUP      MOVE.L   A0,-(SP)
001002 207C00001016                MOVE.L   #TABLE,A0
001008 0280000000FF                AND.L    #$FF,D0
00100E 10300800                    MOVE.B   (A0,D0.L),D0
001012 205F                        MOVE.L   (SP)+,A0
001014 4E75                        RTS

001016 3F              TABLE       DC.B     $3F          ;zero
001017 06                          DC.B     $06          ;one
001018 5B                          DC.B     $5B          ;two
001019 4F                          DC.B     $4F          ;three
00101A 66                          DC.B     $66          ;four
00101B 6D                          DC.B     $6D          ;five
00101C 7D                          DC.B     $7D          ;six
00101D 07                          DC.B     $07          ;seven
00101E 7F                          DC.B     $7F          ;eight
00101F 6F                          DC.B     $6F          ;nine

                                   END
```

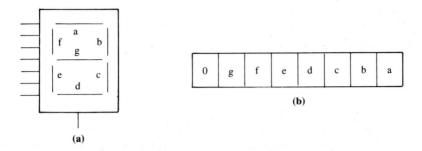

Figure 5-6   (a) The 7-segment numeric display and (b) the binary bit pattern used for displaying data on the output device.

The table included in Example 5-18 contains the 7-segment codes for the BCD numbers 0 through 9. The first entry contains the 7-segment code for a BCD zero, the second contains the 7-segment code for a one, and so forth. (Note: it is assumed here that a logic one will light a segment and a logic zero will not.)

Before the subroutine is executed, register A0 is loaded with the address of the lookup table. In this way, when the indexed MOVE instruction is executed, the data from the table address plus the contents of D0 are added to form the lookup address. The data at the lookup address are then moved into D0 and a return occurs, with D0 equal to the 7-segment code equivalent of the original BCD contents of D0. The 7-segment display is illustrated in Figure 5-6, along with the binary bit pattern used to form the TABLE entries used in Example 5-18.

## Computed Jumping Using a Lookup Table

Another programming technique that requires a lookup table is the *computed jump*. This technique uses a number, located in one of the registers, to select from one of many programs. In the example presented here, if the number in D0 is a 0, program ZERO executes; if the number in D0 is a 1, program ONE executes, etc. Example 5-19 illustrates the sequence of instructions required to implement the computed jump function. (Incidentally, this is identical to a computed GOTO in BASIC.) The computed GOTO is used in menu-driven software, where a number or letter is typed to select a function listed in the menu.

### E X A M P L E   5 - 19

```
001046                      ORG     $1046

001046 207C0000105A         MOVE.L  #JTABLE,A0     ;address JTABLE
00104C 0280000000FF         AND.L   #$FF,D0
001052 E588                 LSL.L   #2,D0          ;multiply by 4
001054 20700800             MOVE.L  (A0,D0.L),A0   ;get address
001058 4ED0                 JMP     (A0)           ;jump

00105A 00002000      JTABLE  DC.L    ONE
00105E 00003000              DC.L    TWO
```

```
001062 00004000                    DC.L    THREE
                                   END
```

In Example 5-19, address register A0 is loaded with the address of the table. The contents of the data register D0 are multiplied by a 4 so that long-word addresses (4 bytes each) in the jump table are referenced. Then A0 is loaded with the long-word address at the location indexed by the sum of A0 plus D0. The JMP (A0) instruction then jumps to the address selected from the table for the next instruction in the program.

If a computed GOSUB is required, this sequence is converted by changing the JMP (A0) instruction to a JSR (A0) instruction. The sequence then will jump to the subroutine whose address is stored in the lookup table. The RTS instruction at the end of the subroutine will return control back to the program following the JSR (A0) instruction.

### 5-3.8    Data Conversions

In many systems data never seem to be in the correct form at the appropriate time. Sometimes the data are in ASCII code when BCD or hexadecimal data are needed. Conversion from an ASCII decimal number ($30–$39) to a BCD number (0–9) is accomplished by subtracting a $30 from the ASCII character. Converting from BCD (0–9) to ASCII ($30–$39) is accomplished by adding a $30 to the BCD number. This is a simple task that doesn't require a program, just a single instruction (ADD.B #$30,D0 or SUB.B #$30,D0) to accomplish.

Other conversions are more complex and require additional effort. Conversions between ASCII and hexadecimal numbers require a short subroutine because of the hexadecimal digits A–F ($41–$46). Hexadecimal digits 0–9 ($30–$39) are converted by adding or subtracting $30, while hexadecimal digits A–F are converted by adding or subtracting a $37. The subroutines for ASCII-to-hexadecimal and hexadecimal-to-ASCII conversion appear in Example 5-20. The same subroutines may also be used for BCD-to-ASCII conversion, but not efficiently.

### E  X  A  M  P  L  E      5 - 20

```
           001000                           ORG      $1000

           001000 06000030    HEXASCII      ADD.B    #$30,D0
           001004 0C000039                  CMP.B    #$39,D0
           001008 63000004                  BLS      HEX1
           00100C 5E00                       ADD.B    #7,D0
           00100E 4E75                       RTS
                               HEX1

           001010 04000030    ASCIIHEX      SUB.B    #$30,D0
           001014 0C000009                  CMP.B    #9,D0
           001018 63000004                  BLS      ASC1
           00101C 5F00                       SUB.B    #7,D0
           00101E 4E75                       RTS
                               ASC1

                                            END
```

In the subroutine that converts from hexadecimal to ASCII, a $30 is added. The result after adding a $30 is then tested to see whether it is a $39 or less. If the result is larger than $39, an additional $07 is added because the original hexadecimal number was a letter A–F. The result, after the $07 has been added, is $41–$46, which represents the letters A–F. The subroutine that converts from ASCII to hexadecimal functions in the reverse manner because a $30 is subtracted before the decision is made whether to subtract an additional $07 if the difference is larger than a 9.

Another common form of conversion is between binary and ASCII. Here the data must be converted from binary to BCD and then to ASCII or from ASCII to BCD and then to binary.

### Binary-to-ASCII Conversion

To convert a binary number into an ASCII number, the number is repeatedly divided by 10. After each division the remainder is saved as a significant digit of the result and the new quotient is again divided by a 10. This process is repeated until the quotient reaches a value of zero.

Example 5-21 illustrates this algorithm, using the binary number 0110 0110. In this example, three divisions are required to complete the conversion process. After the third division, the quotient becomes a zero. Notice that the remainders are 0010 (2), 0000 (0), and 0001 (1). The result is 102 decimal. The only problem with this technique is that the remainders appear in reverse order. The program that performs this conversion rearranges the remainders in the correct order. It also adds a $30 to each remainder to convert it to the appropriate ASCII coded numbers.

E X A M P L E    5 - 21

$$01100110/1010 = \text{quotient of } 1010, \text{ remainder of } 0010$$
$$1010/1010 = \text{quotient of } 0001, \text{ remainder of } 0000$$
$$0001/1010 = \text{quotient of } 0000, \text{ remainder of } 0001$$

Example 5-22 illustrates a subroutine that converts the unsigned number in the word portion of D0 into an ASCII-Z character string (ASCII-Z strings end with a $00) stored in the memory location addressed by address register A0. After the return from the subroutine, A0 addresses the byte following the $00 at the end of the ASCII-Z string. See Figure 5-7 for the flowchart of this subroutine.

E X A M P L E    5 - 22

```
002000                        ORG     $2000

002000 2F01         BINASCII  MOVE.L  D1,-(SP)          ;save D1
002002 4241                   CLR.W   D1                ;clear count
002004 0280FFFF0000 BIN1      AND.L   #$FFFF0000,D0     ;and
00200A 80FC000A               DIVU    #10,D0            ;remainder
00200E 4840                   SWAP    D0                ;divide by 10
```

```
002010 06400030          ADD.W   #$30,DO      ;get
002014 1F00              MOVE.B  DO,-(SP)     remainder
002016 4840              SWAP    DO           ;add $30
002018 5241              ADD.W   #1,D1        ;save ASCII
00201A 4A40              TST.W   DO           ;get quotient
00201C 66E6              BNE     BIN1         ;count rem.
                                              ;test
00201E 5341              SUB.W   #1,D1        quotient
                                              ;if not zero

                                              ;adjust count
002020 101F      BIN2    MOVE.B  (SP)+,DO     ;get ASCII
002022 10C0              MOVE.B  DO,(A0)+     ;save it
002024 51C9FFFA          DBRA    D1,BIN2      ;repeat

002028 4218              CLR.B   (A0)+        ;store $00
00202A 221F              MOVE.L  (SP)+,D1     ;restore D1
00202C 4E75              RTS

                         END
```

## ASCII-to-Binary Conversion

To convert a number from ASCII code into binary requires that the number first be converted to BCD by subtracting a $30 from each digit. To generate a binary number from the BCD version, the result is initially set to a value of zero. Next, the result is multiplied by a 10 ($0A). After the multiplication, a digit of the number, which is converted from ASCII, is added to the result. This process is repeated until there are no additional ASCII characters to be converted.

Example 5-23 illustrates the use of this technique to convert an ASCII number into binary. Notice that the original ASCII coded number, in 3 bytes of memory, is a 351. Also notice that the result is a 351 decimal or a $015F.

E X A M P L E  5 - 23

| ASCII to Binary | Result × 10 | | Result |
|---|---|---|---|
| $33 − $30 = $03 | $0000 × $0A = $0000 | + $03 = | $0003 |
| $35 − $30 = $05 | $0003 × $0A = $001E | + $05 = | $0023 |
| $31 − $30 = $01 | $0023 × $0A = $015E | + $01 = | $015F ($351_{10}$) |

Figure 5-8 illustrates the flowchart of a subroutine that converts a numeric ASCII-Z character string into a binary number. The character string is addressed by A0 and the result (32 bits) is found in register D0 upon a return from the subroutine. This subroutine retrieves data from the ASCII-Z string a character at a time and develops the binary number in D0. The process ends when the character extracted from the memory is a $00.

Example 5-24 illustrates this subroutine, called ASCIIBIN. The only thing this subroutine does not do is test the ASCII data for the numbers 0–9. If a special

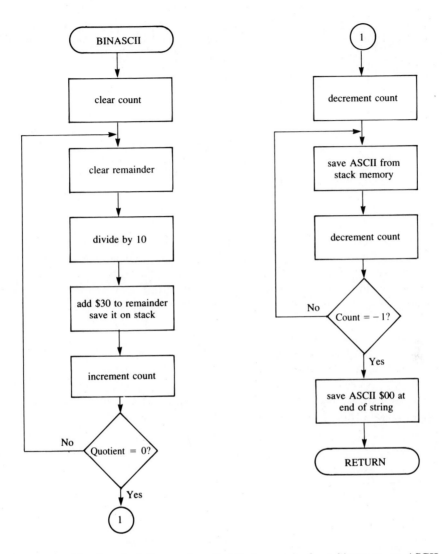

**Figure 5-7** The flowchart for a subroutine that converts from binary to an ASCII Z-string.

character or letter is found, the subroutine assumes that this too is a number and will convert it, with erroneous results. It is therefore wise to test the ASCII-Z string to make certain that it contains only ASCII coded numbers before using this subroutine.

E X A M P L E 5 - 24

```
003000                          ORG      $3000

003000 2F01          ASCIIBIN   MOVE.L  D1,-(SP)    ;save D1
003002 4280                     CLR.L   D0          ;clear result
```

```
003004 4A10          ASCII1    TST.B    (A0)          ;check for $00
003006 66000006                BNE      ASCII2        ;if not $00

00300A 221F                    MOVE.L   (SP)+,D1      ;restore D1
00300C 4E75                    RTS

00300E C0FC000A      ASCII2    MULU     #10,D0        ;X10
003012 1218                    MOVE.B   (A0)+,D1      ;get ASCII
003014 02810000000F            AND.L    #$F,D1        ;to binary
00301A D081                    ADD.L    D1,D0         ;add to result
00301C 60E6                    BRA      ASCII1        ;repeat

                               END
```

### 32-Bit Binary to Floating-Point Conversion

Another conversion often found in systems requiring complex arithmetic is binary integer to floating-point conversions. Floating-point numbers are used for most higher level arithmetic in computer systems, so this is an important building block in a system program. The subroutine illustrated in Example 5-25 takes the 32-bit binary integer contained in register D0 and converts it to a standard 32-bit floating-point number held in register D1. The conversion process is rather simple, because all that is required is a shift of the integer to produce the floating-point number. Figure 5-9 illustrates the flowchart of this conversion process.

To convert to floating-point form, the sign of the integer is extracted and then the integer is made positive, if it is negative. Once in the positive form, the integer is adjusted (by shifting) so that it contains no leading zeros and the most significant bit is erased. This process is accomplished by shifting it to the left until the carry

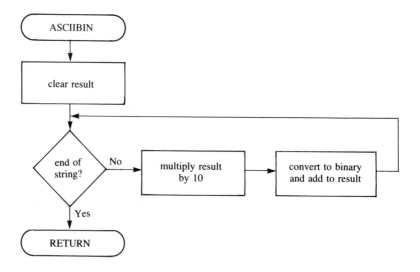

**Figure 5-8   The flowchart of a subroutine that converts from ASCII to binary.**

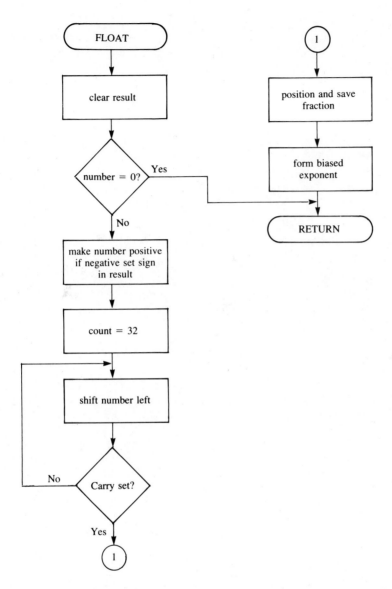

**Figure 5-9** The flowchart of a subroutine that converts a binary integer into a floating-point number.

CCR bit becomes a logic one. This shift not only normalizes the number, but it also removes the most significant bit (the implied bit). As the data are shifted, a count is kept so that the value of the biased exponent can be determined. After each item has been calculated (sign, fraction, and biased exponent), it is added to the result in D1 to form the floating-point version of the original binary integer.

EXAMPLE     5 - 25

```
004000                          ORG      $4000

004000  4281        INTFLO      CLR.L    D1              ;clear result
004002  4A80                    TST.L    D0              ;test for zero
004004  66000004                BNE      INTFLO1         ;if not zero

004008  4E75                    RTS

00400A  6A000008    INTFLO1     BPL      INTFLO2         ;if plus
00400E  08C1001F                BSET     #31,D1          ;set to minus
004012  4480                    NEG.L    D0              ;make positive

004014  3F02        INTFLO2     MOVE.W   D2,-(SP)        ;save D2
004016  343C0020                MOVE.W   #32,D2          ;load count

00401A  E388        INTFLO3     LSL.L    #1,D0           ; shift left
00401C  55CAFFFC                DBCS     D2,INTFLO3

004020  E088                    LSR.L    #8,D0           ;position frac.
004022  E288                    LSR.L    #1,D0
004024  D280                    ADD.L    D0,D1           ;add fraction
004026  707F                    MOVE.L   #$7F,D0         ;form exponent
004028  D002                    ADD.B    D2,D0
00402A  EF88                    LSL.L    #7,D0
00402C  4840                    SWAP     D0
00402E  D280                    ADD.L    D0,D1
004030  341F                    MOVE.W   (SP)+,D2
004032  4E75                    RTS

                                END
```

If a binary fraction is converted to floating-point format, the number is normalized by shifting it to the left one place to delete the original left-most bit. The biased exponent becomes a $7F. Because fractions don't normally contain a sign bit, the result is very simple to obtain. Example 5-26 illustrates how the binary fraction in D0 is converted to a floating-point number in register D1. This subroutine assumes that D0 is not zero and that it contains an unsigned binary fraction.

EXAMPLE     5 - 26

```
004100                          ORG      $4100

004100  223C3F800000  FRACFLO   MOVE.L   #$3F800000,D1   ;set D1
004106  E388                    LSL.L    #1,D0
004108  E088                    LSR.L    #8,D0           ;position
00410A  E288                    LSR.L    #1,D0
00410C  D280                    ADD.L    D0,D1           ;form result
00410E  4E75                    RTS

                                END
```

## 5-3.9 Time Delay Software

Because each 680XX instruction has a predictable execution time, an accurate time delay is realized with software. Instruction execution times are calculated from the information provided in Appendix D. The execution time of each instruction is given in clock periods, which means that execution times are found no matter what system clock speed is chosen. For example, the MOVE.B #$12,D1 instruction requires 8 clock periods for execution. If the system is operated with a clock cycle time of 125 ns, the actual time required to execute this instruction is 8 × 125 ns or 1.0 μs.

Time delays are usually constructed using the DBRA instruction, so the value loaded into the counter determines the amount of time required to execute a time delay.

Example 5-27 illustrates a subroutine used to generate a time delay. Here D0 is loaded with a 10 decimal so that the DBRA instruction is executed 11 times. Ten of the 11 times, it takes DBRA 10 clock periods to execute. The final time that DBRA executes, it takes 14 clock periods. This means that the DBRA instruction requires a total of 100 + 14 clocks (114) to execute with a count of 10. In addition to the 114 clocks required for DBRA, the time required for the MOVE.W #10,D0 and RTS instruction must be included. The MOVE.W #10,D0 instruction requires 8 clocks and the RTS instruction requires 16 clocks, for a total of 138 clocks for the entire subroutine. Note that this does not include the number of clocks required to branch or jump to the subroutine. Because the form of the branch or jump to the subroutine varies, these clocks are not included in the time calculation for the time delay. If the system clock requires 125 ns, this subroutine requires 17.25 μs to execute.

E X A M P L E    5 - 27

```
004200                      ORG     $4200

004200 303C000A  DELAY      MOVE.W  #10,D0    ;load count
004204 51C8FFFE  LOOP       DBRA    D0,LOOP   ;repeat
004208 4E75                 RTS

                            END
```

A general formula is created to determine the value to load into the counter or to find the time required to execute the time delay subroutine, if the count is known. The first formula, illustrated in Example 5-28, is used to calculate the amount of time required to execute the subroutine (DELAY) if the count is known.

E X A M P L E    5 - 28

$$\text{Time} = 4.75 \ \mu\text{s} + \text{XXXX} \ (1.25 \ \mu\text{s})$$

NOTE: XXXX is the number loaded into the counter (D0); time is in microseconds.

If the count is required, as it often is, then the equation given in Example 5-29 is used to determine the count for a given time delay. If the largest time delay (0.0819135 second) is used, the count will become a 65,535 ($FFFF).

E X A M P L E    5 - 29

$$\text{Count} = \frac{\text{Time} - 4.75 \ \mu s}{1.25 \ \mu s}$$

NOTE: Time is in microseconds.

What if you need a count that causes time delays of seconds or even minutes? This is achieved by using two counters in two time delay subroutines. Example 5-30 illustrates two subroutines, one that delays for 0.01 second and another subroutine that calls the 0.01 second time delay subroutine 6000 times. This generates a time delay of approximately 1 minute. Although the one-minute delay is not perfectly accurate, it is to within less than 1% of a minute, which is accurate enough in most applications. If more accuracy is desired, the amount of time required to branch to the subroutine and go through the MINUTE1 part of the MINUTE subroutine should be calculated and added into the total time delay.

E X A M P L E    5 - 30

```
004300                              ORG     $4300
                            ;
                            ;wait  one  minute
                            ;
004300  323C1770    MINUTE      MOVE.W  #6000,D1

004304  61000008    MINUTE1     BSR     DELAY
004308  51C9FFFA                DBRA    D1,MINUTE1
00430C  4E75                    RTS
                            ;
                            ;wait  0.01  second
                            ;
00430E  303C1F3C    DELAY       MOVE.W  #7996,D0

004312  51C8FFFE    DELAY1      DBRA    D0,DELAY1
004316  4E75                    RTS

                                END
```

### 5-3.10   Diagnostic Software

Many times today the software design task also includes test programs that are executed either when a system is first started or by a technician during the field servicing of a piece of equipment. Testing falls into two main categories: memory testing and I/O testing. Memory testing, the subject of this section, requires that a program check each memory location in the system to determine functionality, while I/O testing tests all the I/O devices connected to system, as discussed in connection with I/O devices in later chapters.

### Read/Write Memory Testing

Testing the read/write memory (RAM) in a system can be easy if only a functional or static test is required, or difficult if the memory is to be tested for dynamic errors. *Static memory errors,* often called hard errors, occur when a bit is stuck high (1) or low (0) in a memory device. A static error is easy to find because all that is required for this test is that a zero and a one be stored in every memory location. After the zero has been stored, a test is executed to check each location for a zero, and the same test is also used after all ones have been stored ($FF). If the test fails, a static memory fault has occurred. A *dynamic memory error,* often called a soft error, occurs when one bit in the memory is modified as a result of a change in another bit. The error may also occur if a bit changes on its own after a brief period of time. This occurrence is much more difficult to detect, because it is never known which bit will change another or how long a bit will take to change.

The subroutine listed in Example 5-31 performs a static test on a 1024-byte block of the memory system addressed by address register A0. Notice that this subroutine stores a $00 in each location and then tests to see whether they have all changed to $00. After this test, each location is set to a $FF so that it can be checked for this number. If both tests are passed, a return with carry cleared occurs. If a byte is in error, a return with carry set occurs.

E  X  A  M  P  L  E      5 - 31

```
004400                     ORG       $4400
                     ;
                     ;test 1024 bytes of memory addressed by A0
                     ;
004400 48E7C000   TESTK    MOVEM.L   D0-D1,-(SP)
004404 103C0000            MOVE.B    #0,D0              ;test for $00
004408 6100002C            BSR       SAVE
00440C 61000038            BSR       TEST
004410 6600001A            BNE       TESTF              ;if test fails

004414 4600               NOT.B     D0                 ;test for $FF
004416 6100001E            BSR       SAVE
00441A 6100002A            BSR       TEST
00441E 6600000C            BNE       TESTF              ;if test fails

004422 4CDF0003            MOVEM.L   (SP)+,D0-D1
004426 023C00FE            AND.B     #$FE,CCR           ;clear carry
00442A 4E75               RTS

00442C 4CDF0003   TESTF    MOVEM.L   (SP)+,D0-D1
004430 003C0001            OR.B      #1,CCR             ;set carry
004434 4E75               RTS

004436 2F08       SAVE     MOVE.L    A0,-(SP)
004438 323C03FF            MOVE.W    #1023,D1           ;load count
```

```
00443C 10C0        SAVE1   MOVE.B   D0,(A0)+        ;save number
00443E 51C9FFFC            DBRA     D1,SAVE1        ;repeat

004442 205F                MOVE.L   (SP)+,A0
004444 4E75                RTS

004446 2F08        TEST    MOVE.L   A0,-(SP)
004448 323C03FF            MOVE.W   #1023,D1        ;load count

00444C B018        TEST1   CMP.B    (A0)+,D0        ;compare
00444E 56C9FFFC            DBNE     D1,TEST1        ;repeat

004452 205F                MOVE.L   (SP)+,A0
004454 0C41FFFF            CMP.W    #-1,D1          ;test counter
004458 4E75                RTS

                           END
```

Suppose that you are required to test memory locations $008000–$01FFFF. This amount of memory represents $18000 bytes (96K bytes) of memory. To test this section of memory, the address register A0 is loaded with $00008000 and a counter is initialized with 96 so that the subroutine of Example 5-31 can be used to test each kilobyte block of memory. Example 5-32 illustrates the final test subroutine to statically test this section of the memory. If an error is detected, a branch is made to an error handler (not illustrated here).

**E X A M P L E    5 - 32**

```
004460                          ORG     $4460
                        ;
                        ;test memory from $008000 through $01FFFF
                        ;
004460 207C00008000 TESTM  MOVE.L  #$8000,A0    ;address
004466 7460                MOVE.L  #96,D2       ;load count

004468 6196        TESTM1  BSR     TESTK        ;test 1K block
00446A 65000008            BCS     ERROR        ;if error
00446E 51CAFFF8            DBRA    D2,TESTM1    ;repeat

004472 4E75                RTS

004474 ------      ERROR   ------               ;on error
```

Dynamic errors are much more difficult to test for because a 1-bit change in one memory location can cause a change in a totally unrelated location. For this type of error, therefore, a new type of test is developed. This test, the *walking bit test,* requires much more time to execute than the static test of Example 5-32. In fact, the walking bit test requires 16 times longer to execute than the static bit test, so it is normally reserved for thorough memory testing. The static test, which provides a cursory memory test, is normally used whenever a system is turned on each day.

**Table 5-6 The Walking Bit Pattern Used to Test for Dynamic RAM Errors**

| Sequence Number | Pattern |
|:---:|:---:|
| 1 | 00000000 |
| 2 | 00000001 |
| 3 | 00000011 |
| 4 | 00000111 |
| 5 | 00001111 |
| 6 | 00011111 |
| 7 | 00111111 |
| 8 | 01111111 |
| 9 | 11111111 |
| 10 | 11111110 |
| 11 | 11111100 |
| 12 | 11111000 |
| 13 | 11110000 |
| 14 | 11100000 |
| 15 | 11000000 |
| 16 | 10000000 |
| 17 | 00000000 |

NOTE: Notice that the first number in the sequence is a 00000000, which repeats after 10000000.

Table 5-6 illustrates the binary bit pattern used for the walking bit test. Notice that ones are first shifted through the number and then zeros. It takes 16 memory locations to store each set of these patterns and they are stored 16 times in the memory, with each location receiving each number in the table. This is why this test requires so much time to perform.

The subroutine that is used to test a 1024-byte segment of the memory appears in Example 5-33. Notice that this subroutine must test the 1024-bytes segment 16 times, with the starting location receiving a 00000000 the first time, a 00000001 the second time, a 00000011 the third, and so forth. Notice how the byte in the D0 register is rotated left and then the right-most bit is inverted (with the BCHG instruction), to cause the walking bit pattern to be generated.

E X A M P L E 5 - 33

```
004500                    ORG      $4500
                 ;
                 ;walking bit test for 1024 memory locations
                 ;beginning at the location addressed by A0.
                 ;
004500 48E7E000  WALK     MOVEM.L  D0-D2,-(SP)   ;load count
004504 323C000F           MOVE.W   #15,D1
004508 4240              CLR.W    D0
```

```
00450A 61000034    WALK1   BSR     SAVEW           ;store pattern
00450E 61000046            BSR     TESTP           ;test pattern
004512 66000012            BNE     WALKF           ;if failed
004516 E318               ROL.B   #1,D0           ;rotate pattern
004518 08400000            BCHG    #0,D0           ;invert bit 0
00451C 51C9FFEC            DBRA    D1,WALK1        ;repeat

004520 4CDF0007            MOVEM.L (SP)+,D0-D2
004524 4E75               RTS

004526 -------     WALKF   -------                 ;on error

004540 2F08        SAVEW   MOVE.L  A0,-(SP)
004542 343C03FF            MOVE.W  #1023,D2        ;load count

004546 10C0        SAVEW1  MOVE.B  D0,(A0)+        ;save data
004548 E318               ROL.B   #1,D0           ;new pattern
00454A 08400000            BCHG    #0,D0
00454E 51CAFFF6            DBRA    D2,SAVEW1       ;repeat

004552 205F               MOVE.L  (SP)+,A0
004554 4E75               RTS

004556 2F08        TESTP   MOVE.L  A0,-(SP)
004558 343C03FF            MOVE.W  #1023,D2        ;load count

00455C B018        TESTP1  CMP.B   (A0)+,D0        ;compare
00455E 66000014            BNE     TESTP2          ;if error
004562 E318               ROL.B   #1,D0           ;new pattern
004564 08400000            BCHG    #0,D0
004568 51CAFFF2            DBRA    D2,TESTP1       ;repeat

00456C 205F               MOVE.L  (SP)+,A0
00456E 003C0001            OR.B    #1,CCR          ;equal
004572 4E75               RTS

004574 205F        TESTP2  MOVE.L  (SP)+,A0
004576 023C00FE            AND.B   #$FE,CCR        ;not equal
00457A 4E75               RTS

                          END
```

## Read-Only Memory (ROM) Testing

Read-only memory (ROM) devices are fairly simple to test because they contain a program or data that never change. Knowing this, we can formulate a method for testing ROMs. Suppose that all the data on a ROM are added together. This will produce a particular sum in all cases unless the ROM somehow changes in value because of an error. This type of sum is called a *checksum*. Checksums are formed by either adding or exclusive-ORing all the data together on the ROM. In most cases one location on the ROM will contain a number that causes the checksum to become a zero if no error exists. Although this will not catch all possible ROM errors, it will suffice in most cases.

E X A M P L E 5 - 34

```
004600                     ORG      $4600
004600 48E7C080  CHECKADD   MOVEM.L  DO-D1/A0,-(SP)
004604 303C0FFF             MOVE.W   #4095,D0        ;load count
004608 4201                 CLR.B    D1              ;clear sum
00460A D218      ADD1       ADD.B    (A0)+,D1        ;sum number
00460C 51C8FFFC             DBRA     D0,ADD1         ;repeat
004610 4CDF0103             MOVEM.L  (SP)+,D0-D1/A0
004614 4E75                 RTS
                            END
```

Example 5-34 shows how the checksum of the contents of a 4K-byte ROM is tested. In this program the starting address of the ROM must be in register A0 before the subroutine is called. Upon return from the subroutine, a zero (equal) condition indicates that the checksum was correct, and a not zero (not equal) condition indicates that an error has been discovered. If the exclusive-OR type of checksum is desired, the ADD.B instruction is changed to an EOR.B instruction. This will exclusive-OR all the data together to form a checksum. As with addition, the correct result after an exclusive-OR checksum is zero because a one byte is stored in the ROM, which causes this result. In some systems the addition checksum can be 16 bits in width. Whether an 8- or 16-bit checksum is chosen is up to the software designer. The 16-bit version is more accurate but requires more work to generate and more time to execute.

## 5-3.11 Sorting Data

In many applications, data must be sorted. This section describes the use of a bubble sort to sort numeric data. A *bubble sort* is the most common sorting technique because it works well with a nearly ordered list of data, and in most cases lists of data are already partially sorted.

The term "bubble sort" comes from the way data seem to rise up in the list as they are sorted. Figure 5-10 illustrates a set of data and the way it is sorted with the bubble sort. Notice that the first two numbers are compared, and if the upper one is larger than the lower, they are exchanged. This continues until the bottom of the list is reached. After the first pass, the largest number is at the bottom and the lighter (smaller) numbers appear to be moving up in the list. The second pass is much like the first, because again the top two numbers are compared and exchanged if necessary. Again this continues until the second number from the bottom is reached. There is no need to sort the bottom number again because it is already the largest in the list.

A list of 5 numbers requires a maximum of 4 passes; a list of 20 numbers requires at most 19 passes. The number of required passes can be reduced if a flag is

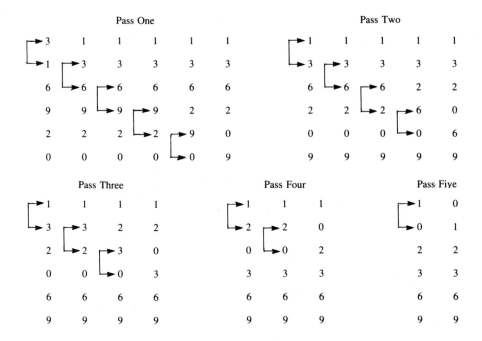

**Figure 5-10   Six numbers and their movement during a bubble sort.**

used to indicate whether numbers are exchanged. When a complete pass occurs in which no numbers are exchanged, the numbers are in numerical order.

Figure 5-11 illustrates the flowchart required to implement a bubble sort. Notice that two counters are needed. One counts the number of passes through the list, and the other determines how many numbers to compare during the pass. Also notice the flag that indicates whether any data are exchanged during a pass.

Example 5-35 lists the subroutine that sorts 32-bit numeric data addressed by address register A0. The quantity of numbers sorted is transferred to the subroutine through the D0 register, which holds the count. This subroutine is capable of sorting up to 64K different 32-bit numbers with the smallest at the top and the largest at the bottom. When numbers are sorted using this technique, the minimum number of passes is one, if the numbers are already in order. The maximum number is one less than the count if the smallest number is at the bottom. It is very rare that the maximum number of passes is needed because of the odds against having the smallest number at the bottom of the list.

E  X  A  M  P  L  E     5 - 35
_____

```
005000                          ORG      $5000
                         ;
                         ;Sort the data addressed by A0. The number
                         ;of 32-bit long-words sorted is held in D0.W.
                         ;
```

```
005000 5540            SORT     SUB.W    #2,D0                ;adjust count
005002 6500003A                 BCS      SORT4                ;if count <2
005006 48E7F060                 MOVEM.L  D0-D3/A1-A2,-(SP)

00500A 2448            SORTA    MOVE.L   A0,A2                ;save A0
00500C 4282                     CLR.L    D2                   ;clear flag
00500E 3200                     MOVE.W   D0,D1
005010 2248                     MOVE.L   A0,A1                ;replicate A0
005012 5889                     ADD.L    #4,A1

005014 B388            SORT1    CMP.L    (A0)+,(A1)+          ;compare data
005016 63000012                 BLS      SORT2
00501A 2628FFFC                 MOVE.L   -4(A0),D3            ;exchange data
00501E 2169FFFCFFFC             MOVE.L   -4(A1),-4(A0)
005024 2343FFFC                 MOVE.L   D3,-4(A1)
005028 7401                     MOVE.L   #1,D2                ;set flag

00502A 51C9FFE8        SORT2    DBRA     D1,SORT1             ;inner loop

00502E 204A                     MOVE.L   A2,A0                ;get address
005030 8482                     OR.L     D2,D2                ;test flag
005032 67000006                 BEQ      SORT3                ;no exchanges
005036 51C8FFD2                 DBRA     D0,SORTA             ;outer loop

00503A 4CDF060F        SORT3    MOVEM.L  (SP)+,D0-D3/A1-A2
00503E 4E75            SORT4    RTS

                                END
```

## 5-3.12   Parsing

Parsing is a technique that is used to separate data typed as an ASCII-coded character string. Many systems require that when data are typed, the data typed in the line
be separated or parsed to permit evaluation. Often data are delimited with spaces,
and in this section spaces serve as delimiters between blocks of information. Other
delimiters include commas, colons, and semicolons.

E X A M P L E   5 - 36

```
001000                          ORG      $1000
                        ;
                        ;Parse the ASCII-coded character string
                        ;addressed by A0. Store the ASCII-code
                        ;word in the location address by A1.
                        ;
001000 1018            PARSE    MOVE.B   (A0)+,D0             ;get character
001002 0C000000                 CMP.B    #0,D0                ;test for end
001006 6700001A                 BEQ      ENDIT                ;if end
00100A 0C000020                 CMP.B    #$20,D0              ;test for space
00100E 67F0                     BEQ      PARSE                ;eliminate spaces

001010 12C0            LOOP1    MOVE.B   D0,(A1)+             ;save character
001012 1018                     MOVE.B   (A0)+,D0             ;get character
```

```
001014  0C000000           CMP.B   #0,D0      ;test for end
001018  67000008           BEQ     ENDIT      ;if end
00101C  0C000020           CMP.B   #$20,D0    ;test for space
001020  66EE               BNE     LOOP1      ;if not space

001022  12BC0000   ENDIT   MOVE.B  #0,(A1)    ;save $00
001026  4E75               RTS

                           END
```

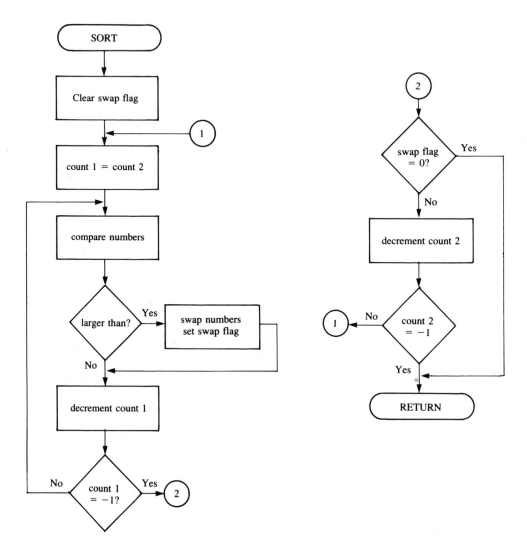

**Figure 5-11   The flowchart for a bubble sort.**

The subroutine listed in Example 5-36 is used to parse a ASCII-coded word from the ASCII character string addressed by register A0. Parsing begins by eliminating any spaces that might precede the ASCII-coded word. Once the initial spaces, if they exist, have been skipped over, the subroutine stores the ASCII-coded word at the location addressed by A1. The end of the word is encountered when a space or a $00 (end of string) is found. The ASCII-coded word stored at the location address by A1 is ended with a $00.

When the return from this subroutine occurs, the byte-sized portion of D0 contains either a $20 (space) or a $00 (end of string). This is used by the calling software to determine whether more data are available, or instead, the end of the string has been reached. This information is used either to parse the next ASCII-coded word by calling PARSE or to terminate the parsing procedure.

## SUMMARY

1. An assembler is a program that converts the source program, written in symbolic assembly language, into the hexadecimal object program. All assemblers today look at a source program two times. The first pass is used to generate a symbol table and check each opcode. The second pass produces the hexadecimal object program from the source program and symbol table.

2. The assembly language statement is composed of four fields: label, opcode, operand, and comment. The label field indicates a symbolic address; the opcode is placed in the opcode field; the operand can be none, one, or two items; and the comment field contains remarks about the statement.

3. Special opcodes that direct the assembly process or place data in the memory are called pseudo opcodes or directives. The 680XX assembler has the following pseudo opcodes: END, LIST, NOLIST, SPC, LLEN, DC, DS, PAGE, ORG, and EQU.

4. Flowcharts are constructed with six flowcharting symbols: process, terminal, predefined process, input/output, decision, and connector. These symbols indicate the flow of a program and are connected with lines bearing arrows to specify the direction of the flow.

5. A data transfer subroutine copies bytes, words, or long-words from one part of the memory to another. In most cases, the source and destination addresses are transferred to the subroutine via address registers, and the number of bytes, words, or long-words is conveyed via a data register.

6. Data exchanges are similar to data transfers except that an additional register stores the data during the transfer.

7. Memory data are often summed for generating averages and for other statistical purposes. To generate sums, a data register is cleared to zero and a string of memory data are added.

8. Differences of memory data are formed by addressing data with two address registers and using a third to address the location of the result.

9. Multiplication by constants is performed by adding together the original number times its powers of 2. To multiply by 12, for example, add 4 times the original number plus 8 times the original number. Multiplying by 4 and 8 is accomplished with shift left operations.

10. Lookup tables convert one numeric code to another. They are also used to form a computed GOTO or computed GOSUB structure.

11. Data conversions that are commonly found in programs convert between ASCII and hexadecimal or ASCII and binary. An intermediate step in the conversion between ASCII and binary is BCD.

12. Time delays are an important part of many real-time control programs. Time delays are generated with a program and are very accurate because each instruction requires a fixed number of clock pulses to execute. The accuracy is due to a crystal-controlled clock that times the operation of the microprocessor.

13. Memory devices are tested in the computer with programs. Programs are used to test for static errors (stuck bits) and dynamic errors (randomly changing bits). Static errors are found by simply storing $00 and $FF in the memory and then checking to make certain they were stored. Dynamic errors are tested with the walking bit test.

14. Read-only memory (ROM) is tested via a checksum. At the time of programming a ROM, all the numbers, except one, are added to generate a sum. The last byte is then programmed with a value that, when added to the sum, will generate a $00. When a ROM is tested, all the data are added; if the result is a $00, the ROM is good.

15. Data are sorted numerically using a technique called a bubble sort, after the way the data are sorted and the way the smaller numbers seem to bubble up to the top of the list.

16. Parsing is an important technique that allows ASCII-coded lines of information to be separated. This technique is valuable in any system that uses ASCII-coded data as typed input to a program. Parsing, for example, is used by the assembler program to remove the label during pass one.

## Questions

1. The assembler program converts a _____ program into a _____ program.

2. The _____ program is in hexadecimal machine language.

3. What events occur during the first pass of the assembler?

4. Which assembler pass generates the object program?

5. What are the four fields found in an assembly language statement?

6. Which of the following labels are in error?
   (a) TEST     (b) TEST3     (c) TEST.3     (d) 4WHAT     (e) THIS—ONE

7. What hexadecimal values are loaded into register D0 by the following instructions?
   (a) MOVE.L #$56,D0
   (b) MOVE.L #56,D0
   (c) MOVE.L #'ABCD',D0
   (d) MOVE.L #4/5,D0

8. If an entire statement is used as a comment, the first character in the statement must be a _____.

9. What is the purpose of the END pseudo opcode?

10. If an ORG $3400 instruction is executed, the program that follows the ORG instruction will be stored beginning at memory location _____.

11. What do each of the following statements accomplish?
    (a) DATA EQU 12
    (b) LISTX DS.W 100
    (c) ARRAY DS.L 200
    (d) NUMB DC.B 12,13,14
    (e) NAME DC.B 'Name',0

12. What pseudo opcode is used to stop from printing a program or a section of a program?

13. Flowcharts are commonly constructed with what six flowcharting symbols?

14. If the decision flowcharting symbol has three lines running from it the lines are labeled: _____, _____, and _____.

15. Develop a program that will copy the contents of memory locations $3000–$305A into locations $4000–$405A and $5000–$505A.

16. Develop a subroutine that exchanges the 64-bit number addressed by A0 with the 64-bit number addressed by A1.

17. Write a subroutine that adds the contents of memory locations $3000–$300F together. Assume that the data are bytes and that the result is a 16-bit sum returned from the subroutine in the D0 register.

18. Write a subroutine that multiplies the contents of word memory location $3000 by a 33 decimal and stores the word result in memory location $3000.

19. Develop a subroutine that will square the numbers 0–9. Assume that the byte portion of D0 contains a number 0–9 when the subroutine is called. Upon a return, the byte portion of D0 must contain the number squared. For example, if a $04 is in D0 when the subroutine is called, D0 must be a $10 upon return. You must use a lookup table to perform this conversion.

**20.** What is an ASCII-Z string?

**21.** Develop a time delay subroutine that will cause a one-hour time delay.

**22.** In Example 5-27, what time delay is generated if the count is $3400?

**23.** Develop a memory test subroutine that will test memory locations $30000– $3FFFF by storing a $55 and $AA to test each location.

**24.** Write a program that will take the contents of memory location $3000–$31FF and add a $16 to each of these byte locations.

**25.** Develop a subroutine that will search through memory from locations $4000– $41FF for the 32-bit number $30000000. If the number is found, set the X-CCR bit. If the number is not found, clear the X-CCR bit.

**26.** Develop a subroutine that searches memory beginning at the address pointed to by the A0 register for an ASCII number ($30–$39). When the number is located, return from the subroutine.

**27.** Write a sort subroutine that sorts bytes of memory data.

**28.** Use the subroutine in Example 5-36 to parse a line containing four ASCII-coded words of information. Store the first ASCII-coded word at location $100000, the second at location $200000, the third at location $300000, and the fourth at location $400000.

# The 68000/68008 Microprocessor

# 6

**OBJECTIVES**

Upon completion of this chapter, you will be able to:

- Describe the purpose and function of each pin connection on both the 68000 and 68008 microprocessors.

- List the drive currents available at each output pin and show the fanout to various logic families.

- Explain the purpose of each state in the timing diagram and indicate the amount of time allowed for memory access.

- Determine whether buffers are required in a 68000-based system and develop the schematic diagram required showing any required buffers.

- Draw the circuitry required to reset the 68000 microprocessor.

- Develop the circuit required to produce the clock signal for the microprocessor.

- Explain how the $\overline{\text{DTACK}}$ signal is used for normal memory access and how it is used to cause wait states for slower memory.

- Describe interrupts and direct memory access or bus arbitration.

**KEY TERMS**

| | | |
|---|---|---|
| upper $\overline{\text{DS}}$, lower $\overline{\text{DS}}$, data strobe | bus bandwidth | interrupt |
| fanout | memory access time | bus arbitration or direct memory access |
| bus cycle | slower memory component | |
| data transfer rate | bus conflict | |

THIS chapter details the hardware pin connections of the 68000 and 68008 microprocessors. It also explains the operation and terminal requirements of each of the 68000 and 68008 microprocessor pin connections.

Once the pin connections have been presented, the ac and dc characteristics of these microprocessors are explained with the required circuitry for clock generation.

Timing diagrams are provided, to promote an understanding of the timing of the microprocessor and the parameters that are important to interfacing.

Additional circuitry required for normal operation is explained. This includes buffers that are often found in larger 68000 and 68008 based systems. The 68008 is only lightly described because of its similarity to the 68000 microprocessor.

## 6-1 The 68000 and 68008 Pinouts

The Motorola 68000 microprocessor is mounted in a 64-pin DIP (dual in-line package). The 68008, also produced by Motorola, is mounted in either a 48- or 52-pin DIP depending on the version. All three of these devices are also available in pin grid array (PGA) packages. Figure 6-1 illustrates the pinouts of both versions of the 68008 microprocessor, the 68008D and 68008Q. The major difference between these versions is the amount of memory that each addresses. The 68008D addresses a 1M byte memory. The 68008Q addresses a 4M byte memory. The 68008Q addresses 4M bytes of memory because it has two more address (A0–A21) connections than the 68008D (A0–A19).

Figure 6-2 illustrates the 68000D microprocessor. If the pinouts of the 68000

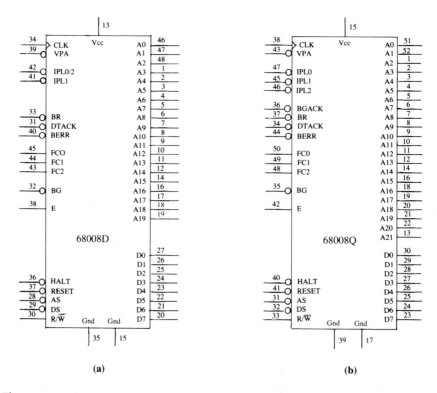

**Figure 6-1** The pinout and block diagrams of the 68008D (a) and 68008Q (b) microprocessors.

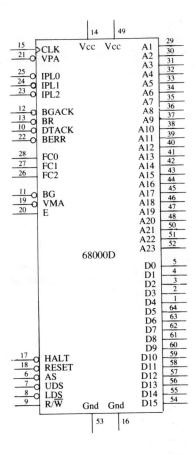

**Figure 6-2** The pinout and block diagram of the 68000D microprocessor.

and 68008 are studied, it is noticed there are very few differences between the 68000 and the 68008. The main difference is the number of pin connections on these microprocessors. These pin differences include the data bus width, the address bus width, and the extra control bus signal that aids in operating the 16-bit-wide memory of the 68000. The extra control signal is not required on the 68008 because its memory data bus is only 8 bits wide.

### 6-1.1 Differences Between the 68000 and 68008

The 68000 contains a 16-bit data bus that allows transfers of 16-bit-wide data between itself and the memory and I/O system. The 68008 contains an 8-bit data bus that transfers a byte (8 bits) at a time. Although the 68000 has a 16-bit data bus, it is still capable of transferring 8 bits through either the upper or the lower half of its data bus. The upper and lower data bus halves are used to transfer all bytes that have even and odd memory addresses, respectively.

The 68000 contains address connections A1–A23 while the 68008 contains only address connections A0–A19 (68008D) or A0–A21 (68008Q). This means that the 68008D addresses a 1M byte memory space, transferring a byte at a time, with its 20-bit address. The 68008Q addresses 4M bytes of memory space, transferring a byte at a time, with its 22-bit address. The 68000 addresses a 16M byte (8M word or 4M long-word) memory space with its 23-bit address bus while transferring either a byte or a 16-bit word.

Memory data in both microprocessors are numbered and addressed by each byte. A word is two consecutive bytes in either the 68000 or 68008, but it must be located at an even memory boundary in the 68000. If not, the 68000 will generate an address error exception. Bytes may be stored at either even or odd memory addresses.

The 68000 contains $\overline{\text{LDS}}$ and $\overline{\text{UDS}}$ pins. The 68008 does not contain these signals. In place of $\overline{\text{LDS}}$ and $\overline{\text{UDS}}$, the 68008 has a $\overline{\text{DS}}$ pin. The $\overline{\text{LDS}}$ (*lower data strobe*) connection indicates that the least significant 8 bits (D7–D0) of the data bus are currently active. The $\overline{\text{UDS}}$ (*upper data strobe*) connection indicates that the most significant 8 bits (D15–D8) of the data bus are active.

$\overline{\text{LDS}}$ and $\overline{\text{UDS}}$ are necessary for the 68000 to read or write bytes (upper or lower) or, if necessary, words of data. Without these two additional control pins, all memory transfers are always 16 bits. Note that when a 16-bit number is stored in memory, the most significant part (upper data bus) is stored in an even-numbered location, the least significant part (lower data bus) is stored at an odd location.

The 68008 uses the $\overline{\text{DS}}$ (*data strobe*) connection to indicate that data are active on the data bus. Other than the few differences listed here, the 68000 and the 68008 are identical. Both have the same instruction set, and all the other hardware connections are basically the same.

### 6-1.2    Pin Connections

Following is a complete listing of the pin connections on the 68000/68008 microprocessor. Each set of pins is described, and any differences that occur between the 68000 and 68008 microprocessors are delineated.

### 68000 and 68008 Pin Connections

**A23–A1 (Address)**    These 23 address connections allow the 68000 microprocessor to directly address 16M bytes or 8M words of memory. Individual bytes are specified by the $\overline{\text{LDS}}$ and $\overline{\text{UDS}}$ signals. The 68008D has 20 address connections, labeled A19–A0, which allow it to address 1M bytes of memory. On the 68008Q there are 22 address connections, labeled A21–A0, which allow the microprocessor to address 4M bytes of memory.

**$\overline{\text{AS}}$ (Address strobe)**    Address strobe becomes a logic zero to indicate that the address bus contains a valid memory address. This signal is often used to enable the $\overline{\text{DTACK}}$ signal if no wait states are required. It is also used to enable the decoders that select memory and I/O devices.

**$\overline{\text{BERR}}$ (Bus error)**    The $\overline{\text{BERR}}$ input is used to request a bus error exception. If $\overline{\text{BERR}}$ is activated with the $\overline{\text{HALT}}$ signal, the current bus cycle will be rerun.

$\overline{BG}$ **(Bus grant)** The $\overline{BG}$ input indicates that the 68000 or 68008 has stopped executing software. It also indicates that the microprocessor has open-circuited its address, control, and data buses. The $\overline{BG}$ signal is a response to the $\overline{BR}$ (bus request) signal used during DMA (direct memory access) or bus arbitration processes.

$\overline{BGACK}$ **(Bus grant acknowledge)** The $\overline{BGACK}$ signal indicates that the external DMA controller has taken control of the system buses. This allows the DMA controller to access the memory and I/O spaces and commands the microprocessor to relinquish its address, data, and control buses. This line is also tested by other DMA controllers to see if the bus is available.

$\overline{BR}$ **(Bus request)** The bus request input is used whenever a DMA or bus arbitration is required. $\overline{BR}$ is used to request a DMA action.

**CLK (Clock)** The clock input controls the basic operating frequency of the 68000 or 68008. The clock signal provides all internal microprocessor components with their basic timing. The standard version of the 68000 or 68008 uses an 8 MHz clock signal. Versions of these microprocessors are available that operate with up to a 12.5 MHz clock.

**D15–D0 (Data)** Data connections are used to transfer information into or out of the 68000 microprocessor in groups of either 8 or 16 bits. On the 68008 there are only eight data bus connections, labeled D7–D0, to transfer a byte of data. On the 68008 a word is transferred via two byte transfers.

$\overline{DS}$ **(Data strobe)** The data strobe signal is present only on the 68008 microprocessor. When this signal is a logic zero, it is used to validate the R/$\overline{W}$ line to the memory and I/O. Data strobe indicates that the data bus either contains data or will accept data, as in a read operation.

$\overline{DTACK}$ **(Data transfer acknowledge)** This input, which indicates to the microprocessor that a bus transfer is complete, must be activated during each bus cycle for the microprocessor to continue normal operation. The $\overline{DTACK}$ signal causes the microprocessor to run at whatever speed is required by the memory or I/O, up to the speed allowed by the clock. This occurs no matter how much time is required in a system.

**E (Enable)** The E signal is generated from the CLK pin at one-tenth the frequency applied to the CLK input. E is low for six CLK pulses and high for four. This signal is most often used when 6800 peripherals are interfaced to the 68000 or 68008; it is also useful wherever a lower frequency clock signal is required.

**FC2, FC1, FC0 (Function code bits)** Function code bits are used to indicate that the 68000 is executing various functions as listed in Table 6-1. The primary use for these pins is to generate an interrupt acknowledge signal if interrupts are used in a system. A code of 111 also indicates that the microprocessor is accessing the CPU space, which is generally used for an interrupt acknowledge. These signals also prove useful if a separate section of memory is required for supervisory or user data.

**Table 6-1**   Function Code Bits FC2, FC1, and FC0

| FC2 | FC1 | FC0 | Function |
|-----|-----|-----|----------|
| 0 | 0 | 0 | not used |
| 0 | 0 | 1 | user data addressed |
| 0 | 1 | 0 | user program addressed |
| 0 | 1 | 1 | not used |
| 1 | 0 | 0 | not used |
| 1 | 0 | 1 | supervisor data addressed |
| 1 | 1 | 0 | supervisor program addressed |
| 1 | 1 | 1 | interrupt acknowledge (CPU space) |

$\overline{\text{HALT}}$   This bidirectional pin is used as an input to cause a halt or a rerun. As an output, it indicates that the 68000 has halted. The $\overline{\text{HALT}}$ pin is normally grounded at the same time as the $\overline{\text{RESET}}$ pin during system reset. This prevents the 68000 from malfunctioning during the system reset operation.

$\overline{\text{IPL2}}$, $\overline{\text{IPL1}}$, $\overline{\text{IPL0}}$ **(Interrupt priority inputs)**   Interrupts are requested by activating one or more of these inputs. Notice that the inputs are active low. A 010 placed on the pins will select interrupt vector number 101 for autovector interrupts.

$\overline{\text{LDS}}$ **(Lower data strobe)**   The lower data strobe signal is a logic zero to indicate that the data bus is about to transfer a byte of data. At this time, the data travel through the data bus connections D7–D0. This pin is not found on the 68008 because of its 8-bit data bus. $\overline{\text{LDS}}$ is often combined with R/$\overline{\text{W}}$ to generate a read and a write signal for the lower memory and I/O bank. Note that the $\overline{\text{LDS}}$ signal is active for an odd-addressed byte transfer and also a word transfer in the 68000 microprocessor.

**R/$\overline{\text{W}}$ (Read/write)**   The read/write signal indicates that the current bus cycle is either a read or a write cycle. If R/$\overline{\text{W}}$ is a logic zero, operation is a write operation, and if R/$\overline{\text{W}}$ is a logic one, it is a read operation.

$\overline{\text{RESET}}$   The $\overline{\text{RESET}}$ pin is a bidirectional pin that is placed at a logic zero level by executing the RESET instruction. If the $\overline{\text{RESET}}$ pin is physically grounded, it causes the 68000 to reset and fetch vectors 0 and 1. These vectors are loaded into the SSP and PC, respectively. Vector 0 is stored in memory locations 0–3 and vector 1 is stored at 4–7. Note that each vector stores a 32-bit address.

$\overline{\text{UDS}}$ **(Upper data strobe)**   The upper data strobe signal is a logic zero to indicate that the data bus is about to transfer a byte of data through data bus connections D15–D8. This pin is not found on the 68008 because of its 8-bit data bus. $\overline{\text{UDS}}$ is often combined with R/$\overline{\text{W}}$ to generate a read and a write signal for the upper memory and I/O bank. Note that the $\overline{\text{UDS}}$ signal is active for an even-addressed byte transfer or a word transfer in the 68000 microprocessor.

**Vcc (Positive power supply connection)**   The Vcc connection requires a +5.0 V power supply connection with a tolerance of ±5%. The power supply must supply an average of about 500 mA of current with a surge capability of at least 1.5 A.

During a reset operation and at other times, power supply current can surge to 1.5 A.

$\overline{\text{VPA}}$ **(Valid peripheral address)**   The $\overline{\text{VPA}}$ pin serves two functions in the 68000 and 68008. It is used during an interrupt acknowledge cycle to cause autovectoring. It is also used to indicate that the peripheral has received a valid address for a 6800 peripheral I/O operation. This signal is provided to interface older, 6800-type interface components to the microprocessor and to select autovectored interrupts.

$\overline{\text{VMA}}$ **(Valid memory address)**   This signal, which indicates that the bus contains a valid memory address if the $\overline{\text{VPA}}$ input is activated, is used to activate older 6800 peripherals.

**Vss (ground power supply connection)**   The Vss pin is connected to the ground terminal of the +5.0 V power supply.

### 6-1.3   DC Characteristics

The 68000 microprocessor requires an average of 500 mA of current for operation with a +5.0 V dc power supply. The supply voltage must have a tolerance of ±5%. The 68008 requires the same tolerance on its power supply connections. The difference is the amount of current required for its operation. The 68008 requires 440 mA of average power supply current. Less power is required because the 68008 contains fewer buffers to external pin connections. An HCMOS version (high speed CMOS) of the 68000 microprocessor is available (68HC000) that requires 50 mA of power supply current. The reason for the much smaller power requirement is because the 68HC000 is a CMOS version of the 68000.

One additional power supply requirement exists for these microprocessors. The power supply must be capable of providing power supply current surges of up to 1.5 A. (For the HCMOS version, 150 mA of surge current is required.) If the power supply cannot provide this surge current, the microprocessor will not operate correctly. Incorrect operation is caused by a power supply voltage droop below +5.0 V with each surge. In practice, if the power supply is not adequate, the 68000 or 68008 will exhibit mysterious changes and malfunctions. These changes occur in the contents of the internal registers and external memory system during a reset and during other operations. A droop in supply voltage may cause a mysterious loss of position in a program.

### Bypass Capacitors

As with any TTL (transistor–transistor logic) or MOS device, the power supply connections must be bypassed to ground. The purpose of the bypass capacitor is to help prevent a droop in power supply voltage to the microprocessor during normal operation (not during the 1.5 A surge). A 0.1 μF capacitor connected from +5.0 V to ground as near to the integrated circuit as possible, accomplishes bypassing (refer to Figure 6-3). A bypass capacitor is needed because the microprocessor is a digital device. With each internal transition of its logic levels, a surge of current is generated. These surges cause external power supply surges. Since the printed circuit

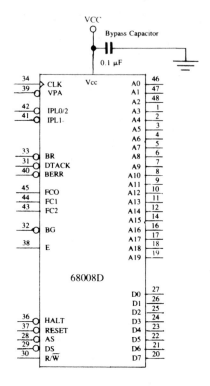

**Figure 6-3**   The bypass capacitor used to bypass the Vcc power input to the micro-processor.

connection has some resistance, the voltage at the Vcc pin will droop below +5.0 V. The capacitor filters or removes the droops. Make certain not to lump this capacitance, because lumping serves no purpose. All integrated circuits in a system, linear or digital, must be bypassed for proper operation.

### Drive Current

The amount of current available at the output pin connections of the 68000 and 68008 varies from one grouping of pins to another. Table 6-2 illustrates the values of the currents available for each grouping of pins.

**Table 6-2    Output Drive Currents for the 68000 and 68008**

| Pins | Logic 0 | Logic 1 |
|------|---------|---------|
| HALT | 1.6 mA | 400 μA |
| A1–A23, $\overline{BG}$, FC0–FC1 | 3.2 mA | 400 μA |
| RESET | 5.0 mA | 400 μA |
| E, $\overline{AS}$, D0–D15, $\overline{LDS}$, $\overline{UDS}$, $R/\overline{W}$ | 5.3 mA | 400 μA |

Standard interface components include TTL and MOS devices, which require different amounts of drive current. Therefore, different numbers of these circuits are connected to an output pin. These logic families, with their respective drive current requirements, are listed in Table 6-3.

### Fanout

The *fanout* (maximum number of connections) is determined by comparing Tables 6-2 and 6-3 when connecting the 68000 and 68008 microprocessors to various logic families. For example, the $\overline{\text{RESET}}$ connection allows up to 5.0 mA of current to flow before the logic one and logic zero voltages degrade too far for proper operation. If more than 5.0 mA of current is allowed to flow, the logic zero voltage will rise above 0.4 V, changing the noise immunity of the system. Too much current will cause the logic zero voltage to become high enough to be interpreted as a logic one level. To prevent problems, always stay within the design criteria of these microprocessors, or any digital circuit.

A standard TTL input requires 1.6 mA at a logic zero level and 40 μA at a logic one level. If the amount of current required at the TTL input is divided into the amount provided on a 68000 output pin, you arrive at the fanout number for the logic family type. With the $\overline{\text{RESET}}$ connection and standard TTL, about three standard TTL circuits (unit loads) may be safely connected to the $\overline{\text{RESET}}$ pin before a problem with the logic voltage levels arises. Other logic families allow different loading because of different current levels. So do other pins on the microprocessor.

Table 6-4 illustrates the fanouts available to various logic families from the 68000 and 68008 microprocessors. Notice the apparent error in the table for the fanout to MOS circuits. No, this is not an error. MOS circuits exhibit a large input capacitance that increases in value each time an additional load is connected to an output pin connection. As the capacitance increases, the timing signals begin to change in shape and position. This is due to increased capacitance in the output of the pin connection's buffer. To prevent a severe problem with this timing degradation, this capacitance must never exceed approximately 150 pF. Considering that the printed circuit connections have capacitance, this means that about 10 MOS loads

**Table 6-3**  Logic Family Drive Current Requirements

| Family | Logic 1 | Logic 0 |
|---|---|---|
| TTL (74XXX) | 40 μA | 1.6 mA |
| TTL (74HXXX) | 50 μA | 2.0 mA |
| TTL (74LSXXX) | 20 μA | 0.4 mA |
| TTL (74SXXX) | 40 μA | 2.0 mA |
| TTL (74ALSXXX) | 20 μA | 0.2 mA |
| TTL (74ASXXX) (74FXXX) | 40 μA | 1.0 mA |
| CMOS (74HCXXX) | ±10 μA | ±10 μA |
| MOS | ±10 μA | ±10 μA |

**Table 6-4**   Fanouts from the 68000 and 68008

| Family | Fanouts | | |
| --- | --- | --- | --- |
| | Data bus | Address bus | Control bus |
| TTL (74XXX) | 3 | 2 | 3 |
| TTL (74HXXX) | 2 | 1 | 2 |
| TTL (74LSXXX) | 10 | 8 | 10 |
| TTL (74SXXX) | 2 | 1 | 2 |
| TTL (74ALSXXX) | 10 | 10 | 10 |
| TTL (74ASXXX) | 5 | 3 | 5 |
| CMOS (74HCXXX) | 10 | 10 | 10 |
| MOS | 10 | 10 | 10 |

are all that may normally be driven from a 68000 or 68008 output connection. To drive additional loads, a buffer circuit is required that can drive high capacitance loads.

### Input Current Loading

The amount of current consumed by the 68000 and 68008 at any input is only about $\pm 2.5$ μA. The exception is $\overline{\text{HALT}}$, where the loading is $\pm 20$ μA. The microprocessor inputs are MOSFET inputs that do not cause any appreciable amount of current to flow. They mainly provide a capacitive load with very little current flow for a logic one or zero. With capacitive loads, the signals can degrade if there are more than 10 connections. This occurs even though the amount of current is negligible. If more than 10 loads are connected, you must use buffers to reduce the capacitive loading.

### 6-1.4   Bus Buffers

Bus buffers are required when the fanout is heavier than that allowed by the 68000 or 68008. A fully buffered 68000-based system is illustrated in Figure 6-4. Notice that buffers appear on the address bus connections, on the data bus connections, and also on many control signal connections.

Figure 6-4 also shows the bypass capacitors required for proper circuit operation. Without the bypass capacitors, this circuit will not function properly. In most schematics, the bypass capacitors are not illustrated. It is assumed that they are present, just as it is assumed that the power supply connections are present. The bypass capacitors are not illustrated on any other schematic in this text because it is not customary to show them. In practice it is often hard to locate the bypass capacitors in existing circuitry because they may be hidden inside the integrated circuit socket, or even built into the socket when it is manufactured.

The buffers found connected to the address bus and the control bus are unidirectional 74ALS244 octal bus buffers. The buffers connected to the data bus are 74ALS245 bidirectional octal bus buffers. Each of these buffer circuits provides up to 32 mA of logic zero current and up to 5.2 mA of logic one current. This increased

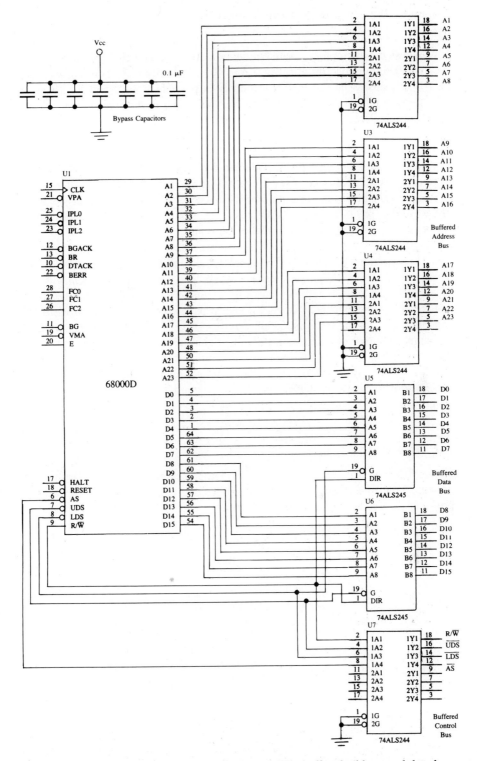

**Figure 6-4**  A 68000 microprocessor illustrating a fully buffered address and data bus. Notice that the R/$\overline{\text{W}}$, $\overline{\text{UDS}}$, $\overline{\text{LDS}}$, and $\overline{\text{AS}}$ control signals are also buffered and that bypass capacitors are shown for each integrated circuit.

drive allows the microprocessor to fan out to more integrated circuits. Buffers have increased the logic one drive current from 400 μA to 5.2 mA. This allows more capacitive loads to be driven than normally is possible from the microprocessor pins. Despite this increase in drive current, you should never exceed about 20–30 loads on a buffered connection. Having too many loads causes too much input capacitance. Figure 6-5 illustrates the effect on timing signals when the amount of capacitive load is increased on a bus connection.

Notice from Figure 6-5 that as the load increases, the amount of time shift and waveform distortion also increases. If the waveshape and position of a timing signal change by very much, the operation of the 68000 or 68008 is placed in jeopardy. The waveform position is changed because it takes longer to charge a large capacitance (more loads) to 5 V than a smaller capacitance (less loads).

Figure 6-6 illustrates the 68008 in a system that has its address, data, and control connections buffered. When comparing the buffered 68000 and 68008 systems, we notice only a slight difference between them. This difference is mainly due to widths of the address and data buses of these two microprocessors. Also notice that the control bus signals lower data bus strobe and upper data bus strobe ($\overline{\text{LDS}}$ and $\overline{\text{UDS}}$) are missing from the 68008. In place of $\overline{\text{LDS}}$ and $\overline{\text{UDS}}$, the 68008 has a $\overline{\text{DS}}$ connection that is buffered in this illustration. There are only two reasons to buffer a microprocessor: if the amount of drive current required exceeds that allowed for the microprocessor, or if the capacitive loading on a pin is excessive. Normally, excessive capacitance is defined as approximately 150 pF on any pin connection.

## 6-2   Bus Timing

To interface memory or I/O devices to the microprocessor, one must understand the timing of the microprocessor. The microprocessor is a synchronous device that produces timing. It expects the external memory and I/O systems to respond to the

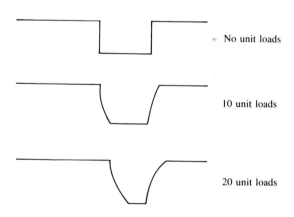

No unit loads

10 unit loads

20 unit loads

**Figure 6-5   The effect on timing with various unit loadings.**

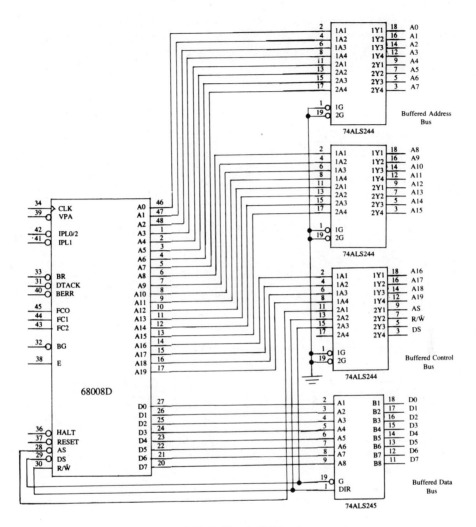

**Figure 6-6**   A fully buffered 68008 microprocessor.

timing within certain timing constraints. The microprocessor drives or controls the memory and I/O through its timing signals. Figure 6-7 illustrates basic read timing for the 68000 microprocessor.

The uppermost waveform in Figure 6-7 represents the clock signal that is provided by an external timing source. The 68000 clock is normally 8 MHz for the standard version and as high as 12.5 MHz for a higher speed version. The enhanced 68020, 68030, and 68040 currently operate at frequencies of up to 25 MHz, with still faster versions on the horizon. The 68040 will eventually operate at clock frequencies of up to 33 MHz and possibly 50 MHz.

All other timing shown in Figure 6-7 is referenced to the system clock waveform. This timing diagram is divided into clocking states $(S_n)$ that represent one half

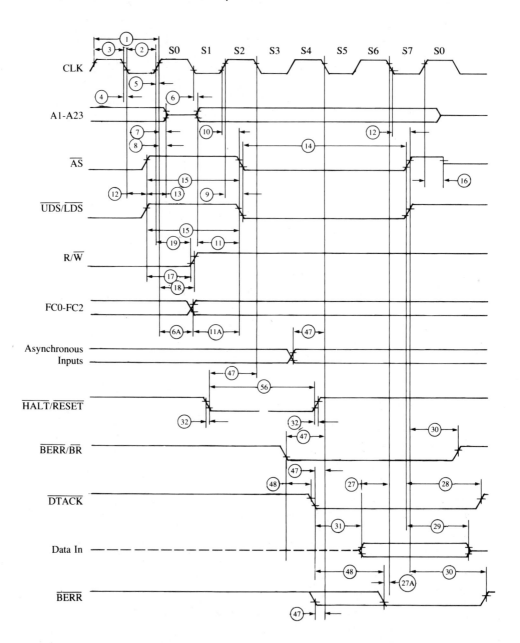

**Figure 6-7**   The read timing diagram of the 68000/68008 microprocessor. (Courtesy of Motorola, Inc.)

a clock cycle. It normally takes eight states ($S_0$–$S_7$) to transfer data between the microprocessor and memory or I/O. These eight states are collectively called a *bus cycle*. During any given bus cycle, data are read from memory or I/O or written to memory or I/O.

If the clock is 8 MHz, the 68000 requires 500 ns (8 states of 67.5 ns each) for one bus cycle. The number of data transfers per second is called the *data transfer rate*. If the clock is 8 MHz, the maximum data transfer rate between the microprocessor and the memory and I/O is 2M bytes (68008) or 2M words (68000) per second. Data transfer rate is also at times specified as *bus bandwidth*. Here the bus bandwidth is said to be 2 MHz. In practice, the data transfer rate is often less because the microprocessor does not continuously read or write data. At times, the microprocessor is executing an instruction and the memory is not referenced: the multiplication instruction, for example, requires more time to execute (70 clocks); during its execution, the microprocessor bus is idle and is not transferring data.

### 6-2.1   States

From the timing diagram in Figure 6-7, notice that during state $S_1$, the microprocessor sends the address to the memory or I/O. This first state is the beginning of the read or write machine cycle. Data from the memory or I/O is not sampled until a point between the end of $S_6$ and the beginning of $S_7$.

An approximate memory access time is then six states or 375 ns if the clock is 8 MHz. If the timing is studied closely, it is seen that access time cannot be determined directly by looking at the timing diagram. Notice, though, that it takes some time less than 3 clocking periods or six states to access memory. This is because time is needed for the address to appear on the address connections after the start of $S_1$. There is also a setup time requirement before the beginning of $S_7$, where the data are sampled.

The amount of time required for the address to appear after the start of $S_1$ is $t_{CLAV}$ time (time number 6). Time specification $t_{CLAV}$ is the amount of time it takes for the address to become valid and stable after the start of clocking state $S_1$. (Refer to Figure 6-8 for the ac timing characteristics of the 68000 microprocessor.) The amount of time required before the data bus is sampled at $S_7$ is called $t_{DICL}$ or data setup time (time number 27). Setup time is the amount of time data must remain valid and stable before it is sampled at the beginning of $S_7$.

*Memory access time* (time allowed the memory to access data) is the time it takes for three complete 68000 clocking periods (six states) minus the time needed for the address to appear after $S_1$ ($t_{CLAV}$), minus the time required for data to be set up on the data bus before $S_7$ ($t_{DICL}$). The access time therefore is $t_{ACC} = 3$ clocks $-$ $t_{CLAV} - t_{DICL}$.

If the 68000 is operated with an 8 MHz clock, each clocking period is 125 ns, so three clocking periods are 375 ns. The amount of time listed for $t_{CLAV}$ is 70 ns, and the time listed for $t_{DICL}$ is 15 ns. Thus the amount of time the microprocessor allows for a memory access is 290 ns when the 68000 clock is 8 MHz. Later it is shown that this may not be enough time for certain memory devices to function properly. In this event, the microprocessor must wait for the slower devices to become ready for operation.

| Num. | Characteristic | Symbol | 8 MHz Min | 8 MHz Max | 10 MHz Min | 10 MHz Max | 12.5 MHz Min | 12.5 MHz Max | Unit |
|------|----------------|--------|-----------|-----------|------------|-------------|--------------|---------------|------|
| 1 | Clock Period | $t_{cyc}$ | 125 | 500 | 100 | 500 | 80 | 250 | ns |
| 2 | Clock Width Low | $t_{CL}$ | 55 | 250 | 45 | 250 | 35 | 125 | ns |
| 3 | Clock Width High | $t_{CH}$ | 55 | 250 | 45 | 250 | 35 | 125 | ns |
| 4 | Clock Fall Time | $t_{Cf}$ | — | 10 | — | 10 | — | 5 | ns |
| 5 | Clock Rise Time | $t_{Cr}$ | — | 10 | — | 10 | — | 5 | ns |
| 6 | Clock Low to Address Valid | $t_{CLAV}$ | — | 70 | — | 55 | — | 55 | ns |
| 6A | Clock High to FC Valid | $t_{CHFCV}$ | — | 70 | — | 60 | — | 55 | ns |
| 7 | Clock High to Address Data High Impedance (Maximum) | $t_{CHAZx}$ | — | 80 | — | 70 | — | 60 | ns |
| 8 | Clock High to Address/FC Invalid (Minimum) | $t_{CHAZn}$ | 0 | — | 0 | — | 0 | — | ns |
| 9[1] | Clock High to $\overline{AS}$, $\overline{DS}$ Low (Maximum) | $t_{CHSLx}$ | — | 60 | — | 55 | — | 55 | ns |
| 10 | Clock High to $\overline{AS}$, $\overline{DS}$ Low (Minimum) | $t_{CHSLn}$ | 0 | — | 0 | — | 0 | — | ns |
| 11[2] | Address Valid to $\overline{AS}$, $\overline{DS}$ (Read) Low/$\overline{AS}$ (Write) | $t_{AVSL}$ | 30 | — | 20 | — | 0 | — | ns |
| 11A[2] | FC Valid to $\overline{AS}$, $\overline{DS}$ (Read) Low/$\overline{AS}$ (Write) | $t_{FCVSL}$ | 60 | — | 50 | — | 40 | — | ns |
| 12[1] | Clock Low to $\overline{AS}$, $\overline{DS}$ High | $t_{CLSH}$ | — | 70 | — | 55 | — | 50 | ns |
| 13[2] | $\overline{AS}$, $\overline{DS}$ High to Address/FC Invalid | $t_{SHAZ}$ | 30 | — | 20 | — | 10 | — | ns |
| 14[2] | $\overline{AS}$, $\overline{DS}$ Width Low (Read)/$\overline{AS}$ (Write) | $t_{SL}$ | 240 | — | 195 | — | 160 | — | ns |
| 14A[2] | $\overline{DS}$ Width Low (Write) | — | 115 | — | 95 | — | 80 | — | ns |
| 15[2] | $\overline{AS}$, $\overline{DS}$ Width High | $t_{SH}$ | 150 | — | 105 | — | 65 | — | ns |
| 16 | Clock High to $\overline{AS}$, $\overline{DS}$ High Impedance | $t_{CHSZ}$ | — | 80 | — | 70 | — | 60 | ns |
| 17[2] | $\overline{AS}$, $\overline{DS}$ High to R/$\overline{W}$ High | $t_{SHRH}$ | 40 | — | 20 | — | 10 | — | ns |
| 18[1] | Clock High to R/$\overline{W}$ High (Maximum) | $t_{CHRHx}$ | — | 70 | — | 60 | — | 60 | ns |
| 19 | Clock High to R/$\overline{W}$ High (Minimum) | $t_{CHRHn}$ | 0 | — | 0 | — | 0 | — | ns |
| 20[1] | Clock High to R/$\overline{W}$ Low | $t_{CHRL}$ | — | 70 | — | 60 | — | 60 | ns |
| 20A[2] | AS Low to R/$\overline{W}$ Valid | $t_{ASRV}$ | — | 20 | — | 20 | — | 20 | ns |
| 21[2] | Address Valid to R/$\overline{W}$ Low | $t_{AVRL}$ | 20 | — | 0 | — | 0 | — | ns |
| 21A[2] | FC Valid to R/$\overline{W}$ Low | $t_{FCVRL}$ | 60 | — | 50 | — | 30 | — | ns |
| 22[2] | R/$\overline{W}$ Low to $\overline{DS}$ Low (Write) | $t_{RLSL}$ | 80 | — | 50 | — | 30 | — | ns |
| 23 | Clock Low to Data Out Valid | $t_{CLDO}$ | — | 70 | — | 55 | — | 55 | ns |
| 24 | Clock High to R/$\overline{W}$, $\overline{VMA}$ High Impedance | $t_{CHRZ}$ | — | 80 | — | 70 | — | 60 | ns |
| 25[2] | $\overline{DS}$ High to Data Out Invalid | $t_{SHDO}$ | 30 | — | 20 | — | 15 | — | ns |
| 26[2] | Data Out Valid to $\overline{DS}$ Low (Write) | $t_{DOSL}$ | 30 | — | 20 | — | 15 | — | ns |
| 27[5] | Data In to Clock Low (Setup Time) | $t_{DICL}$ | 15 | — | 10 | — | 10 | — | ns |
| 27A | Late $\overline{BERR}$ Low to Clock Low (Setup Time) | $t_{BELCL}$ | 45 | — | 45 | — | 45 | — | ns |
| 28[2] | $\overline{AS}$, $\overline{DS}$ High to $\overline{DTACK}$ High | $t_{SHDAH}$ | 0 | 245 | 0 | 190 | 0 | 150 | ns |
| 29 | $\overline{DS}$ High to Data Invalid (Hold Time) | $t_{SHDI}$ | 0 | — | 0 | — | 0 | — | ns |
| 30 | $\overline{AS}$, $\overline{DS}$ High to $\overline{BERR}$ High | $t_{SHBEH}$ | 0 | — | 0 | — | 0 | — | ns |
| 31[2,5] | $\overline{DTACK}$ Low to Data Valid (Setup Time) | $t_{DALDI}$ | — | 90 | — | 65 | — | 50 | ns |
| 32 | $\overline{HALT}$ and $\overline{RESET}$ Input Transition Time | $t_{RHr, f}$ | 0 | 200 | 0 | 200 | 0 | 200 | ns |
| 33 | Clock High to $\overline{BG}$ Low | $t_{CHGL}$ | — | 70 | — | 60 | — | 50 | ns |
| 34 | Clock High to $\overline{BG}$ High | $t_{CHGH}$ | — | 70 | — | 60 | — | 50 | ns |
| 35 | $\overline{BR}$ Low to $\overline{BG}$ Low | $t_{BRLGL}$ | 1.5 | 3.5 | 1.5 | 3.5 | 1.5 | 3.5 | Clk. Per. |
| 36 | $\overline{BG}$ High to $\overline{BG}$ High | $t_{BRHGH}$ | 1.5 | 3.5 | 1.5 | 3.5 | 1.5 | 3.5 | Clk. Per. |
| 37 | $\overline{BGACK}$ Low to $\overline{BG}$ High | $t_{GALGH}$ | 1.5 | 3.0 | 1.5 | 3.0 | 1.5 | 3.0 | Clk. Per. |

—Continued

| Num. | Characteristic | Symbol | 8 MHz Min | 8 MHz Max | 10 MHz Min | 10 MHz Max | 12.5 MHz Min | 12.5 MHz Max | Unit |
|---|---|---|---|---|---|---|---|---|---|
| 37A | $\overline{BGACK}$ Low to $\overline{BR}$ High (to Prevent Rearbitration) | $t_{BGKBR}$ | 20 | — | 20 | — | 20 | — | ns |
| 38 | $\overline{BG}$ Low to Bus High Impedance (with $\overline{AS}$ High) | $t_{GLZ}$ | — | 80 | — | 70 | — | 60 | ns |
| 39 | $\overline{BG}$ Width High | $t_{GH}$ | 1.5 | — | 1.5 | — | 1.5 | — | Clk. Per. |
| 40 | Clock Low to $\overline{VMA}$ Low | $t_{CLVML}$ | — | 70 | — | 70 | — | 70 | ns |
| 41 | Clock Low to E Transition | $t_{CLC}$ | — | 70 | — | 55 | — | 45 | ns |
| 42 | E Output Rise and Fall Time | $t_{Er, f}$ | — | 25 | — | 25 | — | 25 | ns |
| 43 | $\overline{VMA}$ Low to E High | $t_{VMLEH}$ | 200 | — | 150 | — | 90 | — | ns |
| 44 | $\overline{AS}$, $\overline{DS}$ High to $\overline{VPA}$ High | $t_{SHVPH}$ | 0 | 120 | 0 | 90 | 0 | 70 | ns |
| 45 | E Low to Address/$\overline{VMA}$/$\overline{FC}$ Invalid | $t_{ELAI}$ | 30 | — | 10 | — | 10 | — | ns |
| 46 | $\overline{BGACK}$ Width | $t_{BGL}$ | 1.5 | — | 1.5 | — | 1.5 | — | Clk. Per. |
| 47[5] | Asynchronous Input Setup Time | $t_{ASI}$ | 20 | — | 20 | — | 20 | — | ns |
| 48[2,3] | $\overline{DTACK}$ Low to $\overline{BERR}$ Low | $t_{DALBEL}$ | — | 80 | — | 55 | — | 35 | ns |
| 49 | E Low to $\overline{AS}$, $\overline{DS}$ Invalid | $t_{ELSI}$ | −80 | — | −80 | — | −80 | — | ns |
| 50 | E Width High | $t_{EH}$ | 450 | — | 350 | — | 280 | — | ns |
| 51 | E Width Low | $t_{EL}$ | 700 | — | 550 | — | 440 | — | ns |
| 52 | E Extended Rise Time | $t_{CIEHX}$ | — | 80 | — | 80 | — | 80 | ns |
| 53 | Data Hold from Clock High | $t_{CHDO}$ | 0 | — | 0 | — | 0 | — | ns |
| 54 | Data Hold from E Low (Write) | $t_{ELDOZ}$ | 30 | — | 20 | — | 15 | — | ns |
| 55 | R/$\overline{W}$ to Data Bus Impedance Change | $t_{RLDO}$ | 30 | — | 20 | — | 10 | — | ns |
| 56[4] | $\overline{HALT}$/$\overline{RESET}$ Pulse Width | $t_{HRPW}$ | 10 | — | 10 | — | 10 | — | Clk. Per. |

NOTES:
1. For a loading capacitance of less than or equal to 50 picofarads, subtract 5 nanoseconds from the values given in these columns.
2. Actual value depends on clock period.
3. In the absence of $\overline{DTACK}$, $\overline{BERR}$ is an asynchronous input using the asynchronous input setup time (#47).
4. For power up, the MPU must be held in $\overline{RESET}$ state for 100 ms to allow stabilization of on-chip circuitry. After the system is powered up, #56 refers to the minimum pulse width required to reset the system.
5. If the asynchronous setup time (#47) requirements are satisfied, the $\overline{DTACK}$-low to data setup time (#31) and $\overline{DTACK}$-low to $\overline{BERR}$-low setup time (#48) requirements can be ignored. The data must only satisfy the data-in to clock-low setup time (#27) for the following clock cycle, $\overline{BERR}$ must only satisfy the late-$\overline{BERR}$-low to clock-low setup time (#27A) for the following clock cycle.

**Figure 6-8   The ac electrical characteristics of the 68000/68008 microprocessor. (Courtesy of Motorola, Inc.)**

Because the memory access time allowed at an 8 MHz clock is 290 ns, a memory device that is connected to the 68000 must have a maximum access time of no longer than 290 ns. If the access time is 291 ns or more, the data from the memory device are passed over by the microprocessor. The amount of time required to decode the memory device detracts from the access time. Thus, if the memory requires 250 ns maximum for access and the decoder requires 30 ns, the total access time for the memory and its decoder is 280 ns. Because the 68000 running with an 8 MHz clock allows 290 ns for memory access, this memory and its decoder will work properly.

### 6-2.2   Clock

The clock signal input of the 680XX is generated by an external clock generator. The allowable clock frequency is determined by the version of the 680XX connected in a system. The speed of operation that the system designer requires for the microprocessor also may determine clock speed.

If the standard version of the 68000 is used, the clock frequency is as high as 8 MHz and as low as 2 MHz. The lower limit is due to the internal dynamic register storage. Dynamic registers are refreshed by the clock input signal. If they are not refreshed within a certain period, data are lost. The upper limit is due to the speed of the logic circuitry inside the microprocessor. If a higher than allowed clock frequency is used, the propagation delays times cause problems with the internal timing.

The microprocessor may still function at a clocking rate higher than its designed rate, but an early failure may occur, or data may be lost. Early failure is due to the excessive heating that occurs with a higher clock frequency. It is never the proper solution to use a heat sink and a higher than design clock speed. If a clock frequency lower than allowed is used, the dynamic register storage will begin to forget data because it is not being refreshed in the proper time frame.

Figure 6-9 illustrates a typical clock generator circuit for the 68000 microprocessor. Notice that a quartz crystal is used as a timing element so the micro-

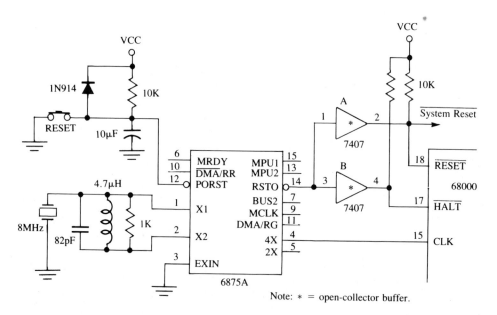

**Figure 6-9   Circuit illustrating the connection of the clock and reset circuitry of the 68000/68008 microprocessor.**

processor operates at a predictable and stable frequency. The clock generator produces a single phase output that is designed to drive a high capacitance load such as the clock input of the 68000 microprocessor.

The clock connection on all microprocessors is connected to many internal MOSFET loads. This means that it has quite a bit of capacitance. The crystal oscillator may also be an integrated oscillator. The integrated oscillator is mounted in a 14-pin integrated circuit. It is purchased with an operating frequency from 2 to more than 50 MHz.

Besides the clock, the circuit illustrated in Figure 6-9 generates the reset signal for the microprocessor. More detail is provided on reset in Section 6-3.1.

It might be desirable to operate the 68000 from an *RC*- or *LC*-based timing source. If this is done, you must design circuit with a resonant frequency so it is not too near to 8 or 2 MHz. *RC* and *LC* elements are not very stable, which results in frequency drift. This drift causes operation above or below the maximum and minimum allowable frequencies for the 68000. Rarely is *LC* or *RC* timing used to generate the clock for a microprocessor, but it is possible.

### 6-2.3   Data Transfer Acknowledge ($\overline{\text{DTACK}}$)

The data transfer acknowledge handshake, provided by the $\overline{\text{DTACK}}$ signal, is required for the microprocessor to perform a memory or I/O read or write. The $\overline{\text{DTACK}}$ signal must become a logic zero within 20 ns before the end of $S_4$ occurs or the 68000 will enter an idle or wait state. $\overline{\text{DTACK}}$ also must be returned to a logic one level within 245 ns after the $\overline{\text{AS}}$ signal has returned to a logic one level, or wait states will occur.

Wait states are useful if slower memory components are interfaced to the microprocessor. (A *slower memory component* is a memory device that requires a longer access time than the 68000 provides.) If inserted, wait states add to the amount of time the 68000 allows the memory to access data. Normally, wait states ($S_w$) are inserted as pairs. This causes the access time to be expanded by multiples of system clocking periods. Figure 6-10 illustrates the effect on the timing if two wait states are inserted into the timing of the 68000.

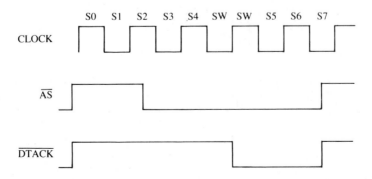

**Figure 6-10   Bus timing when two wait states ($S_w$) are inserted into the 68000/68008 timing with the $\overline{\text{DTACK}}$ signal.**

Notice from Figure 6-10 that the data sampling point (beginning of $S_7$) is shifted to the right by these two wait state clocking periods ($S_w$). If the system clock is 8 MHz, the memory access time is stretched by 125 ns (the two wait states) from 290 ns (the normal access time at 8 MHz) to 420 ns. This is enough access time for most memory devices except the slowest of EPROMs (erasable programmable ROMs).

If more access time is required, more wait states are inserted into the timing. For example, if four wait states are used, the amount of access time allowed by the 68000 increases to 540 ns (250 ns + 290 ns). Actually an infinite number of these wait states is inserted if the $\overline{\text{DTACK}}$ pin is either grounded or held high. $\overline{\text{DTACK}}$ must become a logic zero and must return to a logic one during each bus cycle for operation of the microprocessor to proceed. If $\overline{\text{DTACK}}$ is held high past the ends of the machine cycle, wait states occur. If it is held low through a machine cycle, wait states also occur.

If you refer to Figure 6-11 and back to Figure 6-8 you can see that the timing on the $\overline{\text{DTACK}}$ pin is fairly critical. Provided $\overline{\text{DTACK}}$ has gone high before state $S_4$, the 68000 will now sample $\overline{\text{DTACK}}$ to determine whether it is a logic one or a logic zero. If $\overline{\text{DTACK}}$ is a logic one when sampled at $S_4$, no wait states occur; if it is a logic zero, there will be wait states. After the initial sampling in $S_4$, $\overline{\text{DTACK}}$ is again sampled in each pair of wait states to determine whether additional wait states are required. If they are not, $\overline{\text{DTACK}}$ must be returned to a logic one by 245 ns past the end of the current bus cycle as signaled by $\overline{\text{AS}}$. If no wait states are required, it is fairly common to connect the $\overline{\text{AS}}$ pin to the $\overline{\text{DTACK}}$ pin because $\overline{\text{AS}}$ meets all the timing requirements of $\overline{\text{DTACK}}$. This connection generates no wait states.

Figure 6-12 illustrates a circuit that generates various wait states for the 68000/68008 microprocessor. This is a very flexible circuit because it allows the user to make wait states sensitive to a particular area of the memory. It also allows wait states to be made sensitive to a particular memory component. The circuit allows a different number of wait states for different areas of memory.

Notice the jumper switch connection allows 0W, 2W, etc. numbers of wait states to be inserted. The integrated circuit shown is a shift register. The shift

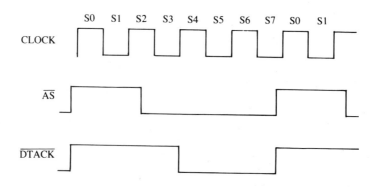

**Figure 6-11**  The 68000/68008 timing diagram illustrating no wait states because $\overline{\text{DTACK}}$ is a logic zero by the end of $S_4$.

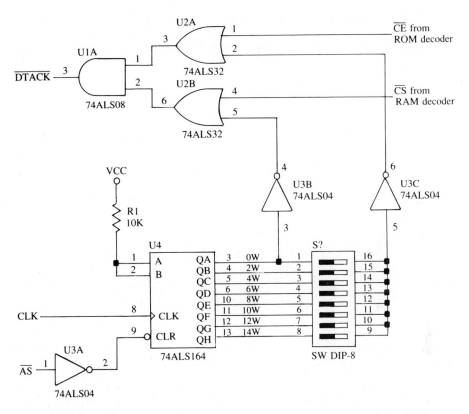

**Figure 6-12** A wait state generator that allows 0–14 wait states. In this circuit, zero wait states are inserted for the RAM and any number are inserted for the ROM.

register is used to generate a hard-wired waveform when the 68000/68008 accesses memory or I/O. This access is signaled by the activation of the $\overline{AS}$ signal, which indicates that the address bus contains a valid memory or I/O address.

In this circuit, the shift register remains cleared (0000 0000) until the $\overline{AS}$ signal becomes a logic zero. The zero on $\overline{AS}$ indicates the start of a memory or I/O read or write. Next, the wait state generator begins to generate or shift logic ones into itself from the serial input. The serial input is connected to a logic one. The contents of the shift register are shifted onto the $\overline{DTACK}$ pin through an inverter and logic circuit. Shift registers are often used to generate simple waveforms like this in digital or microprocessor-based systems.

With the circuit wired as illustrated, access to the RAM causes zero wait states and access to the ROM causes any number of wait states. The switch setting determines the number of wait states for the ROM. This arrangement may be expanded so that any number of different sections of the memory will cause any number of wait states. A section of memory is a single device or an area of memory. Wait states are also used with I/O devices. In most cases I/O devices require no waits for proper operation.

### 6-2.4   Read/Write (R/$\overline{\text{W}}$)

The read/write pin determines whether the memory or I/O in the system does a read or a write. To use this signal and to control the most common forms of memory, R/$\overline{\text{W}}$ is often combined with the $\overline{\text{DS}}$ signal. This generates a separate read and a separate write strobe for the 68008. In the 68000 microprocessor the R/$\overline{\text{W}}$ signal is combined with $\overline{\text{UDS}}$ and $\overline{\text{LDS}}$. Figure 6-13 illustrates how $\overline{\text{RD}}$ and $\overline{\text{WR}}$ are generated from the R/$\overline{\text{W}}$ and data strobe signals.

These new control signals are often required in a system because many memory devices have two or three control inputs. A ROM, for example, often contains an $\overline{\text{OE}}$ and a $\overline{\text{CE}}$ connection. $\overline{\text{CE}}$ is connected to the memory decoder, and $\overline{\text{OE}}$ goes to a control signal that enables its internal bus buffers. Output enable applies data to the data bus from the memory so that it can be read by the microprocessor. $\overline{\text{OE}}$ is normally connected to the $\overline{\text{RD}}$ signal developed here for this purpose. $\overline{\text{RD}}$ becomes valid when the data strobe is valid. $\overline{\text{RD}}$ must be used to time the application of data from a memory or I/O to the 68000 data bus.

Many commonly found RAM (read/write) memory devices contain three control inputs: $\overline{\text{CS}}$, $\overline{\text{OE}}$, and $\overline{\text{WE}}$. The $\overline{\text{CS}}$ input is normally connected to an address decoder, the $\overline{\text{OE}}$ pin is grounded to cause a read operation, and the $\overline{\text{WE}}$ pin is grounded to cause a write operation. The normal connection of $\overline{\text{WE}}$ is to the $\overline{\text{WR}}$ signal, and the normal connection for $\overline{\text{OE}}$ is the $\overline{\text{RD}}$ signal.

Because the 68000 does not have separate read and write control signals, the signals developed in Figure 6-13 provide the required timing for this memory

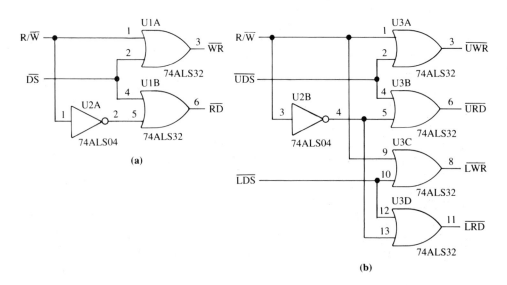

**Figure 6-13**   Circuits used to generate memory and I/O control signals. (a) The $\overline{\text{RD}}$ and $\overline{\text{WR}}$ signals for a 68008 system. (b) The $\overline{\text{UWR}}$, $\overline{\text{LWR}}$, $\overline{\text{URD}}$, and $\overline{\text{LRD}}$ signals for a 68000 system.

device. The $\overline{WR}$ signal causes a write to occur only after $\overline{DS}$ is a logic zero and R/$\overline{W}$ is a logic zero. At this time the microprocessor's data bus contains information to be written to the memory or I/O.

What happens if the read/write signal is not used in a system? Read and write must be used to time the transfer of information between the memory and the microprocessor. If these commands are not used, the data may be lost during this transfer because of *bus conflicts*. A bus conflict occurs when more than one memory or I/O device, are simultaneously activated. It is very important to use the R/$\overline{W}$ signal or $\overline{RD}$ and $\overline{WR}$ as developed in the circuit of Figure 6-13. If these signals are not used, it is important that $\overline{DS}$ (68008) or $\overline{LDS}$ and $\overline{UDS}$ (68000) be used to time the application of data to the data bus.

## 6-3  Other 68000/68008 Signals

Besides the address, data, and control signals presented above, other control and special function signals exist on the 68000 microprocessor. These other signals and control functions include interrupts and bus arbitration. An interrupt is a special way of handling I/O, as is a bus arbitration.

### 6-3.1  $\overline{\text{RESET}}$

Because the 68000 is a synchronous system, it must be initialized to a known state. If not initialized, it will not work properly. Reset initializes the 68000. Resetting is accomplished with the $\overline{RESET}$ connection on the 68000. The $\overline{RESET}$ connection is a dual-purpose (bidirectional) connection. $\overline{RESET}$ is operated as an input for initialization and as an output whenever the RESET instruction is executed in a program.

If the external system physically grounds the $\overline{RESET}$ input for at least 100 ms after Vcc is applied, the 68000 microprocessor fetches the vector (memory address) stored at memory locations $000000–$000003 and places it into the supervisor stack pointer (SSP). After fetching and loading the SSP, it retrieves the contents of memory locations $000004–$000007 and places this material into the program counter (PC). Recall that the program counter always contains the address of the next instruction in a program. If $\overline{RESET}$ initializes the program counter during a reset, it programs the 68000 to begin executing an instruction at a known memory location. Figure 6-14 illustrates the simple circuit often used to reset the 68000. Note that the $\overline{HALT}$ and $\overline{RESET}$ pins must be activated together, to ensure that the 68000 is properly reset upon the application of system power.

The circuit in Figure 6-14 operates in the following manner.

1. Upon the application of +5.0 V dc, the capacitor begins to charge toward +5.0 V. Initially it is discharged to zero volts, which means that the $\overline{RESET}$ and $\overline{HALT}$ inputs are both a logic zero level. The application of the logic zero on $\overline{RESET}$ and $\overline{HALT}$ resets the 68000.

2. As time passes, the capacitor begins to charge toward +5.0 V. Eventually, its voltage crosses the logic one threshold for the $\overline{RESET}$ and $\overline{HALT}$ inputs. As it

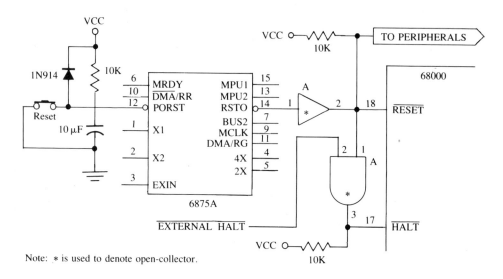

**Figure 6-14   The reset circuitry for the 68000/68008 microprocessor using the 6875A.**

does this, both pins return to a logic one level. This allows the 68000 to begin executing instructions normally from the address fetched for the program counter from locations \$000004–\$000007.

3. From this time forward, until power is disconnected or the reset button is pressed, the $\overline{\text{RESET}}$ and $\overline{\text{HALT}}$ connections remain at a logic one level, allowing normal operation.

If the RESET instruction is executed, the $\overline{\text{RESET}}$ pin becomes a logic zero level for 124 clocking periods. The $\overline{\text{RESET}}$ pin is normally connected to any peripheral in the system that requires resetting for initialization. Because $\overline{\text{RESET}}$ is connected to the peripherals, the RESET instruction will reset them or they are reset whenever power is applied by the *RC* circuit. The RESET instruction does not fetch the SSP and PC from the memory as a hardware reset input did. The RESET instruction only activates the $\overline{\text{RESET}}$ pin for 124 clocks to reset peripherals; it does not reset the microprocessor.

### 6-3.2   Halt

The $\overline{\text{HALT}}$ pin, besides being used for reset, is a bidirectional pin. It is used as an output to indicate that the microprocessor is halted (STOP instruction). It is also an input used to cause a halt, or with the $\overline{\text{BERR}}$ input, to cause a rerun. If $\overline{\text{HALT}}$ is placed at a logic zero level and $\overline{\text{BERR}}$ is a logic one level, the 68000 will halt or suspend the execution of all instructions. This is its use during the reset described earlier. If $\overline{\text{HALT}}$ and $\overline{\text{BERR}}$ are both placed at their logic zero levels, the 68000 will reexecute the current bus cycle. (See Table 6-5.) This feature is useful for memory errors and other applications.

**Table 6-5**   Function of the $\overline{\text{HALT}}$ and $\overline{\text{BERR}}$ Pin Connections

| $\overline{\text{HALT}}$ | $\overline{\text{BERR}}$ | Function |
|------|------|----------|
| 0 | 0 | rerun |
| 0 | 1 | halt |
| 1 | 0 | bus error interrupt |
| 1 | 1 | no function |

For example, if a parity check is accomplished each time data are read from the memory, the $\overline{\text{HALT}}$ and $\overline{\text{BERR}}$ inputs are grounded whenever a parity error is detected. In this way, the 68000 will automatically rerun the current bus cycle. This is to see whether the error is due to noise (soft error) or whether it is a hard error. If a second consecutive error occurs, the $\overline{\text{BERR}}$ input is grounded by itself to cause a bus error interrupt. This terminates the program at the point of the parity error and calls an interrupt service subroutine to handle the bus error.

## 6-3.3   Interrupts

An *interrupt* is a hardware-initiated subroutine branch that interrupts the program that is currently executing. An interrupt branches to a subroutine. If the hardware activates an interrupt input, and the interrupt input is enabled, the 68000 branches to an interrupt service subroutine. This is a very useful feature, especially if an I/O device transfers data somewhat infrequently.

An example I/O system that benefits from interrupt processing is a keyboard. The benefit occurs if information is typed on a computer keyboard because even a good typist can optimally type only a few characters per second. The computer is much faster. So as data are typed at this slow rate, the operation of the computer is delayed. The computer cannot do anything but look at the keyboard and wait for another character to be typed by the typist.

If the keyboard is interfaced to the microprocessor so that whenever a key is pressed an interrupt occurs, the microprocessor is free to perform other tasks until a key is pressed. When the key is pressed, the microprocessor's program is interrupted and an interrupt service subroutine is branched to, causing keyboard data to be read. After the keyboard has been read with the interrupt service subroutine, a return from the interrupt occurs. This permits the interrupted program to resume execution at the exact point of interruption. The subroutine branch that is used to go to the interrupt service subroutine stores the address of the point of interruption (return address) on the stack. This allows the return to the interrupted program. This sequence of events is exactly the same as if you had executed a BSR instruction.

The 68000 interrupt structure contains several input pins and one output signal that is generated by a circuit that combines FC2, FC1, and FC0 called $\overline{\text{INTA}}$ (see Figure 6-15). The inputs include $\overline{\text{IPL0}}$, $\overline{\text{IPL1}}$, $\overline{\text{IPL2}}$, and $\overline{\text{BERR}}$, and the output derived by the circuit is $\overline{\text{INTA}}$. The $\overline{\text{BERR}}$ interrupt input is an edge-triggered, nonmaskable interrupt, while the $\overline{\text{IPL}}$ inputs are level sensitive and maskable. A maskable interrupt input can be turned on and off via software or hardware. The nonmaskable interrupt is always active and can never be shut off.

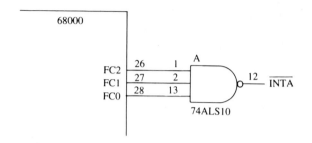

**Figure 6-15   A circuit that generates the $\overline{\text{INTA}}$ signal for interrupts.**

The $\overline{\text{BERR}}$ input (bus error) is a special interrupt input that is used alone or with the $\overline{\text{HALT}}$ input. In a system that indicates parity errors by the memory, $\overline{\text{BERR}}$ and $\overline{\text{HALT}}$ are used to either rerun a bus cycle or to terminate execution in a fatal error. If both $\overline{\text{BERR}}$ and $\overline{\text{HALT}}$ are grounded, a rerun occurs; if only $\overline{\text{BERR}}$ is grounded, a fatal interrupt to the bus error interrupt vector occurs.

The $\overline{\text{IPL}}$ inputs are used in a few different ways in the 68000 system. One method for using these inputs is autovectoring, while in another, an external vector is supplied to the 68000 during the $\overline{\text{INTA}}$ cycle. More detail on this is provided in Chapters 8 and 9, which deal with I/O circuitry and interrupts.

Besides hardware interrupts, the 68000 contains software interrupts. Software interrupts include a conditional interrupt called TRAPV and 16 software interrupts, TRAP 0–TRAP 15. These software interrupts function like the hardware interrupts except that they must be stored in the flow of the program as instructions. Actually, they are jump to subroutine instructions that require only 2 bytes of memory to store and reference vectors, in a vector table, for the subroutine's address. Refer to Chapter 9, on interrupts and exceptions, for more detail on the software interrupt instructions.

### 6-3.4   Bus Arbitration

Another method of handling I/O is called *bus arbitration* or *direct memory access*. This I/O technique uses three 68000 connections that are specifically designed for this purpose. The $\overline{\text{BR}}$ input (bus request) is activated whenever a DMA is requested. By activating this input, the 68000 will shortly produce a logic zero on the $\overline{\text{BG}}$ pin. $\overline{\text{BG}}$ indicates that the 68000 has suspended execution of software and has open-circuited its address, data, and control bus connections. This action allows an external DMA controller, or even another microprocessor, to enter the micro-processor's I/O and memory space, thus allowing the external controller to directly access memory and I/O. This is why this technique is often called direct memory access (DMA).

The $\overline{\text{BGACK}}$ connection is activated by the external bus controller when it begins to use the memory and I/O space. It is important that $\overline{\text{BGACK}}$ not be activated until (1) a bus grant has been received, (2) the $\overline{\text{AS}}$ signal is a logic one, (3) the $\overline{\text{DTACK}}$ signal is a logic one, and (4) the $\overline{\text{BGACK}}$ signal is a logic one.

$\overline{BGACK}$, which is used as a signal to other DMA controllers in a system, indicates that another DMA controller has access to the system. The DMA controller always tests the $\overline{BGACK}$ connection to determine whether a DMA action can occur. If the controller discovers logic one on $\overline{BGACK}$, it then activates $\overline{BR}$. If it discovers a logic zero on $\overline{BGACK}$, it enters idle states and waits for $\overline{BGACK}$ to return to a logic one before requesting the bus.

## Summary

1. The 68000 is packaged in a 64-pin dual in-line processor. The 68008 is packaged in either a 48- or 52-pin DIP. Both devices are also available in pin grid array packages.

2. The 68000 and 68008 have a few differences. The 68000 can address 16M bytes of memory with a 16-bit data bus and a 24-bit address. The 68008D can address 1M byte of memory with an 8-bit data bus and a 20-bit address. The 68000 contains $\overline{LDS}$ and $\overline{UDS}$ control signals, while the 68008 does not. Instead, the 68008 contains a $\overline{DS}$ signal.

3. The $\overline{LDS}$ and $\overline{UDS}$ signals are used by the 68000 to indicate that an 8-bit bank of memory is used for the memory or I/O transfer. $\overline{LDS}$ is active when the least significant 8 bits (D7–D0) are accessed, and $\overline{UDS}$ is active when the most significant 8 bits (D15–D8) are accessed. The 68008 has a data strobe signal ($\overline{DS}$) used to qualify the read and write control signals.

4. The fanout from most of the system bus pins is 10 unit loads. This rule holds if the 74LSXXX or 74ALSXXX series of TTL integrated circuits are used or if MOS or CMOS parts are used. If a fanout of 10 is too low, the system buses must be buffered.

5. A bus cycle has four clocking periods or eight states. It is used to read or write a byte or word of data between the microprocessor and the memory or I/O.

6. The amount of time the 68000 microprocessor allows the memory or I/O to function is computed by subtracting $t_{CLAV}$ and $t_{DICL}$ from three 68000 clocking periods. If the clock is operated at 8 MHz, access time allowed to the memory and I/O is 290 ns.

7. In the standard version of the 68000, the clock frequency may be set to anything as long as it doesn't exceed 8 MHz or drop below 2 MHz.

8. The $\overline{DTACK}$ (data transfer acknowledge) signal must be active to transfer data. If $\overline{DTACK}$ is held low or high, no information will be transferred in the 68000-based system.

9. Because wait states are inserted in the timing diagram of the 68000, memory that has an access time longer than 290 ns can be used with the microprocessor. Wait states are inserted by delaying the application of the $\overline{DTACK}$ signal to the 68000.

10. To reset the 68000 microprocessor, both the $\overline{\text{HALT}}$ and $\overline{\text{RESET}}$ inputs must be grounded for at least 100 ms. If the RESET instruction is executed, the $\overline{\text{RESET}}$ pin becomes a logic zero for 124 clocking periods.

11. The $\overline{\text{HALT}}$ pin is a bidirectional pin that is grounded to halt execution of software or becomes a logic zero to indicate the execution of the STOP instruction.

12. The $\overline{\text{BERR}}$ input is a dual-purpose connection that will cause the 68000 to execute a nonmaskable bus error interrupt if activated by itself. It will rerun the current bus cycle if activated with the $\overline{\text{HALT}}$ input.

13. The 68000 has four interrupt input connections. The $\overline{\text{BERR}}$ input is a nonmaskable interrupt input, and the $\overline{\text{IPL2}}$, $\overline{\text{IPL1}}$, and $\overline{\text{IPL0}}$ inputs are maskable interrupt inputs.

14. The function code bits (FC2, FC1, and FC0) are decoded to produce an $\overline{\text{INTA}}$ (interrupt acknowledge) signal.

15. An interrupt is a hardware- or software-initiated subroutine jump that interrupts the currently executing program to execute a subroutine. This is called an *interrupt service subroutine* because it services the interrupt.

16. A bus arbitration or direct memory access is an I/O technique that allows an external microprocessor or controller to deactivate the 68000 and gain control of its memory and I/O space.

17. The 68000 has three pins that are used for bus arbitration or DMA: $\overline{\text{BR}}$ (bus request), $\overline{\text{BG}}$ (bus grant), and $\overline{\text{BGACK}}$ (bus grant acknowledge). The $\overline{\text{BR}}$ input is used by an external system to gain control of the memory and I/O space of the 68000. The $\overline{\text{BG}}$ output pin indicates that the 68000 has granted control of its memory and I/O. The $\overline{\text{BGACK}}$ input is used by the external device to acknowledge that it has taken over the memory and I/O space of the 68000.

## Questions

1. The 68000 microprocessor is packaged in a _____-pin integrated circuit.

2. The 68008 microprocessor is packaged in a _____-pin integrated circuit.

3. The 68000 microprocessor can address _____ bytes of memory.

4. The 68008 microprocessor can address _____ bytes of memory.

5. The 68000 transfers _____ or _____ between itself and the memory or I/O through its data bus.

6. What is the width of the 68000 data bus?

7. What is the width of the 68008 data bus?

**8.** If the 68000 is connected to 74LSXXX TTL circuits, how many of these circuits can be connected to the A19 pin connection?

**9.** If the 68000 is connected to a large system, what pins must be buffered for it to function properly?

**10.** Describe the purpose of the $\overline{\text{LDS}}$ and $\overline{\text{UDS}}$ connections on the 68000 microprocessor.

**11.** What are the allowable clock frequencies on the 68000?

**12.** Why does the clock input to the 68000 have an upper and lower limit?

**13.** Define the following terms:
(a) bus cycle
(b) data transfer rate
(c) state
(d) memory access time

**14.** Where does the address first appear in the timing diagram of the 68000 microprocessor?

**15.** At what point in the timing of the 68000 does the microprocessor read the data from the memory or I/O?

**16.** How is the access time allowed the memory or I/O by the 68000 microprocessor calculated?

**17.** Calculate the access times allowed the memory and I/O for the 68000 when it is operated at the following clock frequencies:
(a) 5 MHz
(b) 6 MHz
(c) 7 MHz
(d) 7.5 MHz

**18.** Draw the waveform required for $\overline{\text{DTACK}}$ with the identification of each clock state so the following numbers of wait states are generated.
(a) 0 waits
(b) 2 waits
(c) 4 waits

**19.** Explain the operation of the wait state generator illustrated in Figure 6-12.

**20.** If the 68000 is operated with an 8 MHz clock, determine the amount of memory access time it allows for the following numbers of wait states.
(a) 0 waits
(b) 2 waits
(c) 4 waits

**21.** When the 68000 is reset, where does it get the address of the first instruction to be executed after a reset?

**22.** Which two 68000 control pins must be grounded to cause the 68000 to reset?

23. What instruction is executed to cause the $\overline{\text{RESET}}$ pin connection to become a logic zero for 124 clock periods?

24. What instruction is used to halt execution of software in the 68000?

25. Define the term interrupt.

26. What is an interrupt service subroutine?

27. When an interrupt occurs, what is interrupted?

28. The $\overline{\text{BERR}}$ and $\overline{\text{HALT}}$ pins are used together to cause the 68000 to perform what operation?

29. What is a nonmaskable interrupt compared to a maskable interrupt?

30. How is the $\overline{\text{INTA}}$ signal generated by the 68000 system?

31. What is a DMA?

32. Describe the effect of placing a logic zero on the $\overline{\text{BR}}$ pin of the 68000 microprocessor.

33. What is the purpose of the $\overline{\text{BG}}$ connection on the 68000 microprocessor?

34. What device generates the $\overline{\text{BGACK}}$ signal?

35. What must occur before the $\overline{\text{BGACK}}$ signal can be applied?

# Memory Interface

# 7

**OBJECTIVES**

Upon completion of this chapter, you will be able to:

- Define the following terms as they apply to memory: access time, address connections, data connections, and control connections.

- Describe the operation of each of the following memory types: ROM, PROM, EPROM, EEPROM, SRAM, and DRAM.

- Explain the operation of a decoder, whether an integrated decoder, a PROM decoder, or a PLD.

- Given a schematic of a memory system, determine the address range of each memory circuit by analyzing the operation of the decoder.

- Design a memory system that includes both EPROM for program and fixed data storage and SRAM for variable data storage.

- Explain the operation of the circuit that is used to refresh a dynamic memory.

- Develop a memory system that uses both EPROM for program and fixed data storage and DRAM for variable data storage.

**KEY TERMS**

| | | |
|---|---|---|
| read-only memory or ROM | volatile memory | glue |
| nonvolatile, nonvolatile memory | refreshing | clean ASCII file |
| mask-programmed ROM | address | fully, partially decoded (or populated) memory |
| | common separate data connections | |
| PROM programmer | access time | overlay, shadow |
| EPROM programmmer | don't care | RAS-only refresh |
| EEPROM | programmable/generic array logic or logic arrays | hidden refresh or zero wait state |
| NOVRAM | | |

I F THE block diagram of a computer system is recalled (refer to Figure 1-1), it is noticed that it contains three main sections: a microprocessor, a memory system, and an I/O system. This chapter describes the operation and design of the memory system as it applies to the 68000 and 68008 microprocessors.

Memory systems are constructed with three main components:

Random access, read/write memory (RAM).

Read-only memory (ROM).

A device to decode the memory address, which selects either RAM or ROM for the appropriate area in the memory.

This chapter provides information on the operation of the RAM and ROM and many commonly found decoders. The discussion of decoding also includes programmable logic devices (PLDs). The operation of memory with the microprocessor is also described. After an understanding of these basic circuits and their operation has been developed, we investigate a method of interfacing any memory device at any area of the system memory.

## 7-1   Memory Components

Before we can consider how a memory component is interfaced to the microprocessor, its operation and function must be understood. This section details the operation and function of both the read-only memory (ROM) and read/write memory (RAM). The ROM memory types consist of ROM, PROM, EPROM, and EEPROM. The RAM memory types consist of static RAM (SRAM) and dynamic RAM (DRAM).

### 7-1.1   Read-Only Memory

The *read-only memory* or ROM is so named because no data are written to it during its normal operation in a system. The ROM is read only during its operation in a memory system.

Many different types of read-only memory device are available to the system designer, including ROM (read-only memory), PROM (programmable read-only memory), EPROM (erasable programmable read-only memory), and EEPROM (electrically erasable programmable read-only memory).

With a ROM, the data or programs remain valid even after electrical power has been removed from the device. When data are stored in this manner, it is called *nonvolatile* storage. "Nonvolatile" means not easily changed. All ROM memories are examples of *nonvolatile memory*. A system normally contains one of the ROM forms to store information and system programs that normally are not changed over the useful life of the system.

### ROM

The read-only memory (ROM) is one of the first types of nonvolatile memory component to be introduced. Programmed at the factory when it is manufactured, the ROM device is sometimes called a *mask-programmed ROM*. Programming is accomplished by internally connecting circuits so that ones and zeros are permanently stored in the appropriate memory locations. This type of read-only memory is the most stable, but also the most expensive if only a few devices are required.

The high cost is due to a one-time mask charge imposed by the manufacturer. The mask can cost more than $10,000. The mask, the final step in manufacturing the ROM, selects logic ones or zeros for each bit position within the ROM. This type of ROM is so stable because it is wired, with the final mask, to store ones and zeros. The wires do not normally change unless the entire device fails.

## PROM

The programmable read-only memory (PROM) is a device that is programmed by the end user in a machine called a *PROM programmer,* which burns open tiny fuses of nichrome or polysilicon inside the PROM. Most PROM memory devices contain logic ones in all bits until a bit or its fuse is burned open by the PROM programmer. The act of burning open a fuse causes an output bit to become a logic zero.

The main advantage of the PROM is that it is a bipolar memory device with access times of 25 ns or less. All other types of ROM memory device are currently constructed with MOSFET technology, which makes their access times much slower. The MOSFET ROMs may be as slow as 450 ns. Some higher speed MOSFET ROM devices currently have access times to 100 ns.

The main disadvantage of the PROM is its lower density (number of bits per circuit component). The PROM which is a TTL, bipolar memory, also requires a much larger power supply current compared to MOSFET memory devices. PROM devices also sometimes fail because the fuses have been known to heal or grow closed after many hours of use in a system.

## EPROM

The erasable programmable read-only memory (EPROM) is a device that is programmed in an *EPROM programmer* by the end user. Its main advantage is that unlike the ROM and PROM, it is erasable. Once a PROM has been programmed by burning open fuses, it is programmed for its useful life. The EPROM memory device, on the other hand, finds wide application in systems because it can be erased and reprogrammed with new information.

The EPROM is different from the ROM or PROM because of its construction. An EPROM is a MOSFET logic circuit that uses a trapped charge on a floating gate for programming. A floating gate is a metal gate region that is completely surrounded with an insulator. To program the EPROM, a voltage of approximately 21–25 V is applied, to remove electrons from the gate region. This higher than normal voltage breaks down the insulator, thus removing electrons from the gate, which becomes charged. Because the gate is surrounded by a very good insulator, it remains charged for a long period. It is estimated that the gate holds a usable charge for at least 20 years. This is much longer than the useful life of most products in a system, or even the system itself.

The EPROM is erased by shining an ultraviolet light on the gate region through a quartz window located on the surface of the package. The ultraviolet light causes a photocurrent to flow, neutralizing the trapped charge stored on the floating gate. This effectively erases the stored program. Exposure times vary from 6 to 20 minutes under high intensity ultraviolet light. The amount of time depends on the device and the intensity of the light source. Information pertaining to erasure is listed in the manufacturer's literature for the device.

The main advantages of the EPROM are that it is erasable and reprogrammable. Its main disadvantages are that it takes a long time to erase, and both erasing and programming must be done outside the system. Since the EPROM is erased by ambient lighting, you must make sure that the quartz window is covered by an opaque label after programming. Another disadvantage is that an incorrectly programmed EPROM may erase itself after time. Unintended erasure also may occur if a devise is erased often. The EPROM has a limited number of erasures. In practice an EPROM can be safely erased, if the exposure to UV light is correct, up to about 100 times.

### EEPROM

The electrically erasable programmable read-only memory (EEPROM) solves the problem of removing the read-only memory from the machine to erase it and program it. The *EEPROM* is erased and reprogrammed inside the machine in which it resides. The main problem with this device is that it takes many milliseconds (up to 10 ms) to erase a single memory location. The EEPROM also has a limited life span. Many current EEPROMs have a life of no more than 10,000 cycles of erasure and reprogramming.

The EEPROM is an excellent device for storing tax tables in cash registers and setup information for video display terminals. A newer use is storing the DOS (disk operating system) on this type of device rather than on the disk drive. Later DOS can be changed or updated by merely reprogramming the EEPROM in the system. Reprogramming may occur through a communications link and the telephone lines.

In some EEPROMs, called *NOVRAMs* for nonvolatile RAM, the function of the EEPROM is replaced with a battery-powered CMOS static memory. These devices retain information for years on just the supply current provided by a small lithium battery. They tend to cost less than an EEPROM. They also don't require extra circuitry, and they can be erased in less time than is needed by the EEPROM.

### 7-1.2   Read/Write Random Access Memory

The read/write random access memory (RAM) is available in two forms: the static RAM (SRAM) and the dynamic RAM (DRAM). Both the SRAM and DRAM are called *volatile memory* devices to indicate that they lose stored information when the power supply is interrupted.

The main difference between the SRAM and the DRAM is that the SRAM retains data for as long as power is applied. The DRAM retains data for only 2–4 ms before it must be rewritten. The act of rewriting the data in a DRAM is called *refreshing*. RAM memory is used in a system to store transitory data.

## SRAM

SRAM memory is commonly available in sizes of up to 32K × 8. An SRAM of this size stores 32K (32,768) different 8-bit numbers. The SRAM is normally found in systems that usually contain no more than 256K bytes of read/write memory. The main disadvantages of SRAM storage are the requirements of more power to operate than DRAM and more integrated circuits for a large memory system. This is why systems that contain more than 256K bytes of storage use DRAM memory. An SRAM will remain a viable memory component for use in control systems, because control systems rarely contain a huge memory system.

## DRAM

DRAM memory is available in sizes of up to 4M × 1; on the horizon are 16M × 1 or much larger memory devices. SIMMs (single in-line memory modules) are commonly available in sizes of 1M × 8. Soon SIMMs will be commonly available in sizes of 4M × 8. Some 9-bit-wide SIMMs are also available for systems that store parity with each byte of data. As explained previously, parity is a check bit that is encoded with a logic one or a zero. It is set or cleared to indicate that a byte contains an even or an odd number of ones. If, when a memory location is read, it contains the wrong parity, the microprocessor is signaled that a parity error has occurred. The parity error generally indicates a memory component failure.

Any memory system that requires a vast amount of memory will normally use the DRAM. A DRAM results in a reduction in the number of circuit components required to store the data in large memory systems. Again, the main disadvantage of this form of memory is that without refreshing, the data stored will be lost. Refreshing is accomplished with dynamic RAM controllers that supply the necessary control and address data to accomplish a periodic refresh.

### 7-1.3 Memory Pin Connections

All memory components have similar memory pin connections. These connections are used to address data, to pass data into or out of the memory component, and to control the type of data transfer and its timing. The pins found common to all memory components are address, data, and control connections. If these three connections sound familiar, they should, because the microprocessor also contains the same three types of pin connections or buses. These buses are known as address, data, and control buses on the microprocessor. The memory components have address, data, and control connections.

## Address Connections

All memory components contain a grouping of pins called *address connections*. The address connections are used to select a memory location inside the memory component and are always labeled $A_0$, $A_1$, $A_2$, . . ., $A_n$.

The number of address connections on a memory device determines the number of locations within the memory. For example, a memory component with address connections $A_0$–$A_9$ has 10 address pins and selects any of 1024 different memory locations because $2^{10} = 1024$ (1K). It is a good idea to remember that a memory with 10 address connections has 1024 memory locations. If the number of address pins is increased to 11, the memory has twice as many locations or 2048 (2K). If it is increased to 12, the memory has 4096 (4K) locations.

It is also important to remember that a 1K memory device contains $400 memory locations. If you have 13 address connections, the memory has 8K memory locations or $2000 locations. This is arrived at by remembering that a 10-address pin memory has 1K or $400 locations. Thus an 11-address pin memory has 2K or $800 locations, a 12-address pin memory has 4K or $1000 locations, and a 13-address pin memory has 8K or $2000 locations. The relationship between memory size and number of hexadecimal locations is very important and must be remembered if proficiency with memory and memory interface is desired. It might also be a good idea to remember that $1000 is equal to 4K.

Refer to Figure 7-1 for an illustration of a generic RAM and a generic ROM. Notice that both memory types contain address input connections that are labeled in the same manner, although the number of connections often differs.

## Data Connections

Most memory components contain eight data connections that are attached to the microprocessor data bus. Some older memory components and some larger DRAM memories contain one, two, or four data connections.

Usually the least significant data connection is labeled D0. The most significant connection is labeled D7 for the memories with 8 bits per location. These pins are also labeled IO0–IO7 on some memory components. The data connections on a read-only memory are unidirectional, and data flow out of the memory. The same connections on most read/write memories are bidirectional. If the memory has bidirectional data connections, they are often called *common data connections*.

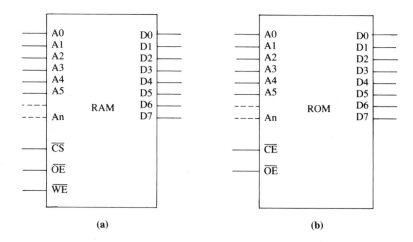

**Figure 7-1**    (a) A generic RAM and (b) a generic ROM.

Some DRAM memory circuits have separate pins for each direction of data flow, and these are called *separate data connections*. Separate data connections are usually labeled DIn for input and DOn for output, but not always.

## Control Connections

Address and data connections are essentially identical on memory devices of all types. The main difference between all memories lies in the control connections. Even control connections are not very different, as shall be shown.

All memory devices have at least one input that is used to select or enable the memory device. This pin is most often labeled $\overline{CS}$ (chip select), $\overline{CE}$ (chip enable), or simply $\overline{S}$ (select) or $\overline{E}$ (enable). Whenever this input is placed at a logic zero level, if it is an active low input, the memory device is enabled. When enabled, it begins to access the memory location addressed by the binary code placed on its address connections. Some memories have more than one of these enable inputs. Most have just one, though. If more than one enable input is present, all must be placed at their active levels to read or write data. For example, suppose that a memory device has the following enable inputs: CE1, $\overline{CE2}$, and CE3. To activate this memory, CE1 and CE3 must be placed at a logic one and $\overline{CE2}$ must be placed at a logic zero.

If we examine the read-only memory in Figure 7-1, we notice that it also contains one additional control connection called $\overline{OE}$ (output enable). The $\overline{OE}$ connection is used to enable or activate a set of internal buffers that drive the data bus attached to the data connections. If the $\overline{OE}$ connection is not activated, no data will ever appear at the output connections of the read-only memory. So, both the $\overline{CE}$ and $\overline{OE}$ connections must be active for any data to be read from this device. If both are not active, the output connections remain at their high impedance state.

In practice we will learn that the $\overline{CE}$ connection is attached to a memory address decoder. The $\overline{OE}$ connection is connected to some form of signal that indicates that a read will take effect. Most read-only memories contain the $\overline{CE}$ and $\overline{OE}$ connections. At times the $\overline{OE}$ connection is also labeled $\overline{G}$ (gate) or $\overline{OC}$ (output control).

If you take another look at the RAM in Figure 7-1, you will notice that it contains three control connections: $\overline{CS}$, $\overline{OE}$, and $\overline{WE}$. The new connection is for write enable ($\overline{WE}$). $\overline{WE}$ is used to cause the RAM to write information to the selected memory location if the $\overline{CS}$ connection is also active. In most RAM memory systems the $\overline{CS}$ connection is connected to an address decoder. The $\overline{OE}$ connection is connected to some type of read signal. The $\overline{WE}$ connection is attached to a write signal. The $\overline{WE}$ connection is also at times labeled $\overline{W}$ (write).

Some RAMs contain a $\overline{CS}$ and an $R/\overline{W}$ connection for control. Most of these are older devices and are not encountered as often. If these two control pins are found, the $\overline{CS}$ connection is grounded by a decoder to select the memory. Once selected, a logic one is placed on $R/\overline{W}$ to cause a read or a zero to cause a write. Many DRAM memory components use these two control inputs.

### 7-1.4 Memory Timing

Figure 7-2 illustrates the timing diagram of a read-only memory, showing the address, data, chip enable, and output enable connections. From the illustration, it is clear how the read-only memory is operated. First the memory address is applied

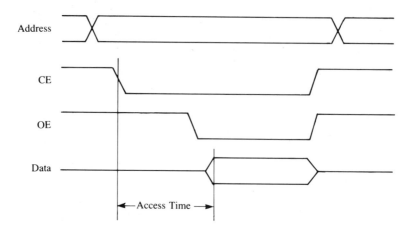

**Figure 7-2   The timing diagram for an EPROM or a ROM.**

to the address connections. After a short time, the chip enable connection is activated by some form of address decoder that selects the memory device. Once the device has been selected, a read signal appears on the output enable connection, causing the output buffers to be activated, whereupon data from the location addressed by the address connections flow onto the data connections.

Notice that before the $\overline{\text{OE}}$ connection becomes active, the data output connections are in their high impedance state. They also return to their high impedance state whenever $\overline{\text{OE}}$ or $\overline{\text{CE}}$ deactivates. This allows many memory components to be placed on a bus without interaction or conflict with other devices. A bus conflict occurs when two devices drive the bus at the same time. This causes data to be lost.

The one major timing event that exists for a memory device is called *access time*. The access time of a memory device is by definition the time needed by the memory to look up the contents of a memory location and present it at the output data connections. In a read-only memory, the access time is measured from the application of the address or the chip enable signal, whichever occurs last, to the time the data appear on the output connections. Access time of the slower EPROM read-only memory versions is as long as 450 ns; with the bipolar PROM circuits, it may be 15 ns or even shorter. The slower EPROM versions are usually very large, with capacities of up to 64K bytes and greater. The PROM devices are usually much smaller, as small as 32 bytes.

Figure 7-3 illustrates the timing for a typical RAM. Notice that it is very similar to the read-only memory timing except that a RAM performs both a read and a write operation. This is why the timing diagram has an extra signal, $\overline{\text{WE}}$. With the RAM, as with the read-only memory, access time is defined in the same manner. Most RAM memory components today can access data in no more than 250 ns, and as quickly as 15 ns for the very high speed bipolar RAM devices. Higher speed memory is available as ECL (emitter-coupled logic). The ECL memory has access

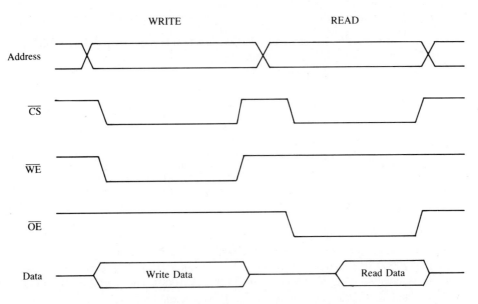

**Figure 7-3**   **The timing diagram for a typical RAM device.**

times of 2–4 ns. ECL devices are seldom used with present microprocessor-based systems. This is because ECL and standard microprocessor components use different power supply voltage and logic levels.

## 7-2   Memory Address Decoders

To interface a memory device to a microprocessor, memory address decoding and decoders must be understood. This section of the chapter explains how some of the more common decoders function and provides a method of decoding memory addresses.

### 7-2.1   Decoders

Decoders are devices that are used to select a memory component when a particular range of addresses is encountered on the address bus. For example, suppose that you are connecting a 4K $\times$ 8 EPROM to the 68008 microprocessor. The 68008 has a 20-bit address bus, while an EPROM of this size has only 12 address connections. This memory device does not fill the entire 1M byte memory space of the 68008. If the EPROM is not selected to operate at only a 4K byte segment of this memory, however, no other memory component may be connected to the microprocessor. The purpose of the decoder is to select the EPROM for just 4K of the available memory space.

## NAND Gate Decoder

Suppose that you decide to have the EPROM function at memory location $20000–$20FFF (a 4K byte section of the memory) for a 68008 microprocessor. (Recall that $400 is 1K of memory, $800 is 2K, and $1000 is 4K.) Example 7-1 shows both the first and last address of this block of memory, converted into binary for examination.

E X A M P L E   7 - 1

```
$20000  =   0010  0000  0000  0000  0000
$20FFF  =   0010  0000  1111  1111  1111
```

Notice in this example that the first 8 address bits ($20 or 0010 0000) remain constant in the entire range of memory addresses listed. If you drop one location below $20000, the first 8 bits become 0001 1111 ($1FFFF), and if you go one location above $20FFF, they become 0011 0001 ($21000). Thus a binary 0010 0000 ($20) is unique to this range of addresses. If we decode this binary bit pattern, the memory device is selected or enabled for this section of the memory only.

Figure 7-4 illustrates how a simple NAND gate is used to decode this binary bit pattern. When all eight inputs of the NAND gate are high, its output becomes a logic zero. In this circuit, this occurs only when the binary number 0010 0000 appears. Here some of the bits are passed through inverters and onto the inputs of the NAND gate. The NAND gate is used to generate a product term that describes the 0010 0000 code.

The output of this NAND gate becomes a zero for this binary address only. If its output is connected to the $\overline{CE}$ connection on the EPROM, the EPROM will activate for this section of the memory only. Thus the EPROM is decoded at memory addresses $20000–$20FFF and will not function elsewhere in the memory system.

Decoding a memory address with a NAND gate is seldom done today because of the variety of other techniques that are available. Decoders are used in place of NAND gates because there are so many address lines to decode. Of these other decoders, the most common are integrated decoder circuits, PROM decoders, and programmable logic devices (PLDs) such as PLAs (programmable logic arrays), PALs and GALs (programmable and generic array logic).

## Integrated Decoders

Before we can use an integrated decoder to decode a memory address, the decoder itself must be understood. Figure 7-5 illustrates the pinout and function table of the 74ALS138, 3-to-8 line decoder, which is common in many microprocessor-based systems. This device has three address inputs labeled A, B, and C and three enable inputs, $\overline{G2A}$, $\overline{G2B}$, and G1. The device is simple to understand if you first realize that all the outputs remain inactive (logic 1) if the device is not enabled. To enable this decoder, $\overline{G2A}$ and $\overline{G2B}$ must be a logic zero and G1 a logic one.

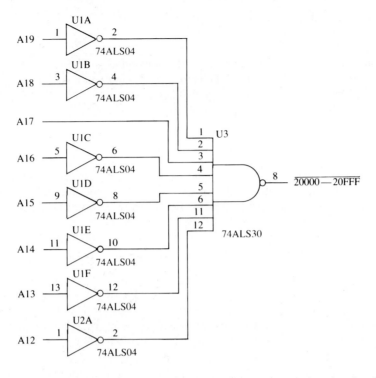

**Figure 7-4**  A NAND gate decoder for the 68008 microprocessor that decodes the address range $20000–$20FFF.

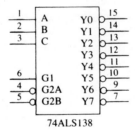

**Figure 7-5**  The pinout and function table of the 74ALS138 decoder.

| Inputs | | | | | | Outputs | | | | | | | |
|---|---|---|---|---|---|---|---|---|---|---|---|---|---|
| G1 | $\overline{G2A}$ | $\overline{G2B}$ | C | B | A | Y0 | Y1 | Y2 | Y3 | Y4 | Y5 | Y6 | Y7 |
| 0 | x | x | x | x | x | 1 | 1 | 1 | 1 | 1 | 1 | 1 | 1 |
| 1 | 1 | x | x | x | x | 1 | 1 | 1 | 1 | 1 | 1 | 1 | 1 |
| 1 | x | 1 | x | x | x | 1 | 1 | 1 | 1 | 1 | 1 | 1 | 1 |
| 1 | 0 | 0 | 0 | 0 | 0 | 0 | 1 | 1 | 1 | 1 | 1 | 1 | 1 |
| 1 | 0 | 0 | 0 | 0 | 1 | 1 | 0 | 1 | 1 | 1 | 1 | 1 | 1 |
| 1 | 0 | 0 | 0 | 1 | 0 | 1 | 1 | 0 | 1 | 1 | 1 | 1 | 1 |
| 1 | 0 | 0 | 0 | 1 | 1 | 1 | 1 | 1 | 0 | 1 | 1 | 1 | 1 |
| 1 | 0 | 0 | 1 | 0 | 0 | 1 | 1 | 1 | 1 | 0 | 1 | 1 | 1 |
| 1 | 0 | 0 | 1 | 0 | 1 | 1 | 1 | 1 | 1 | 1 | 0 | 1 | 1 |
| 1 | 0 | 0 | 1 | 1 | 0 | 1 | 1 | 1 | 1 | 1 | 1 | 0 | 1 |
| 1 | 0 | 0 | 1 | 1 | 1 | 1 | 1 | 1 | 1 | 1 | 1 | 1 | 0 |

Once enabled, the 74ALS138 responds to its address inputs and selects the output that becomes a logic zero. Notice that the C connection is most significant and the A connection is least significant address connection. If a 110 is applied to the address inputs, and the decoder is enabled, output number 6 will become a logic zero. This means that the output selected by the address inputs will become a logic zero if the decoder is enabled. Verify this by looking at the function table in Figure 7-5.

Figure 7-6 illustrates yet another decoder that is at times found in memory decoding schemes. The 74ALS139 decoder is a dual 2-to-4 line decoder. Notice that this device has two completely separate halves, each with two address connections and one enable connection. With this decoder, once the enable input has been grounded, the output selected by the A and B address inputs becomes a logic zero. If enable is held high, then none of the output connections become active (a logic zero).

### Example Decoder

Figure 7-7 illustrates a 74ALS138 connected to the address bus of the 68008 microprocessor. Here address connection A19 is connected to G1, A18 is to $\overline{G2A}$, and A17 is connected to $\overline{G2B}$. An output becomes active only if the memory address placed on the address bus by the microprocessor begins with a 100. This means, if you examine Example 7-2, that the range of addresses decoded by this decoder is $80000–$9FFFF. This happens to be a 128K byte block of the 68008 memory. Notice how the range of addresses is determined in Example 7-2. The first 3 bits must be a 100, and the remaining bits may be any value X. (X is a *don't care* that may be either a logic one or a zero.) In this example, the bottom-most address is determined by placing all zeros in the number for the don't cares; the upper-most address was determined by using all ones.

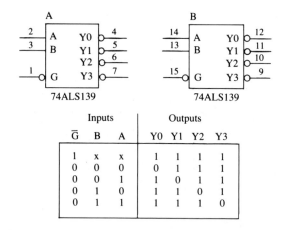

| Inputs | | | Outputs | | | |
|---|---|---|---|---|---|---|
| $\overline{G}$ | B | A | Y0 | Y1 | Y2 | Y3 |
| 1 | x | x | 1 | 1 | 1 | 1 |
| 0 | 0 | 0 | 0 | 1 | 1 | 1 |
| 0 | 0 | 1 | 1 | 0 | 1 | 1 |
| 0 | 1 | 0 | 1 | 1 | 0 | 1 |
| 0 | 1 | 1 | 1 | 1 | 1 | 0 |

**Figure 7-6**   The pinout and function table of the 74ALS139 decoder.

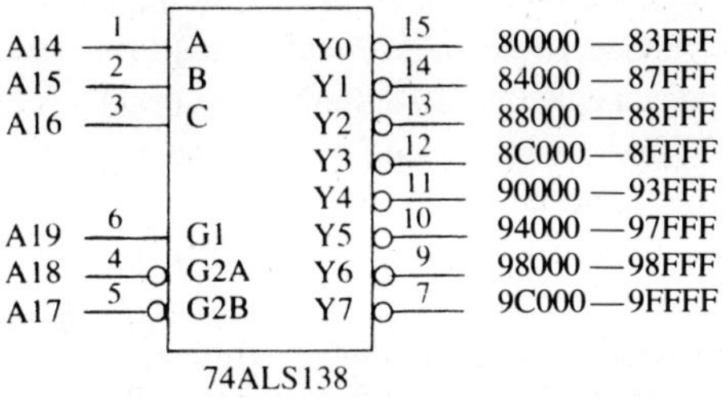

| A14 | 1 | A | Y0 | 15 | 80000 —83FFF |
| A15 | 2 | B | Y1 | 14 | 84000 —87FFF |
| A16 | 3 | C | Y2 | 13 | 88000 —88FFF |
| | | | Y3 | 12 | 8C000 —8FFFF |
| | | | Y4 | 11 | 90000 —93FFF |
| A19 | 6 | G1 | Y5 | 10 | 94000 —97FFF |
| A18 | 4 | G2A | Y6 | 9 | 98000 —98FFF |
| A17 | 5 | G2B | Y7 | 7 | 9C000 —9FFFF |

74ALS138

**Figure 7-7** A 74ALS138 connected to decode memory beginning at location $80000 through location $9FFFF in blocks of 16K bytes.

E X A M P L E  7 - 2

```
100X   XXXX  XXXX  XXXX  XXXX
1000   0000  0000  0000  0000  =   $80000
                .
                .
                .
1001   1111  1111  1111  1111  =   $9FFFF
```

A closer examination of Figure 7-7 shows that besides the address connections wired to the enable inputs, there are three more address pins connected to the decoder at address inputs A, B, and C. The three address inputs select which of the eight output connections become active within the address range of $80000–$9FFFF. For example, if A16, A15, and A14 are all zeros, then the decoder will select an output 0. Example 7-3 shows how the range of addresses decoded at output 0 are calculated. Here again the don't cares are used to determine the addresses that are decoded.

E X A M P L E  7 - 3

```
       C   BA
1000   00XX  XXXX  XXXX  XXXX
1000   0000  0000  0000  0000  =   $80000
                .
                .
                .
1000   0011  1111  1111  1111  =   $83FFF
```

The difference in Example 7-3 is there are fewer don't cares because of the additional three address connections on C, B, and A. The range of addresses decoded at output zero is $80000–$83FFF, or a 16K × 8 section of the 68008 memory. This means that this output is connected to the enable input of a 16K × 8 memory device. The device could be a RAM or a ROM. We know that this is a 16K memory device because there are 14 don't cares or address connections that are not decoded by the decoder. These 14 address connections are decoded inside the memory component to select one of the different memory locations on the memory device. A memory component with 14 address connections contains 16K memory locations.

Output 1 is determined in a like manner, as illustrated by Example 7-4. Here address connections C, B, and A contain a 001. Each succeeding output is determined in the same manner by changing the binary code applied to the C, B, and A inputs to match the output connection being decoded. For example, to find what address range is decoded by output 4, place a 100 (CBA) on these inputs. Output 4 decodes memory addresses $90000–$93FFF.

E  X  A  M  P  L  E    7 - 4

```
        C    BA
      1000  01XX  XXXX  XXXX  XXXX
      1000  0100  0000  0000  0000  =   $84000
                    .
                    .
                    .
      1000  0111  1111  1111  1111  =   $87FFF
```

## 7-2.2  PROM Address Decoders

Programmable read-only memories, too, are used for decoding memory addresses because of their high speed. The PROM also contains more address connections than decoders. The greater number of address connections makes the PROM more useful for decoding. This is especially true if you are decoding the address of the 68000 (23 address connections) or the 68020, 68030, or 68040 microprocessors (30 address connections).

All PROM devices are available with 10 or more address connections and are usually constructed with TTL components. The PROM is very fast. Access times of less than 25 ns are common, by virtue of the TTL construction of the PROM. This speed is important because it does not impact on the timing of the memory system. Recall from Chapter 6 that the time required to decode the memory address detracts from the access time allowed to the memory by the microprocessor.

Figure 7-8 illustrates a 512 × 8 PROM decoder (82S147). Notice from the function table that this device decodes 4K blocks of memory. Why is this true? The device decodes blocks of this size because 8 of the 20 address connections from a 68008 microprocessor are connected to the 8 address inputs of the PROM. The remaining address connections from the microprocessor, A11–A0, are not decoded by the PROM. If we use the PROM as we did with the 74ALS138 decoder, we know

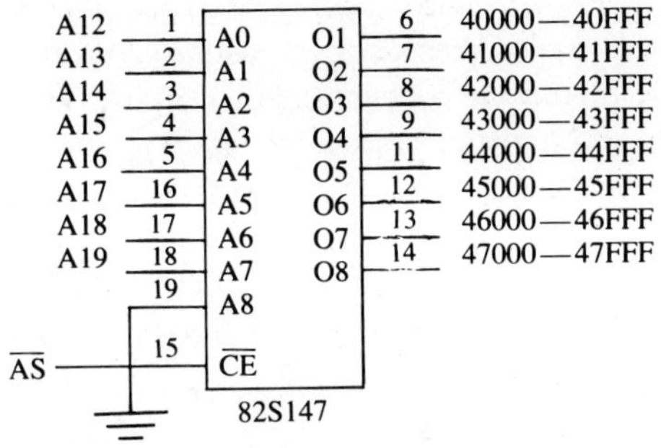


| Inputs | | | | | | | | Outputs | | | | | | | |
|---|---|---|---|---|---|---|---|---|---|---|---|---|---|---|---|
| A19 | A18 | A17 | A16 | A15 | A14 | A13 | A12 | O1 | O2 | O3 | O4 | O5 | O6 | O7 | O8 |
| 0 | 1 | 0 | 0 | 0 | 0 | 0 | 0 | 0 | 1 | 1 | 1 | 1 | 1 | 1 | 1 |
| 0 | 1 | 0 | 0 | 0 | 0 | 0 | 1 | 1 | 0 | 1 | 1 | 1 | 1 | 1 | 1 |
| 0 | 1 | 0 | 0 | 0 | 0 | 1 | 0 | 1 | 1 | 0 | 1 | 1 | 1 | 1 | 1 |
| 0 | 1 | 0 | 0 | 0 | 0 | 1 | 1 | 1 | 1 | 1 | 0 | 1 | 1 | 1 | 1 |
| 0 | 1 | 0 | 0 | 0 | 1 | 0 | 0 | 1 | 1 | 1 | 1 | 0 | 1 | 1 | 1 |
| 0 | 1 | 0 | 0 | 0 | 1 | 0 | 1 | 1 | 1 | 1 | 1 | 1 | 0 | 1 | 1 |
| 0 | 1 | 0 | 0 | 0 | 1 | 1 | 0 | 1 | 1 | 1 | 1 | 1 | 1 | 0 | 1 |
| 0 | 1 | 0 | 0 | 0 | 1 | 1 | 1 | 1 | 1 | 1 | 1 | 1 | 1 | 1 | 0 |
| for all other codes | | | | | | | | 1 | 1 | 1 | 1 | 1 | 1 | 1 | 1 |

**Figure 7-8 Pinout and function table for a PROM decoder that decodes memory from location \$40000 to \$47FFF. Notice that $\overline{AS}$ is used to enable the PROM.**

that this PROM decoder decodes 4K byte blocks of the memory. (See Example 7-5.) In this example, memory is decoded beginning at location \$40000 and continues to location \$40FFF for a total of 4K bytes of the memory.

EXAMPLE 7-5

```
0100  0000  XXXX  XXXX  XXXX
0100  0000  0000  0000  0000  ($40000)
              .
              .
              .
0100  0000  1111  1111  1111  ($40FFF)
```

The attractiveness of the PROM decoder is that only eight memory locations need to be programmed, so programming the PROM really doesn't cost much money or require much time. There is also hardly ever a need to add external logic circuitry with the PROM decoder, as is true of the same decoder scheme as implemented using the 74ALS138.

Figure 7-9 illustrates the same decoding task using the 74ALS138. Notice that extra logic circuitry is required because eight address pins from the microprocessor are decoded, and the 74ALS138 contains only six inputs. This circuit uses inverters and a NAND gate to accomplish the decoding task with the 74ALS138. The cost of the 74ALS138 is higher than the cost of the PROM decoder in this example. In this context, "cost" means number of components required to decode the memory, amount of room required on the printed circuit board, time required to troubleshoot a problem, and time required to construct a prototype circuit for testing.

### 7-2.3 PAL, PLA, or GAL Decoders

The PAL (*programmable array logic*), PLA (*programmable logic array*), or GAL (*generic array logic*) decoder is available in many different versions for use as decoders and other circuit elements. The PAL, PLA, or GAL looks exactly like a PROM decoder in a system because unlike the PROM decoder, it requires no additional circuitry for its implementation. The difference is the way that the decoder is internally constructed.

Figure 7-10 illustrates the internal structure of a PAL 10L8 device. The PAL is programmed by burning fuses, just like the PROM. PALs contain logic gates that are wired, by burning fuses, to perform logic functions. Many PAL circuits also contain flip-flops and many other digital circuits that allow complex functions to be programmed into the PAL. PALs are often called *glue* because they connect microprocessors, memory, I/O, and other circuits without the use of any additional logic gates or circuits.

The PAL illustrated in Figure 7-10 has 10 input pins and 8 output pins. Each input pin has its true and inverted forms, which are connected to any output. For example, if you look closely at input I1, you will notice that there are two outputs from the buffer. One output is in true form and the other is inverted. A close look at

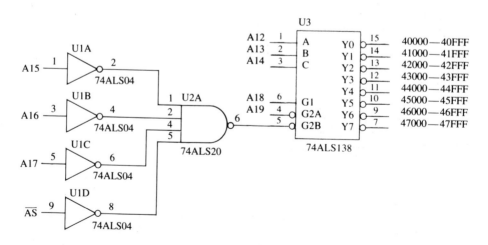

**Figure 7-9** A decoder that uses the 74ALS138 to decode memory locations $40000–$47FFF.

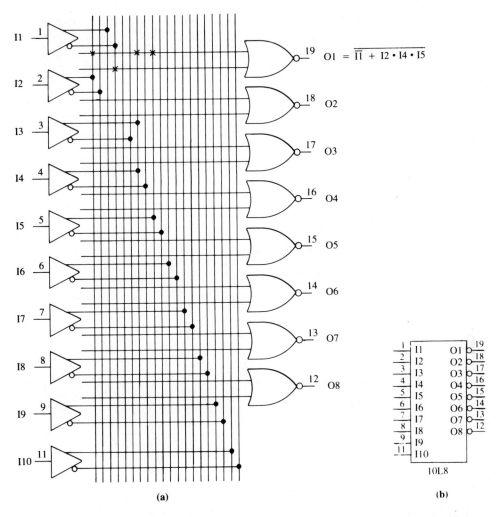

$O1 = \overline{\overline{I1} + I2 \cdot I4 \cdot I5}$

**Figure 7-10**   (a) The internal structure of the PAL 10L8 showing O1 programmed with the logic function illustrated. (b) The pinout of the PAL 10L8.

output $\overline{I1}$ will show an X connection to one input of the NOR gates connected to pin 19 or O1. The other pin on the NOR gate is connected to three places: I2, I4, and I5. These three connections are wire-ANDed together so that they form an AND gate. The output function found on O1 is $\overline{I1} + I2 \cdot I4 \cdot I5$. None of the other outputs are wired in this illustration.

Programming any PAL is accomplished through software rather than through the logic diagram illustrated in Figure 7-10a. This is fortunate because for some advanced PAL designs, the logic circuit contains many hundreds of logic gates. Example 7-6 illustrates the software required to program the PAL 10L8 from Figure 7-10. Notice that this very short program is easy to understand. Such a listing could be produced with any word processor. First, however, the output of the word processor must be set to produce a *clean ASCII file*—that is, one that doesn't contain control characters.

Example 7-6 illustrates the exact steps required to set up a file that is used to program the PAL. Notice that the first six instructions entail information that identifies the project, date, and author's name. The CHIP statement identifies the name of the circuit (PAL), which can be any PAL type. Next the pins are defined with any name that the author desires. Finally, the equations for the PAL are entered. Note that the / is used to indicate inversion, * is used for AND, and + is used to OR. So the equation illustrated as $/O1 = /I1 + I2 * I4 * I5$ matches the equation in Figure 7-10. The equation also can be entered as $O1 = /(/I1 + I2 * I4 * I5)$.

**E  X  A  M  P  L  E     7 - 6**

```
TITLE        Example
PATTERN      Test
REVISION     A
AUTHOR       BARRY BREY
COMPANY      DeVRY
DATE         2/7/91
CHIP         Gates PAL10L8

;PINS        1     2     3     4     5     6     7     8     9     10
             I1    I2    I3    I4    I5    I6    I7    I8    I9    GND

;PINS        11    12    13    14    15    16    17    18    19    20
             I10   08    07    06    05    04    03    02    01    VCC

EQUATIONS
/O1  =  /I1  +  I2  *  I4  *  I5
```

## 7-3   Static Memory Systems

Now that decoders are better understood, the interface of memory to the 68008 and 68000 microprocessors can be discussed. This section details the fully decoded and partially decoded memory methods, which are used to design memory systems for these microprocessors. A fully decoded memory system is one that contains or will eventually contain memory or I/O in every memory location. The memory is said to be fully populated. A partially decoded memory system is one that contains only some memory and will never contain memory or I/O at every memory location. This approach affords certain advantages and economies for decoding, as described later.

### 7-3.1 · 68008 Memory Interface

The 68008 memory was discussed in Section 7-1. More detail is required before a memory system can be properly constructed for this microprocessor. The 68008 has 20 address connections, labeled A19–A0. Each of these locations stores a byte of

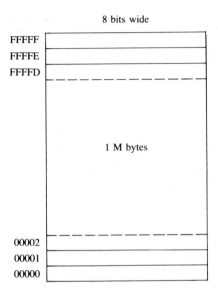

**Figure 7-11** The memory map for the 68008, illustrating its 1M bytes of memory address space.

data. The memory map for the 68008 is illustrated in Figure 7-11. Notice that memory begins at address $00000 and extends to address $FFFFF. This means that when memory is interfaced to the 68008, all 20 address connections must be used in the decoder. This is true only if we plan to fully populate (decode) the memory. As indicated above, a memory that eventually contains all locations for data storage, is called a *fully decoded memory* or *fully populated memory.* Later, we discuss examples that do not use all the address connections with partially populated or partially decoded memory systems. A memory system that will never contain all its memory by design is often called a *partially decoded memory* or *partially populated memory.*

### Fully Decoded Memory for the 68008

Suppose that you are required to design a memory system containing 128k bytes of EPROM and 64k bytes of SRAM. You are given the memory map in Figure 7-12 and told to implement it in any way that you decide. All the memory map shows is that you are to place the SRAM at locations $F0000–$FFFFF and the EPROM at locations $00000–$1FFFF. You are allowed to order and specify the components required to build this system.

You call vendors and discover that you can obtain quick delivery on 32K byte EPROMs (27,256) and 8K × 8 SRAMs (6164). You will need four of the EPROMs and eight of the SRAMs to build the system. The SRAM memory has an access time of 250 ns, which presents no problem with the 8 MHz version of the 68008 that you plan to interface. The EPROM, on the other hand, does present a problem: its access time of 350 ns is too slow for the 68008 running at 8 MHz to use without wait states.

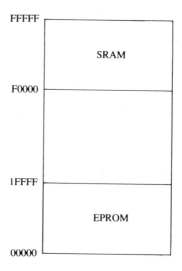

**Figure 7-12   A memory map.**

Recall that for the 68008 to function without any wait states, the memory must access data in 290 ns. The EPROM specified in this example has an access time of 350 ns.

If two wait states are inserted whenever the EPROM is accessed, the access time allowed will be 290 ns plus 125 ns or a total of 415 ns. This is enough time to access the EPROM if the decoder that is selected has a propagation delay time of less than 65 ns. The access time allowed by the microprocessor of 415 ns is sufficient, because the 74ALS138 has a propagation delay time of only 25 ns and the PROM or PAL has an even lower propagation delay time. So any PROM decoder, PAL decoder, or a 74ALS138 decoder will function properly in this memory system.

The first step in designing the memory system is to write the address range of each section of the memory in binary, as illustrated in Example 7-7. This example shows that two 74ALS138 decoders are required to construct the interface. This is because of the difference in the addresses and because there are 12 memory devices to interface. If the EPROM section is examined, we notice that the 32K byte memory devices internally decode address connections A0–A14, as illustrated with don't cares in Example 7-8. If a 74ALS138 is used to decode this section of the memory, it is activated whenever the first three address connections are 000. The next two address connections are used to select the four EPROMs.

E  X  A  M  P  L  E    7 - 7

```
                          SRAM
$F0000  =   1111  0000  0000  0000  0000
                    •
                    •
                    •
$FFFFF  =   1111  1111  1111  1111  1111
```

```
                              EPROM
$00000 =  ‾0‾0‾0‾0‾ ‾0‾0‾0‾0‾ ‾0‾0‾0‾0‾ ‾0‾0‾0‾0‾ ‾0‾0‾0‾0‾
                ‡
                ‡
                ‡
$1FFFF =  0001 1111 1111 1111 1111
```

---

**E X A M P L E   7 - 8**

---

```
0000 0XXX XXXX XXXX XXXX
         ‡
         ‡
         ‡
0001 1XXX XXXX XXXX XXXX
```

---

Figure 7-13 illustrates the 74ALS138 connected so that it decodes this section of the memory and selects each of the four EPROMs. Notice that the output of the NAND gate is labeled for connection to the wait state generator as presented in Figure 6-12. The wait state generator delays the application of the $\overline{\text{DTACK}}$ signal on the 68008, so wait states are inserted into the 68008 timing. This connection causes two wait states each time memory location $00000–$1FFFF is accessed. The wait states slow down the 68008, by inserting wait states, permitting it to access this slower EPROM.

The SRAM section of the memory is decoded by another 74ALS138. Example 7-9 shows the address range of the SRAM section of the memory with the don't cares in place for the right-most 13 address connections. The first four bits of this address are 1111 for any location in this range and are therefore used to enable the 74ALS138.

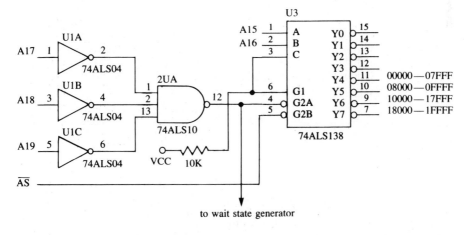

**Figure 7-13** A decoder that selects EPROM for the memory map of Figure 7-12.

E X A M P L E    7 - 9

| | | | | |
|---|---|---|---|---|
| 1111 | 000X | XXXX | XXXX | XXXX |
| | . | | | |
| | . | | | |
| | . | | | |
| 1111 | 111X | XXXX | XXXX | XXXX |

Unlike the EPROM decoder, no wait states are required for SRAM, but because there is an output for the wait state generator, zero wait states are inserted into the timing. Address connections A15–A13 are used as address inputs to the decoder to select any one of the eight outputs when A19–A16 are 1111. Figure 7-14 illustrates the connection of this decoder.

To fully appreciate the way the entire system is connected to the 68008, study the system schematic in Figure 7-15. Here both decoders are shown with a wait state generator used to cause two wait states for the EPROM and zero wait states for the SRAM. Also pay attention to the $\overline{\text{WE}}$ connection on the SRAM as well as the $\overline{\text{OE}}$ connections on both the SRAM and the EPROMs. Notice that the data strobe signal ($\overline{\text{DS}}$) is used with R/$\overline{\text{W}}$ to generate a write signal ($\overline{\text{WR}}$) and a read signal ($\overline{\text{RD}}$) for the memory. As mentioned in Chapter 6, $\overline{\text{DS}}$ is used to qualify the R/$\overline{\text{W}}$ signal.

## Partially Decoded Memory for the 68008

Often the entire memory is never fully decoded. This is especially true in small, dedicated task control systems. In such cases, some address connections are ignored completely, which simplifies the task of decoding. Systems that use partially de-

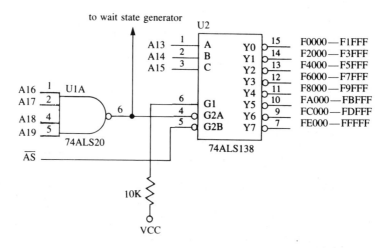

**Figure 7-14** The SRAM decoder for the memory map of Figure 7-12.

coded memory are systems that are installed and not later modified (e.g., control systems and microprocessor-based communications systems). About the only system that is ever fully populated is a system like a home or business computer. In this type of system, the user has the option to add more memory at some future point after the initial purchase.

Take the example developed for the 68008 for a fully populated environment. If the memory is partitioned with 12 or more parts, it will function properly if additional memory is never added. Because we are working with a binary system, the memory must be divided into 2, 4, 8, 16, etc. parts. In this example the memory is divided into 16 parts with only 12 of these sections populated. Figure 7-16 illustrates the memory map divided into 16 sections, with each portion used for EPROM and SRAM as labeled. To break the memory in 16 parts, a 4-bit binary code is required. If the first 4 bits of the address are used, the task is simple.

Figure 7-17 illustrates the memory system decoded with a single 4-to-16 line decoder. Notice that the decoder has four address connections A, B, C, and D, and one enable input $\overline{E}$. Besides the decoder there is a circuit that is used to generate a signal for the wait state generator whenever the microprocessor addresses the EPROM to cause two wait states. As before, the wait states allow additional access time for the EPROM. The decoder is connected, so its address inputs (A, B, C, and D) are attached to A19–A16.

In this memory system, 12 of the 16 available spaces are filled. The remaining spaces can have additional memory added or can be used for I/O. Each output connection of the decoder becomes active for a 64K segment of the memory. You might think that this would cause a problem, but it doesn't, since the addresses of the EPROM and SRAM are listed for the person developing the software. The software is developed so that data are stored and read from only the areas of memory identified.

The number 15 output of the decoder is connected to an 8K byte SRAM. This output becomes a logic zero for memory addresses $F0000–$FFFFF, which is a 64K byte section of the memory. How can this memory component function properly? It can if the person developing the software is told that there are 8K bytes of memory at locations $F0000–$F1FFF. Figure 7-18 depicts this section of the memory map. Notice there are eight places where the 8K byte SRAM appears. Any of these eight places can be the SRAM, while the remaining seven spaces are overlays or shadows. An *overlay* or a *shadow* is a space in the memory where an actual device appears again or is repeated. Here if a $00 is stored at location $F0000, it will also appear at that location plus the following locations as shadows: $F2000, $F4000, $F6000, $F8000, $FA000, $FC000, and $FE000. The $00 appears in these other seven locations because the SRAM decodes address connections A0–A12 and the decoder decodes A16–A19. Address connections A13, A14, and A15, which are not decoded, are don't cares that cause the same memory location to appear in eight different places in the memory system. Again this creates no problem when the software is developed because the software will not use these shadow areas. In this case the person developing the software might be told that the memory exists at location $F0000–$F1FFF. This is where the software is written.

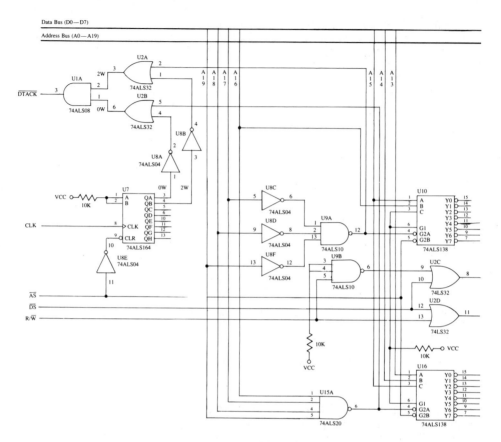

**Figure 7-15   A memory interface for the 68008 implemented from the memory map of Figure 7-12.**

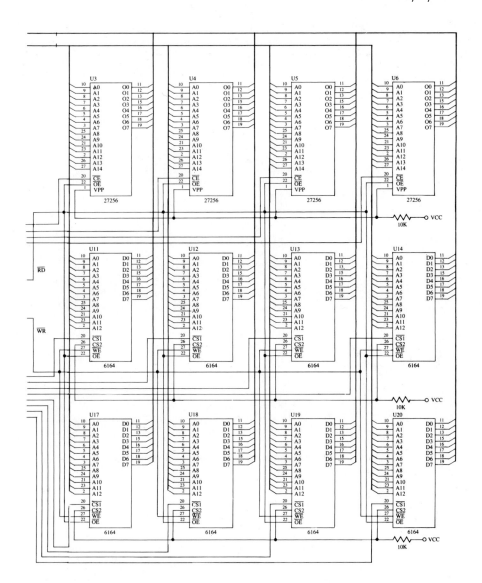

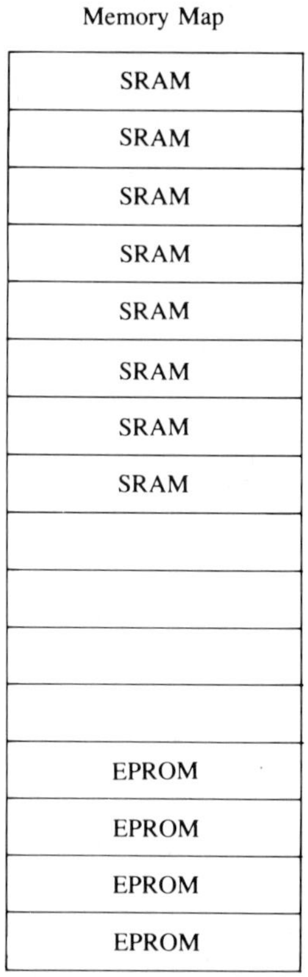

Memory Map

| SRAM |
|------|
| SRAM |
| SRAM |
| SRAM |
| SRAM |
| SRAM |
| SRAM |
| SRAM |
|      |
|      |
|      |
|      |
| EPROM |
| EPROM |
| EPROM |
| EPROM |

**Figure 7-16**   The memory map for an incompletely decoded memory system containing eight SRAMs and four EPROMs.

### 7-3.2   68000 Memory Interface

The main difference between the 68008 and the 68000 memory interface lies in the organization of the 68000 memory. Figure 7-19 shows the physical organization of the 68000 in memory map form. Notice from this map that the memory is 16 bits wide and organized into two separate memory banks, each 8 bits wide. This organization allows the 68000 to read or write a byte of data from either memory bank or to read or write a word (16 bits) from both banks simultaneously. Because it can read or write a word at one time, the 68000 is faster than the 68008 whenever word-sized memory data are manipulated.

The 68000 issues two additional control signals not found on the 68008 to control the operation of separate memory banks. The $\overline{\text{LDS}}$ (lower data strobe) and $\overline{\text{UDS}}$ (upper data strobe) control signals indicate which bank of the memory is active at any given time. These signals replace the $\overline{\text{DS}}$ (data strobe) signal found in the 68008 to control its single bank of memory. Table 7-1 illustrates what these two control signals specify to the memory system during a read or a write.

Besides the $\overline{\text{LDS}}$ and $\overline{\text{UDS}}$ signals, the 68000 has additional address connections, which allow it to access up to 16M bytes of memory instead of 1M bytes, as with the 68008. The 68008 has address connections A19–A0, while the 68000 has address connections A23–A1.

Notice that the 68000 does not have an A0 address connection, as did the 68008. This is because the 68000 addresses words of data, with the upper or lower byte accessed through the $\overline{\text{LDS}}$ and $\overline{\text{UDS}}$ signals. The 68008 accesses only bytes and requires the A0 signal to accomplish byte addressing. The A0 pin is used to select an even or odd byte of memory in a word and therefore does not appear as a pin connection on the 68000 microprocessor. Instead, the A0 connection is encoded as part of the $\overline{\text{LDS}}$ and $\overline{\text{UDS}}$ strobes on the 68000 microprocessor.

## Fully Decoded Memory for the 68000 Using Separate Decoders

Suppose that you are required to place memory at location $300000–$30FFFF in a 68000-based microprocessor and that the system must be fully decoded. This is a 64K byte section of the memory. Let us also suppose that this area of the memory is to be coded with 6164 SRAMs that each contain 8k bytes of memory. This means that four of these SRAMs will operate in the upper bank and four in the lower bank of the memory.

The lower bank memory devices must be activated only when $\overline{\text{LDS}}$ is a logic zero. The upper bank memory devices must be activated only when $\overline{\text{UDS}}$ is a logic zero. This is accomplished by setting up a separate decoder for each memory bank or by generating a separate write signal for each memory bank. We need not worry about a separate read signal for each bank because the microprocessor will just ignore the half of the data bus not being read for an 8-bit read. This is not true with a write, and that is why we use a separate write signal for each memory bank. If separate control signals are used to select memory, instead of separate decoders, no separate signal is needed for read.

When memory for the 68000 is decoded, the least significant address connection is not present on the microprocessor, so it becomes a don't care. Example 7-10 illustrates memory address range $300000–$30FFFF, converted to binary. From this example, notice that the first 8 bits are the same for any location in this section of the memory. These left-most 8 bits (A23–A16) are used to enable the decoder. The next 2 bits (A15 and A14) are used to select one of four 16K byte (8K word) sections of the memory. With the 68000, two 8-bit banks of the memory are selected simultaneously by the decoder. The upper and lower data strobes are then used to select one or both banks for the memory operation.

E  X  A  M  P  L  E    7 - 10

| | | | | | | | |
|---|---|---|---|---|---|---|---|
| $300000 | = | 0011 | 0000 | 0000 | 0000 | 0000 | 0000 |
| | | | | · | | | |
| | | | | · | | | |
| $30FFFF | = | 0011 | 0000 | 1111 | 1111 | 1111 | 1111 |

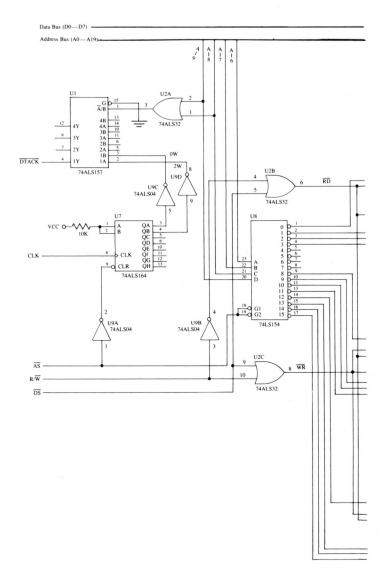

**Figure 7-17**  A system that implements the memory map of Figure 7-16 for the 68008 microprocessor.

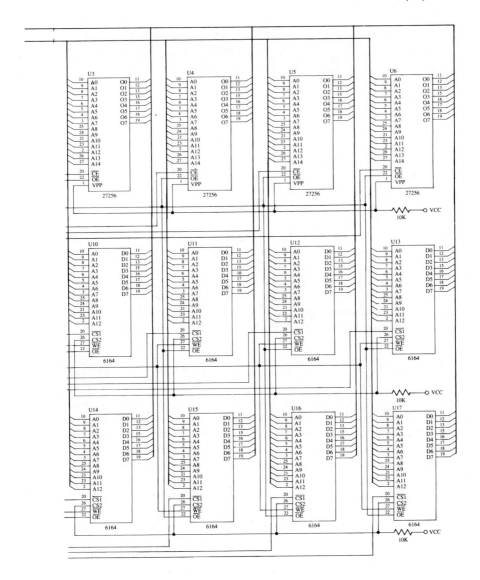

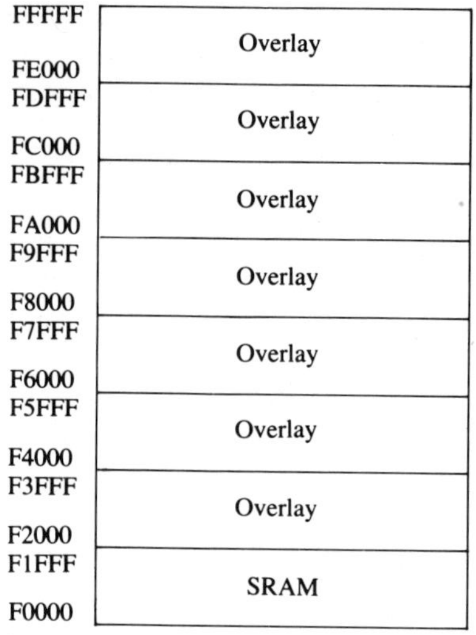

| | |
|---|---|
| FFFFF | Overlay |
| FE000 | |
| FDFFF | Overlay |
| FC000 | |
| FBFFF | Overlay |
| FA000 | |
| F9FFF | Overlay |
| F8000 | |
| F7FFF | Overlay |
| F6000 | |
| F5FFF | Overlay |
| F4000 | |
| F3FFF | Overlay |
| F2000 | |
| F1FFF | SRAM |
| F0000 | |

**Figure 7-18    The memory map of the SRAM placed at decoder output 15. Notice how it overlays seven parts of this memory block and appears in only one 8K byte section.**

Figure 7-20 illustrates two 74ALS138 decoders that are used to select memory for this example. One of the decoders selects four upper bank memory components, while the other selects four lower bank memory components. Notice how the upper bank decoder uses $\overline{UDS}$ for one of its enable inputs, while the lower bank decoder uses $\overline{LDS}$. Notice also how the memory address bus connections are attached to the memory devices. Address bus connection A1 is connected to memory pin A0, address bus connection A2 is connected to memory pin A1, etc. The address connections are skewed because memory is addressed as a word (16 bits wide). The $\overline{LDS}$ and $\overline{UDS}$ signals, which encode address bit A0, are used to select one or both memory banks.

## Fully Decoded Memory for the 68000 Using Separate Write Signals

Most likely a better way to handle memory banks is to decode them as 16-bit-wide memory, but to use one decoder that sends each bank a separate write signal. The

**Table 7-1    Upper and Lower Data Strobe Signals**

| $\overline{LDS}$ | $\overline{UDS}$ | Function |
|---|---|---|
| 0 | 0 | 16 bit data bus transfer |
| 0 | 1 | 8 bit lower data bus transfer |
| 1 | 0 | 8 bit upper data bus transfer |
| 1 | 1 | no transfer (bus idle) |

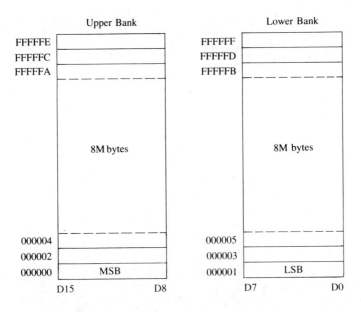

**Figure 7-19** The memory map of the 68000 microprocessor illustrating its 16-bit wide memory, organized into two 8-bit banks.

separate write signals for the banks are developed by combining R/$\overline{\text{W}}$ and the $\overline{\text{LDS}}$ and $\overline{\text{UDS}}$ signals. Figure 7-21 illustrates the simple circuit that generates $\overline{\text{UWR}}$ (upper write) and $\overline{\text{LWR}}$ (lower write)—the two separate memory bank write signals.

In Figure 7-22 the same memory interface shown in Figure 7-20 is illustrated with separate write signals rather than separate bank decoders. Notice that the amount of circuitry is reduced in this example because one 74ALS154 decoder is used instead of two 74ALS138 decoders. This reduction in decoder components is not always found. That is why both techniques of decoding memory for the 68000 are presented. The designer should choose the circuit that requires the fewest components, both to reduce total system cost and to make repair and troubleshooting easier for the technician.

## Fully Decoded Memory Using PAL Circuitry

As discussed in Section 7-2.3, PAL circuitry is often used to reduce the component count in a system. A PAL logic circuit is used in Figure 7-23 to reduce the circuitry used in Figure 7-22 to a bare minimum. In this circuit, both the 74ALS138 and the 74ASL257 are replaced with a single PAL 10L8. The program used for the PAL is listed in Example 7-11. Notice that pin $\overline{\text{DEC}}$ is programmed to replace the 74ALS138 decoder. The remaining four output pins generate the upper and lower

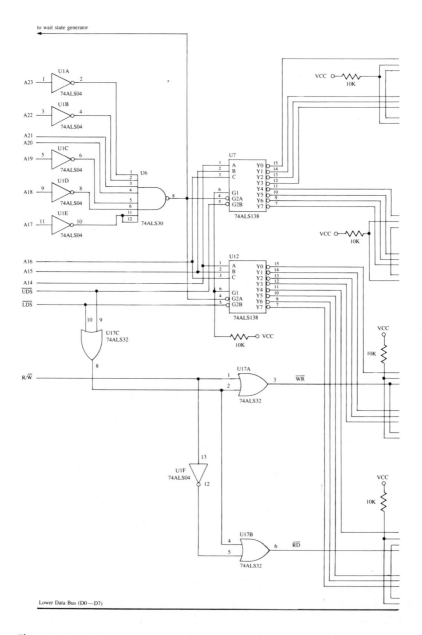

**Figure 7-20   Using separate decoders for each memory bank in a 68000 system.**

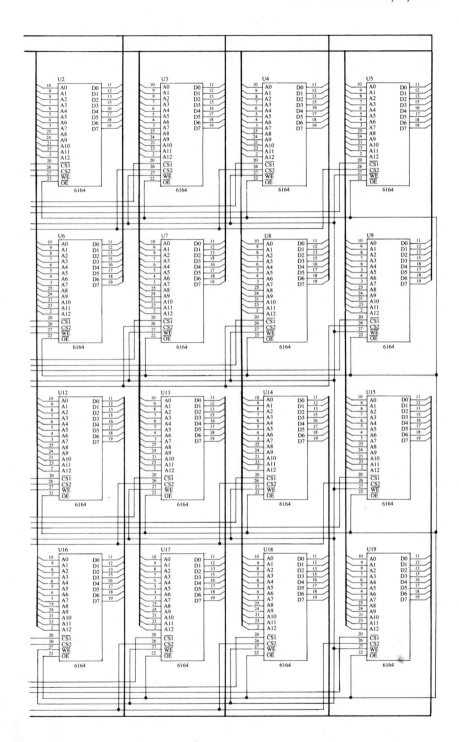

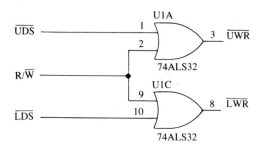

**Figure 7-21**   The circuit used to generate separate write signals for the upper and lower memory banks.

read and write strobes. PAL circuitry is very useful in memory decoders, as this example shows.

E  X  A  M  P  L  E     7 - 11

```
TITLE      Decoder/strobe generator
PATTERN    P0000
REVISION   A
AUTHOR     BARRY BREY
COMPANY    DeVRY
DATE       2/7/91
CHIP   Decoder PAL10L8

;PINS      1      2      3      4      5      6      7      8      9      10
           A23    A22    A21    A20    A19    A18    /UDS   /LDS   RW     GND

;PINS      11     12     13     14     15     16     17     18     19     20
           NC     NC     NC     NC     LRD    LWR    UWR    URD    DEC    VCC

EQUATIONS
/DEC = /A23 * /A22 * A21 * A20 * /A19 * /A18
/LWR = /LDS + RW
/LRD = /LDS + /RW
/UWR = /UDS + RW
/URD = /UDS + /RW
```

## 7-4   Dynamic Memory Systems

Dynamic memory is used in memory systems that require more than approximately 256K bytes for read/write memory. This type of memory isn't used until the memory exceeds 256K bytes mainly because it requires auxiliary circuitry. The extra circuitry is normally used to refresh memory and to handle address multiplexing for dynamic memory. These additional costs cannot be justified in small memory systems. In large systems, however, the extra circuitry does not add to the cost significantly because the number of memory components required to implement a large system is reduced with dynamic memory when compared to static memory.

## 7-4.1 Dynamic Memory Devices

Before we discuss the interfacing of dynamic memory systems to the 68000 or 68008, the dynamic RAM (DRAM) must be understood. The main difference between the DRAM and SRAM is that more bits are packed into the same integrated circuit with the DRAM. The reasons for the higher bit density are: (1) the storage element in the DRAM calls for half the circuitry that is required to store a bit in a SRAM, and (2) data are stored on capacitors inside the DRAM. Lower power is required to store data on capacitors. Because little power is dissipated inside the DRAM, the storage transistors are much smaller, which also increases packaging density of the DRAM. Density is at least 8–16 times greater with the DRAM than with the SRAM.

Figure 7-24 illustrates the internal structure of both the SRAM and the DRAM memory cells. Notice that the SRAM memory cell, which stores one bit of information, requires two inverters, while the DRAM cell requires only one inverter. Because the SRAM has twice as many inverters for data storage, the size of an SRAM device is at least doubled.

Data are stored in the DRAM cell by using the gate region capacitance (shown as a capacitor in Figure 7-24b) of the MOSFET. The current flows in the DRAM cell only when the gate capacitance is either charged to a logic one level or discharged to a logic zero level. Current does not flow through the transistor in the DRAM cell until the cell is read. This is accomplished by switching off the supply voltage to the DRAM cell whenever it is inactive. In all, the reduction in the current and in the number of data storage transistors reduces the size of the DRAM cell significantly when compared to an SRAM of the same size of memory bits.

## 7-4.2 Pinout of DRAM Memory

The DRAM is different from both the ROM and SRAM discussed earlier in this chapter because the control and address connections are different. The address connections on a DRAM are multiplexed to reduce the total number of pins required to address memory. This is not done on the SRAM and ROM.

The control pins are different because of this multiplexed address arrangement. Changed are the $\overline{CS}$ and $\overline{OE}$ connections which, on the DRAM, become an $\overline{RAS}$ and a $\overline{CAS}$ connection. $\overline{RAS}$ is used to strobe (clock) the row address through the address connections, and the $\overline{CAS}$ input is used to strobe the column address through the address connections. Besides clocking the column address through the address connections, the $\overline{CAS}$ pin functions as a chip select input. The $\overline{WE}$ and $\overline{OE}$ connections, often found on modern SRAM, are replaced with an $R/\overline{W}$ connection on the DRAM. If $R/\overline{W}$ is a logic one, and $\overline{CAS}$ occurs, a read operation is performed by the DRAM. If $R/\overline{W}$ is a logic zero, and $\overline{CAS}$ occurs, a write operation is performed.

Refer to Figure 7-25 for the internal structure of a 256K × 1 dynamic RAM (41,256). Notice that this memory device contains nine address connections, labeled A0–A8. Through these nine address pins, an 18-bit memory address is entered into the DRAM. This is accomplished by sending 9 bits to the row address latch and 9 bits to the column address latch through nine address connections. The $\overline{RAS}$ and

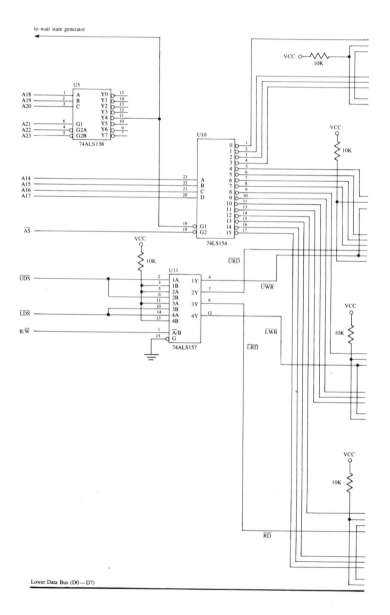

**Figure 7-22** **A memory system using separate read and write signals.**

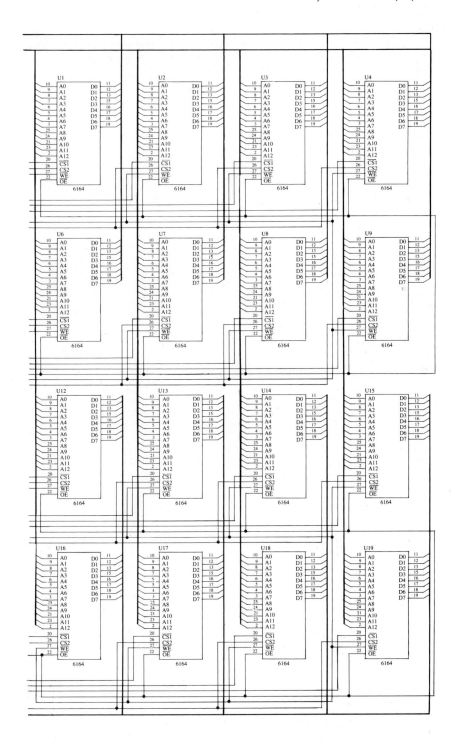

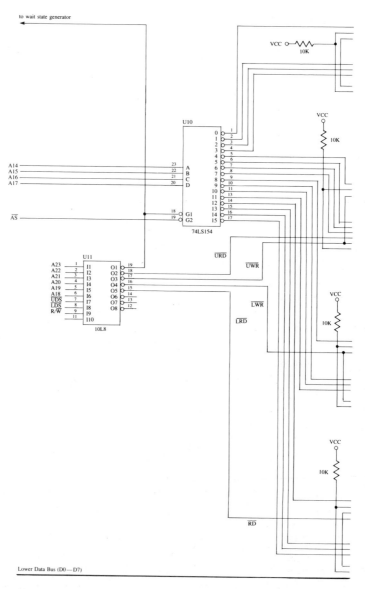

Figure 7-23    A memory system using separate read and write signals developed by a PLD.

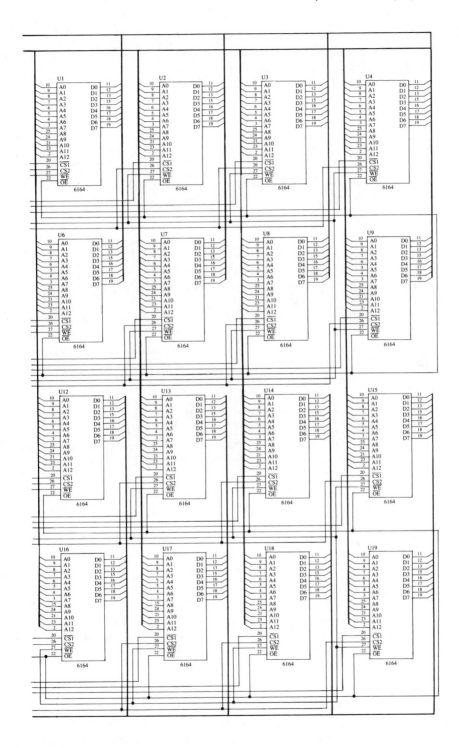

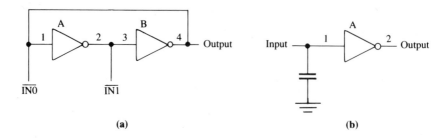

**Figure 7-24**    The internal structure of an SRAM memory cell (a) and a DRAM memory cell (b). Note that the capacitor in the DRAM cell is its gate capacitance.

$\overline{CAS}$ signals clock these internal latches and cause each of them to hold a 9-bit part of the 18-bit address. The row and column address latches hold the 18-bit address, so one bit of the 256K-bit memory array is accessed. Once accessed, the bit is either written or read.

Notice how the internal memory is organized. The memory is set up as an array of four 64K-bit sections. Each section is organized as a 256 × 256 memory. Eight bits of the address, stored in the row address latch, are used to select a row (internal word that is 256 bits wide) in each section. Also one bit of the row address latch and one bit of the column address latch are used to select a bit from one of the four sections of internal memory.

The remaining 8 bits of the column latch are used to select one of 256 bits of data of the selected 256-bit-wide word of memory. Thus, each internal section of the memory contains 256 words that are each 256 bits wide. This means that each section contains 64K bits of data. Because there are four sections of memory, the entire chip contains 256K bits of data.

This organization allows the memory to be refreshed in large sections each time the row address changes to select a new row in the memory. With this memory device, 8 bits of the row address are used to select a word of data in each memory bank. Each time a new 8-bit row address is sent to the memory, four 256-bit words (1024 bits) are selected and automatically refreshed by the memory. To refresh the entire memory, the user must provide the memory with all possible combinations of the 8-bit row address every 4 ms. This means a new row (1024 bits) of the memory must be refreshed every 15.625 μs. Any read, write, or refresh operation will always refresh 1024 bits of memory in this DRAM. Refresh occurs because 1024 refresh amplifiers are switched on to refresh all bits of a row whenever the $\overline{RAS}$ signal strobes a new address into the row address latch.

### 7-4.3    Address Multiplexer

Figure 7-26 shows how the nine address connections on the DRAM are made to accept an 18-bit memory address from the microprocessor. Here a multiplexer circuit that uses three 74AS157 quadrupole, 2-to-1 line multiplexers, sends the address into the nine DRAM address connections. The 74AS157 has A and B inputs

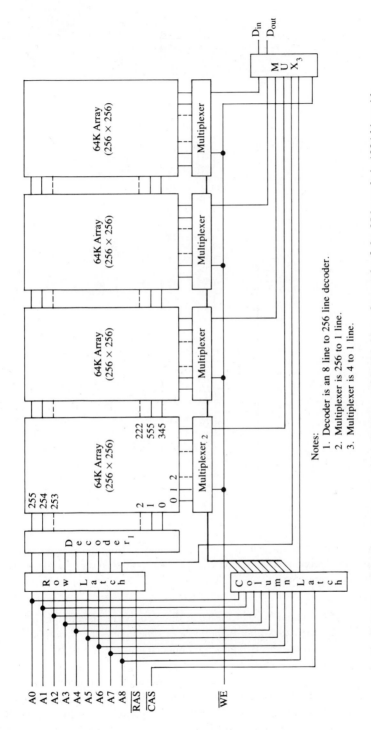

**Figure 7-25** The internal structure of a 256K × 1 DRAM. Note that each of the 256 words is 1024 bits wide.

245

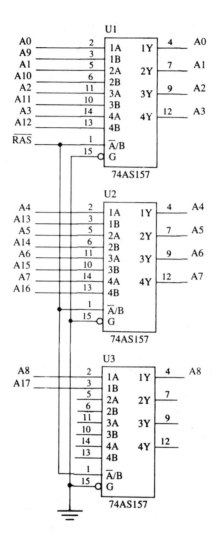

**Figure 7-26** A multiplexer used to apply an 18-bit address from the microprocessor to the nine address connections on a 256k bit DRAM. This multiplexer is meant to function with a 68008 microprocessor.

that are passed to the output Y connections as directed by the select input ($\overline{A}/B$). If the select input is a logic zero, the A inputs are connected to the Y outputs. If the select input is a logic one, the B inputs are connected to the Y outputs.

The $\overline{RAS}$ signal is connected to both the select input of the 74AS157 and the DRAM $\overline{RAS}$ input. When $\overline{RAS}$ is a logic one, address connections A9–A17 are connected to the nine address connections of the DRAM through the 74AS157. When $\overline{RAS}$ goes from a logic one to a logic zero, it causes the DRAM to latch these address signals. It also causes the 74AS157 to begin to switch its outputs to the A connections. This switching does not occur instantaneously. For the 74AS157 there is a propagation delay time of about 10 ns. After 10 ns, the output connections of the 74AS157 change to A0–A8. A short time later, the $\overline{CAS}$ signal (not shown in Figure 7-26) changes to a logic zero, latching this part of the address into the DRAM column address latch. In this way all 18 bits of the address are sent into the DRAM through the 74AS157 multiplexers.

### Refresh Address

The circuit of Figure 7-26 functions perfectly until it's time to refresh the DRAM. To refresh the DRAM, a refresh address must be connected to the DRAM. Figure 7-27 shows the same circuit of Figure 7-26 modified to permit the refresh address to be applied to the address connections of the DRAM for a refresh operation. The refresh address is an 8-bit address (A0–A7) that is sent into the row address latch so that a selected row can be refreshed. Earlier it was learned that each time the row address changes, 1024 bits of this 256K × 1 DRAM are refreshed. If you multiply 1024 times the 256 possible 8-bit addresses latched into the row address latch, you will see that all 256K bits of the memory are refreshed. The 8-bit address sent into the row address latch selects all rows for refreshing.

The circuit of Figure 7-27 uses a set of two 74AS157s to apply a refresh address from an 8-bit binary counter each time the $\overline{RFSH}$ (refresh) signal becomes a logic zero. Shortly after $\overline{RFSH}$ has become a logic zero, the $\overline{RAS}$ signal becomes a logic zero, causing the refresh address from the binary counter to be sent to the row address latch in the DRAM. This refreshes a new 1024-bit row of the DRAM. When $\overline{RFSH}$ returns to a logic one level, the refresh counter is incremented to the next refresh address. In this manner all 256 rows can be refreshed if the $\overline{RFSH}$ signal is activated at least once every 15.625 μs. If it is not, the memory device will start to forget or lose bits of information.

### 7-4.4 DRAM Timing Diagram

Figure 7-28 illustrates the read, write, and refresh timing diagram of the 256K × 1 DRAM integrated circuit. To read or write data, the $\overline{RAS}$ signal is activated, sending the row address into the DRAM through its address connections. After a short delay, the $\overline{CAS}$ is activated, sending the column address through the address connections. Shortly after $\overline{CAS}$ activation, data are read from the DRAM and appear at the output connection. For a write, data are written into the DRAM through the input connection.

The time delay between $\overline{RAS}$ and $\overline{CAS}$ is critical if the timing diagram and its corresponding timing characteristics are studied. The amount of time between $\overline{RAS}$ and $\overline{CAS}$ directly affects the access time of the DRAM. When interfacing the DRAM to a microprocessor, this timing requirement must be met or the access time will be increased. As with any memory device, access time is calculated from the application of the address. With the DRAM, this occurs from the application of the $\overline{RAS}$ signal. $\overline{CAS}$ is used to time the application of data on the output connections. If the application of $\overline{CAS}$ is delayed, access time is increased because it also applies part of the address to the DRAM.

Refresh occurs without using the $\overline{CAS}$ signal. $\overline{CAS}$ performs two duties with a

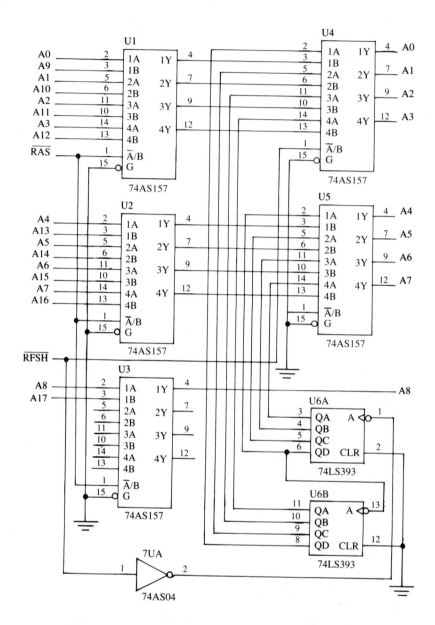

**Figure 7-27    An address multiplexer with a refresh counter.**

DRAM. First it strobes the column address into the column address latch. Finally, it selects the DRAM for a read or a write. Because no read or write occurs for a refresh and no column address is required, only the $\overline{RAS}$ signal is activated to refresh the DRAM. Whenever $\overline{RAS}$ is used for a refresh, the operation is called an *RAS-only refresh*. Recall that $\overline{RAS}$ applies the row address that is used to refresh a row of memory inside the DRAM.

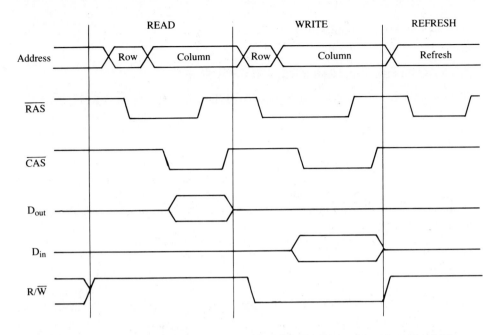

Figure 7-28  The timing diagram of a DRAM illustrating read, write, and refresh.

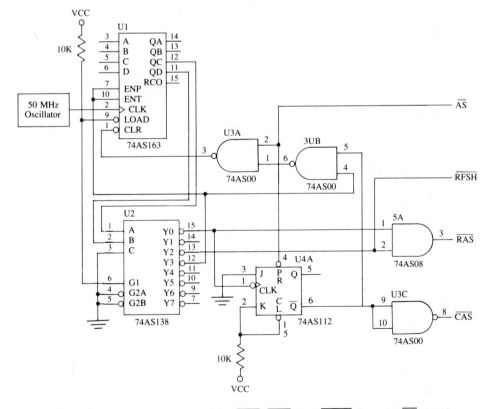

Figure 7-29  A circuit that generates $\overline{RAS}$, $\overline{CAS}$, and $\overline{RFSH}$ from the $\overline{AS}$ signal.

### 7-4.5    Generating the $\overline{\text{RAS}}$, $\overline{\text{CAS}}$, and $\overline{\text{RFSH}}$ Signals

The circuit in Figure 7-29 is used to generate the DRAM control signals $\overline{\text{RAS}}$, $\overline{\text{CAS}}$, and $\overline{\text{RFSH}}$ (refresh). The $\overline{\text{RAS}}$ signal is generated in two ways by this circuit. First, $\overline{\text{RAS}}$ is generated each time the system accesses memory, requesting a read or write operation. After the read or write has been completed, $\overline{\text{RAS}}$ is again generated to permit a refresh to be accomplished. Because the access time of the DRAM is 100 ns and the microprocessor allows 290 ns for the memory to function, time exists after each read or write operation for the memory to be refreshed. After each read or write, the $\overline{\text{RAS}}$ signal is again generated, and a *hidden refresh,* also called a *zero wait state,* is accomplished.

The $\overline{\text{CAS}}$ signal is generated after $\overline{\text{RAS}}$ if the operation requested is a read or a write. The $\overline{\text{CAS}}$ signal is not generated if the operation is a refresh. For the refresh operation, the timing circuit generates $\overline{\text{RFSH}}$ instead of the $\overline{\text{CAS}}$ signal. $\overline{\text{RFSH}}$ is used by the memory system to apply a refresh address to the DRAM. It applies the contents of the refresh counter, and after 256 memory read operations, the memory is completely refreshed.

Although the zero wait state/hidden type of refresh may increase memory power consumption slightly, it eliminates the need to cause the microprocessor to wait for the memory refresh. This increases system performance. If the access time allowed by the microprocessor is nearer to 100 ns, then hidden refresh is not possible and wait states will periodically be inserted whenever a refresh operation is due. When this condition exists, a circuit is required that causes wait states in the microprocessor timing so that a refresh operation can occur.

Other refresh systems are found in application. In some cases no refresh counter is used. In place of the counter, the least significant address bits are used as a row address. Because most programs increment the address up through the memory, all refresh rows are sent to the memory by the program. This system calls for some monitoring because tight loops in programs may not send all addresses to the row address latch. In this case a refresh of all unselected rows must be performed.

Yet another technique uses a direct memory access (DMA) operation that periodically causes each row address to be sent to the memory for refresh. What typically happens is that every 4 ms, the DMA controller gains access to the system and transfers all 256 row addresses to the DRAM to accomplish a refresh operation.

### 7-4.6    A DRAM Memory System

Figure 7-30 illustrates a complete DRAM memory system containing 4M bytes of DRAM for a 68000 microprocessor. Here no wait states are required because the DRAM selected has an access time of only 100 ns, much shorter than the maximum of 290 ns for the 68000 microprocessor. In this system the decoder selects memory for locations \$000000–\$3FFFFF. This system uses 510001 (1M × 1) memory devices to form a 4M × 8 memory system. The circuit of Figure 7-29 provides the DRAM system with its timing signals.

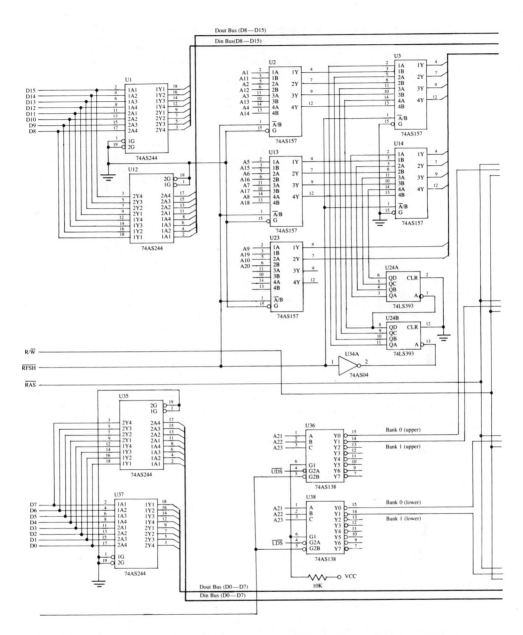

**Figure 7-30**  A 68000 microprocessor interfaced to a DRAM memory system containing 4M bytes of memory. This memory system is decoded at locations $000000–$3FFFFF.

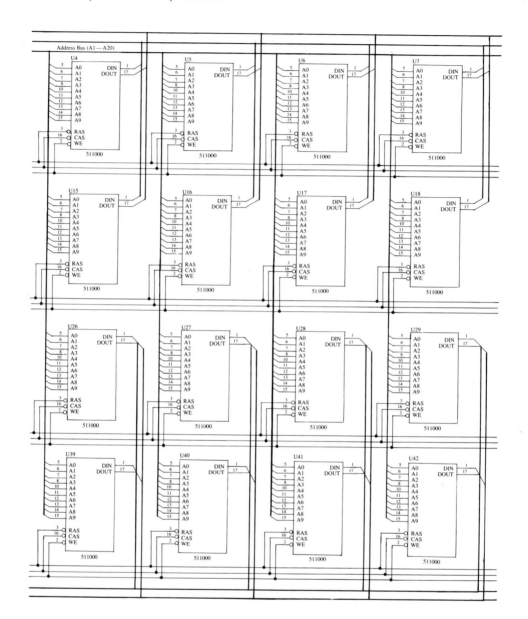

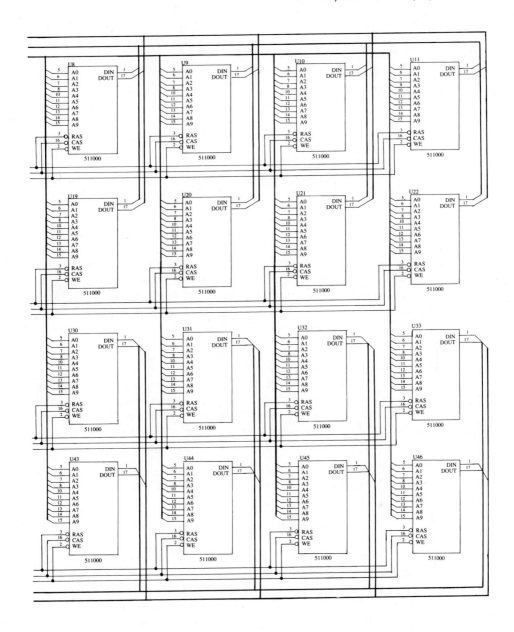

## Summary

1. Memory is available in two basic forms: read-only and read/write. Read-only memory consists of ROM (factory mask-programmed), PROM (fuse-programmed), EPROM (electrically programmed, can be erased with ultraviolet light), and EEPROM (electrically programmed, electrically erasable). Read/write memory consists of static (SRAM) and dynamic (DRAM) random access memory.

2. ROM is nonvolatile memory because it does not change when power is removed from the memory component. RAM is volatile because it changes or loses information when power is removed from the system.

3. All memory devices have address pins, data pins, and control pins. The ROM and SRAM contain address connections that are labeled A0–An, data connections that are usually labeled D0–Dn, and control connections. The ROM has two control connections, $\overline{CE}$ and $\overline{OE}$, while the RAM has three, $\overline{CS}$, $\overline{OE}$, and $\overline{WE}$. The $\overline{CE}$ (ROM) or $\overline{CS}$ (RAM) connection is used to select or enable the memory component, while the $\overline{OE}$ connection is used to enable the output connections for a read operation. The $\overline{WE}$ connection in the RAM is used to cause a write.

4. One very important timing consideration for any memory component is access time, the time needed by the memory component to output data after the address and control signals have been applied. In most memory components this time is measured from the instant of application of the address and enable signal until the data first appear on the output connections. Memory access time must fall within the access time allowed by the microprocessor.

5. Decoders are used to select a memory component for a unique range of memory addresses. Common decoders include the 3-to-8 line decoder, the 74ALS138, the PROM, and programmable logic devices (PLDs).

6. When a memory component is decoded, the address connections on the memory device itself are treated as don't cares and are ignored by the decoder. These address connections are already decoded by the memory component. The additional address connections that are not decoded by the memory device are decoded by the external 3-to-8 line decoder, PROM, or PLD. Decoder time is added to memory access time to determine whether the memory and its decoder will function within the access time allowed for the memory by the microprocessor.

7. Two methods are employed for decoding memory: fully decoded and partially decoded. In the fully decoded memory, all address connections are either decoded by the memory or by the memory and the decoder. In the partially decoded memory only some address signals are decoded, which leaves overlapping areas in the memory called overlays or shadows. Partially decoded memory systems are often used in special-purpose applications of the microprocessor.

8. The 68000 uses memory that is 16 bits in width, but addressable in 8-bit sections called banks. The upper bank contains all the even-numbered memory locations and is selected using the $\overline{\text{UDS}}$ (upper data strobe). The lower bank contains all the odd-numbered memory addresses and is selected by the $\overline{\text{LDS}}$ (lower data strobe). In practice two ways are used to decode 68000 memory. One method uses a separate decoder for each memory bank, while the other uses separate write control signals. Both systems are used in practice. The 68008 has a memory that is 8 bits in width. The $\overline{\text{DS}}$ (data strobe) signal is used to enable the memory read or write operation.

9. Dynamic memory is different from static memory because if it is not periodically refreshed, it loses the stored data. Refreshing is accomplished by selecting 256 row addresses in a period of 4 ms. The static RAM requires no refresh because it remembers data for as long as power is applied to the memory component. The main reason for the wide usage of dynamic RAM is that it offers a much higher packaging density than does static RAM.

10. The address connections on a DRAM are different from those on an SRAM or a ROM. Address connections on the DRAM are multiplexed to save on the number of pin connections required. If the DRAM has nine pin connections, 18 address bits exist because two sets of nine address signals are sent through the same nine pins. The row address is sent into the DRAM whenever the $\overline{\text{RAS}}$ signal is activated. The column address is sent into the DRAM whenever the $\overline{\text{CAS}}$ signal is activated.

11. The $\overline{\text{RAS}}$ signal is used to strobe the row address into the DRAM, which selects the row inside the DRAM to be read or written. This signal also causes the entire row of memory to be refreshed.

12. The $\overline{\text{CAS}}$ signal is used to strobe the column address into the DRAM, which selects the column to be read out or written into. This signal also selects the DRAM so a read or a write can occur. Without a $\overline{\text{CAS}}$ signal, the DRAM will execute an $\overline{\text{RAS}}$-only refresh.

## Questions

1. What memory component is programmed during construction by the manufacturer?

2. What type of memory is programmed in the field by burning open fuses?

3. Which two read-only memory types can be erased?

4. What device is used to program a PROM?

5. What is the purpose of the $\overline{\text{CE}}$ pin on a memory component?

6. If more than one $\overline{\text{CE}}$ pin is present on a memory component, when is the memory selected or enabled?

7. Do data appear on the output of a ROM if only the $\overline{OE}$ connection is activated?

8. When the $\overline{WE}$ pin is placed at a logic zero level, the RAM will _____ data.

9. Define the term "access time."

10. How is access time for a memory component measured?

11. If a memory component has 12 address connections, it is said to have _____ memory locations.

12. A 4K × 8 memory that is placed in memory beginning at memory address $10000 will have its last location at _____.

13. If a memory component is placed at locations $20000–$2FFFF, how many bytes of memory does it contain?

14. An 8K × 8 memory device is to be placed in memory at location $02000–$03FFF. If the microprocessor is a 68008, determine the binary bit pattern that must be decoded to select this memory device.

15. Explain the operation of the 74ALS138 decoder.

16. Develop a circuit that will select three 16K × 8 EPROM memory devices so that they function beginning at memory location $00000. Assume that the microprocessor is a 68008.

17. Develop a circuit that will select four 32K × 8 EPROM memory devices so that they function beginning at memory location $E0000. Assume that the microprocessor is a 68008.

18. Develop a circuit that will select six 64K × 8 SRAM memory devices to occupy memory locations $00000–$5FFFF. Assume that the microprocessor is a 68008.

19. Develop a memory system for the 68008 that uses partial decoding to select four 16K × 8 EPROMs and two 8K × 8 SRAM memories.

20. Develop a memory system for the 68008 that uses partial decoding to select six 32K × 8 EPROMs and four 16K × 8 SRAM memories.

21. Explain how a PROM is used to decode memory addresses.

22. Explain how a PLD is used to decode memory addresses.

23. Develop a memory system for the 68008 using six 64K × 8 EPROMs placed beginning at memory location $80000. The decoder must be a PAL 10L8. Show all hardware and also the program for the PAL.

24. What bank selection signal is used to enable the memory bank that contains all odd-numbered memory locations in the 68000 memory system?

25. If both the $\overline{LDS}$ and $\overline{UDS}$ memory bank selection signals in the 68000 microprocessor are active, what size memory transfer operation is being performed by the microprocessor?

26. Develop a memory system for the 68000 microprocessor that uses separate bank decoders to interface six 32K × 8 EPROMs beginning at memory location $100000.

27. Develop a memory system for the 68000 microprocessor that uses separate bank decoders to interface a dozen 64K × 8 EPROMs beginning at memory location $300000.

28. Using separate bank read signals, interface six 16K × 8 EPROMs to a 68000 microprocessor beginning at memory location $F00000.

29. Using separate bank read and write signals, interface four 32K × 8 EPROMs to a 68000 microprocessor beginning at memory location $000000 and six 32K × 8 SRAMs beginning at location $200000.

30. Why can the DRAM memory component store more bits in the same area as a SRAM?

31. What is a refresh?

32. Explain how the address is entered into a DRAM using the $\overline{RAS}$ and $\overline{CAS}$ control signals.

33. What control signal on a DRAM is used to select the DRAM for a read or a write?

34. What control signal on a DRAM is used to start a refresh operation?

35. Explain how the 74AS157 multiplexer operates.

36. Is the memory address decoder different from an SRAM whenever a DRAM is interfaced to the 68000 microprocessor?

37. What control signals are activated to send an address into the DRAM? Please use the correct sequence.

# 8

# Basic Input/Output Interfacing

## OBJECTIVES

Upon completion of this chapter, you will be able to:

- Design a decoder circuit that allows I/O operations with the microprocessor.
- Explain how parallel data are interfaced to the microprocessor and construct a simple parallel interface.
- Interface a simple keyboard to the microprocessor and develop the software required to scan the keyboard for a keystroke.
- Connect seven-segment numeric displays to the microprocessor and develop the software required to display information on these displays.
- Explain how serial data are interfaced to the microprocessor and construct a serial interface.
- Interface an analog-to-digital converter to the microprocessor.
- Interface a digital-to-analog converter to the microprocessor.
- Interface a stepper motor and a dc motor to the microprocessor.

## KEY TERMS

| | | |
|---|---|---|
| memory-mapped I/O | backlit | parity error |
| isolated I/O | pixel | RS-232C |
| common-anode display | stop bit | half, full duplexes |
| | start bit | full-scale |
| common-cathode display | Baud rate | full step |
| | modem | half-step |

A MICROPROCESSOR is not a very useful device unless it communicates between itself and the outside world. This chapter introduces input/output interfacing by showing how the microprocessor is connected to other machines and to humans. This human–machine symbiotic interface is accomplished through such devices as keyboards, displays, and parallel or serial interfaces. Decoders are also explained, with the emphasis on input/output decoding rather than on memory system decoding.

Humans connect to a microprocessor through keyboards for data entry and displays for data output. Microprocessors connect to other machines through parallel interfaces. Parallel devices include printers, video displays, plotters, and even disk memory systems. Serial interfaces are used to connect the microprocessor to a variety of equipment in the industrial environment. They are also used with the telephone lines for long distance digital data communications. Although this chapter cannot possibly explain all applications of the microprocessor, it does introduce these basic interfaces with the decoding required to operate them.

Because humans are analog creatures, this chapter also provides a basic coverage of the analog-to-digital and digital-to-analog converters that serve to interface the analog world to the digital world. In addition to all these devices, interfaces to motors are introduced.

## 8-1    Simple Input/Output Interfaces

Before input/output decoding and interfacing are discussed, an introduction to I/O devices is in order. This section of the chapter presents basic I/O interfacing and decoding after explaining some simple, but extremely important, I/O devices. It also introduces the basic input and output interfaces.

### 8-1.1    Basic Input and Output Circuits

To function correctly, an input or output device must be electronically connected to the microprocessor at the appropriate time. In the 680XX microprocessor system, any memory data transfer operation is used to perform input/output operations. In the 68000, the MOVEP (move peripheral) instruction is sometimes used for word transfers.

An example input device is a keyboard that might be assigned to memory address $200000. If this is the case, you would use a memory read operation to read a character from the keyboard. You could use the MOVE.B $200000,D0 instruction to read a character from memory location $200000 (the keyboard) into the byte-sized D0 register. Memory and I/O are treated the same in the 680XX microprocessor. In this example, the address is decoded and the keyboard data are read when the R/$\overline{\text{W}}$ signal is a logic one and both the $\overline{\text{AS}}$ and the data strobe signal ($\overline{\text{DS}}$) are a logic zero.

### The MOVEP Instruction

The MOVEP (move peripheral) instruction causes both bytes of a 16-bit number to be output to either the upper or lower data bus in the 68000 microprocessor. For example, if the MOVEP.W D0,$E0000 instruction is executed, the 68000 will send both bytes of information to the upper data bus connections (D15–D8).

Figure 8-1 illustrates how the data appear on the data bus of the microprocessor. With this instruction, the most significant byte is sent to I/O address $E0000 and the least significant byte is sent to $E0002.

If the instruction has an odd address, then both bytes of a word are transferred to the lower data bus half (D7–D0). Figure 8-1 also illustrates the MOVEP.W D0,$E0001 instruction.

The MOVEP instruction also is used to input or output long-word data. This is illustrated with the MOVEP.L D0,$E0000 instruction, also shown in Figure 8-1, which moves all 4 bytes to the upper data bus bank. In this case 4 bytes are moved to locations $E0000, $E0002, $E0004, and $E0006. If the address were odd, the bytes would be moved through the lower data bus half.

In most cases data are output to 8-bit I/O devices, so the MOVEP instruction does not find much application. It is basically designed to allow word or long-word data to be output to 8-bit peripherals.

### The Basic Input Circuit

Figure 8-2 depicts the circuit that is used to interface a set of eight DIP switches to the 68000 or 68008 microprocessor. Notice that the switches are connected to the inputs of a three-state octal buffer (74ALS244). The outputs of the buffer are connected to the microprocessor's data bus. (In a 68000-based system, the outputs may be connected to either D0–D7 or D8–D15.)

In this circuit if the output enable ($\overline{G}$) inputs of the buffer are a logic zero, the switches are connected to the data bus. If the $\overline{G}$ inputs are a logic one, the output of the buffer enters its high impedance state (disconnected). A logic zero on output enable causes the buffer to function as a set of eight wires. This connects the switches to the data bus. A logic one on output enable causes the switches to be

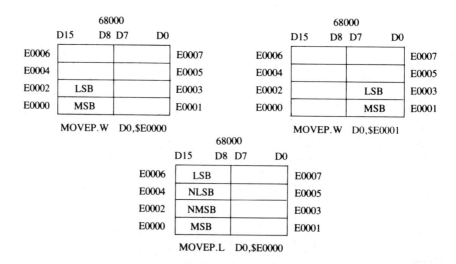

**Figure 8-1    The MOVEP instruction and its mode of storing data in the I/O space.**

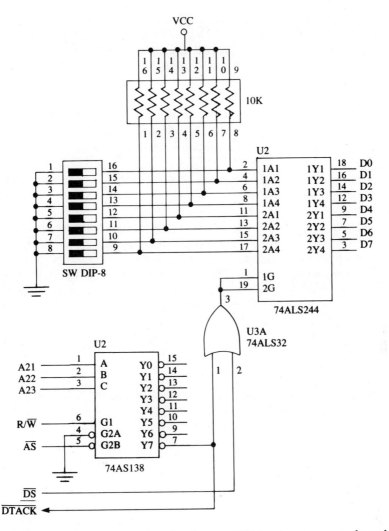

**Figure 8-2** Eight DIP switches interfaced to a 68008 microprocessor through a 74ALS244 buffer.

disconnected from the data bus because the buffer's outputs are at their high impedance state.

The decoder illustrated decodes address connections A23, A22, and A21. It also combines them with control signals $\overline{AS}$, $\overline{DS}$, and R/$\overline{W}$ to generate a control signal for the buffer. The output of the decoder does not become a logic zero unless $\overline{AS}$ and $\overline{DS}$ are a zero, R/$\overline{W}$ is a one, and address bits A23, A22, and A21 are all a logic one. If an instruction reads data from a memory location whose address begins 111, the three-state buffer is activated. This connects the switches to the data bus so that they can be read. Notice that the output of the decoder also generates the $\overline{DTACK}$ signal for the microprocessor, with the result that there are zero wait states inserted into the timing.

In this example, the MOVE.B $E00000,D0 instruction is used to read the contents of the eight switches into the byte portion of data register D0. The interface illustrated assumes that it is connected to a 68008 microprocessor because $\overline{DS}$ is connected to the decoder. Most input devices, except for the simplest, like a set of DIP switches, have the three-state buffers built into them.

The buffer times the application of the input data to ensure that data appear on the data bus only when its location is read from the memory. This type of I/O interface is called *memory-mapped I/O*. With memory-mapped I/O, any instruction that reads the contents of a memory location is used to read the contents of the input device.

Some microprocessors have special instructions for I/O operations and even a separate area of addresses that are unique to I/O operations. These microprocessors use separate I/O schemes because of the separate I/O addresses. This technique is often referred to as *isolated I/O*. The Motorola series of microprocessors supports memory-mapped I/O only; these devices do not support isolated I/O.

If this interface of Figure 8-2 is used with the 68000 microprocessor, the $\overline{DS}$ signal is replaced by either the $\overline{LDS}$ or $\overline{UDS}$ signal. If $\overline{LDS}$ is connected to the decoder, the memory address must be odd. If $\overline{UDS}$ is connected to the decoder, the memory address must be even. A MOVE.B $E00000,D0 transfers data from the upper data bus half to the byte-sized D0 data register. A MOVE.B $E00001,D0 transfers data from the lower data bus half to the byte-sized D0 data register.

## The Basic Output Circuit

Like the basic input circuit, the basic output circuit requires a decoder to decode a memory location so that the output device will function. The memory address decoder combines address connections from the microprocessor with the $\overline{AS}$, $\overline{DS}$, and R/$\overline{W}$ connections. As with the input circuit, the decoder's output activates when an operation addresses the decoded memory location.

There is only one difference between the basic input circuit and the basic output decoder, and it is minor, involving the activity level of R/$\overline{W}$ that determines whether the output of the decoder activates for a read or a write. The input circuit's decoder enables a three-state buffer that applies data to the data bus from the input device. The output circuit's decoder clocks or gates a latch circuit. The latch then captures the data present on the data bus at the time of the memory write operation.

Figure 8-3 illustrates a set of eight LED indicators that are connected to the output connections or an octal latch (74ALS374). Because the memory address begins with a 101, the latch receives a clock pulse from the decoder whenever an instruction writes data to a memory location whose address begins with a 101. For example, if you want to place a 1001 0000 on the LED indicators, a MOVE.B #$90,$A00000 instruction must be executed, causing the microprocessor to send out an address that begins with a 101 at the time the data bus contains a $90.

As with the input circuit, the technique used to transfer data between the microprocessor and the I/O device is memory-mapped I/O. This technique allows the I/O device to be operated by any instruction that references the memory. The

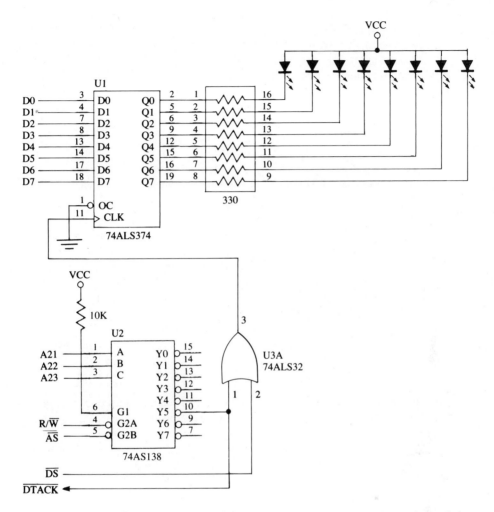

**Figure 8-3   Eight LED indicators interfaced to the 68008 microprocessor and decoded at location $AXXXXX.**

latch is required for the basic output circuit because data appear on the data bus for just a very short time when you execute the MOVE.B #$90,$A00000 instruction. If the latch were not present, the LED displays would light up for less than 300 ns, certainly not long enough to see much of anything. Most output devices contain the latch either built into the device or separate as illustrated in this example.

The circuit shown for the LEDs is decoded to function with a 68008 microprocessor. If the 68000 is used in place of the 68008, the $\overline{DS}$ connection becomes either $\overline{UDS}$ or $\overline{LDS}$. As with the basic input decoder for the 68000, the $\overline{LDS}$ signal is active for an odd memory address and the $\overline{UDS}$ signal is active for an even memory address.

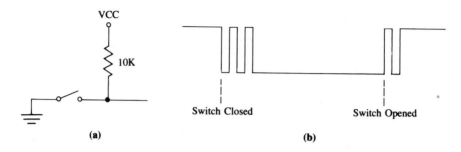

**Figure 8-4** (a) A simple SPST switch. (b) The waveform found at the output of a switch as it is closed and opened.

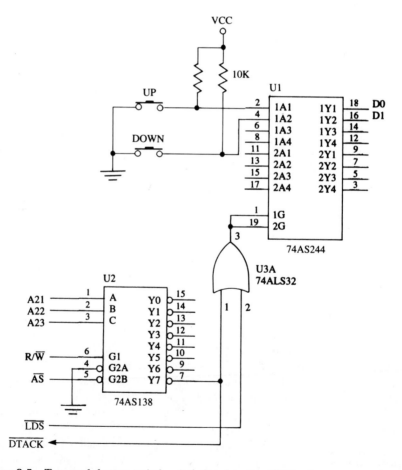

**Figure 8-5** Two push-button switches interfaced to the 68000 microprocessor for the program in Example 8-1.

## 8-1.2 Input Devices

An input device is any device that sends a binary number to the microprocessor through a set of three-state buffers. Example input devices include switches, keyboards, ADC (analog-to-digital converters), and similar devices. Keyboards and ADCs are interfaced to the microprocessor in Section 8-3, but the simple switch is discussed at this point.

Many input devices and sensors are switch based. Switches, however, don't always perform exactly as you might expect. What unforeseen problems occur with switches? Switches mechanically bounce. A bounce or bounces occur whenever a switch is closed and sometimes when it is opened. The bouncing happens because the switch is a mechanical device that has contacts that have resilience. Figure 8-4 illustrates a simple switch and the electrical signal found across it when the device is closed and opened. Notice that there is more than one contact connection when the switch is closed. A bounce may also occur when the switch contact is opened. This happens as a switch ages and dirt begins to accumulate on the contacts. Bouncing is often undesirable in a digital system because one pulse per switch depression is normally required. Digital circuitry is often used to debounce the switch, but this is an unneeded additional expense in a system that contains a microprocessor. This is because microprocessors are usually used to debounce switch contacts.

Figure 8-5 shows a pair of switches interfaced to the microprocessor with the basic input circuit that appeared in Figure 8-2. In this example, one push-button switch is labeled UP and the other is labeled DOWN. The software that appears in Example 8-1 is used to read the switches and debounce them. It then either causes the contents of register D0 to be incremented by one (UP) or decremented by one (DOWN). Either operation occurs only once for each depression of the respective switch. The port address, decoded in this illustration, is any address that begins with a 111. Also, because $\overline{\text{LDS}}$ is connected to enable the circuit, the address must be odd since the microprocessor is a 68000.

E X A M P L E   8 - 1

```
                        ORG     $1000

001000  61000030  START BSR     TEST        ;test switches
001004  67FA            BEQ     START       ;if no switch
001006  6100003A        BSR     DELAY       ;wait 20 ms
00100A  61000026        BSR     TEST        ;test switches
00100E  67F0            BEQ     START       ;if no switches
001010  08010000        BTST    #0,D1       ;test UP
001014  67000008        BEQ     UP          ;if up
001018  5380            SUB.L   #1,D0       ;decrement D0
00101A  60000004        BRA     START1
00101E  5280      UP    ADD.L   #1,D0       ;increment D0
001020  61000010  START1 BSR    TEST        ;test switches
001024  66FA            BNE     START1      ;if switch pressed
001026  6100001A        BSR     DELAY       ;wait 20 ms
00102A  61000006        BSR     TEST        ;test switches
00102E  66F0            BNE     START1      ;if switch pressed
001030  60CE            BRA     START       ;if no switch pressed
```

```
                      ;
                      ;test switches
                      ;
001032  123900E00001  TEST    MOVE.B   $E00001,D1   ;read switches
001038  000100FC              OR.B     #$FC,D1      ;set bits 2-7
00103C  0C0100FF              CMP.B    #$FF,D1      ;test switches
001040  4E75                  RTS
                      ;
                      ;20 ms time delay
                      ;
001042  343C3E78      DELAY   MOVE.W   #15992,D2
001046  51CAFFFE      DELAY1  DBRA     D2,DELAY1
00104A  4E75                  RTS

                              END
```

To debounce a switch, the software waits until the switch stops bouncing. This is most often accomplished by using a time delay. The delay must be long enough to skip the bounces that occur at the switch. Since switches typically bounce for less than 20 ms, a time delay, which causes 20 ms of delay, is used to skip the bounces. In the software listed in Example 8-1, the switches are first tested to see whether both are released. Then they are tested to see whether either is closed. If a switch is closed, a time delay subroutine is called to give the switch time to stop its mechanical bounce. After time has been allowed for bouncing to cease, the switches are again tested to see which, if any, are active.

## 8-1.3 Output Devices

Many more types of output than input device are commonly connected to a microprocessor. Some of these devices are LED indicators, segmented displays constructed from LEDs, liquid crystal displays (LCD), and even vacuum tube devices such as fluorescent displays, motors, relays, and DACs (digit-to-analog converters).

### A Single LED

LED indicators are simple to interface to the microprocessor if the interface circuit has at least 10 mA of current available to drive the LED. Figure 8-6 depicts a single LED indicator connected so that a logic one causes it to illuminate. When the LED is lit, it glows red, green, or yellow. Most LEDs are red.

Notice in this interface that an inverter provides the required 10 mA of current through a series current-limiting resistor. The voltage drop across the lit LED is about 2 V in this circuit. (The LED nominally drops 1.65 V, but in practice the drop more often is closer to 2.0 V.) The remaining 3 V is dropped across the series current-limiting resistor. To limit the current to 10 mA, a 300 Ω resistor is used. In this example, a 330 Ω device is used because it is the nearest 20% resistor available. This interface, or one that is similar, must be used if the current available to drive the LED is less than 10 mA.

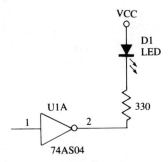

**Figure 8-6** A simple LED connected to a TTL inverter through a current-limiting resistor.

## The Seven-Segment LED Display.

Figure 8-7 illustrates a seven-segment LED indicator and its connection to a set of segment drivers. Notice that each segment is lettered. The segments are lettered a through g. Also notice that this type of display is called a *common-anode* display because all seven anodes are tied together to form a common connection. *Common-*

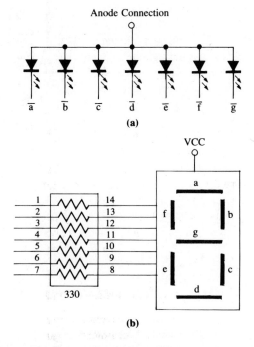

**Figure 8-7** (a) The internal structure of a seven-segment, common-anode LED display. (b) A seven-segment LED display connected to current-limiting resistors.

*cathode* displays are also available, in which all the cathodes are tied in common. The common-anode display requires a cathode to be grounded to cause a segment to light. The common-cathode display requires that an anode be connected to 5.0 V to light a segment. In either case, each segment must have its current limited to 10 mA for most LED segmented displays. Both types of display device are common. Notice that the segment drivers are basically the same circuit used to drive a single LED.

### LCD Display

The liquid crystal display is probably the most familiar of the display devices because it is found on many digital wristwatches and in most calculators. The main advantage of the LCD display is that it has very high contrast, unlike the LED display, and can be seen extremely well in very bright light. The main problem with the LCD display is that it requires a light source in dim or dark areas because it produces no light of its own. Light sources are often included at the edge of the glass to flood the LCD display with light in dimly lit environments. This is a disadvantage because the light consumes more power than the entire display.

Figure 8-8 illustrates the basic construction of the LCD display. The LCD type of display that is most common today allows light to pass through it whenever it is activated. Earlier LCD displays absorbed light. Activation of a segment requires a low frequency bipolar excitation voltage of 30–1000 Hz. The polarity of this voltage must change or the LCD will not be able to change very quickly.

The device functions in the following manner. When a voltage is placed across the segment, an electrostatic field is set up that aligns the crystals in the liquid. This alignment allows light to pass through the segment. If no voltage is applied across a segment, the crystals appear to be opaque because they are randomly aligned. Random alignment is assured by the ac excitation voltages applied to each segment.

In a digital watch, the segments appear to darken when they are activated because light passes through the segment where a black cardboard backing is located to absorb all light. This causes the segment to darken. The area surrounding the activated segment appears lighter in color because much of the light is reflected by the randomly aligned crystals.

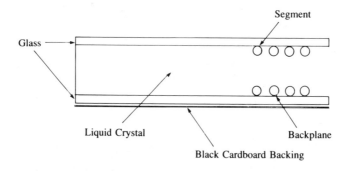

**Figure 8-8   A liquid crystal display (LCD).**

In a *backlit* computer LCD display, the segment appears to grow brighter because of a light placed behind the display. The light is allowed to pass through when the segment is activated. Currently a few manufacturers have developed color LCD displays for use with computers and small color televisions. This display uses three segments (dots) for each picture element (*pixel*). These three dots are filtered so that they pass red, blue, and green light. By varying the amount of time each of the three dots is active, and the number of dots, just about any color and intensity can be displayed. White light consists of 59% green, 30% red, and 11% blue light. Secondary colors are magenta (red and blue), cyan (blue and green), and yellow (red and green). Not only secondary colors but also any other colors are obtained by mixing red, green, and blue light.

## Fluorescent Display

The fluorescent display is popular in calculators, bedroom alarm clocks, automobile clocks, and many point-of-sale terminals (cash registers). The main reason is that this type of display is visible under almost any lighting condition except bright direct sunlight. The fluorescent display exhibits a blue-green glow that is unique to this type of display device. Figure 8-9 illustrates the seven-segment fluorescent display which is a vacuum tube. This device contains the following major components: a filament/cathode, a control grid, and seven anode segment connections.

The filament, which acts as a cathode, is heated to generate electron flow for the tube. The control grid controls the amount of electron flow past it to the anodes in the tube. The anodes are coated with a phosphor that glows when bombarded with a stream of electrons.

A small voltage (usually 1.5 V) is applied to the filament to produce a cloud of free electrons. If a voltage (usually 15 V) is applied to an anode, free electrons are attracted to the anode, striking it with enough force to generate secondary emission

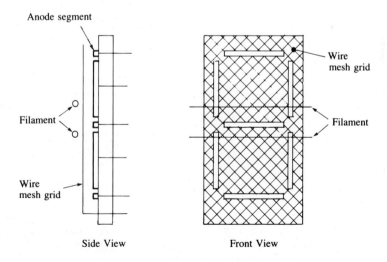

**Figure 8-9   The structure of the fluorescent display.**

and subsequently visible photons of light. The control grid usually has a small negative voltage applied to it to control the number of electrons that pass to the anode. By controlling the electron flow, the brightness of the display may be controlled. This is the only display device that can easily have its intensity changed, which is another advantage of the fluorescent display when compared to other such devices.

### Relay/Solenoid

The relay or solenoid is interfaced to the microprocessor through a driver because it requires more current than is available from the microprocessor—often several amperes of current. Figure 8-10a depicts a 12 V relay connected to the microprocessor so that a small current from the microprocessor can drive it. Here a Darlington pair is used to drive the relay.

Notice that this interface uses a diode to prevent damage to the Darlington. When the Darlington is cut off, the current flow through the relay coil stops flowing, causing the magnetic field surrounding its coil to collapse. This collapsing field produces a reverse voltage across the relay coil that will exceed the breakdown voltage rating of the Darlington. This reverse voltage often approaches 10,000 V if no protection is provided to the Darlington driver. The diode conducts to dissipate this reverse voltage and protects the Darlington.

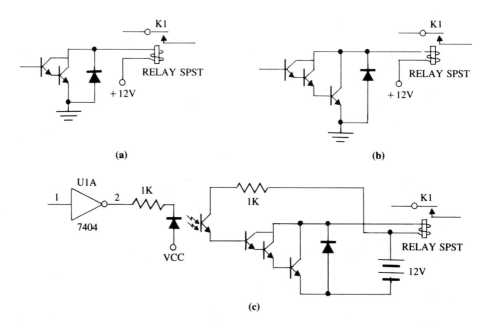

**Figure 8-10**    (a) A Darlington pair used to drive a relay. (b) A Darlington pair with an external driver used to supply current to a relay. (c) An optical isolator used to isolate the TTL power supply from the relay power supply.

The Darlington in this circuit has a current gain of 2000. If the relay coil requires 500 mA of current to energize, the amount of base current required for the Darlington is 500 mA/2000 or 250 μA. Any microprocessor circuit is able to provide 250 μA of current. The base resistor is designed using the worst-case logic one voltage of 2.4 V at 250 μA.

Suppose that a solenoid or relay is used that requires 10 A of current. This is interfaced using a Darlington that has a gain of 2000 and a power transistor that has a gain of 20 (Figure 8-10b). Here the total current gain is approximately 20 × 2000 or 40,000. The amount of base current for the Darlington is 10 A/40,000 or 250 μA, so the base resistor in this circuit is the same as for the first circuit.

A word about large current devices that are connected to the microprocessor. Often the surge in current required to operate a large solenoid or relay will cause problems with the supply voltage to the microprocessor and its memory. To prevent the ill effects of current surges a separate power supply is often provided for the solenoid or relay.

In addition to the separate supply, an optical isolator may also be found to further isolate the relay or solenoid from the microprocessor. Figure 8-10c shows the 10 A solenoid interfaced using an optical isolator. Notice that this separates the TTL power supply, from the relay power supply, preventing any interface to the TTL supply. Besides separate power supplies, it is important to heat sink the power transistor or Darlington. In many cases, the relay or solenoid is energized long enough to produce heat at the Darlington amplifier. If not heat sinked, the amplifier will destroy itself.

## 8-2   The Peripheral Interface Adapter (PIA)

The peripheral interface adapter is a device that allows the microprocessor to transfer information between itself and parallel I/O devices. The 68000 often uses the 6821 PIA, or an updated version, the 68230. This chapter covers the 6821. The next chapter explains the 68230, which offers a more flexible approach to I/O interfacing. The 68230 is a parallel interface that also contains a 24-bit timer.

Parallel interface adapters are used whenever the microprocessor requires or needs to transmit parallel data. Some examples of parallel data include the ASCII code transmitted between the microprocessor and a printer or between a keyboard and the microprocessor.

### 8-2.1   The 6821 PIA

Figure 8-11 illustrates the pinout of the 6821 PIA. Notice from this pinout that this device has two 8-bit parallel I/O data registers or ports. The pinout shows there are eight data bus connections, D0–D7, and two 8-bit I/O data paths, which we label data interface A (PA0–PA7) and data interface B (PB0–PB7). Selection is accomplished via three chip selection inputs (CS0, CS1, and $\overline{CS2}$) and by an enable input. Whenever the chip selection and enable inputs are all active, the register selection inputs (RS0 and RS1) select an internal register.

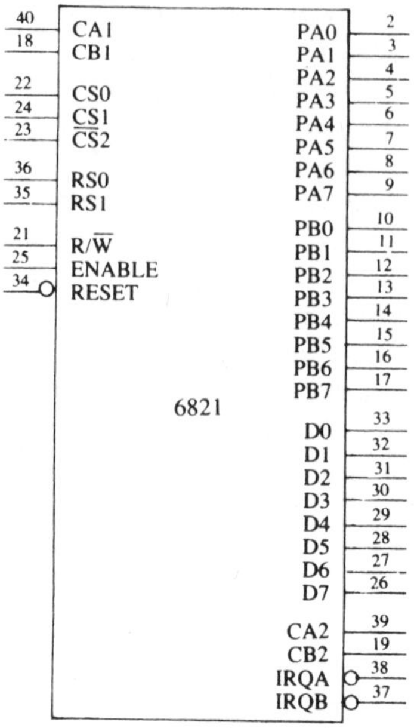

```
     40
   ─────   CA1                    PA0  ── 2 ─
     18     CB1                   PA1  ── 3 ─
   ─────                          PA2  ── 4 ─
     22     CS0                   PA3  ── 5 ─
   ─────   CS1                    PA4  ── 6 ─
     24                           PA5  ── 7 ─
   ─────   CS2                    PA6  ── 8 ─
     23                           PA7  ── 9 ─
     36     RS0
   ─────   RS1                    PB0  ── 10 ─
     35                           PB1  ── 11 ─
                                  PB2  ── 12 ─
     21     R/W̄                   PB3  ── 13 ─
   ─────   ENABLE                 PB4  ── 14 ─
     25                           PB5  ── 15 ─
   ─────o  RESET                  PB6  ── 16 ─
     34                           PB7  ── 17 ─

                    6821
                                  D0  ── 33 ─
                                  D1  ── 32 ─
                                  D2  ── 31 ─
                                  D3  ── 30 ─
                                  D4  ── 29 ─
                                  D5  ── 28 ─
                                  D6  ── 27 ─
                                  D7  ── 26 ─

                                  CA2  ── 39 ─
                                  CB2  ── 19 ─
                                  IRQA o─ 38 ─
                                  IRQB o─ 37 ─
```

**Figure 8-11   The pinout of the 6821 peripheral interface adapter (PIA).**

*Connection of the 6821 to the 68000 or 68008 Microprocessor*

Figure 8-12 illustrates how the 6821 is connected to the 68008 microprocessor so that it functions at memory addresses $10000–$17FFFH. Obviously the device does not contain this many I/O addresses. The interface is so designed that the memory address is only partially decoded. Actually, there are only four different I/O addresses associated with this device, as selected by the register selection input, RS1 and RS0.

The 68000 and 68008 function differently with the 6821 (a 6800 peripheral) and with peripherals and memory designed for the 68000 or 68008. The 68000/68008 issues a memory address with the $\overline{AS}$ signal as it does with any memory address. The difference with the 6821 or any of the 6800 peripherals is that the peripheral interface decodes the address and returns the $\overline{VPA}$ signal to the 68000/68008 in place of $\overline{DTACK}$. $\overline{VPA}$ informs the 68000/68008 that the I/O device is a 6800-compatible device.

Once $\overline{VPA}$ has been received, the microprocessor modifies the bus timing so that the slower 6821 will function correctly with the 68000/68008. Memory timing is modified by the insertion of wait states. The data strobe signal from the 68008 microprocessor is not used when a 6800 peripheral is interfaced to the microprocessor. The enable (E) signal performs the same function as data strobe for the 6800 peripheral. With the 68000 microprocessor, $\overline{LDS}$ or $\overline{UDS}$ must be used to select the device for an upper or lower data bus transfer.

Besides the $\overline{VPA}$ signal sent to the 68000/68008, two other 6800 peripheral signals are connected to the 6821 interface. The $\overline{VMA}$ (valid memory address) is

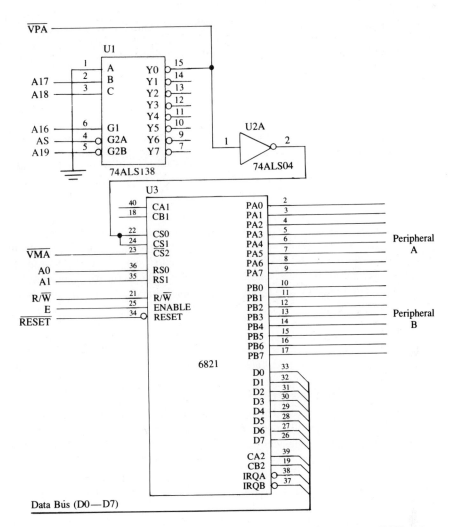

**Figure 8-12**  A 6821 peripheral interface adapter connected to the 68008 micro-processor. Notice from this circuit that the 6821 is decoded at locations $10000–$17FFF.

generated by the 68000/68008 when it receives $\overline{\text{VPA}}$. $\overline{\text{VMA}}$ indicates that the 68000/68008 is issuing a valid memory address for a 6800 type peripheral. The E (signal) is also sent from the 68000/68008 and used to enable the 6821.

Table 8-1 illustrates the effect of the register selection inputs and the effect of some bits in control register A (CRA) and control register B (CRB). Notice that the registers selected in Table 8-1 depend on the register selection inputs and also on the state of two internal control register bits. The internal selection bits are the control register A, position 2 ($CRA_2$) and control register B, position 2 ($CRB_2$) bits. Before this device is programmed, the state of control registers A and B must be pro-grammed.

**Table 8-1    The Effect of RS0 and RS1 Register Selection Inputs**

| RS1 | RS0 | CRA$_2$ | CRB$_2$ | Function |
|-----|-----|---------|---------|----------|
| 0 | 0 | 1 | x | Peripheral register A |
| 0 | 0 | 0 | x | Data direction register A |
| 0 | 1 | x | x | Control register A |
| 1 | 0 | x | 1 | Peripheral register B |
| 1 | 0 | x | 0 | Data direction register B |
| 1 | 1 | x | x | Control register B |

The control registers are programmed by placing the register selection inputs at a 11 to program control register B and a 01 to program control register A. In Figure 8-12 the register selection bits cause the 6821 to select various internal devices using address connections A0 and A1, which are attached to the RS0 and RS1 inputs, respectively. Here is a possible set of I/O addresses: $10000 for peripheral register A or data direction register A, $10001 for control register A, $10002 for peripheral register B and data direction register B, and $10003 for control register B.

## Programming the 6821 Control Register

Before the 6821 is programmed, the effect of the reset input must be known. The reset pin will initialize the 6821, clearing all its internal registers to $00. This programs peripheral data interfaces A and B as input ports and disables connections IRQA and IRQB. If peripheral data interfaces A and B are required as input devices and IRQA and IRQB are not used, no further programming is necessary after a system reset. If these interfaces are programmed differently—as outputs, for example—then the internal registers must be programmed.

Figure 8-13 illustrates the structures of control registers A and B, which are used to program the 6821. Bits 7 and 6 of both control registers convey information

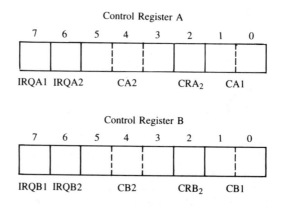

**Figure 8-13    The internal control register structure of the 6821 PIA.**

**Table 8-2**  The CA1 Control Bits $CRA_1$ and $CRA_0$: Also Applies to CB1 Control

| CA1 bits | | Interrupt input | Interrupt flag | |
| --- | --- | --- | --- | --- |
| $CRA_1$ | $CRA_0$ | CA1 | $CRA_7$ | MPU |
| 0 | 0 | Negative edge | Set high on negative edge of CA1. | Disabled for CA1. |
| 0 | 1 | Negative edge | Set high on negative edge of CA1. | Active for CA1. |
| 1 | 0 | Positive edge | Set high on positive edge of CA1. | Disabled for CA1. |
| 1 | 1 | Positive edge | Set high on positive edge of CA1. | Active for CA1. |

**Table 8-3**  Control of CA2 as an Interrupt Input: Also Applies to CB2

| CA2 bits | | | Interrupt input | Interrupt flag | |
| --- | --- | --- | --- | --- | --- |
| $CRA_5$ | $CRA_4$ | $CRA_3$ | CA2 | $CRA_6$ | MPU |
| 0 | 0 | 0 | Negative edge | Set high on negative edge of CA2. | Disabled for CA2. |
| 0 | 0 | 1 | Negative edge | Set high on negative edge of CA2. | Active for CA2. |
| 0 | 1 | 0 | Positive edge | Set high on positive edge of CA2. | Disabled for CA2. |
| 0 | 1 | 1 | Positive edge | Set high on positive edge of CA2. | Active for CA2. |

**Table 8-4**  Control of CA2 as an Output Connection

| CA2 bits | | | CA2 cleared | CA2 set |
| --- | --- | --- | --- | --- |
| $CRA_5$ | $CRA_4$ | $CRA_3$ | | |
| 1 | 0 | 0 | When peripheral register A is read | Upon active transition of CA1 |
| 1 | 0 | 1 | When peripheral register A is read | After 6821 has been deselected |
| 1 | 1 | 0 | [CA2 is cleared.] | — |
| 1 | 1 | 1 | — | [CA2 is set.] |

**Table 8-5   Control of CB2 as an Output**

| CB2 bits | | | | |
|---|---|---|---|---|
| $CBA_5$ | $CBA_4$ | $CBA_3$ | CB2 cleared | CB2 set |
| 1 | 0 | 0 | When peripheral register B is read | Upon active transition of CB1 |
| 1 | 0 | 1 | When peripheral register B is read | After 6821 has been deselected |
| 1 | 1 | 0 | [CB2 is cleared.] | — |
| 1 | 1 | 1 | — | [CB2 is set.] |

to the microprocessor whenever the control register is read. The remaining bits convey no information on a read. Bits 7 and 6 indicate conditions of interrupts as specified by the CA2 and CB1 fields of the control registers. Refer to Tables 8-2 through 8-5 for the operation of the $\overline{IRQA}$ and $\overline{IRQB}$ status bits of the control registers.

Table 8-2 illustrates how bits 1 and 0 of either control register are programmed to affect the operation of the CA1 or CB1 input pin and the $\overline{IRQA}$ or $\overline{IRQB}$ output pins. Notice that CA1 or CB1 is programmed as either a positive or negative edge-triggered input. Pins $\overline{IRQA}$ or $\overline{IRQB}$ are programmed on or off (active or disabled). Bits CRA7 or CRB7 are affected by the change on interrupt input CA1.

Table 8-3 illustrates the operation of the CA2 input connection and the $\overline{IRQA}$ output connections as well as the CRA6 bit of the control register. This table performs the same function as Table 8-2 does for the CA1 input connection. The remaining combinations of CRA5, CRA4, and CRA3 appear in Table 8-4 when CA2 is used as an output pin. The remaining combinations of CRB5, CRB4, and CRB3 appear in Table 8-5 when CB2 is used as an output connection.

## Programming the Data Direction Registers of the 6821

To program the pins of peripheral data registers A (PDRA) and B (PDRB) as input or output connections, the $CRA_2$ and $CRB_2$ bits of the control registers are first cleared to zero. This is accomplished automatically after a reset operation, which clears all the bits of both control registers. The reset also sets each data peripheral register as an input device. Once the $CRA_2$ and $CRB_2$ bits have been cleared, the data direction registers for both A and B are programmed. If a one is placed in a bit position of the data direction register, the corresponding peripheral pin is programmed as an output connection. If a zero is placed in a bit position of the data direction register, the corresponding peripheral pin is programmed as an input connection.

Suppose that the 6821 is interfaced to the 68008 as illustrated in Figure 8-14. In this circuit, the seven least significant peripheral data register A connections are attached to a two-digit display. The two most significant peripheral data register B connections are used to select one of the display devices. Finally, the least significant two peripheral data register B connections are connected to two push-button switches. The 6821 is decoded at locations $20000, $20001, $20002, and $20003.

Example 8-2 illustrates the software required to program the 6821. It is assumed that this software is executed after a hardware reset: with the control registers thus set to $00, the 6821 can accept programming for the data direction registers.

E X A M P L E   8 - 2

```
                              ORG      $A000
00A000  13FC00FF00020000  SETUP  MOVE.B  #$FF,$20000  ;program A as out
00A008  13FC000000020002         MOVE.B  #0,$20002    ;program B as in
00A010  13FC000200020001         MOVE.B  #2,$20001    ;set CRA2
00A018  13FC000200020003         MOVE.B  #2,$20003    ;set CRB2
00A020  4E75                      RTS

                              END
```

In this software example, the contents of data direction register A are adjusted so that peripheral data register A is programmed as an output device. The contents of data direction register B are programmed so that the least significant 2 bits of peripheral data register B are programmed as input bits. The most significant 2 bits are programmed as output bits. Once both data direction registers have been programmed, the $CRA_2$ and $CRB_2$ bits are set, to permit the peripheral data registers to be used in the program.

Figure 8-15 illustrates the flowcharts used to read the UP and DOWN switches and debounce them. It also shows how these switches are used to increment (UP) or decrement (DOWN) a counter. The contents of the counter are displayed in decimal on the two-digit display. Display is accomplished by converting the counter, which counts in binary-coded decimal, into seven-segment code for the displays. This conversion is accomplished by using a lookup table that contains the seven-segment codes for each BCD number.

The main program calls the read subroutine that reads the switches. Each time the switches are read, they are debounced with a time delay. The time delay subroutine not only causes a 10 ms time delay, but it also displays the contents of D0 on the LED displays.

Example 8-3 lists the software that implements the flowchart of Figure 8-15. When reviewing this software, pay close attention to the portion of the time delay that locates the seven-segment code in a lookup table and displays it on the displays.

E X A M P L E   8 - 3

```
                              ORG      $B000
00B000  13FC00FF00020000  START  MOVE.B  #$FF,$20000  ;program A
00B008  13FC00C000020002         MOVE.B  #$C0,$20002  ;program B
00B010  13FC000200020001         MOVE.B  #2,$20001    ;program CRA2
00B018  13FC000200020003         MOVE.B  #2,$20003    ;program CRB2
                          ;
```

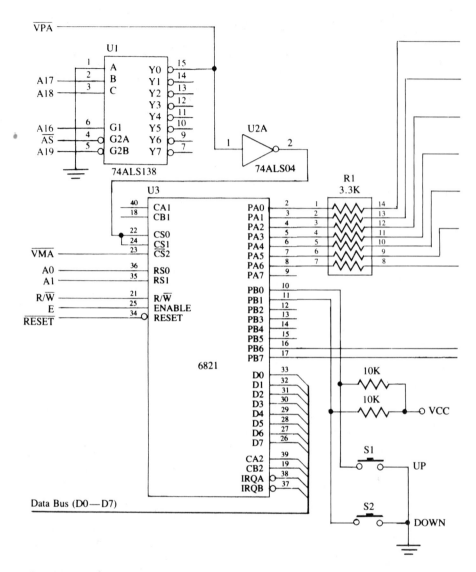

**Figure 8-14**   Two switches and a two-digit display interfaced to the 68008 micro-processor through a 6821 PIA.

```
00B020   103C0000                  MOVE.B   #0,D0        ;initialize D0
00B024   143C0001                  MOVE.B   #1,D2        ;setup one
                             ;
00B028   61000024        START1    BSR      READ         ;read switches
00B02C   67FA                      BEQ      START1       ;if no key
00B02E   08010000                  BTST     #0,D1        ;test UP
00B032   6700000C                  BEQ      START2       ;if UP
00B036   023C00EF                  AND.B    #$EF,CCR     ;clear extend
00B03A   8102                      SBCD     D2,D0        ;decrement count
00B03C   60000008                  BRA      START3
```

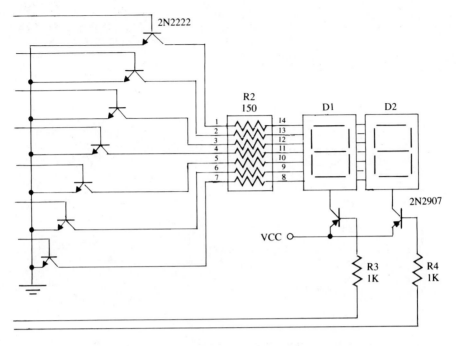

**Figure 8-14   Continued.**

```
00B040   023C00EF      START2   AND.B    #$EF,CCR      ;clear extend
00B044   C102                   ABCD     D2,D0         ;increment count
                                ;
00B046   61000006      START3   BSR      READ          ;read switches
00B04A   66FA                   BNE      START3        ;key pressed
00B04C   60DA                   BRA      START1
                       ;
                       ;read subroutine
                       ;
00B04E   123900020002  READ     MOVE.B   $20002,D1     ;read switches
00B054   000100FC               OR.B     #$FC,D1       ;set bits 2-7
00B058   61000016               BSR      DELAY         ;wait 10 ms
00B05C   163900020002           MOVE.B   $20002,D3
00B062   000300FC               OR.B     #$FC,D3       ;set bits 2-7
00B066   B203                   CMP.B    D3,D1         ;compare
00B068   66E4                   BNE      READ          ;repeat if not same
00B06A   0C0100FF               CMP.B    #$FF,D1       ;test switches
00B06E   4E75                   RTS
                       ;
                       ;delay and display
                       ;
00B070   6100003C      DELAY    BSR      CONVERT       ;get 7-seg code
00B074   13C300020000           MOVE.B   D3,$20000     ;display code
00B07A   13FC004000020002       MOVE.B   #$40,$20002   ;select D2
00B082   61000020               BSR      FIVE          ;wait 5 ms
00B086   1F00                   MOVE.B   D0,-(SP)      ;save D0
00B088   E808                   LSR.B    #4,D0
00B08A   61000022               BSR      CONVERT       ;get 7-seg code
00B08E   33C300020000           MOVE     D3,$20000     ;display code
00B094   13FC008000020002       MOVE.B   #$80,$20002   ;select D1
```

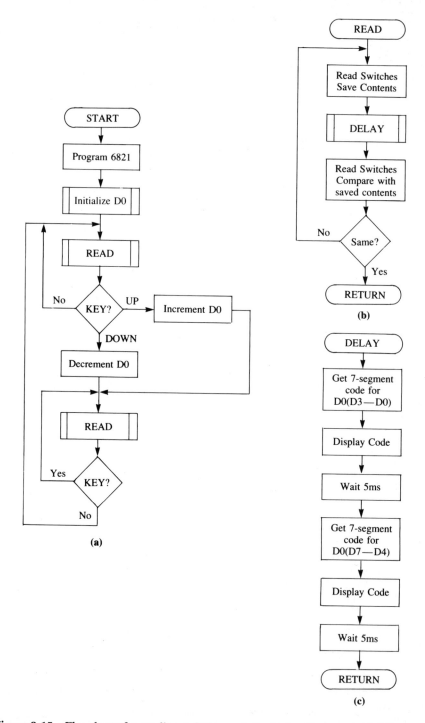

**Figure 8-15** Flowcharts for reading switches and displaying the count. (a) The main flowchart. (b) Flowchart of a subroutine that reads a key switch. (c) Flowchart of a subroutine that generates a time delay and also displays the contents of register D0 on the two-digit display.

```
00B09C   101F              MOVE.B   (SP)+,D0      ;restore D0
00B09E   61000004          BSR      FIVE          ;wait 5 ms
00B0A2   4E75              RTS
                        ;
                        ;five ms delay
                        ;
00B0A4   3A3C0F9E   FIVE    MOVE     #3998,D5
00B0A8   51CDFFFE   DELAY6  DBRA     D5,DELAY6
00B0AC   4E75               RTS
                        ;
                        ;convert to 7-seg code
                        ;
00B0AE   4243       CONVERT CLR.W    D3
00B0B0   1600       MOVE.B  D0,D3
00B0B2   0243000F           AND.W    #$F,D3
00B0B6   207C0000B0C2       MOVE.L   #TABLE,A0
00B0BC   16303000           MOVE.B   0(A0,D3.W),D3
00B0C0   4E75               RTS
                        ;
                        ;lookup table
                        ;
00B0C2   3F         TABLE   DC.B     $3F          ;0
00B0C6   06                 DC.B     6            ;1
00B0CA   5B                 DC.B     $5B          ;2
00B0CE   4F                 DC.B     $4F          ;3
00B0D2   66                 DC.B     $66          ;4
00B0D6   6D                 DC.B     $6D          ;5
00B0DA   7D                 DC.B     $7D          ;6
00B0DE   07                 DC.B     7            ;7
00B0E2   7F                 DC.B     $7F          ;8
00B0E6   6F                 DC.B     $6F          ;9

                           END
```

## 8-3  Keyboard and Display Interfaces

The PIA is often used to interface the microprocessor to a keyboard or a display. This section illustrates how a hexadecimal keypad and an 8-digit display are interfaced to the 68000 family. In both interfaces, a 6821 PIA serves as the interfacing component.

### 8-3.1  Keyboard Interface

In many small systems, keyboards are interfaced directly to the microprocessor. The 6821 is an ideal gateway to the microprocessor for a keyboard. Figure 8-16 illustrates a 16-key hexadecimal keypad interfaced to the 68000 microprocessor through a 6821. Peripheral data connections PA0–PA3 and PB0–PB3 are used to interface to the keypad. In this interface, PA0–PA3 are used as output signals to the keypad. Pins PB0–PB3 are used as inputs from the keypad.

Table 8-6 illustrates the binary bit pattern sent to the keyboard to select keyboard columns. This pattern is placed on the least significant 4 bits of peripheral data register A. Notice with the patterns listed that a zero selects a column of four switches. This binary pattern is developed with software that searches for a contact on a push-button keyswitch. The switches on this keyboard are connected as a

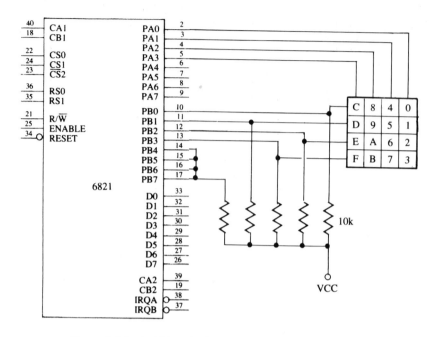

**Figure 8-16   A 16-key keypad connected to the 6821 PIA.**

matrix. There are four switches per row and four per column. If a switch is pressed, it connects one row to one column. If no switches are pressed, no row is connected to any column.

The rows are connected to peripheral data register B connections PB0–PB3. These connections are programmed as input connections. Each row is pulled high through a 10 kΩ resistor. If no keys are pressed, all these input connections are connected to a logic one through the resistors. If a key is pressed on a column that is selected by the code in Table 8-6, one of these four input connections becomes a logic zero. The selected column becomes a logic zero, which is passed through a closed contact to a row.

Figure 8-17 illustrates the flowchart for the software that detects and reads a key. Because software often takes a little time to process data, if a key is not released, it may be detected a second and even a third time. To prevent such errors,

**Table 8-6   Pattern Found on Pins PA0–PA3 in the Circuit of Figure 8-16**

| PA3 | PA2 | PA1 | PA0 | Function |
|-----|-----|-----|-----|----------|
| 1 | 1 | 1 | 0 | Selects keys 0, 1, 2, and 3. |
| 1 | 1 | 0 | 1 | Selects keys 4, 5, 6, and 7. |
| 1 | 0 | 1 | 0 | Selects keys 8, 9, A, and B. |
| 0 | 1 | 1 | 1 | Selects keys C, D, E, and F. |

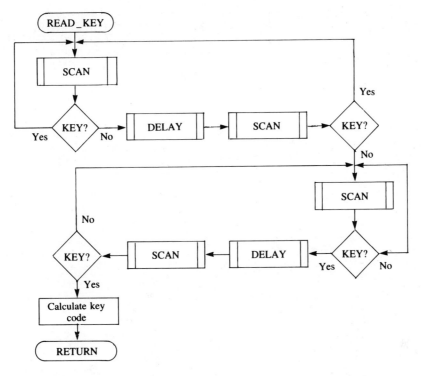

**Figure 8-17** The flowchart used to detect a key and return with the key code.

it is advisable to wait for a key to be released before testing for a key. This software first waits for a key to be released. The second part of the flowchart shows that the software tests for a key. If the key is detected, the key code is calculated by the software.

Time delays appear in the flowchart to debounce keys. In most cases keys will bounce for 10 ms or less. The time delay used here wastes 10 ms of time to debounce a key. Keys bounce when pressed and when released. The flowchart illustrates how both conditions are tested. The first delay is used to debounce a release. The second delay debounces a keystroke. In this way, the software will detect only a valid keystroke.

E X A M P L E     8 - 4

```
                        ORG     $C000
                  ;
                  ;read keyboard and return with key code in D1
                  ;
00C000  6100002A  READ    BSR     SCAN    ;test keys
00C004  66FA              BNE     READ    ;if key down
00C006  61000050          BSR     DELAY   ;wait 10 ms
00C00A  61000020          BSR     SCAN    ;test keys
00C00E  66F0              BNE     READ    ;if key down
                  ;
```

```
00C010    6100001A    READ1    BSR      SCAN         ;test keys
00C014    67FA                 BEQ      READ1        ;if no key
00C016    61000040             BSR      DELAY        ;wait 10 ms
00C01A    61000010             BSR      SCAN         ;test keys
00C01E    67F0                 BEQ      READ1        ;if no key
00C020    04010001             SUB.B    #$1,D1       ;adjust D1
                            ;
00C024    5201        READ2    ADD.B    #1,D1        ;adjust code
00C026    E208                 LSR.B    #1,D0        ;shift right
00C028    65FA                 BCS      READ2        ;repeat until found
00C02A    4E75                 RTS                   ;return with code
                            ;
                            ;scan keys
                            ;
00C02C    123C0000    SCAN     MOVE.B   #0,D1        ;set code
00C030    163C00FE             MOVE.B   #$FE,D3      ;set select code
00C034    383C0003             MOVE.W   #3,D4        ;column count-1
                            ;
00C038    13C300020000 SCAN1   MOVE.B   D3,PORTA     ;select column
00C03E    E31B                 ROL.B    #1,D3        ;setup for next
00C040    103900020002         MOVE.B   PORTB,D0     ;read rows
00C046    0C0000FF             CMP.B    #$FF,D0      ;test row
00C04A    6600000A             BNE      SCAN2        ;if key found
00C04E    5801                 ADD.B    #4,D1        ;row count
00C050    51CCFFE6             DBRA     D4,SCAN1     ;repeat
00C054    4200                 CLR.B    D0
00C056    4E75        SCAN2    RTS
                            ;
                            ;delay 10 ms
                            ;
00C058    3A3C1F3C    DELAY    MOVE.W   #7996,D5
00C05C    51CDFFFE    DELAY1   DBRA     D5,DELAY1
00C060    4E75                 RTS

                             END
```

Example 8-4 illustrates the software written from the flowchart of Figure 8-17. Note that the scan subroutine may be modified to scan keyboards of other sizes by changing the counter and the number added to the register; in certain cases, the peripheral data registers also must be modified to connect a larger keypad. The same basic software and interface will function with keyboard matrices of sizes 2 × 2 to 8 × 8. This allows from 4 to 64 keys to be connected with this hardware and software, with only a slight software modification.

## 8-3.2    Multiplexed Displays

Another common interface is a set of multiplexed displays. The circuit used to drive eight common-anode LED displays is illustrated in Figure 8-18. Because the displays are multiplexed, a set of common segment drivers is used. One segment driver powers all the a segments. Another powers all of the b segments, and so forth. Besides segment drivers, there are anode switches, used to enable one display position at a time.

A closer look at the segment driver reveals an NPN transistor, with its collector connected through a resistor to a segment. The emitter of the transistor is grounded. The base is connected through a resistor to a peripheral data pin. The amount of segment current is determined by the number of display positions. Here there are eight display positions, and each one requires a nominal current of 10 mA for maximum brightness. Because the displays are multiplexed and turned on only an eighth of the time, the amount of segment current must be increased by a factor of 8. This maintains an average current of 10 mA in each display segment. Here, the segment current is set to 80 mA. If there were six displays, it would be set to 60 mA.

The resistor connected to the collector is chosen by using 80 mA of current and a voltage drop of 3.0 V. About 2.0 V is dropped across the LED display and the anode switch. The value of this resistor is 3.0 V/80 mA or 37.5 $\Omega$. A 39 $\Omega$ resistor is used because this is the closest standard resistor value.

The base resistor is chosen by using the minimum gain of the transistor—here 100. Since the collector current is 80 $\mu$A, the base current is 800 $\mu$A. The value of the base resistor is determined using 800 $\mu$A and a voltage of 1.7 V. This is the difference between the 2.4 V guaranteed at the peripheral data output pin for a logic one level and the drop across the emitter–base junction (0.7 V). In this circuit, the base resistor is 1.7 V/800 $\mu$A or 2.125 $\Omega$. A 2.2 k$\Omega$ resistor is used because it is the nearest standard value.

The anode switch has only one resistor to select. In this system, there are seven segments per LED. This means that 7 times 80 mA of current (560 mA) will flow through the anode switch for the number 8. The number 8 causes all segments to light, so the current due to this number is used in the calculation for the anode switch. Because the gain of the anode transistor is 100 minimum, the base current in this transistor is 5.6 mA. The voltage across the base transistor is 3.9 V. The value of the base resistor is then 3.9 V/5.6 mA or 696 $\Omega$. Here a 680 $\Omega$ resistor is used because it is the nearest standard resistor value.

Now that the circuit has been designed, an explanation of its operation follows. To multiplex this display, each anode driver is enabled (logic zero on the base), one position at a time. After the anode driver has been enabled, the seven-segment code is sent to the segment drivers. A time delay is entered so that time is allowed for the display to illuminate. Typically the amount of time is around one millisecond per display position. After the 1 ms time delay, the next anode switch is enabled and the next seven-segment code is sent to it.

Often the seven-segment codes are stored in a section of the memory called a display RAM. For an 8-digit display, this means that 8 bytes of memory are used for the display RAM. Also required are a pointer and the code used to select a display. Table 8-7 illustrates the codes required to select the various display positions.

As Table 8-7 indicates, the select code is developed using a shift instruction. The selection code is normally stored in the display RAM along with the seven-segment codes for each display position. The pointer value, also stored in the display RAM, is used to address display RAM data for each display position.

Figure 8-19 illustrates the flowchart of a subroutine that displays data from the display RAM on one display position. This subroutine also causes a 1 ms time delay. To display data properly, this subroutine must be called often. If this sub-

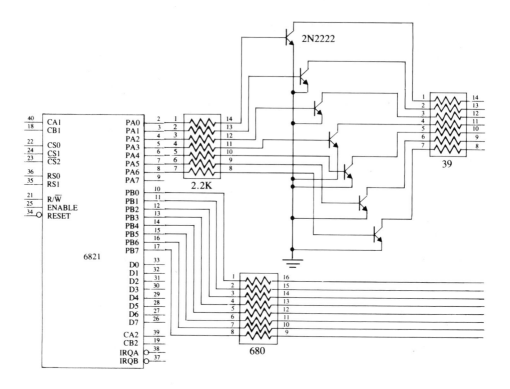

**Figure 8-18   A multiplexed LED display.**

routine is not called for an extended period, the display will appear to stop on one digit and the digit will become very bright.

E X A M P L E   8 - 5

```
                          ORG      $D000
00D000  48E7C080    DISPLAY   MOVEM.L   D0-D1/A0,-(SP)        ;save registers
00D004  207C00010000          MOVE.L    #DISRAM,A0           ;address display
00D00A  13E8000800020002      MOVE.B    8(A0),PORTB          ;select display
00D012  10280008              MOVE.B    8(A0),D0
00D016  E218                  ROR.B     #1,D0                ;rotate select
00D018  11400008              MOVE.B    D0,8(A0)
00D01C  4280                  CLR.L     D0
00D01E  10280009              MOVE.B    9(A0),D0             ;get code
00D022  13F0080000020000      MOVE.B    0(A0,D0.L),PORTA     ;display 7-seg code
00D02A  5200                  ADD.B     #1,D0                ;adjust code
00D02C  0C000007              CMP.B     #7,D0                ;test against 7
00D030  6300000A              BLS       DISPLAY1             ;if 7 or less
00D034  4200                  CLR.B     D0                   ;clear code
00D036  1178007F0008          MOVE.B    $7F,8(A0)            ;save new select
00D03C  11400009    DISPLAY1  MOVE.B    D0,9(A0)             ;save code
00D040  61000008              BSR       DELAY
00D044  4CDF0103              MOVEM.L   (SP)+,D0-D1/A0       ;restore registers
00D048  4E75                  RTS
                          ;
```

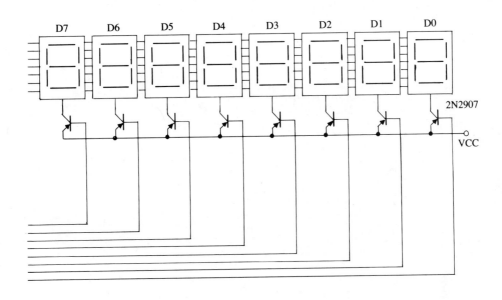

```
                                          ;delay 1 ms
                                          ;
00D04A   323C0190          DELAY     MOVE.W    #400,D1        ;load count
00D04E   51C9FFFE          DELAY1    DBRA      D1,DELAY1
00D052   4E75              RTS

                                          END
```

Software used to display data appears in Example 8-5. This subroutine must be called often to ensure that the display lights evenly. When interrupts are discussed,

**Table 8-7  Bit Patterns Used to Select Various Displays**

| Code | Selected digit | Pointer value |
|------|----------------|---------------|
| 01111111 | D0 | 00 |
| 10111111 | D1 | 01 |
| 11011111 | D2 | 02 |
| 11101111 | D3 | 03 |
| 11110111 | D4 | 04 |
| 11111011 | D5 | 05 |
| 11111101 | D6 | 06 |
| 11111110 | D7 | 07 |

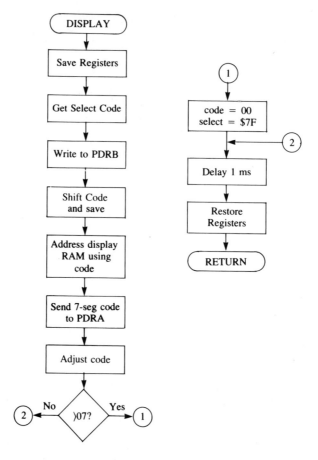

**Figure 8-19   The flowchart for the software used to multiplex an 8-digit LED display.**

this interface will again appear, to illustrate a typical method for generating the display.

## 8-4   Serial Data Interface

Many systems require serial digital data. To produce such data, the microprocessor usually uses an interface component called an asynchronous communications interface adapter (ACIA). The 68000 often uses the 6850 ACIA, which is a 6800 peripheral.

### 8-4.1   Asynchronous Serial Data

Before discussing the ACIA, we must consider the structure of asynchronous serial data. Figure 8-20 illustrates two ASCII-coded characters of data in an asynchronous serial data stream. Notice that the data are preceded by stop bits, which function as separators between characters of information. At least one stop bit is placed be-

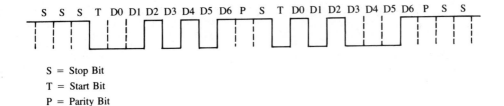

S = Stop Bit
T = Start Bit
P = Parity Bit

**Figure 8-20** Asynchronous serial data illustrating the letter T followed by the letter E.

tween each pair of ASCII characters. There is no maximum number of stop bits that appear between characters.

The *stop bit* is used to synchronize the receiver, as is the start bit. ASC II data are preceded by a *start bit* and followed by a parity bit. In Figure 8-20 the ASCII T is transmitted first, followed by an ASCII E. Notice that these ASCII codes are transmitted with the least significant bit first. Parity in the illustration is even. Many data communications systems use even parity.

The parity bit is coded as a one or a zero. If parity is even, then all ASCII data bits plus the parity are an even number. In the waveform illustrated in Figure 8-20, ASCII T = 1010100. Because an ASCII T has three ones, the parity bit is set to send four ones—an even number of ones. To send odd parity, the total number of ones transmitted must be an odd number.

The Baud rate of a serial asynchronous transmission is determined by counting the number of data bits, parity bits, start bits, and stop bits sent per second. In many data communications systems, each ASCII character is sent with one stop, one start, one parity, and seven data bits. Each ASCII character is therefore sent with 10 bits. If a system has a Baud rate of 300, it is sending 30 ASCII characters per second. The *Baud rate* is the number of bits sent per second. Common Baud rates are: 110, 300, 1200, 2400, and 9600. In a 9600 Baud system, the number of ASCII characters transmitted per second is 960, using asynchronous data transmission.

### 8-4.2 The 6850 (ACIA) Pinout

Figure 8-21 illustrates the pinout of the 6850 asynchronous communications interface adapter. This device is capable of simultaneous transmission and reception of serial asynchronous data. The 6850 is able to send and receive serial data at Baud rates of up to 19,200. The 6850 is compatible with just about any microprocessor, but it is specifically designed to interface to the 6800 microprocessor.

The clock inputs, RX and TX, control the Baud rates of the receiver and the transmitter. Since in many systems these rates are the same, these pins are often connected in common. The ACIA is programmable. This means that the Baud rate is selected, to some extent, by the software. In addition, the numbers of data, stop, and parity bits are also programmable. The RS (register select) connection is used to select data or control/status registers within the ACIA. If RS is a one, data status is selected, and if RS is a zero, control status is selected.

Modem control pins, $\overline{RTS}$, $\overline{CTS}$, and $\overline{DCD}$ are found on the ACIA. A *modem* (modulator–demodulator) converts TTL-level serial data into audio signals that are

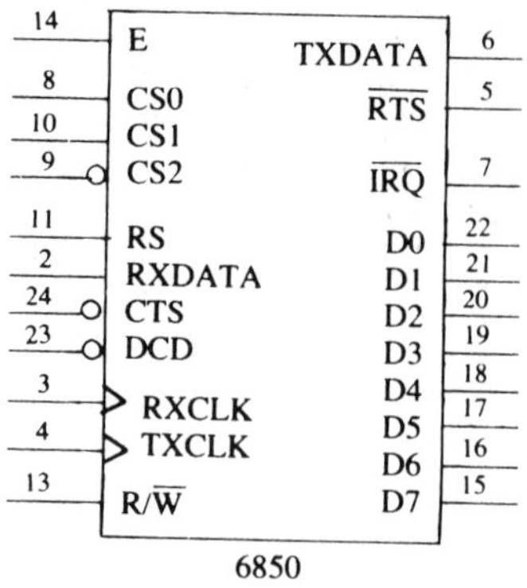

```
        14 ┌─────────────────────────┐
    ──────┤ E             TXDATA ├── 6
         8 │                      │
    ──────┤ CS0              RTS ├── 5
        10 │                      │
    ──────┤ CS1                   │
         9 │                      │
    ─────o┤ CS2              IRQ ├── 7
        11 │                      │
    ──────┤ RS               D0 ├── 22
         2 │                  D1 ├── 21
    ──────┤ RXDATA           D2 ├── 20
        24 │                      │
    ─────o┤ CTS              D3 ├── 19
        23 │                  D4 ├── 18
    ─────o┤ DCD              D5 ├── 17
         3 │                  D6 ├── 16
    ─────▷┤ RXCLK            D7 ├── 15
         4 │                      │
    ─────▷┤ TXCLK                 │
        13 │                      │
    ──────┤ R/W                   │
          └─────────────────────────┘
                   6850
```

**Figure 8-21**   The pinout of the 6850 asynchronous communications interface adapter (ACIA).

transmitted over the telephone system. It also converts audio tones back into TTL serial data.

### 8-4.3   Programming the ACIA

Programming is accomplished by sending an 8-bit control word to the ACIA. The control word is sent to the ACIA if a logic zero exists on the RS pin. The format for this control word is listed in Table 8-8.

Bits CR0 and CR1 are used to select the appropriate Baud rate multiplier. These bits also allow the ACIA to be reset with software. If the input frequency to the ACIA is 19,200 Hz, a divide by one will cause operation at 19,200 Baud. If divide by 16 is chosen, the ACIA will operate at 1200 Baud. If divide by 64 is chosen, the ACIA will operate at 300 Baud. Although the Baud rate is not fully programmable, some latitude is allowed with these divide-by rates.

Bits CR2–CR4 are used to select the format of each character. Notice that each ASCII character can be transmitted as 7 or 8 bits. Bits CR2–CR4 also program how many stop bits are sent and the type of parity. If, for example, these bits are programmed as 000, the ACIA will transmit and receive 7 data bits, even parity, and 2 stop bits between characters.

Bits CR5 and CR6 control the transmitter interrupt and the RTS pin. A break character also may be sent using these two bits as a control. A break is two complete character times or frames of start bits. If data are sent with a start bit, a stop bit, 7 data bits, and even parity, then 20 bits of logic zeros (starts) are sent for a break.

Bit CR7 enables the IRQ pin for the receiver section of the ACIA. If the IRQ pin is enabled, it becomes a logic zero each time the receiver receives data. It also activates each time a receiver error occurs. Receiver errors include parity, framing, and overrun errors. This signal also activates on the positive edge of the DCD pin.

### 8-4.4   ACIA Status

The status register is read by selecting the device and placing a zero on the RS pin. The status register, as illustrated in Table 8-9, indicates errors, the condition of some modem control pins, and the general operating condition of the ACIA.

**Table 8-8**  The 6850 ACIA Control Register

### Control register

| CR7 | CR6 | CR5 | CR4 | CR3 | CR2 | CR1 | CR0 |
|-----|-----|-----|-----|-----|-----|-----|-----|

| CR1 | CR0 | Function |
|-----|-----|----------|
| 0 | 0 | Divide by 1 |
| 0 | 1 | Divide by 16 |
| 1 | 0 | Divide by 64 |
| 1 | 1 | Software reset |

| CR4 | CR3 | CR2 | Function |
|-----|-----|-----|----------|
| 0 | 0 | 0 | 7 data bits, even parity, and 2 stops |
| 0 | 0 | 1 | 7 data bits, odd parity, and 2 stops |
| 0 | 1 | 0 | 7 data bits, even parity, and 1 stop |
| 0 | 1 | 1 | 7 data bits, odd parity, and 1 stop |
| 1 | 0 | 0 | 8 data bits, no parity, and 2 stops |
| 1 | 0 | 1 | 8 data bits, no parity, and 1 stop |
| 1 | 1 | 0 | 8 data bits, even parity, and 1 stop |
| 1 | 1 | 1 | 8 data bits, odd parity, and 1 stop |

| CR6 | CR5 | Function |
|-----|-----|----------|
| 0 | 0 | $\overline{RTS}$ = 0, transmit interrupt disabled |
| 0 | 1 | $\overline{RTS}$ = 0, transmit interrupt enabled |
| 1 | 0 | $\overline{RTS}$ = 1, transmit interrupt disabled |
| 1 | 1 | $\overline{RTS}$ = 1, transmit interrupt enabled and transmit a break character on transmit data output. |

| CR7 | Function |
|-----|----------|
| 0 | Disables receiver interrupt. |
| 1 | Enables receiver interrupt. |

The RDRF bit indicates that the receiver has data for the microprocessor. The microprocessor must remove the data before the next data are received. If data are not removed from the receiver before the next character is received, an overrun error occurs. The RO bit in the status register indicates an overrun error.

Other errors are also detected by the receiver and indicated by the status register. The parity error bit PE is a logic one if a *parity error* is detected on the received data. The framing error bit FE indicates that the received data did not contain the stop and start bits in the correct position. This occurs if the data are received at an incorrect Baud rate.

**Table 8-9   The 6850 Status Register**

Status register

| IRQ | PE | RO | FE | $\overline{\text{CTS}}$ | $\overline{\text{DCD}}$ | TDRE | RDRF |
|-----|----|----|----|----|----|------|------|

| Bit | Function |
|-----|----------|
| IRQ | Interrupt request |
| PE | Parity error |
| RO | Overrun error |
| FE | Framing error |
| $\overline{\text{CTS}}$ | $\overline{\text{CTS}}$ pin |
| $\overline{\text{DCD}}$ | $\overline{\text{DCD}}$ pin |
| TDRE | Transmitter empty |
| RDRF | Receiver full |

The IRQ status bit indicates that the input buffer is full, the transmitter is empty, there is an overrun error, or there is a positive transition on the $\overline{\text{DCD}}$ pin. If the external $\overline{\text{IRQ}}$ pin is connected to the microprocessor, the software in the microprocessor tests the status word to see what caused the interrupt.

It is important to note at this point that the $\overline{\text{CTS}}$ pin must be grounded for the 6850 to transmit data. Also note that the $\overline{\text{DCD}}$ pin must be grounded for the receiver to function properly.

The transmit empty bit (TDRE) indicates that the transmitter is empty, hence ready to receive another byte of information for transmission. This bit is typically polled by the software to determine whether another byte can be transmitted.

### 8-4.5   ACIA Interface to the 68000 Microprocessor

Figure 8-22 illustrates the 6850 interfaced to the 68000 microprocessor. The ACIA is at address $E00000 for the control/status register and location $E00002 for the data register. The data connections on the 6850 are attached to the 68000 upper data bus (D15–D8) connections. The decoder decodes only the most significant eight address connections or $E0 of the I/O address. The remaining bits, except for the A1 address bit, are don't cares.

Notice that the PAL 10L8 is used to decode the first eight address lines. It is also used as an inverter to generate an active high chip enable signal for the $\overline{\text{UDS}}$ signal. The program for the PAL is listed in Example 8-6. The PAL 10L8 is an AND/NOR gate that has active low outputs. Notice that only the NAND gate is used for O1 and only an internal inverter is used to generate O2. Because an active high select input is required for the 6850, the O1 connection is passed through the inverter at I10 and O3 is connected to the select input of the 6850.

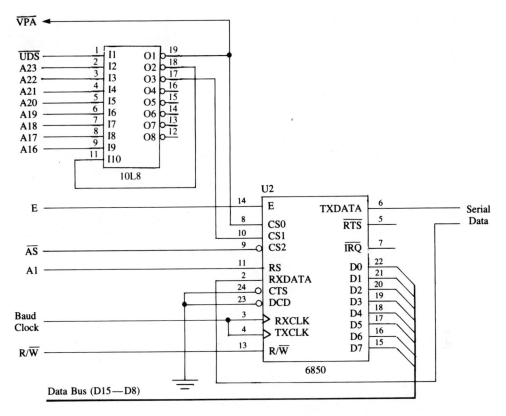

**Figure 8-22** The ACIA interfaced to a 68000 microprocessor through a PAL 10L8.

```
E X A M P L E    8 - 6

TITLE       Example
PATTERN     Test
REVISION    A
AUTHOR      BARRY BREY
COMPANY     DeVRY
DATE        2/7/91
CHIP        Decode PAL10L8

;PINS       1     2     3     4     5     6     7     8     9      10
            A23   A22   A21   A20   A19   A18   A17   A16   /UDS   GND

;PINS       11    12    13    14    15    16    17    18    19     20
            I10   NC    NC    NC    NC    NC    O3    O2    O1     VCC

EQUATIONS
/O1 = A23*A22*A21*/A20*/A19*/A18*/A17*/A16
/O2 = UDS
/O3 = I10
```

### 8-4.6 Programming the 6850

Initialization, the first step in programming the 6850, is accomplished by first resetting the 6850 with a software reset. Refer to Table 8-8, above, for the configuration of the control register. Bit positions CR1 and CR0 are both set to reset the 6850. After resetting, the 6850 is ready to be programmed for operation. The control register is used to set the Baud rate divider, the number of data bits, the number of stop bits, and the logic level placed in the $\overline{\text{RTS}}$ connection.

Example 8-7 illustrates the short sequence of instructions required to reset the 6850 and to program it. In this example, the 6850 is programmed so that 7 data bits are transmitted and received. The number of stop bits is one and parity is set for even. This is a very common setup in many data communications environments. Because the Baud rate divider is set to divide by 1, the Baud clock frequency placed on the Baud clock input connection of Figure 8-22 will decide the Baud rate of the 6850.

E  X  A  M  P  L  E     8 - 7

```
                              ORG     $E000
00E000   13FC0003000E0002   SETUP   MOVE.B   #3,COMM     ;reset ACIA
00E008   13FC0008000E0002           MOVE.B   #$08,COMM   ;program ACIA
00E010   4E75                       RTS
                              END
```

*Transmit Software*

Once initialized, the 6850 is available for use. Example 8-8 lists a subroutine that will transmit a block of data through the 6850. This subroutine uses the A0 register to address the starting location of the data block. Register D1 is used as a counter to select the number of bytes that are transmitted. Before this subroutine is branched to in a program, both A0 and D1 are loaded with the address and count. Notice that the subroutine first tests the status register (refer to Table 8-9, above) to see whether the transmitter is empty. It does this by testing the TDRE bit of the status register. If the transmitter is empty, the subroutine transfers data from the memory location addressed by A0 and sends it to the 6850 data register for transmission. This process is repeated until the number of data, indicated by the count in D1, have been transmitted.

E  X  A  M  P  L  E     8 - 8

```
00E012   5341                 SEND    SUB.W    #1,D1        ;adjust count
00E014   08390001000E0002     SEND1   BTST     #1,COMM      ;test TDRE
00E01C   67F6                         BEQ      SEND1        ;if busy
00E01E   13D8000E0000                 MOVE.B   (A0)+,DATA   ;send data
00E024   51C9FFEE                     DBRA     D1,SEND1     ;repeat
00E028   4E75                         RTS
                               END
```

## Receive Software

As with the transmission software, the status register contains information that is tested. Example 8-9 illustrates a subroutine that reads one byte of data from the 6850. First the status register is tested to determine whether the receiver is full. This is accomplished by testing the TDRF bit of the status register. If the receiver is full, the software tests the error bits PR, RO, and FE for errors. If no errors are detected, the subroutine reads the data from the receiver and returns with them in the byte portion of D0. If errors are encountered, the receiver is read, but the data read from it are discarded. In their place, a question mark is returned in D0. On an error, the 6850 is also reset to reset the error flags.

E X A M P L E   8 - 9

```
00E02A   08390000000E0002    READ    BTST    #0,COMM    ;test RDRF
00E032   67F6                        BEQ     READ       ;if busy
00E034   08390004000E0002            BTST    #4,COMM    ;test FE
00E03C   66000022                    BNE     ERROR      ;if FE
00E040   08390005000E0002            BTST    #5,COMM    ;test RO
00E048   66000016                    BNE     ERROR      ;if RO
00E04C   08390006000E0002            BTST    #6,COMM    ;test PE
00E054   6600000A                    BNE     ERROR      ;if PE
00E058   1039000E0000                MOVE.B  DATA,D0    ;get data
00E05E   4E75                        RTS
00E060   619E                ERROR   BSR     SETUP      ;reset error
00E062   103C003F                    MOVE.B  #$3F,D0    ;get?
00E066   4E75                        RTS

                                     END
```

### 8-4.7   The Interface to RS-232C

Serial data are often transferred through an interface standard called *RS-232C*. This standard specifies the voltage levels for logic signals. It also specifies the function of some pins on the 6850 such as $\overline{\text{RTS}}$, $\overline{\text{CTS}}$, and $\overline{\text{DCD}}$.

## Logic Levels

The logic levels used for transmission of RS-232C serial data (see Figure 8-23) are different from standard TTL levels. Notice that a logic one level is a negative voltage and a logic zero level is a positive voltage. Zero voltage is not used to convey any information. In a data communications environment where cables may be long, noise can exist. Noise normally rides on zero volts. The levels used with RS-232C help to prevent problems from noise that exists on ground.

The RS-232C interface standard specifies a logic one level anywhere between $-3.0$ and $-25$ V. The logic zero level is anywhere between $+3.0$ and $+25$ V. In many systems $\pm 12$ V is commonly used for these levels because it allows a 9.0 V noise margin (12 V $-$ 3 V).

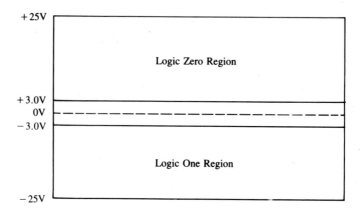

**Figure 8-23   The RS-232C logic levels.**

Conversion between RS-232C and TTL levels is performed by using line drivers and line receivers. Figure 8-24 illustrates the pinouts of the devices commonly used for this conversion. The MC1488 is a line driver that converts from TTL to RS-232C levels. The MC1489 is a line receiver that converts from RS-232C levels to TTL. The third input of the line receiver is used to set the threshold voltage of the line receiver. If this pin is left open, standard threshold voltages of ±3.0 V are used.

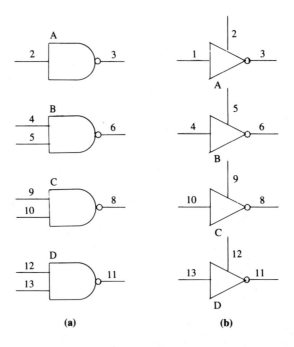

**Figure 8-24   (a) The MC 1488 line driver. (b) The MC 1489 line receiver.**

If a resistor is connected to this pin and one of the power supplies, this threshold voltage can be changed. Usually a connection is made to this pin. If the normal threshold is required, a capacitor is connected from this pin to ground, to prevent noise from interfering with the operation of the receiver. The value of the capacitor typically ranges from 1.0 to 2.2 μF.

### Line Characteristics

The transmission line is normally a pair of twisted wires that contains a shield, which is connected to earth (chassis) ground. The twisted pair is connected to the signal ground and the signal. The standard requires that the capacitance of the line be between 300 and 1200 pF. Often, the transmit end of the cable contains a 300 pF capacitor to ensure that the line has at least 300 pF of capacitance. Transmission line lengths are limited to a maximum of 50 meters, but in practice longer lengths have been used successfully.

### Connectors

RS-232C connectors can take the 25-pin form or the 9-pin form, as illustrated in Figure 8-25. The 25-pin connector, called a DB25, is found in older serial data equipment. The DB9 connector (9-pin) is found in newer data communications equipment. The main difference between these two connectors is that the DB25 handles two channels of data. Figure 8-25 also gives the function of each pin on both connectors.

### Modem Control Signals

The RS-232C interface has several connections that are used to control a modem: $\overline{CTS}$, $\overline{DSR}$, $\overline{DTR}$, $\overline{RTS}$, and signal detection. The 6850 contains $\overline{CTS}$, $\overline{DCD}$, and $\overline{RTS}$, but the remaining signals are not provided or tested by this microprocessor.

The DSR and DTR signals are handshaking signals between a modem and a terminal (computer). The DSR (data set ready) signal becomes active to show that the data set (modem) is ready. This means that the data set has power applied and is ready to function. The DTR (data terminal ready) signal is from the terminal, indicating that the terminal is ready to operate. These signals are not tested or present on the 6850.

The $\overline{RTS}$ and $\overline{CTS}$ signals are used in applications that require half duplex operation. Two modes of operation are available for a modem. One is called *half duplex* and the other *full duplex*. In full duplex operation, data flow in both directions just as in a telephone conversation. You talk while you hear someone talking. Half duplex operation allows data to flow in only one direction. If you use a CB radio, you are using a half duplex system. You can hear someone talk or you can talk. You cannot hear and talk simultaneously. With a modem, the $\overline{RTS}$ (request to send) signal is activated each time you wish to send data through the modem, much like the push-to-talk button on your CB radio. The $\overline{CTS}$ (clear to send) signal is a signal back from the modem, indicating that the modem is ready to transmit data.

The $\overline{DCD}$ (data carrier detect) signal is an input to the 6850 that is normally connected to the signal detection output of the modem. The signal detection output

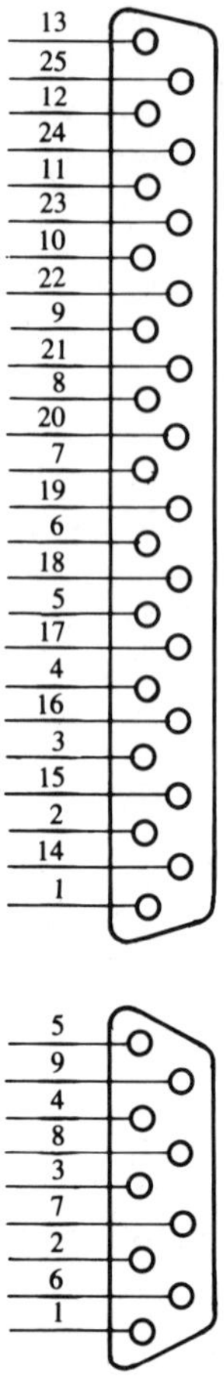

| | | Pin Connections | |
|---|---|---|
| DB25 | DB9 | Function |
| 1 | — | Protective ground |
| 2 | 3 | Transmit date |
| 3 | 2 | Receive date |
| 4 | 7 | RTS |
| 5 | 8 | CTS |
| 6 | 6 | DSR |
| 7 | 5 | Signal ground |
| 8 | 1 | Received line signal detect |
| 9 | — | Test |
| 10 | — | Test |
| 11 | — | — |
| 12 | — | Secondary received line signal detect |
| 13 | — | Secondary CTS |
| 14 | — | Secondary transmit data |
| 15 | — | Transmit signal timing |
| 16 | — | Secondary receive data |
| 17 | — | Receiver signal timing |
| 18 | — | — |
| 19 | — | Secondary RTS |
| 20 | 4 | DTR |
| 21 | — | Signal quality detector |
| 22 | 9 | Ring indicator |
| 23 | — | Data signal rate detect |
| 24 | — | Transmit signal timing |
| 25 | — | — |

**Figure 8-25**    The DB25 and DB9 connectors used with the RS-232C serial interface.

from the modem indicates that the device is receiving a signal. This signal normally indicates that telephone communication has been established.

A 6850 connected to a DB9 connector and RS-232C interface is illustrated in Figure 8-26. Notice that the MC1488 and MC1489 line drivers and receivers are used to interface the TTL signals from the 6850 to the RS-232C levels of the serial interface.

## 8-5    Analog-to-Digital and Digital-to-Analog Converters

The last of the common basic I/O devices to be covered are the ADC (analog-to-digital converter) and the DAC (digital-to-analog converter). These devices are used to interface digital systems to the analog world. This section introduces the 8-bit DAC and the 8-bit ADC. Note that these are not the only types available. In fact, DAC and ADC circuits are available in widths up to 16 bits.

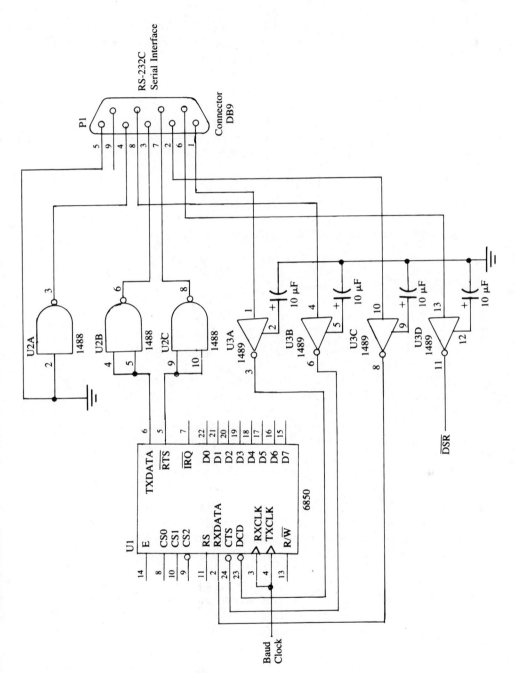

**Figure 8-26   An RS-232C serial interface using the DB9 connector.**

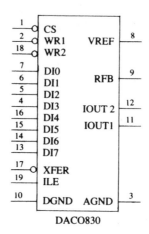

**Figure 8-27    The pinout of the DAC0830 digital-to-analog converter (DAC).**

### 8-5.1    The DAC

The DAC is a digital-to-analog converter; it converts a digital code into an analog voltage. For example, an 8-bit DAC with a step voltage of 0.01 V will generate output voltages between 0.0 and 2.55 V in 0.01 V steps. A 0000 0000 input to this type of DAC generates 0.0 V out. A 1111 1111 input to the DAC generates 2.55 V out. Any voltage in this range is generated with the appropriate digital number applied to the inputs. The maximum output voltage is called *full-scale*.

The step voltage is not always 0.01 V. Step voltages vary with the full-scale voltage of the converter. For example, if an 8-bit DAC has a full-scale voltage of +5.0 V, the step voltage is +5.0 V/255 or 0.0196 V per step. The step voltage is always the full-scale voltage divided by $2^n - 1$. A 10-bit converter using +5.0 V as full-scale has a step voltage of $+5.0 \text{ V}/2^{10} - 1$ or +5.0 V/1023, which, is 0.00489 V per step.

Figure 8-27 illustrates the pinout of the DAC0830 8-bit DAC. This device functions from a single power supply with a range of +5.0 to +15 V. The DAC0830 is designed to interface to a microprocessor. The time required to convert a digital code into an analog voltage is 1.0 μs. This converter uses an R/2R ladder network for the conversion.

### Pin Functions

**Vcc (supply voltage input)**    Where a +5.0 to +15 V dc voltage is applied.

**AGND (analog ground)**    Normally connected to the ground of the analog system.

**DGND (digital ground)**    Normally connected to the ground of the digital system.

**$DI_0$–$DI_7$ (data inputs)**    Where the digital data are applied. These connections are connected to the microprocessor data bus.

**V$_{ref}$ (voltage reference)**   The voltage reference for the internal R/2R ladder network.

**R$_{fb}$ (feedback resistor)**   Provided to set the gain of an external operational amplifier.

**IOUT (1) (output terminal 1)**   Provides an output current that is proportional to the digital input signal.

**IOUT (2) (output terminal 2)**   Provides an output current that is equal to the current generated by the voltage reference minus the current available at IOUT (1).

**$\overline{XFER}$ (transfer input)**   Used to enable or gate the $\overline{WR2}$ input to the DAC.

**$\overline{CS}$ (chip select)**   Used to enable or gate the $\overline{WR1}$ input to the DAC.

**$\overline{WR1}$ (write input 1)**   Strobes the digital signal into an internal holding register.

**$\overline{WR2}$ (write input 2)**   Strobes the data from the internal latch into the DAC.

**ILE (internal latch enable)**   Allows the $\overline{WR1}$ input to strobe data into the internal holding register.

### Operation of the DAC0830

Four pins determine the final analog output voltage of the DAC0830. These pins are Rfb, IOUT (1), IOUT (2), and Vref. The Vref input sets the reference voltage for the internal R/2R ladder network. The polarity of the Vref input is the opposite polarity of the analog output voltage. If Vref is −5.1 V, the output will swing to a +5.1 V maximum full-scale value. The voltage step is +5.1 V/255 or +0.02 V per step. This means that if a 255 ($FF) is sent to the DAC, the analog output voltage will be 255 × 0.02 V or +5.1 V. If a 128 ($80) is sent, the output will be +2.56 V.

Figure 8-28 illustrates the output circuit commonly found connected to the DAC0830. This configuration will produce an analog output voltage between 0.0 and +5.0 V. The operational amplifier used with this circuit is a 741 operational amplifier or its equivalent. It is important to note that the supply voltage to the DAC and the op-amp must be 3.0 V higher than the analog output voltage. Here a ±12 V supply is used.

Notice that separate grounds are used in this circuit. This is important if a clean analog output voltage is desired. Digital circuits generate much power supply noise. Thus to ensure a clean analog output voltage, separate grounds must be used. Also notice the bypass capacitors illustrated for the operational amplifier power connections. Again, these bypass capacitors are needed to ensure a clean output.

### The DAC0830 Interfaced to the 68008

Figure 8-29 illustrates the DAC0830 interfaced to the 68008 microprocessor at location $40000. Not all the address connections are decoded, so the DAC responds to I/O addresses $40000–$43FFF. Here the $\overline{WR1}$ and $\overline{CS}$ are grounded so that the transparent latch connected to these two pins is passive. Also notice that $\overline{WR2}$ and $\overline{XFER}$ are connected to the output of the decoder so that when I/O address

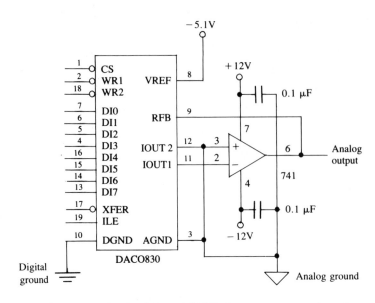

**Figure 8-28   The output circuit of the DAC0830 that generates a voltage between 0.0 and +5.1 V.**

$40000 is written, data are captured in the internal latch whose clock is connected to these pins.

In certain cases this may cause the analog output to become noisy. If this occurs, two I/O addresses must be decoded: one to send data into latch one ($\overline{WR1}$) and a second to transfer the data from the first latch into the second ($\overline{WR2}$). Refer to Example 8-10 for the program of the PAL 10L8 decoder.

E  X  A  M  P  L  E      8 - 10

```
TITLE        Example
PATTERN      Test
REVISION     A
AUTHOR       BARRY BREY
COMPANY      DeVRY
DATE         2/7/91
CHIP         Decode PAL10L8

;PINS        1     2     3     4     5     6     7     8     9     10
             /AS   /DS   RW    A19   A18   A17   A16   A15   A14   GND

;PINS        11    12    13    14    15    16    17    18    19    20
             DT    O8    NC    NC    NC    NC    NC    NC    O1    VCC

EQUATIONS
/O8 = /A19*A18*/A17*/A16*/A15*/A14*AS
/O1 = /DT*DS*/RW
```

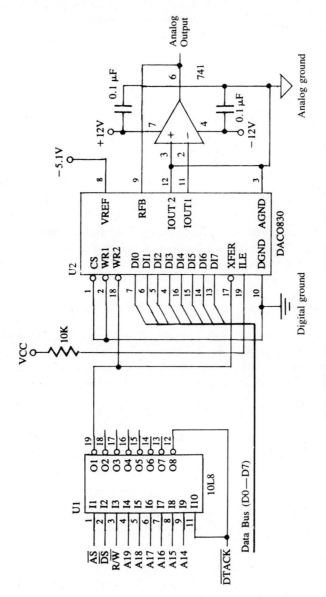

**Figure 8-29** The DAC0830 interfaced to the 68008 microprocessor at I/O address $40000.

303

*Software to Generate a Sawtooth of Voltage*

Example 8-11 illustrates a short program that generates a sawtooth of voltage at the analog output of Figure 8-29. The byte portion of D0 contains a count of between zero and $FF. This program increments the contents of D0 and outputs it to the DAC indefinitely. As the count continues from $00 to $FF, the output voltage rises at a linear rate from 0 to +5.1 V.

**E X A M P L E   8 - 11**

```
                         ORG    $F000
00F000  5200     DAC     ADD.B  #1,D0       ;increment count
00F002  13C000040000     MOVE.B D0,$40000   ;write to DAC
00F008  60F6             BRA    DAC
                         END
```

Recall that the conversion time for the DAC0830 is 1.0 μs. In this example, the amount of time required to increment the counter, and to branch to the instruction that sends the DAC its digital code, is longer than 1.0 μs. The frequency of the output is changed by adding extra instructions in this loop, or even a time delay.

### 8-5.2   The ADC

The analog-to-digital converter (ADC) is often found today in integrated circuit form. Most integrated converters are microprocessor compatible and are interfaced to the microprocessor rather easily. This section of the text explains the operation of the ADC0804 and illustrates its interface to the 68000 microprocessor.

*The ADC0804 Pinout*

Figure 8-30 presents the pinout of the ADC0804 analog-to-digital converter. This converter converts an analog input voltage to a digital output in 10 μs or less. The

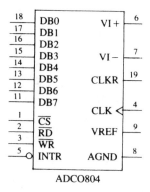

**Figure 8-30   The pinout of the ADC0804 analog-to-digital convert (ADC).**

ADC starts the conversion when the $\overline{\text{WR}}$ input is pulsed while $\overline{\text{CS}}$ is a logic zero. After conversion has begun, the $\overline{\text{INTR}}$ output becomes a logic one until conversion is complete. Once $\overline{\text{INTR}}$ has gone low, the conversion is complete and the data are available on the data bus connections. Data are read when both $\overline{\text{CS}}$ and $\overline{\text{RD}}$ are placed at a logic zero.

## Pin Functions

**DB$_0$–DB$_7$ (data bus connection)**  Pins that convey the digital data to the microprocessor. These connections are at their high impedance state until both $\overline{\text{CS}}$ and $\overline{\text{RD}}$ are placed at a logic zero.

**DGND (digital ground)**  Connected to the digital ground bus.

**AGND (analog ground)**  Connected to the analog ground bus.

**Vcc (power supply input)**  Connected to the +5.0 V digital power supply.

**V$_{\text{ref}}$/2 (voltage reference)**  This pin is not normally connected.

**VIN (+) [analog input (+)]**  Connected to the unknown analog input voltage.

**VIN (−) [analog input (−)]**  Connected to ground or another reference voltage in a system.

**CLK IN (clock input)**  This pin is attached to an external TTL level clock or used for clock generation with the CLK R pin.

**CLK R (clock resistor)**  This pin is used as a clock feedback path.

**$\overline{\text{CS}}$ (chip select)**  This pin enables the $\overline{\text{RD}}$ and $\overline{\text{WR}}$ connections.

**$\overline{\text{RD}}$ (read input)**  This pin allows data to appear on the data bus connections if the $\overline{\text{CS}}$ input is a logic zero.

**$\overline{\text{WR}}$ (write input)**  This pin causes the ADC to begin a conversion if the $\overline{\text{CS}}$ input is a logic zero.

**$\overline{\text{INTR}}$ (interrupt request output)**  This output shows that the ADC is busy when it's a logic one. The logic one to logic zero transition indicates that conversion is complete.

## The Analog Inputs

There are two analog inputs on the ADC0804 converter, VIN (+) and VIN (−). The inputs are connected to an internal operational amplifier as illustrated in Figure 8-31. These differential inputs are used to sum external voltages that are sent to the internal analog-to-digital converter. For example, if a +3.0 V is applied to the VIN (+) connection and a +2.0 V is applied to the VIN (−) connection, the input to the analog-to-digital converter is the difference or +1.0 V. Sometimes the connection shown in Figure 8-31 is used. With this connection, the permissible range of input voltages is 0 to +5.0 V.

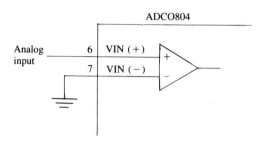

**Figure 8-31    The analog inputs of the ADC0804 converter.**

In certain cases it is desired to offset the input voltage. This is accomplished by raising the voltage on VIN (−) from ground. This connection is illustrated in Figure 8-32. Here a 1 kΩ potentiometer is used to raise pin VIN (−) off ground potential. This connection allows the user to adjust the zero reference for the analog input voltage.

## Clock Generation

The ADC0804 is designed to operate from an external clock or, if needed, it will generate its own internal clock signal. The permissible range of clock frequencies is 100–1460 kHz. Usually the higher the clock frequency, the better. The clock frequency determines the speed of conversion, so it is important to keep the clock frequency as close to 1460 kHz as possible.

If the clock is generated internally, the ADC operates with an *RC* circuit for timing the clock. Figure 8-33 illustrates an *RC* circuit that generates the clock. Here a resistor is connected between the CLK R and CLK IN pins and a capacitor between CLK IN and ground. If this circuit is used to generate the clock, the following equation is used to calculate the operating frequency:

$$F_{\text{CLK}} \approx \frac{1}{1.1RC}$$

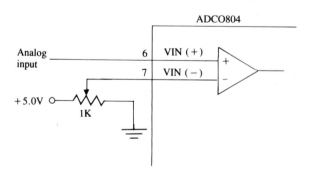

**Figure 8-32    Raising the analog input above ground potential.**

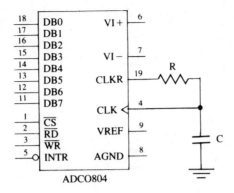

**Figure 8-33   The clock circuit of the ADC0804 analog-to-digital converter.**

## Controlling the ADC0804

The ADC0804 is designed to function with any microprocessor. Four pins ($\overline{CS}$, $\overline{RD}$, $\overline{WR}$, and $\overline{INTR}$) are used to interface the ADC with the data bus connections.

The $\overline{CS}$ pin is connected to the output of a decoder that determines the I/O address. The $\overline{RD}$ input is activated to read the ADC digital output when $\overline{CS}$ is active. The $\overline{WR}$ input is activated to start the conversion process if $\overline{CS}$ is active. Finally, the $\overline{INTR}$ output indicates if the converter is busy when it is a logic one.

The software that operates the ADC is simple. First the conversion process is started by writing to the ADC. Next, the $\overline{INTR}$ output pin is tested to see whether the conversion process is complete. If complete, the data are read from the convert-

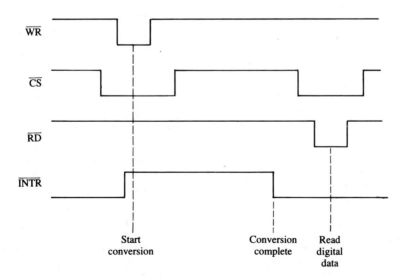

**Figure 8-34   The timing diagram of the ADC0804 analog-to-digital converter.**

er by pulsing the $\overline{RD}$ pin. Figure 8-34 illustrates the timing required to operate the ADC.

### The ADC0804 Used to Measure Temperature

An example use for the ADC0804 is to measure temperature. There are many methods for sensing temperature. Some systems use a thermistor, which is a resistor that changes in value with a change in temperature. Some systems use a transistor or a diode biased just at the point of conduction: as the temperature changes, so do the dynamic resistance and the voltage drop across of the diode or transistor. When a diode or transistor is biased at the point of conduction, this voltage change is the greatest.

Figure 8-35 illustrates a simple circuit using the ADC that monitors temperature. Here the voltage across the diode is connected to the ADC so that a temperature is detected. The software used to translate the voltage into a temperature uses a lookup table, which contains the temperature referenced to the binary numbers obtained from the ADC. Example 8-12 illustrates the software used to read the voltage on the diode and to reference the lookup table.

E  X  A  M  P  L  E    8 - 12

```
                             ORG     $F300
00F300  13C0000F0001    TEMP   MOVE.B  D0,$F0001     ;start conversion
00F306  08390000000E0001 TEMP1 BTST    #0,$E0001     ;test INTR
00F30E  66F6                   BNE     TEMP1         ;if INTR = 1
00F310  4280                   CLR.L   D0
00F312  1039000F0001           MOVE.B  $F0001,D0     ;read ADC
00F318  207C0000F234           MOVE.L  #LOOKUP,A0    ;address lookup
00F31E  10300800               MOVE.B  0(A0,D0.L),D0 ;convert
00F322  4E75                   RTS
                             END
```

## 8-6   Interfacing Motors

Two types of motor are commonly connected to microprocessor-based systems: the dc motor and the stepper motor. The dc motor is an analog motor, while the stepper motor is a digital motor. Stepper motors are available in small sizes that produce low torque. The dc motor is available in just about any size desired and is therefore more common to many applications, especially those that require a large torque.

### 8-6.1   The Stepper Motor

The stepper motor is digital in the sense that it is moved in discrete steps, whereas the dc motor is more difficult to move in discrete steps. Stepper motors find application in devices such as printers, to position the printhead and also to move the paper through the printer. They also are used in plotters, to move the paper

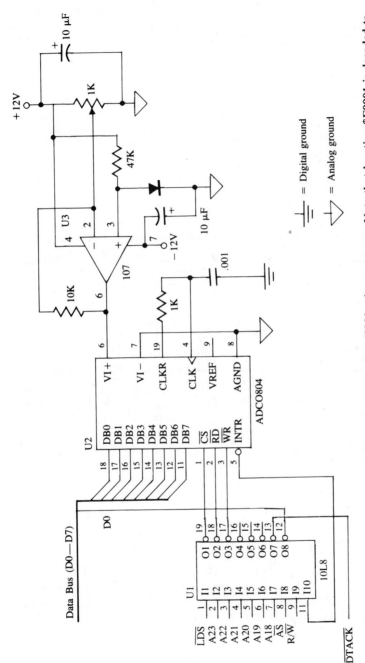

**Figure 8-35** A temperature sensing device connected to the 68000 microprocessor. Note that location $F0001 is decoded to start the converter and also to read it. Location $E0001 is decoded to read the INTR bit from the converter.

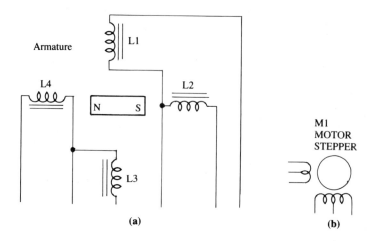

**Figure 8-36** The stepper motor: internal construction (a) and schematic diagram (b).

beneath the pen. Other applications include light industrial devices such as small milling machines, lathes, and drill presses. Stepper motors cannot move large masses because their power is usually small.

Figure 8-36 illustrates the construction of a stepper motor. Notice that the stepper contains four coils. Each coil acts as a separate field winding for the motor. The armature of the stepper motor is a permanent magnet, which is positioned by changing the currents, hence the magnetic fields, in the four field windings. This stepper motor is said to contain four poles. Most stepper motors contain more than four poles, but normally poles are grouped in fours, so the discussion of stepper motors that follows applies to all stepper motors.

A stepper with four poles is positioned in four discrete positions at 90° angles. This is called the step angle or resolution of the stepper motor. In practice the stepper with the largest resolution is 15°. This means that it internally contains 24 poles. A stepper motor that has 360 poles will have a step resolution of 1° per step.

## Full-Step Operation

Figure 8-37 illustrates the effect of magnetizing by applying currents to the four coils to position the stepper motor to the four positions. Notice that two of the four coils are energized for each of the four positions. By following this pattern in sequence, the stepper motor's armature is caused to rotate in either direction. Table 8-10 illustrates a possible bit pattern for rotating the stepper in either the clockwise or counterclockwise direction: the full-step bit pattern. A *full step* occurs when the armature is moved from one pole to the next, each time the field currents are changed. This is the most common way to move the armature of a stepper motor. Note that the binary bit patterns represented in Table 8-10 determine which field coils are activated.

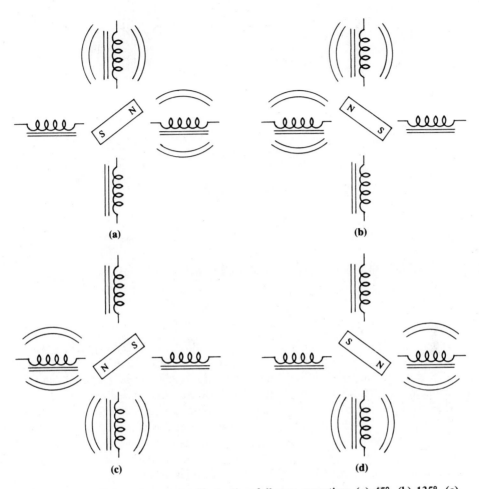

**Figure 8-37**  The stepper motor illustrating full-step operation: (a) 45°, (b) 135°, (c) 225°, and (d) 315°.

**Table 8-10**  Full-Step Bit Patterns for a Stepper Motor

| | Clockwise | | | | | Counterclockwise | | | | |
|---|---|---|---|---|---|---|---|---|---|---|
| Step | L4 | L3 | L2 | L1 | Angle | L4 | L3 | L2 | L1 | Angle |
| 0 | 0 | 0 | 1 | 1 | 45° | 0 | 0 | 1 | 1 | 45° |
| 1 | 0 | 1 | 1 | 0 | 135° | 1 | 0 | 0 | 1 | 315° |
| 2 | 1 | 1 | 0 | 0 | 225° | 1 | 1 | 0 | 0 | 225° |
| 3 | 1 | 0 | 0 | 1 | 315° | 0 | 1 | 1 | 0 | 135° |

NOTE: A one indicates where a coil is energized; refer to Figure 8-37.

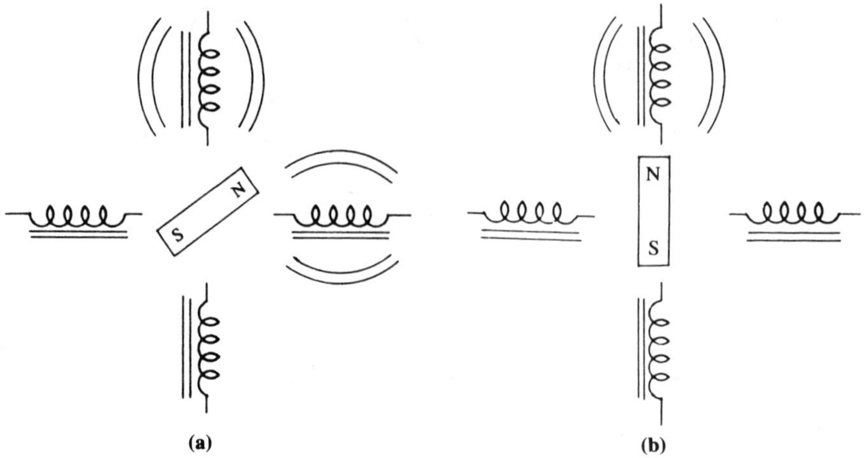

**Figure 8-38**   **The stepper motor illustrating half-steps: (a) 45° and (b) 90°.**

## Half-Step Operation

The stepper motor may also be operated with half-steps. A *half-step* occurs when the armature (in a four-pole stepper) is moved to eight discrete positions. Figure 8-38 illustrates the armature and fields for positioning the stepper motor in both full and half-steps. Notice that for the full steps, one coil is energized and for the half-steps two coils are energized (see Table 8-11, which illustrates all eight steps). The full-step mode here is different from the one presented with Figure 8-37.

One problem exists for a half-step motor: the amount of torque applied to the mechanical system being driven by the stepper motor varies with the steps. This is unavoidable and in many cases causes no difficulties when the device being positioned is a lightweight device. If torque is a consideration, half-steps should be avoided because of this limitation.

**Table 8-11   Half-Step Bit Patterns for the Stepper Motor**

|      | Clockwise |    |    |    |       | Counterclockwise |    |    |    |       |
|------|-----------|----|----|----|-------|------------------|----|----|----|-------|
| Step | L4 | L3 | L2 | L1 | Angle | L4 | L3 | L2 | L1 | Angle |
| 0    | 0  | 0  | 0  | 1  | 0°    | 0  | 0  | 0  | 1  | 0°    |
| 1    | 0  | 0  | 1  | 1  | 45°   | 1  | 0  | 0  | 1  | 315°  |
| 2    | 0  | 0  | 1  | 0  | 90°   | 1  | 0  | 0  | 0  | 270°  |
| 3    | 0  | 1  | 1  | 0  | 135°  | 1  | 1  | 0  | 0  | 225°  |
| 4    | 0  | 1  | 0  | 0  | 180°  | 0  | 1  | 0  | 0  | 180°  |
| 5    | 1  | 1  | 0  | 0  | 225°  | 0  | 1  | 1  | 0  | 135°  |
| 6    | 1  | 0  | 0  | 0  | 270°  | 0  | 0  | 1  | 0  | 90°   |
| 7    | 1  | 0  | 0  | 1  | 315°  | 0  | 0  | 1  | 1  | 45°   |

### Stepper Motor Drivers

Figure 8-39 illustrates the drivers and interface of a 12 V stepper motor to a microprocessor. The same circuit is used for driving the stepper motor with full or half-steps. Stepper motors are available in different voltages from 5.0 to 24 V.

Notice in this illustration that a 6821, used to interface the stepper motor to the microprocessor, is decoded so that it functions at any memory location between $40000 and $47FFF.

The stepper driver has five input connections. Four cause current to flow through any or all of the four coils. The fifth input is labeled STEP and is used to control the amount of current through the energized coils.

Upon closer examination, the STEP input either applies $+12$ V to the coils or limits current through a 47 $\Omega$ resistor. When $+12$ V is applied, the stepper coils that are energized allow quite a bit of current flow. When the current-limiting resistor is switched into the circuit, there is still current flow, but a much smaller amount. The

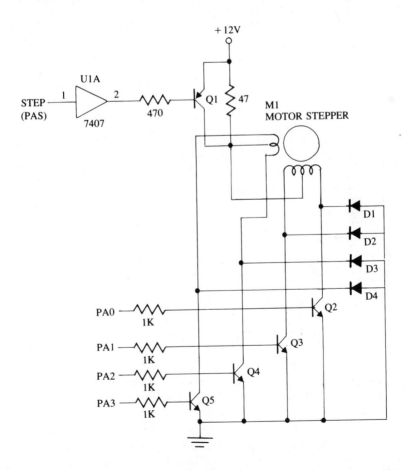

**Figure 8-39   The stepper motor connected to a driver network. Note that PA0–PA5 are connected to a 6821 decoded at addresses $40000–$47FFF.**

+12 V step is used to move the armature and overcome any rest inertia. The current is limited to hold the armature in position. Holding requires much less current than moving the armature, which must overcome rest inertia.

## Controlling the Stepper Motor

Now that the operation and driver circuit of the stepper motor are understood, we examine the software that is required to move the motor. Example 8-13 lists a subroutine that moves the stepper motor a fixed number of positions, either clockwise or counterclockwise.

E X A M P L E     8 - 13

```
                              ORG       $F500
                        ;
                        ;Note that memory location $30000 is
                        ;initialized to a $11 (zero degrees) when the
                        ;system is reset.
                        ;
00F500  5340            STEPS    SUB.W    #1,D0          ;adjust count
00F502  123900030000    STEPS1   MOVE.B   $30000,D1      ;get pattern
00F508  0800001F                 BTST     #31,D0         ;check direction
00F50C  66000008                 BNE      STEPS2         ;if clockwise
00F510  E219                     ROR.B    #1,D1
00F512  60000004                 BRA      STEPS3
00F516  E319            STEPS2   ROL.B    #1,D1
00F518  13C100030000    STEPS3   MOVE.B   D1,$30000      ;save position
00F51E  08810005                 BCLR     #5,D1          ;clear STEP
00F522  13C100040000             MOVE.B   D1,$40000      ;step motor
00F528  61000012                 BSR      DELAY          ;wait 1 ms
00F52C  08C10005                 BSET     #5,D1          ;set STEP
00F530  13C100040000             MOVE.B   D1,$40000      ;hold motor
00F536  51C8FFCA                 DBRA     D0,STEPS1
00F53A  4E75                     RTS
                        ;
                        ;delay 1 ms
                        ;
00F53C  343C0190        DELAY    MOVE.W   #400,D2
00F540  51CAFFFE        DELAY1   DBRA     D2,DELAY1
00F544  4E75                     RTS

                                 END
```

Each time this subroutine is called, the contents of D0 specify the number of steps and the direction of travel. The word portion of D0 specifies the count and the upper 16 bits specify the direction of rotation. The direction is counterclockwise if the upper word is $0000 and clockwise if it is $FFFF.

The subroutine also calls a time delay, so that only one step per millisecond is sent to the stepper motor drivers. This time varies with different sized stepper motors and different applications. The amount of time delay is determined by the maximum allowable step rate for the motor.

The first thing the subroutine tests is the direction portion of register D0. This allows it to rotate the motor either counterclockwise or clockwise. Next the old value for the stepper motor position is removed from memory location $30000 and rotated right or left to form the next step value. After rotation, it is once again stored at $30000 and the STEP bit (bit position 5) is cleared before it is sent to the 6821 to control the motor. Next a time delay is called that waits one millisecond.

After the time delay, the code that was sent to the stepper motor with the STEP bit cleared is now set and again is sent to the 6821. Finally the counter is decremented to determine whether the required number of steps has been reached.

### 8-6.2 DC Motors

The other type of motor found connected to the microprocessor, the dc motor, differs from the stepper motor because it has a permanent magnet field. The armature is a coil in the dc motor. When a voltage and subsequent current flow are applied to the armature, the motor begins to spin. The speed of rotation is determined by the dc voltage applied across the armature.

Figure 8-40 illustrates a dc motor connected to a Darlington driver circuit. The input to the Darlington is connected to a DAC0830 digital-to-analog converter. The converter is interfaced to the microprocessor at I/O address $40000. Each time the value sent to the DAC is changed, the speed of the motor changes. Speed is varied from a full stop to full speed by changing the digital code applied to the DAC.

The subroutines listed in Example 8-14 are called to increase the speed by one step (UP) or to decrease the speed by one step (DOWN). Here a step is 12 V/255 or 0.047 V. The motor has 256 different speeds with this software. Each time the speed of the motor needs to be increased, UP is called. Each time the speed needs to be decreased, DOWN is called. In this way, a control system can adjust the speed of the motor as it operates in a system.

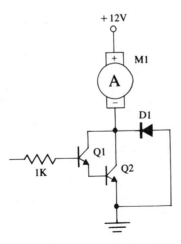

**Figure 8-40.   The DC motor connected to a Darlington driver.**

E  X  A  M  P  L  E     8 - 14

```
                              ORG        $11000
                     ;
                     ;The speed is at location $30000, which is
                     ;initially cleared to zero upon a system reset.
                     ;
011000  103900030000  UP      MOVE.B     SPEED,D0     ;get current speed
011006  0C0000FF              CMP.B      #$FF,D0      ;test max
01100A  67000010              BEQ        UP1          ;if max
01100E  5200                  ADD.B      #1,D0        ;increment count
011010  13C000030000          MOVE.B     D0,SPEED     ;save count
011016  13C000040000          MOVE.B     D0,$40000    ;send to DAC
01101C  4E75          UP1     RTS
                     ;
01101E  103900030000  DOWN    MOVE.B     SPEED,D0     ;get current speed
011024  67000010              BEQ        DOWN1        ;if min speed
011028  5300                  SUB.B      #1,D0        ;decrement count
01102A  13C000030000          MOVE.B     D0,SPEED     ;save count
011030  13C000040000          MOVE.B     D0,$40000    ;send to DAC
011036  4E75          DOWN1   RTS

                              END
```

One way to adjust the speed to the situation is through feedback from the system. Figure 8-41 illustrates a dc motor used to control the speed of an industrial drill. It is important that the speed of the drill remain constant; otherwise the work may be damaged or the drill bit may break. To monitor the speed, the shaft of the drill rotates a small dc generator that provides feedback. The faster the drill bit spins, the higher the amount of feedback voltage.

When the generator is connected to an ADC, the speed of the drill bit can be monitored and adjusted by the microprocessor. The desired speed is set by changing the value stored at memory location SPEED. If the signal returning from the ADC is higher than the value in SPEED, the DOWN subroutine is called to reduce the speed. If the value returned from the ADC is less than the value in speed, the UP subroutine is called. This increases the speed of the motor.

The software to control the speed of this drill press motor is listed in Example 8-15. Note that this example uses the subroutines listed in Example 8-14 for proper operation. Also note that no attempt to enter the speed of the motor into memory location SPEED is illustrated. This subroutine makes no attempt to calibrate the motor speed. Calibration is accomplished by biasing the speed fed to the DAC from the speed read from the ADC.

E  X  A  M  P  L  E     8 - 15

```
011038  13C000050000      SPEEDX   MOVE.B  D0,$50000     ;start ADC
01103E  083900000060000   SPEED1   BTST    #0,$60000     ;test INTR
011046  66F6                       BNE     SPEED1        ;if INTR = 1
011048  103900050000               MOVE.B  $50000,D0     ;get speed
01104E  B03900030000               CMP.B   SPEED,D0      ;compare
011054  62000006                   BHI     SPEED2        ;if higher
011058  61A6                       BSR     UP            ;increase speed
```

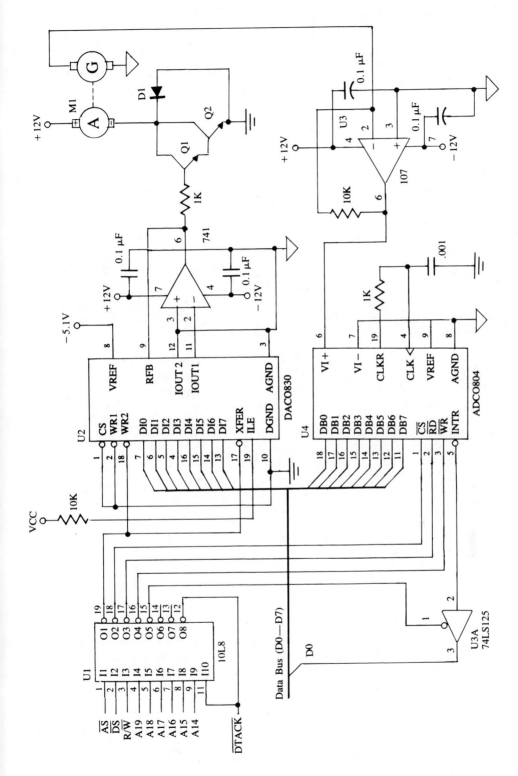

**Figure 8-41**  A motor with feedback through a generator attached to the 68008 microprocessor.

```
01105A    600C                                    BRA      SPEEDX       ;repeat
01105C    61C0                    SPEED2   BSR     DOWN                  ;decrease speed
01105E    60D8                                    BRA      SPEEDX       ;repeat
```

## Summary

1. The basic input circuit uses a set of three-state buffers that apply input data to the data bus. The data are applied when $\overline{AS}$ becomes active for the range of memory decoded by an address decoder. The data strobe signal from the microprocessor is used to activate the buffers along with the address decoder.

2. The basic output circuit uses a set of D-type flip-flops (latch) to capture data from the data bus. The clock input to the latch is connected to an address decoder. This selects the latch for a unique I/O address.

3. Input devices are often switch-based. The most common input devices include a switch and a keyboard. Switches bounce. To eliminate bouncing, the microprocessor uses a time delay.

4. Numeric output devices include LEDs, LCDs, and fluorescent displays. These devices are easily interfaced to the microprocessor through driver circuitry. LED and fluorescent displays require drivers. LCD displays are TTL compatible and require no special driver circuitry.

5. Relays and solenoids are often used to control external events. The relay and solenoid circuits require drivers. Relays and solenoids are noisy and produce voltage spikes. To prevent problems with this noise, the driver circuit is often isolated from the microprocessor. Isolation is often provided by optical isolators for large current relays and solenoids.

6. The PIA (peripheral interface adapter) is often used to interface the microprocessor to external input or output devices. The 6821 PIA contains two 8-bit I/O peripheral data registers. These registers are programmable, which means that any of the 16 bits of I/O are programmable as input or outputs. Besides peripheral data registers, the 6821 contains pins that are used for system control.

7. Keyboards are scanned with software and debounced with software. Often the keyboard is tested for a keystroke release before being tested for a keystroke. This is done so that the software will prevent multiple keystrokes if a key is held down for an extended period.

8. A multiplexed display is driven with software through a PIA. Multiplexed displays require segment drivers and anode switches. The segment drivers must pass enough current to illuminate the multiplexed displays at a normal brilliance. Often the amount of current is equal to the number of display positions times 10 mA. The anode switch must pass the current from all seven segments on the display.

9. The ACIA (asynchronous communications interface adapter) converts between parallel microprocessor data and serial data. The serial data are often transmitted across the phone lines to remote computer systems. Terms that apply to asynchronous data include stop, start, parity, and Baud rate.

10. A modem (modulator/demodulator) is a device that converts serial digital data into signals transmitted across the telephone lines. The modem contains control connections that accomplish an orderly transfer of data. These controls include two, $\overline{DTR}$ and $\overline{DTS}$, that indicate that both modem and computer are active. It also contains controls, $\overline{RTS}$ and $\overline{CTS}$, that are used to control transmission. The $\overline{RTS}$ signal is used to request transmission, and the $\overline{CTS}$ signal indicates "clear to send."

11. RS-232C is a standard interface used with many serial devices. The standard defines the voltage levels and pin connections on the interface cable; it also specifies the length of the interface cable.

12. The DAC (digital-to-analog converter) converts digital data into an analog voltage. This analog voltage is often used to control the speed of motors, to generate speech, to generate video, etc. Many DACs are microprocessor compatible, thus are easily interfaced to the microprocessor.

13. The ADC (analog-to-digital converter) converts an analog voltage into a digital signal. ADCs are used to monitor temperature, to capture speech, and in many other applications. Many ADCs are microprocessor compatible.

14. A stepper motor is a device that is moved in discrete steps. This makes it ideal for connecting to a microprocessor-based system. Stepper motors are operated in full-step or half-step mode. The full-step mode moves the armature of the stepper motor from one pole to another each time it is stepped. The half-step moves the armature of the stepper motor half-way from one pole to the next pole.

15. A dc motor is a device that is controlled by an analog voltage applied across its armature. The dc motor cannot be easily stepped, but it can be rotated at high speeds and also has much more torque than a stepper motor.

## Questions

1. What device is used to connect an input signal to the microprocessor?

2. Develop a decoder that selects an input device for memory location $6XXXXX for the 68008 microprocessor. You need to decode only the most significant four address bits.

3. What device is used to connect the output information to the external output device?

4. Develop a decoder that selects an output device for memory location $7XXXX

for the 68000 microprocessor. This device must function only in the lower bank.

5. Describe mechanical switch bouncing.

6. In a microprocessor-based system, how is contact bouncing eliminated with software?

7. How much current is normally required to light an LED?

8. If an LED requires 12 mA of current, what series current-limiting resistor is used in the circuit of Figure 8-6?

9. What two types of LED, seven-segment display are available?

10. A fluorescent display glows with what color?

11. What is the main disadvantage of a fluorescent display?

12. What is the main disadvantage of the LCD display?

13. Why is an optical isolator often used with a solenoid or relay?

14. Why is a Darlington pair often used to drive a solenoid or a relay?

15. What does PIA stand for?

16. The 6821 contains two programmable peripheral data registers. Is it possible to program these as 4 output bits and 12 input bits?

17. Describe how PDRA is programmed.

18. Develop a sequence of instructions to program PDRA so that all 8 bits are output bits. Assume that this is not after a reset. The PIA is decoded at addresses $60000–$60003.

19. Develop a sequence of instructions to program PDRB so that the most significant 4 bits are output bits and the least significant 4 bits are input bits. Assume that this is not after a reset. The PIA is decoded at addresses $40100–$41003.

20. How long does a switch normally bounce?

21. Modify the keyboard interface of Figure 8-16 so that it contains 20 key switches. Use PDRA for the rows and PDRB for the columns. Connect the keyboard so that there are five rows and four columns.

22. Develop the software to scan the keyboard of question 21. Make sure to include the software to program the 6821.

23. If a multiplexed display contains nine display positions, how much peak current is allowed to flow through a segment? Assume that the nominal segment current is 10 mA.

24. Design the segment driver for the display in question 23. Assume that this display is a common anode display.

**25.** Design the anode switch for the display in question 23. Assume that this display is a common anode display.

**26.** What does ACIA stand for?

**27.** What is Baud rate?

**28.** Describe the frame contents of asynchronous serial data.

**29.** What is even parity?

**30.** Program a 6850 connected to the microprocessor at I/O addresses $60000 and $60001 so that it works with 7 data bits, odd parity, and a divider of 1.

**31.** What is the purpose of the $\overline{\text{CTS}}$ signal?

**32.** What is the purpose of $\overline{\text{RTS}}$?

**33.** What does $\overline{\text{DSR}}$ indicate?

**34.** What is a modem?

**35.** What is a framing error?

**36.** What is an overrun error?

**37.** What voltage level is used with RS-232C to indicate a logic one?

**38.** Interface the DAC at I/O address $30000.

**39.** Connect the circuit of question 38 to a speaker, through an audio amplifier. (No detail required on the speaker and audio amplifier.) Develop the software to send data to the DAC 2000 times a second for 10 seconds. Send the data beginning at memory location $50000.

**40.** What is the purpose of the $\overline{\text{INTR}}$ pin on the ADC?

**41.** Interface the ADC so that it takes data from I/O address $40000. Connect $\overline{\text{INTR}}$ as an input device at location $50000.

**42.** Using the circuit of question 40, assume that it is connected to a microphone and audio amplifier. Develop the software required to sample the output of the microphone 2000 times a second for 10 seconds. Store the sampled data in memory beginning at location $50000.

**43.** What type of motor uses a permanent magnet armature?

**44.** What type of motor uses a permanent magnet field?

**45.** In the stepper motor, explain the difference between a half-step and a full step.

**46.** If the amplitude of the voltage applied to a dc motor is changed, what happens to the speed of the motor?

**47.** Compare the stepper motor with the dc motor for the following factors:
(a) speed    (b) torque    (c) ease of positioning

# 9

# *Interrupt Processed I/O*

**OBJECTIVES**

Upon completion of this chapter, you will be able to:

- Describe the exception structure of the 68000 microprocessor.
- Interface a device as an interrupt processed device and develop the software required to service the interrupt.
- Design the circuitry required to expand the interrupt structure of the 68000 using a daisy chain and other techniques.
- Explain the operation of a real-time clock using a periodic interrupt.
- Interface a parallel printer to the 68000 using interrupts and a queue.
- Program the 68230 parallel interface and timer.
- Use the 68230 parallel interface and timer as an interrupting device.

**KEY TERMS**

| | | |
|---|---|---|
| exception handler | vectors | spurious interrupt |
| interrupt service | nonmaskable, | polling |
|   subroutine |   maskable interrupts | terminal count |
| interrupt, exceptions | glue | centronics interface |

INTERRUPT processed I/O is a very useful I/O technique found with all microprocessors. This chapter details both the external and internal interrupts. Internal interrupts are generated by instructions and internal events. All interrupts are classed together as exceptions to the normal processing state of the microprocessor. These exceptions interrupt a program and jump to a subroutine so that the exception can be handled. This subroutine is often called an *exception handler* or an *interrupt service subroutine*.

I/O devices that benefit from interrupts include any device that requires only occasional attention from the microprocessor. Many I/O devices fit this category. Keyboards, displays, printers, and plotters are examples of devices that are often interrupt processed. Any device that requires attention less than 1000 times a second may be a good candidate for interrupt processing.

## 9-1 Introduction to Exceptions

Exceptions are designed to handle unusual events in a microprocessor. In the 68000/68008 microprocessor, exceptions occur as instructions are executed, when the microprocessor is reset, and when an external event triggers an interrupt. External events are said to *interrupt* the microprocessor, while internal events are said to cause *exceptions*. These techniques function in an identical manner. The terms are often used synonymously.

### 9-1.1 The Exception

Most exceptions occur only after an instruction has been fully executed. The only exceptions that occur sooner are reset, bus error, and address error. These exceptions occur within two clocking periods of the exception request. Table 9-1 illustrates the priority of these exceptions and different types of exceptions. Note that the highest priority exceptions are reset, bus error, and address error. The lowest priority are the software exceptions TRAP, TRAPV, CHK, and divide by zero. Priority is important only if more than one exception occur simultaneously; otherwise priority lacks a role. If more than one exception are active, the one with the highest priority takes effect.

#### Group 0 Exceptions

Group 0 exceptions are the most urgent, so they have the highest priority. If a reset occurs, the contents of memory locations $000000–$000003 are fetched and placed into the supervisor stack pointer. The contents of the program counter are also fetched from memory (locations $000004–$000007). A hardware reset is the only exception that uses two exception vectors (0 and 1).

The bus error exception occurs when a logic signal is placed on the $\overline{BERR}$ input pin. The address error exception occurs whenever an instruction addresses word- or long-word-sized data at an odd-numbered memory location. An address error also occurs when an instruction is executed from an odd-numbered memory location.

**Table 9-1  Exception Priority**

| Group | Type | Comment |
|---|---|---|
| 0 | reset<br>bus error<br>address error | Processing begins within two clocks. |
| 1 | trace<br>interrupt<br>illegal<br>privilege | Processing begins after the current instruction has been completed. |
| 2 | TRAP<br>TRAPV<br>CHK<br>divide by zero | Processing begins after the instruction has been executed. |

Therefore words and long-words only may be stored at even-numbered memory locations as well as instructions. Bytes may be stored at either even or odd locations.

## Group 1 Exceptions

Group 1 exceptions are caused by unusual events that occur during normal system operation. These events include trace, hardware interrupts, illegal instructions, and privilege violations. The trace exception occurs whenever the trace bit in the status register is set. The hardware interrupts occur when any of the $\overline{IPL}$ inputs are activated and the interrupt level that is requested is unmasked. Illegal exceptions occur when an undefined instruction is executed. The privilege violation exception occurs when a privileged instruction (e.g., RESET or STOP) is executed in the user mode. Privileged instructions also include any that modify the contents of the status register.

## Group 2 Exceptions

Group 2 exceptions are all software generated. These occur as a result of the TRAP, TRAPV, CHK or divide instructions. The divide instruction causes a divide by zero error exception if division by zero is attempted. Divide will not cause this exception if a divide overflow occurs.

### 9-1.2    Exception Vectors

Besides priority, exceptions are guided with vectors stored in a vector table. Table 9-2 illustrates the vectors used in the 68000/68008 microprocessor for exceptions. The exception vector table is stored in the first 1k bytes of the memory at locations $000000–$0003FF. Each vector is a 4-byte number in the vector table.

The vector table holds 256 *vectors,* each referenced by vector number. The first vector in the table is vector number zero and the last is vector $FF. The address stored in a vector is stored with the most significant byte in the lowest numbered vector location.

The address stored in the vector is the address of the exception handler or interrupt service subroutine. This is not true only for vector number 0, which holds the initial value of the supervisor stack pointer after a hardware reset. If memory locations $000014 = $00, $000015 = $00, $000016 = $FF, and $000017 = $DC, the vector contains address $0000FFDC. This is the address of the exception handler for a divide by zero error, which is stored at these memory locations.

When an exception or hardware interrupt is processed by the microprocessor, the following series of events occurs.

**1.** The status register is copied into an internal holding register.

**2.** The S (supervisor) bit is set and the T (trace) bit is cleared in the status register.

**3.** The vector number of the exception is generated and the interrupt vector is fetched.

**Table 9-2** Exception Vector Assignments for the 68000/68008 Microprocessor

| Vector | Address | Function |
|--------|---------|----------|
| 0 | $000000 | Initial value of SSP after reset |
| 1 | $000004 | Initial value of program counter after reset |
| 2 | $000008 | Bus error ($\overline{\text{BERR}}$ pin) |
| 3 | $00000C | Address error |
| 4 | $000010 | Illegal instruction |
| 5 | $000014 | Divide by zero |
| 6 | $000018 | CHK instruction |
| 7 | $00001C | TRAPV instruction |
| 8 | $000020 | Privilege violation |
| 9 | $000024 | Trace |
| 10 | $000028 | Line 1010 emulation ($AXXX) |
| 11 | $00002C | Line 1111 emulation ($FXXX) |
| 12 | $000030 | [reserved] |
| 13 | $000034 | [reserved] |
| 14 | $000038 | [reserved] |
| 15 | $00003C | Uninitialized interrupt |
| 16–23 | $000040 | [reserved] |
| 24 | $000060 | Spurious interrupt |
| 25 | $000064 | Level 1 autovector |
| 26 | $000068 | Level 2 autovector |
| 27 | $00006C | Level 3 autovector |
| 28 | $000070 | Level 4 autovector |
| 29 | $000074 | Level 5 autovector |
| 30 | $000078 | Level 6 autovector |
| 31 | $00007C | Level 7 autovector |
| 32–47 | $000080 | TRAP instructions |
| 48–63 | $0000C0 | [reserved] |
| 64–255 | $000100 | User-defined interrupts |

**4.** The contents of the status register (from the holding register), program counter, and a stack frame are placed on the supervisor stack.

**5.** A jump to the address stored at the exception vector occurs.

Thus an exception has begun when a copy of the status register is held in a holding register. This copy indicates the state of the machine immediately before the exception. Next the supervisor bit is set so that the supervisor stack pointer is selected. This allows the state of the microprocessor to be placed into the supervisor stack. Next the trace bit is cleared so that tracing stops during the execution of software by the exception.

Once the status of the machine has been saved and the supervisor mode selected, the microprocessor calculates the exception vector number. It then fetches the exception vector address that is used to jump to the exception handler.

The contents of the status register and program counter, and other information, are now stored on the stack. This information is unloaded from the stack when a return occurs from the exception handler. Refer to Figure 9-1 for the contents of the stack after the machine status is placed there. Notice that there are two types of stack frame for the 68000/68008 microprocessor. Bus error and address error exceptions, which store more information about the machine than do other exceptions, have a different stack frame from the other exceptions. More information is needed because bus error and address error exceptions occur before the end of an instruction, which means that more information is required by the exception handler to determine exactly what event caused the exception.

In the bus error and address error stack frame, both the program counter and the status register are placed on the stack. This is the same as in the normal exception stack frame. Besides this information, bus and address error exceptions place the contents of the instruction register, the access address, and one additional word. The additional word contains the function code bits of the operation that caused the bus or address error. It also shows whether the operation that caused the exception was a read or a write ($R/\overline{W}$). The $\overline{I}/N$ bit shows whether an instruction ($\overline{I}$) caused the exception or not an instruction (N). Not an instruction occurs if the exception took effect during the operand fetch or store portion of an instruction.

This extra information is placed on the stack for a bus error or address error exception so that the error can be recovered. For example, suppose that a bus error exception occurs. The stack frame holds the instruction that caused the error. It also holds the address that was being accessed by the instruction. In addition, it shows whether a read or a write was executing. If the instruction is fetched from memory, the $\overline{I}/N$ bit is a logic zero. With this information, the bus error exception handler can process the error and possibly recover from it. In many cases, the instruction is reexecuted, or at least the cause of the error is discovered.

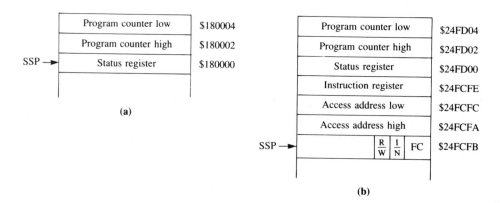

**Figure 9-1**    The stack frames used by (a) all exceptions except bus error and address error and (b) bus error and address error.

A new instruction, RTE, is added to the 68000/68008 instruction set to return from an interrupt or exception. The RTE instruction differs from a normal subroutine RTS instruction in that RTE removes the status register and the program counter from the stack, whereas RTS removes only the program counter.

It is interesting to recall that the status register, which is placed on the stack for an exception, contains the status of the microprocessor before the exception took effect. This means that when the RTE instruction is executed, the prior state of the microprocessor is restored.

For example, suppose that external hardware interrupt levels 6 and 7 are active. A type 6 interrupt occurs. This disables the type 6 interrupt while the microprocessor is executing the type 6 interrupt service subroutine. Upon return from the interrupt service subroutine, the prior state of the machine is restored. Because level 6 and 7 interrupts were enabled before the interrupt, they are again enabled after the interrupt. The same is true of the supervisor and trace status register bits.

### 9-1.3   The Status Register and Exceptions

The system byte of the status register (most significant half) is used with exceptions and hardware interrupts. Figure 9-2 illustrates the entire status register so that the system byte can be located. The system byte's bit positions are changed only if the 68000/68008 is operated in the supervisor mode. If an attempt is made to change any of these bits in the user mode, the microprocessor executes a privilege violation exception. The system byte is a privileged register that may be changed only in the supervisor mode of operation.

### Trace

The system trace bit (T), located in the system byte of the status register, is used to select the trace mode of operation. If trace is enabled, by setting the T bit, the 68000/68008 will interrupt the program after each instruction executes. This is useful when debugging software and is usually a function enabled by the operating system. To set the trace bit, so that debugging may begin, the 68000/68008 must be operating in the supervisor mode.

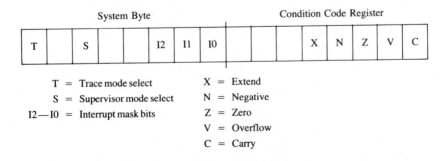

**Figure 9-2   The status register.**

Often a TRAP exception instruction is used to enable the T bit. TRAP is a software exception that causes a context switch to the supervisor mode, allowing T to be set. Recall that any exception or interrupt causes the switch to the supervisor mode.

E X A M P L E    9 - 1

```
                        ;
                        ;TRON is a software interrupt that enables
                        ;tracing by setting the TRACE status
                        ;register bit,
                        ;
011000    00578000    TRON   OR.W    #$8000,(SP)    ;set TRACE bit
011004    4E73               RTE                    ;return
```

Example 9-1 illustrates a TRAP subroutine that is used to enable the trace mode. Notice how the OR instruction in this subroutine is used to set the trace bit. This subroutine is called TRON for "trace on." Here the OR instruction sets the trace bit by addressing the status register stored at the location address by the stack pointer. Refer to the stack frame in Figure 9-1a for the location of the status register in the stack after the software TRAP instruction is executed.

E X A M P L E    9 - 2

```
                        ;
                        ;TROFF is a software interrupt that disables
                        ;tracing by clearing the TRACE status
                        ;register bit,
                        ;
011006    02577FFF    TROFF  AND.W   #$7FFF,(SP)    ;clear TRACE bit
01100A    4E73               RTE                    ;return
```

Example 9-2 illustrates a subroutine that disables trace. This subroutine is called TROFF for "trace off." Notice that tracing is disabled by the AND instruction, which clears the trace bit. Again note that when this subroutine is called, the microprocessor switches to the supervisor mode. Any TRAP instruction causes the supervisor mode to be entered. The TROFF subroutine is called by the TRAP instruction in this example.

## Supervisor Bit

As mentioned earlier, when a hardware reset or an exception occurs, the 68000/68008 is automatically placed in the supervisor mode. There is no other way to enter supervisor mode from the user mode. If the user attempts to set or clear the supervisor bit, a privilege violation exception occurs. This feature allows the

68000/68008 to function in a multiuser environment by preventing the users from tampering with the interrupt structure of the machine and other bits of the system byte of the status register. A user cannot affect the system byte when the microprocessor is operated in the user mode.

### Interrupt Masks

The three interrupt mask bits (I2–I0) are used to enable various hardware interrupt levels. Hardware interrupts are requested through the $\overline{\text{IPL}}$ inputs. Table 9-3 illustrates the effect of the three interrupt mask bits on the interrupt structure of the 68000 and 68008 microprocessors. Note that the 68000 has access to all seven interrupt levels, while the 68008 can only access three: 2, 5, and 7.

Table 9-3 illustrates that interrupt level 7 is a *nonmaskable interrupt*. Nonmaskable interrupts cannot be disabled. Also notice from this table that the interrupt mask bits decide which interrupt level is off plus all lower priority interrupts. For example, if a 101 is placed in the interrupt mask bits, levels 5 and lower are disabled. Interrupt level 7 has the highest priority and interrupt level 1 the lowest.

Whenever a hardware interrupt is requested through the $\overline{\text{IPL}}$ interrupt inputs, the microprocessor completes the current instruction. When the instruction is completed, the microprocessor checks the I2–I0 interrupt mask bits. If the interrupt level that is requested is enabled, the microprocessor begins the hardware interrupt exception processing. If the level requested is disabled, no interrupt exception is processed.

Once the interrupt has been accepted, the microprocessor places the requested interrupt level number into the I2–I0 mask bits. For example, suppose that a level 011 interrupt is requested. If the interrupt mask bits contain a 010, 001, or 000, the interrupt will be accepted, and the microprocessor will place a 011 into the mask bits, disabling levels 3, 2, and 1. This effectively blocks the current interrupt level and all lower priority interrupts. The prior state of the interrupt mask bits is reinstated upon an RTE when the status word is restored.

Table 9-3 The 68000 and 68008 Interrupt Mask Bits

| I2 | I1 | I0 | Levels enabled 60008 | Levels enabled 68000 |
|----|----|----|--------|----------------------|
| 0 | 0 | 0 | 2, 5, and 7 | 1, 2, 3, 4, 5, 6, and 7 |
| 0 | 0 | 1 | 2, 5, and 7 | 2, 3, 4, 5, 6, and 7 |
| 0 | 1 | 0 | 5 and 7 | 3, 4, 5, 6, and 7 |
| 0 | 1 | 1 | 5 and 7 | 4, 5, 6, and 7 |
| 1 | 0 | 0 | 5 and 7 | 5, 6, and 7 |
| 1 | 0 | 1 | 7 | 6 and 7 |
| 1 | 1 | 0 | 7 | 7 |
| 1 | 1 | 1 | 7 | 7 |

### 9-1.4   TRAP and TRAPV

The TRAP and TRAPV instructions are unconditional and conditional software exception instructions, respectively. The TRAPV instruction interrupts the program only if the content of the overflow flag is a logic one. If the overflow flag is a logic zero, the TRAPV instruction performs as a NOP (no operation).

The TRAP instruction is an unconditional exception. There are 16 TRAP instructions. Each TRAP is used to call a different interrupt service subroutine for any task that the user desires (TRAP 0 uses vector number 32, TRAP 1 uses vector 33, etc.; refer to Table 9-2). The last TRAP instruction is TRAP 15. The TRAP and TRAPV instructions execute in the same manner as any other exception. Neither instruction has any effect on the I2–I0 mask bits. This means that the external interrupt inputs have a higher priority than the TRAP and TRAPV instructions. So a hardware interrupt can interrupt a TRAP or TRAPV exception handler.

### 9-1.5   The CHK Instruction

The CHK (check register against boundary) instruction is used to compare the contents of a data register to the contents of the effective address. This instruction only compares word data. For example, CHK UPPER,D2 compares the contents of D2 with UPPER. If the contents of D2 are less than zero or D2 is greater than the contents of memory location UPPER, an exception occurs. This instruction compares the two's complement upper boundary in memory location UPPER with D2. The CHK instruction is useful for testing memory boundaries in multiuser environments.

### 9-1.6   STOP

The STOP instruction is not really an interrupt or exception instruction, although it does test the microprocessor to see whether an exception has occurred. The STOP instruction will stop execution of software until either a hardware reset or a hardware interrupt occurs.

When STOP is executed, the 16-bit operand is stored in the status register. An example is STOP $FFFF. This instruction places a $FFFF into the status register when executed. If an interrupt occurs, the machine processes it and executes the interrupt handler. Upon return from the interrupt handler, the 68000/68008 will return to the instruction following the STOP.

The number used as an operand can mask off external interrupts because it is loaded into the status register when STOP executes. This feature can be used beneficially to disable certain external interrupts when the microprocessor is stopped.

### 9-1.7   Line Emulation Exceptions

The line emulator exceptions are used to cause either a line 1111 ($FXXX) or a line 1010 ($AXXX) exception. If an instruction is placed in memory that begins with either a 1111 or a 1010, the 68000/68008 will interrupt the program to process the exception.

For example, if the instruction $A000 is stored in a program, the microprocessor will use exception vector 10. This is treated as any other exception. Notice that only the first 4 bits of the 16-bit instruction are defined. This allows you to use the remaining 12 bits in any manner. One application is to use these bits to specify various instructions to the type 11 exception handler.

For example, the type 10 exception may be used to emulate another microprocessor. Suppose that the 6800 is emulated using any instruction that begins with the letter $A. The opcodes are emulated and passed to the exception handler as instructions $A000–$A0FF for 6800 opcodes $00–$FF. Each time the $A0?? instruction is encountered, the exception handler examines the right-most 8 bits of the opcode to decide which 6800 instruction to emulate. This technique is applied to any microprocessor or system to be emulated.

The line emulator exceptions are also used by the floating-point coprocessor (68881/68882) and the paged memory management unit (68851). Chapter 11 explains how line emulator 1111 is used to communicate with the floating-point coprocessor.

### 9-1.8 Interrupt Service Subroutine

The interrupt service subroutine or exception handler is a subroutine that is called by an interrupt or exception. In all cases the subroutine must end with the RTE instruction. The RTE instruction, as mentioned earlier, removes the status register and program counter from the stack. This allows the prior state of the machine to be restored. It also allows the subroutine to return to the point of interruption.

An exception or interrupt occurs at any point in the system software, provided the interrupt is enabled. Because this point of interruption cannot always be predicted, the contents of any register used within the interrupt service subroutine must be saved. Usually registers are stored on the supervisor stack during the interrupt service subroutine. Before returning to the point of interrupt, the registers that were saved are reloaded from the supervisor stack before the RTE instruction is executed. Refer to Example 9-3 for an interrupt service subroutine.

E X A M P L E   9 - 3

```
                        ;
                        ;An example interrupt service subroutine or
                        ;exception handler illustrating how the
                        ;registers used by the subroutine are saved on
                        ;and restored from the supervisor stack.
                        ;
012000  48E73004  SUBR  MOVEM.L D2-D3/A5,-(SP)  ;save registers

                        (body of subroutine)

012064  4CDF200C        MOVEM.L(SP)+,D2-D3/A5   ;restore registers
012068  4E73            RTE                     ;return
```

This example places the D2, D3, and A5 registers on the stack by a MOVEM instruction before the subroutine begins. Upon completion of the subroutine, the same registers are restored with another MOVEM instruction from the stack before the return is executed, with the RTE instruction.

## 9-2    Using the Interrupt Inputs

The 68000 microprocessor contains three maskable interrupt inputs labeled $\overline{IPL2}$–$\overline{IPL0}$. These inputs are used to request an interrupt at various interrupt levels. The 68008 contains either these three interrupt inputs or $\overline{IPL0/2}$ and $\overline{IPL1}$. Each microprocessor also contains a $\overline{BERR}$ input, which differs from the $\overline{IPL}$ inputs because it is nonmaskable. A *maskable interrupt* is one that can be turned off. A nonmaskable interrupt can never be turned off.

### 9-2.1    The Interrupt Inputs

Figure 9-3 illustrates the interrupt input connections for both the 68000 and 68008 microprocessors. Notice that there are two versions of the 68008. One version (68008Q) has the same interrupt inputs as the 68000. The other version (68008D) has one less interrupt input. The 68008D uses only interrupt vectors 2, 5, and 7 because of the reduction in interrupt priority inputs.

Both the 68000 and 68008 have a $\overline{BERR}$ input. The $\overline{BERR}$ input is designed to use with a catastrophic bus error (memory failure, power failure, etc.). The $\overline{BERR}$ input can be used for other applications as well, if desired. As mentioned, the $\overline{BERR}$ input is different from the other interrupt inputs in that it can never be turned off or disabled. The other interrupt inputs can be disabled. Another difference is that the information placed on the stack for a $\overline{BERR}$ interrupt is much more detailed, as described above.

### 9-2.2    Autovector Interrupts

The $\overline{IPL}$ inputs are used in two different ways to request an interrupt in the 680XX microprocessor. The first technique uses the autovectors, whereas the second relies

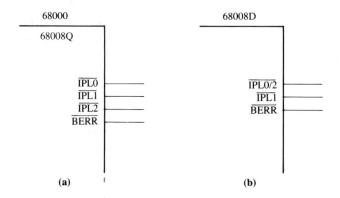

**Figure 9-3**    The interrupt inputs found on (a) the 68000 and 68008Q and (b) the 68008D microprocessors.

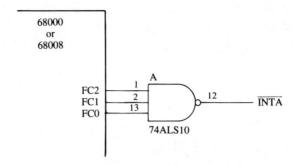

**Figure 9-4** Generating the $\overline{\text{INTA}}$ signal using the function code bits.

on user-specified vectors. In small systems, autovectors are more common because they allow up to seven external interrupt inputs. In larger systems, user interrupts are chosen because they allow almost any number of interrupt vectors ($40–$FF).

Both interrupt schemes require that an interrupt acknowledge signal be available. Figure 9-4 illustrates how the $\overline{\text{INTA}}$ (interrupt acknowledge) signal is generated. When all three FC outputs are a logic one, an interrupt acknowledge is occurring. This is also sometimes referred to as the CPU space for the microprocessor. In this illustration, a three-input NAND gate is used to decode this event and generate $\overline{\text{INTA}}$. The $\overline{\text{INTA}}$ signal becomes active to show that an interrupt has been requested through the $\overline{\text{IPL}}$ inputs. It does not indicate that a $\overline{\text{BERR}}$ interrupt is requested.

The $\overline{\text{INTA}}$ signal causes either an autovector interrupt or a user interrupt. If $\overline{\text{INTA}}$ asserts the $\overline{\text{DTACK}}$ signal, a user interrupt is selected. If $\overline{\text{INTA}}$ asserts the $\overline{\text{VPA}}$ signal, an autovector interrupt is selected.

Figure 9-5 illustrates how a system is connected so that one interrupt input is available. Here all three $\overline{\text{IPL}}$ inputs are connected in common. If they are placed at a logic one level, no interrupt is requested. If they are grounded, interrupt autovector seven is selected. Note that the $\overline{\text{IPL}}$ inputs are active low. This means that a 000 selects autovector seven (111).

This circuit uses a 74ALS138 to steer the $\overline{\text{AS}}$ signal to either $\overline{\text{DTACK}}$ or $\overline{\text{VPA}}$. If the $\overline{\text{INTA}}$ signal is a logic one, then $\overline{\text{AS}}$ is sent to $\overline{\text{DTACK}}$. Notice that this places a 010 on the select inputs of the 74ALS138. The 010, on the select inputs, sends $\overline{\text{AS}}$ through to output $\overline{\text{Y2}}$, which allows normal memory operation without wait states. If wait states are desired, the wait state generator's output is placed on the enable input of the 74ALS138 instead of $\overline{\text{AS}}$.

When an interrupt is requested, by placing a logic zero on the interrupt request input, the $\overline{\text{INTA}}$ signal is generated. Notice that the $\overline{\text{INTA}}$ signal places a 000 on the select inputs of the 74ALS138 at this time. This causes the 74ALS138 to steer the $\overline{\text{AS}}$ signal to the $\overline{\text{VPA}}$ pin instead of the $\overline{\text{DTACK}}$ pin. If $\overline{\text{VPA}}$ is asserted in response to an $\overline{\text{INTA}}$, the 68000/68008 responds with an autovector interrupt. Here, the response is with autovector interrupt number seven because all three $\overline{\text{IPL}}$ inputs are grounded.

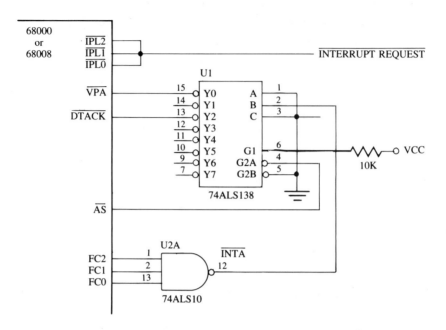

**Figure 9-5**    The 68000/68008 connected so that the interrupt request uses autovector level 7. This circuit is connected so that no wait states are generated.

Suppose that there are three external interrupts instead of one. The basic circuit of Figure 9-5 is used to handle three external interrupts. Figure 9-6 shows how a slight modification in the connections of the $\overline{\text{IPL}}$ inputs allows three external interrupts. These three connections are labeled $\overline{\text{INT4}}$, $\overline{\text{INT2}}$, and $\overline{\text{INT1}}$. The $\overline{\text{INT4}}$ input causes autovector number 4 to be used when this input is solely activated. If $\overline{\text{INT2}}$ is activated, vector 2 is used, and $\overline{\text{INT1}}$ uses vector 1. This assumes that each is activated by itself. If two more are activated, then other interrupt vectors are used. Table 9-4 shows the other interrupt vectors used for various input combinations on these pins.

How are these different interrupt vector levels handled with the interrupt service software? Suppose we assign a disk drive to interrupt $\overline{\text{INT4}}$, a printer to $\overline{\text{INT2}}$, and a keyboard to $\overline{\text{INT1}}$. Obviously these three devices access all seven interrupts at one time or another. How are seven interrupt vectors translated to three interrupting devices? This is handled by using a software interrupt priority scheme. If the disk drive has the highest priority and the keyboard has the lowest priority, the priority would be resolved by placing the correct interrupt service subroutine addresses at the vectors indicated in Table 9-5.

Notice in Table 9-5 that the disk interrupt service subroutine is used for levels 4–7. This occurs because the address of the disk interrupt service subroutine is stored at these vectors. The disk interrupt service subroutine is used whenever the disk requests an interrupt. If the printer and keyboard request an interrupt, the assignment causes the printer interrupt service subroutine to execute. These assign-

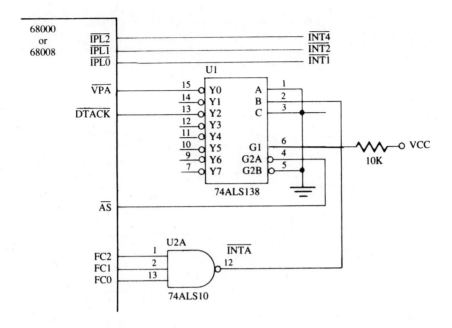

**Figure 9-6** The 68000/68008 connected so that three external interrupts are active using autovectors.

ments are changed if the addresses stored at these vectors are changed. Any assignment can be made for any vector.

Suppose that even more interrupt inputs are required. Up to seven external interrupts are available if an additional circuit is connected. Figure 9-7 illustrates yet another modification to the circuit of Figure 9-5. This change allows up to seven external interrupt inputs.

The circuit of Figure 9-7 adds a 74LS148 priority encoder. Here active low interrupt inputs $\overline{INT7}$–$\overline{INT1}$ are used to cause autovector interrupts to levels 7–1. The priority encoder uses input 7 as its highest priority input. If input $\overline{INT7}$ is placed

**Table 9-4** Interrupt Vector Responses for the Circuit of Figure 9-6

| $\overline{INT4}$ | $\overline{INT2}$ | $\overline{INT1}$ | Autovector response |
|-------------------|-------------------|-------------------|---------------------|
| 0 | 0 | 0 | Level 7 |
| 0 | 0 | 1 | Level 6 |
| 0 | 1 | 0 | Level 5 |
| 0 | 1 | 1 | Level 4 |
| 1 | 0 | 0 | Level 3 |
| 1 | 0 | 1 | Level 2 |
| 1 | 1 | 0 | Level 1 |
| 1 | 1 | 1 | No interrupt requested |

**Table 9-5** Vector Assignments for a Disk Drive, Printer, and Keyboard Using the Circuit of Figure 9-6

| Requested vector | Requesting devices | Assignment |
|---|---|---|
| Level 1 | Keyboard | Keyboard |
| Level 2 | Printer | Printer |
| Level 3 | Printer and keyboard | Printer |
| Level 4 | Disk | Disk |
| Level 5 | Keyboard and disk | Disk |
| Level 6 | Printer and disk | Disk |
| Level 7 | All three | Disk |

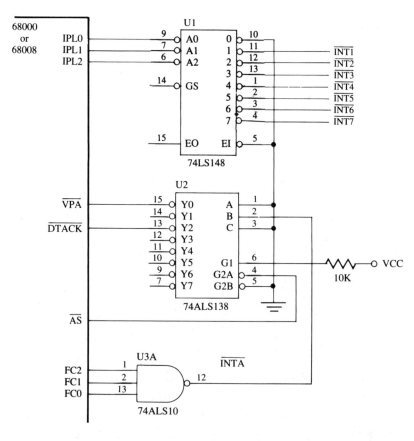

**Figure 9-7** Using seven interrupt inputs with the 68000/68008 microprocessor.

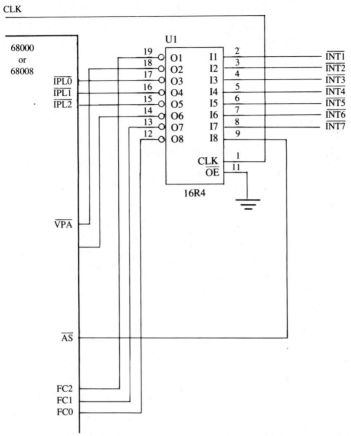

**Figure 9-8**  Using a PAL 16R4 to connect seven interrupt inputs to the 68000/68008 microprocessor.

at a logic zero level, the 74LS148 places a 000 on the $\overline{\text{IPL}}$ inputs requesting a level 7 interrupt. $\overline{\text{INT7}}$ has the highest priority and $\overline{\text{INT1}}$ the lowest. If both $\overline{\text{INT4}}$ and $\overline{\text{INT6}}$ are placed at a logic zero level, the priority encoder requests a level 4 interrupt by placing a 011 on the $\overline{\text{IPL}}$ pins.

All the circuitry in Figure 9-7, except the 68000 or 68008, can be placed on one programmable logic device. In the new circuit created (Figure 9-8), a PAL 16R4 replaces the 74ALS10, 74ALS138, and the 74LS148. The programmable logic array is a worthwhile replacement for the circuitry illustrated in the prior examples.

The program listing for the PAL appears in Example 9-4. Notice how the program replaces the three TTL circuits. Note that the $\overline{\text{AS}}$ input is often connected to a wait state generator if wait states are desired. This program enables the $\overline{\text{VPA}}$ pin and causes it to go to a logic zero whenever $\overline{\text{AS}}$ is low while FC2, FC1, and FC0 are all high. As mentioned, the $\overline{\text{AS}}$ input can come from a wait state generator. The $\overline{\text{DTACK}}$ output activates for all other function codes when qualified by $\overline{\text{AS}}$. The remaining equations generate the three $\overline{\text{IPL}}$ output signals to the microprocessor.

E X A M P L E    9 - 4

---

TITLE        Example
PATTERN      Test
REVISION     A
AUTHOR       BARRY BREY
COMPANY      DeVRY
DATE         2/7/91
CHIP         Decode PAL16R4

;PINS        1       2       3       4       5       6       7       8       9       10
             CLK     INT1    INT2    INT3    INT4    INT5    INT6    INT7    AS      GND

;PINS        11      12      13      14      15      16      17      18      19      20
             OE      FC0     FC1     DTACK   IPL2    IPL1    IPL0    VPA     FC2     VCC

EQUATIONS
VPA.TRST = VCC                           ;enable VPA pin
/VPA = FC2 * FC1 * FC0 * /AS

/DTACK : = /FC2 * /FC1 * /FC0 * /AS
         + /FC2 * /FC1 *  FC0 * /AS
         + /FC2 *  FC1 * /FC0 * /AS
         + /FC2 *  FC1 *  FC0 * /AS
         +  FC2 * /FC1 * /FC0 * /AS
         +  FC2 * /FC1 *  FC0 * /AS
         +  FC2 *  FC1 * /FC0 * /AS

/IPL2 : = /INT7
        + INT7 * /INT6
        + INT7 *  INT6 * /INT5
        + INT7 *  INT6 *  INT5 * /INT4

/IPL1 : = /INT7
        + INT7 * /INT6
        + INT7 *  INT6 *  INT5 *  INT4 * /INT3
        + INT7 *  INT6 *  INT5 *  INT4 *  INT3 * /INT2

/IPL0 : = /INT7
        + INT7 * /INT6
        + INT7 *  INT6 *  INT5 *  INT4 * /INT3
        + INT7 *  INT6 *  INT5 *  INT4 *  INT3 *  INT2 * /INT1

---

### 9-2.3    User Interrupts

If autovector interrupts are not desired, $\overline{\text{VPA}}$ is not used. In place of $\overline{\text{VPA}}$, $\overline{\text{DTACK}}$ is returned to the microprocessor to cause user interrupt vector processing. User interrupts require the vector number to be placed on the data bus in response to the interrupt acknowledge. Figure 9-9 illustrates the simplest method of using the user interrupt vector. Here interrupt vector $FF is applied to the data bus in response to the interrupt acknowledge signal. The vector number is always applied to the least significant data bus connections D0–D7. This circuit uses pullup resistors to apply the $FF to the data bus during the interrupt acknowledge. This connection reduces the cost of such an interrupt to a minimum. Usually, if only one interrupt is required, this is the best circuit to use.

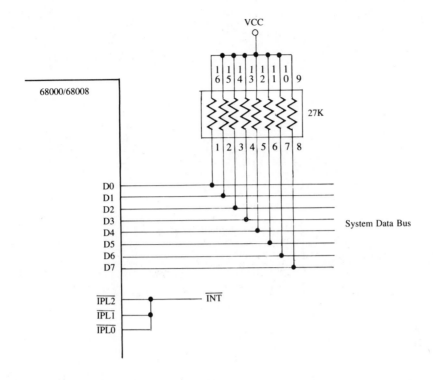

**Figure 9-9** Connecting the 68000/68008 for one external interrupt input using vector $FF.

If more than one external interrupt is required using the user vector scheme, another circuit must be chosen. Figure 9-10 illustrates a circuit that applies any user interrupt vector in response to an interrupt. This circuit uses a 74ALS244 octal buffer to apply the vector number to the data bus for an interrupt acknowledge. In this example, vector number $B2 is applied to the data bus in response to the interrupt request input $\overline{\text{INT}}$. Vector $B2 is applied because it is hard-wired to the inputs of the 74ALS244 buffer. Note that the $\overline{\text{DTACK}}$ input must be activated by the $\overline{\text{INTA}}$ output. This is not shown in this circuit.

Suppose that 16 external interrupts are required. This is accomplished by using two 74LS148 priority encoders that are connected to a 74ALS244 octal buffer. This circuit (see Figure 9-11) causes user interrupt vectors $80–$8F. Other vector numbers can be used if the hardware connections to the 74ALS244 are changed. The circuit used to apply $\overline{\text{DTACK}}$ is also illustrated for the interrupt acknowledge. The interrupt request input is set to function as interrupt level 1 so that it may be disabled with the interrupt masks in the status register.

From this schematic it is clear that many small-scale integrated circuits can be replaced with a PLD. The same circuit is illustrated again in Figure 9-12, with a PAL used in place of the SSI *glue*.

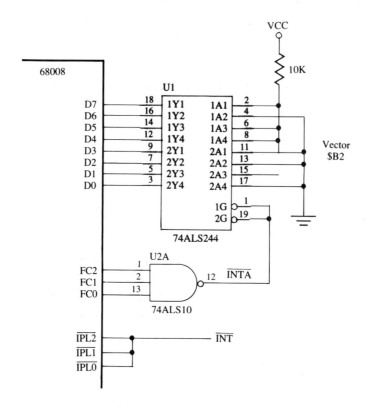

**Figure 9-10   A circuit that responds with interrupt vector $82.**

A larger PAL could have been used in this circuit, but then a 24-pin PAL would have been necessary, compared to the 20-pin PAL used in this example. It was decided that the larger integrated circuit would not be cost effective. This meant, however, that one AND gate was still required.

Example 9-5 illustrates the program for the PAL 16L8. Because the outputs of this device are three-state, they must be enabled. Some outputs are bidirectional and are programmed as either inputs or outputs. In the program listed, the .TRST indicates the three-state output. To program a three-state output pin as active, VCC is applied. To program an output to function as an input, GND is applied to the three-state connection.

**E X A M P L E   9 - 5**

```
TITLE       Interrupts
PATTERN     Test
REVISION    A
AUTHOR      BARRY BREY
COMPANY     DeVRY
DATE        2/7/91
CHIP        Decode PAL16R8
```

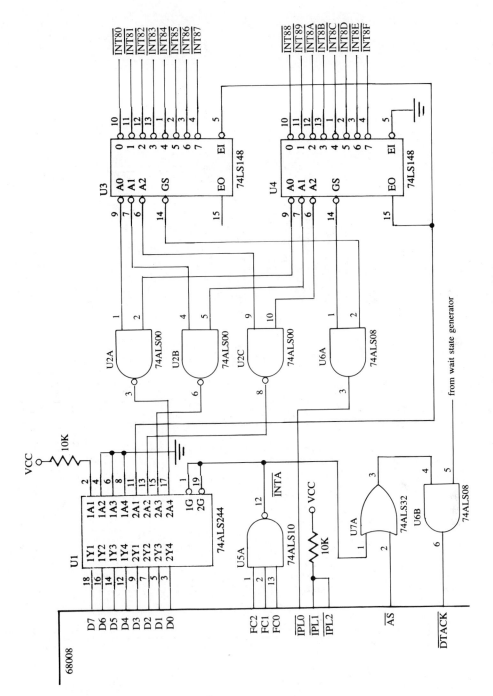

**Figure 9-11  A circuit that has 16 interrupt inputs located at user vectors $80–$8F.**

341

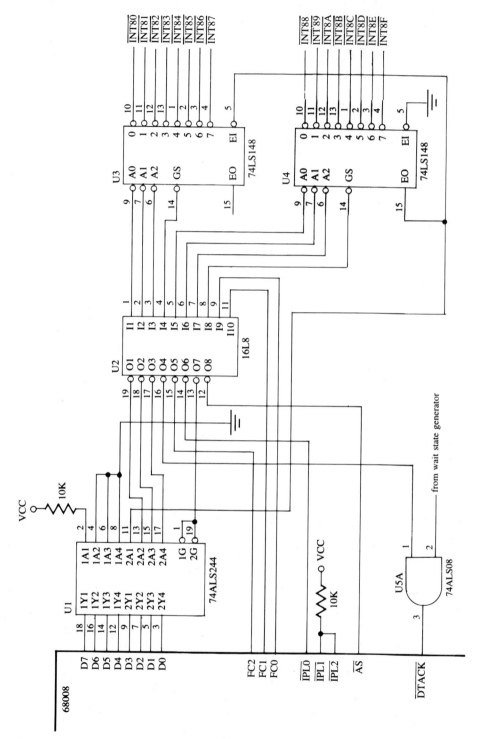

**Figure 9-12** The circuit of Figure 9-11 using a PAL 16L8.

```
;PINS       1    2    3    4    5    6    7    8    9    10
            A0   A1   A2   GS   A0A  A1A  A2A  GSA  FC0  GND

;PINS       11   12   13   14   15   16   17   18   19   20
            FC1  AS   G    IPL0 FC2  DT   2A4  2A3  2A2  VCC
```

EQUATIONS

```
;enable output pins
2A2.TRST = VCC
2A3.TRST = VCC
2A4.TRST = VCC
DT.TRST  = VCC
IPL0.TRST = VCC
G.TRST   = VCC

;disable output pins and program as input pins

FC2.TRST = GND
AS.TRST  = GND
;program pin functions
/G  = FC2 * FC1 * FC0              ;enables 74ALS244
/DT = FC2 * FC1 * FC0 * /AS        ;DTACK
IPL0 = GS * GSA
/2A2 = /A2 * /A2A
/2A3 = /A1 * /A1A
/2A4 = /A0 * /A0A
```

## The Uninitialized Interrupt

The uninitialized interrupt is reserved for use by an external device. If the external device determines that the interrupt vector in the interrupt vector table has not been initialized, the external device causes a type 15 interrupt vector to be placed on the data bus in response to the interrupt request. This calls software that shows that the vector is not initialized. To use this function, the external interrupting device must be able to apply a user interrupt vector number 15 to the data bus during the interrupt acknowledge cycle. The operating system or the interrupting device determines whether an interrupt is uninitialized.

## The Spurious Interrupt

The *spurious interrupt* is designed to handle noise on the $\overline{\text{IPL}}$ inputs. Normally whenever a logic zero is applied to an $\overline{\text{IPL}}$ input, the 68000/68008 responds with an interrupt acknowledge cycle, because FC2, FC1, and FC0 are 111. Normally the external hardware responds to the interrupt acknowledge by applying a pulse to $\overline{\text{VPA}}$ or $\overline{\text{DTACK}}$. If the external hardware does not respond with $\overline{\text{VPA}}$ or $\overline{\text{DTACK}}$, a spurious interrupt occurs.

The external hardware must respond to this type of interrupt with a $\overline{\text{BERR}}$ signal. When $\overline{\text{BERR}}$ is asserted in place of $\overline{\text{VPA}}$ or $\overline{\text{DTACK}}$, the microprocessor uses the spurious interrupt vector. Here, the microprocessor uses the short stack frame for the $\overline{\text{BERR}}$-inspired interrupt. Normally $\overline{\text{BERR}}$ causes the machine to use the long stack frame for a bus error.

### 9-2.4    Daisy-Chained Interrupt Expansion

One additional choice for expanding interrupts exists. The daisy-chained interrupt scheme is perhaps one of the older methods of expanding interrupts that still exists. A daisy-chained interrupt uses one interrupt vector level to service many interrupts. Software is used to distinguish between interrupting devices rather than hardware.

Figure 9-13 illustrates a simple daisy-chained interrupt system. Here four external interrupting devices are attached to the microprocessor using one interrupt autovector. Each 6821 PIA contains two interrupt request pins that are connected together ($\overline{IRQA}$ and $\overline{IRQB}$). The 6821 PIA interrupt request pins are all open-collector devices that allow them to be connected common. All four interrupt requests are connected to the $\overline{IPL0}$ input. This forms a wired-AND gate. If any of the four interrupt requests becomes a logic zero, a zero is applied to the $\overline{IPL0}$ input. This zero input requests an interrupt.

When $\overline{IPL0}$ becomes active, the microprocessor responds with interrupt vector 1 or a user vector. The microprocessor responds with the same interrupt vector for any of the four different interrupts. How does the microprocessor decide which device caused the interrupt? The determination is accomplished with the interrupt service subroutine. The technique used to find which external device requested the interrupt is called *polling*.

E X A M P L E    9 - 6

```
                                 ;
                                 ;Software interrupt service
                                 ;subroutine that polls the 6821s to
                                 ;determine which one caused the
                                 ;interrupt.
                                 ;
013000    039000700020001    POLL    BTST    #7,$20001
013008    6646                       BNE     U2A        ;if U2 IRQA
01300A    0839000700020003           BTST    #7,$20003
013012    660000EC                   BNE     U2B        ;if U2 IRQB
013016    0839000700020101           BTST    #7,$20101
01301E    660001E0                   BNE     U3A        ;if U3 IRQA
013022    6000030C                   BRA     U3B        ;if U3 IRQB
```

Example 9-6 illustrates the portion of the interrupt service subroutine that polls the external 6821s to determine which device caused the interrupt. The port addresses used for these devices are $20000–$20003 for U2 and $20100–$20103 for U3. The decoder is not shown in Figure 9-13 and neither is the circuit required to cause an autovector interrupt or a user interrupt. In this example polling subroutine, it is assumed that the interrupts are requested with the CA1 and CB1 inputs to the 6821s. The control register bits tested are IRQA1 and IRQB1 in control registers A and B.

The polling subroutine first checks U2 to determine whether either its $\overline{IRQA}$ or $\overline{IRQB}$ interrupt is active. If $\overline{IRQA}$ is active, the software continues at location U2A.

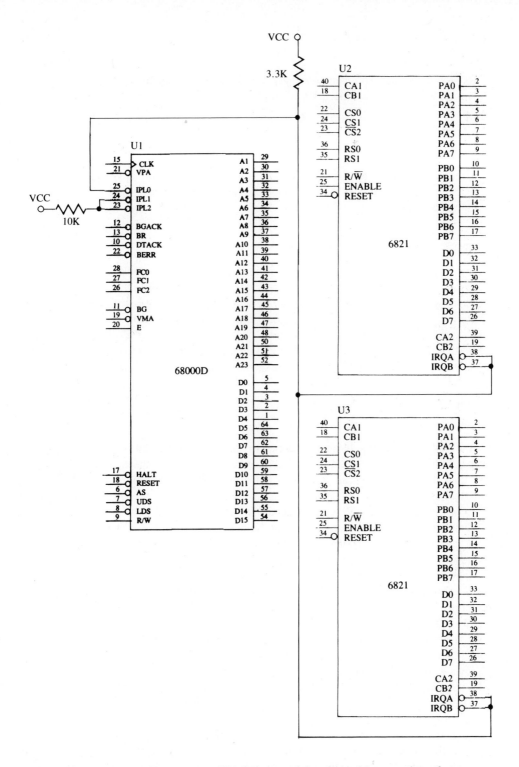

**Figure 9-13** Connecting two 6821 PIAs as a daisy-chained interrupting scheme.

If $\overline{\text{IRQB}}$ is active, the software continues at U2B. Next both interrupt requests on U3 are tested and a branch occurs to either U3A or U3B.

## 9-3 Examples of Interrupt Processed I/O

This section is devoted to two application examples that show how interrupt hardware and interrupt service subroutines support interrupting I/O devices: a real-time clock and the Centronics printer interface.

### 9-3.1 The Real-Time Clock

A simple application of interrupts is the real-time clock. Real-time clocks keep track of time (of day) or are used to time events (that is, to determine the amount of time required for executing software or a hardware action). Event timing is accomplished by storing the time from the real-time clock in memory at the start of the application. At the end of the application, the time is again read from the real-time clock. The difference between the starting time and the ending time determines the exact amount of time required to execute an application. This section deals with time-of-day, real-time clocks.

#### Clock Hardware

Figure 9-14 illustrates the hardware connection of the real-time clock. Notice that very little hardware is required for its implementation. Such a connection costs far less than the inclusion of an integrated clock chip or circuit. This is why this technique is so popular in many systems.

The circuit of Figure 9-14 is connected directly to the 120 V ac power line. Extreme care must be exercised when making this connection. The system ground must be tied to the neutral connection on the ac power line. This is accomplished by connecting the white wire (neutral) or large prong in the ac line cord to the ground connection. The black wire is the hot side of the ac power line or the small prong on the plug. If this connection is reversed, the system ground will be at 120 V ac and presents a shock hazard.

The diode rectifies the ac voltage and the resistive network reduces it to a TTL level. Here the voltage applied to the 74ALS14 Schmitt trigger inverter is 4.3 V peak. The capacitor filters the input to the circuit, and the filter removes any high frequency noise that might exist on the power line. The 74ALS14 produces a 60 Hz TTL-compatible square wave for the JK flip-flop (U3B). The 60 Hz input to the flip-flop is divided by 2 to produce an interrupt signal 30 times a second through flip-flop U3A. This interrupt is the basis for timing the real-time clock.

The second JK flip-flop (U3A) is set by each negative edge at the output the first flip-flop (U3B). This requests an interrupt. The interrupt service subroutine has the responsibility of clearing the JK flip-flop. The circuitry to clear the flip-flop is not shown; often this is accomplished by an I/O write to the clear input.

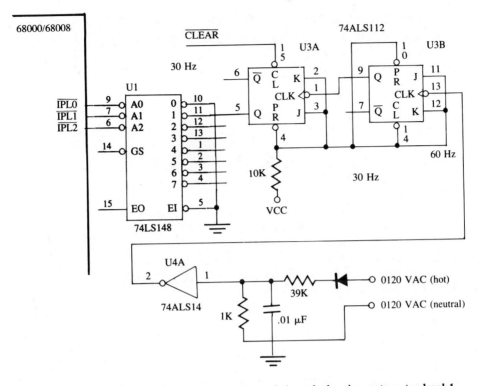

**Figure 9-14** The hardware interface for the real-time clock using autovector level 1.

## Clock Software

The software for the real-time clock is simple. In this system the time is kept in memory at four locations. The memory contains the time in binary-coded decimal (BCD). Each location performs as a counter. The first location ($2000000) is a divide by 30 counter that is used to divide the 30 interrupts per second into one-second pulses. The second location ($200001) is a divide by 60 counter used to count seconds. The third memory location ($200002) counts minutes and the fourth ($200003) hours. This scheme can be expanded to count days of the month, days of the week, months, and years. The counters and their memory locations are illustrated in Figure 9-15.

The interrupt service subroutine uses one additional subroutine, called UP-DATE, which is responsible for incrementing a BCD counter from the real-time clock in the memory.

E X A M P L E   9 - 7

```
;
;The UPDATE subroutine that increments the BCD
;stored at the locations addressed by A0. The
```

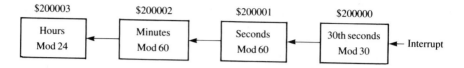

**Figure 9-15    The memory locations and their contents for the real-time clock.**

```
                              ;modulus of the counter is in D0.
                              ;
014000  48A76000  UPDATE  MOVEM.W  D1/D2,-(SP)   ;save registers
014004  1210              MOVE.B   (A0),D1       ;get count
014006  143C0001          MOVE.B   #1,D2         ;get one
01400A  C302              ABCD     D2,D1         ;increment
01400C  10C1              MOVE.B   D1,(A0)+      ;save count
01400E  B200              CMP.B    D0,D1         ;test modulus
014010  66000006          BNE      UP1           ;if good count
014014  4228FFFF          CLR.B    -1(A0)        ;clear count
014018  4C9F0006  UP1     MOVEM.W  (SP)+,D1/D2   ;restore registers
01401C  4E75              RTS
```

Example 9-7 illustrates the UPDATE subroutine. To use UPDATE, the byte portion of D0 is loaded with the modulus of the counter. This is either $30, $60, or $24. Address register A0 is loaded with the memory location of the counter to increment. The return from this subroutine indicates whether another counter needs to be incremented. The subroutine also increments the pointer in A0 in case the next counter must be incremented.

For example, the first counter, Mod 30, is incremented 30 times per second. Once per second, its contents are returned to zero. (When a counter has returned to zero, this state is often called the *terminal count*.) At this time the next counter must be incremented. The return from update must indicate whether the terminal count has been reached. The UPDATE subroutine does this by returning with a zero condition if the counter is cleared. If it is not cleared, it returns with a not zero condition. This return indicating zero or not zero is used to determine whether another counter has been incremented.

E X A M P L E    9 - 8

```
                              ;
                              ;Interrupt service subroutine that updates the
                              ;time stored in four bytes of memory beginning at
                              ;location TIME.
                              ;
01401E  48E78080  CLOCK   MOVEM.L  D0/A0,-(SP)   ;save registers
014022  207C00200000      MOVE.L   #TIME,A0      ;address TIME
014028  103C0030          MOVE.B   #$30,D0       ;set MOD 30
01402C  61D2              BSR      UPDATE        ;update MOD 30
01402E  66000018          BNE      CLOCK1        ;if finished
014032  103C0060          MOVE.B   #$60,D0       ;set MOD 60
014036  61C8              BSR      UPDATE        ;update seconds
```

```
014038    6600000E                 BNE       CLOCK1          ;if finished
01403C    61C2                     BSR       UPDATE          ;update minutes
01403E    66000008                 BNE       CLOCK1          ;if finished
014042    103C0024                 MOVE.B    #$24,D0         ;set MOD 24
014046    61B8                     BSR       UPDATE          ;update hours
014048    423900210000    CLOCK1   CLR.B     $210000         ;clear flip-flop
01404E    4CDF0101                 MOVEM.L   (SP)+,D0/A0     ;restore registers
014052    4E73                     RTE                       ;return
```

The interrupt service subroutine (CLOCK) is listed in Example 9-8. Notice that this subroutine uses the UPDATE subroutine to increment a counter to keep time. Before returning, it also clears the flip-flop (U3A) by writing a $00 to I/O address $210000. The circuitry for clearing the flip-flop is not shown. The interrupt service subroutine uses the D0 and A0 registers. Notice that these registers are saved at the beginning of the subroutine and restored at its end. This is very important. Any registers that are used in an interrupt service subroutine must be saved. If not, these registers will change in the main program of the system. Such changes are not acceptable because they cause unpredictable results.

The time is stored in the subroutine's first address memory location $200000. After addressing the time, the D0 register is loaded with the modulus of the first counter ($30), which is then incremented with the UPDATE subroutine. If the counter reaches a $30, it is cleared and a return equal (zero) occurs. If the counter is incremented to any number between $01 and $29, a return not equal (zero) occurs and the subroutine ends with a branch to CLOCK1.

If the 1/30 second counter reaches $30, the subroutine does not end. Instead the modulus is changed to $60 for the seconds counter and UPDATE is again called. This continues either until all counters have been incremented once per hour, or until a counter is reached that does not become cleared.

This interrupt is set to function at interrupt vector and level 1. This is the lowest priority external interrupt. The system hardware and software must ensure that this interrupt can take effect 30 times per second. If not, the clock will not keep the correct time. In most systems this presents no problem.

### 9-3.2   Centronics Printer Interface with a Queue

A fairly common type of parallel interface for printers and other I/O devices is the Centronics parallel interface. The *Centronics interface* is a TTL interface that allows high speed data transfer between the microprocessor and a printer or other device. Figure 9-16 illustrates the pinout of the printer connector and also the computer connector. Today, the parallel interface uses a DB25, 25-pin connector on the computer and a 36-pin Centronics connector on the printer. Both connector types are illustrated, along with their pin connections.

Note from the illustration that both connectors have eight data connections for data transfer, and a data strobe signal to send the data into the printer. The $\overline{ACK}$ and Busy lines are used for handshaking with the printer. Select in is used to select the printer, and select shows that the printer has been selected.

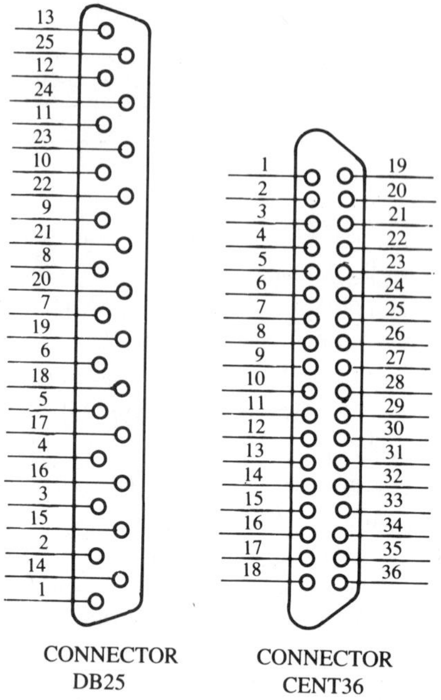

| DB25 Pin Number | CENT36 Pin Number | Function |
|---|---|---|
| 1 | 1 | $\overline{\text{Data Strobe}}$ |
| 2 | 2 | Data 0 (D0) |
| 3 | 3 | Data 1 (D1) |
| 4 | 4 | Data 2 (D2) |
| 5 | 5 | Data 3 (D3) |
| 6 | 6 | Data 4 (D4) |
| 7 | 7 | Data 5 (D5) |
| 8 | 8 | Data 6 (D6) |
| 9 | 9 | Data 7 (D7) |
| 10 | 10 | $\overline{\text{Ack}}$ |
| 11 | 11 | Busy |
| 12 | 12 | Paper Empty |
| 13 | 13 | Select |
| 14 | 14 | Add |
| 15 | 32 | $\overline{\text{Error}}$ |
| 16 | — | $\overline{\text{RESET}}$ |
| 17 | 31 | Select in |
| 18—25 | 19—30 | Ground |
| — | 17 | Frame Ground |
| — | 16 | Ground |
| — | 33 | Ground |

CONNECTOR DB25    CONNECTOR CENT36

**Figure 9-16** **The DB25 connector (found on computers) and the Centronics 36-pin connector (found on printers) for the Centronics parallel printer interface.**

Figure 9-17 shows the operation of the interface through timing diagrams. Notice that the data (ASCII code) are sent to the printer through the data connections. Next, the data strobe is sent to the printer to inform it that data are available. Once the printer has accepted the data and has begun to print, the busy signal becomes a logic one. Busy indicates that the printer is printing a character. Finally, the $\overline{\text{ACK}}$ signal is sent back from the printer when it is ready to receive the next character. Note that $\overline{\text{ACK}}$ also appears when the printer is placed on-line or reset. The $\overline{\text{DS}}$ (data strobe) pulse width is 0.5 μs minimum. The time preceding and following the $\overline{\text{DS}}$ pulse to the data is also 0.5 μs. The width of the $\overline{\text{ACK}}$ (acknowledge) pulse is also 0.5 μs minimum. There are no restrictions on the other times for this interface.

### Queue

A *queue* is a buffer memory that operates as a FIFO (first in, first out) memory. A queue requires two pointers: one to locate the current entry point in the queue, the other to locate the current exit point. A queue is a cyclic memory that uses the same area of memory repeatedly. The bottom of the queue is found one location above the top. Queues are also often called *FIFOs* or *print spoolers*.

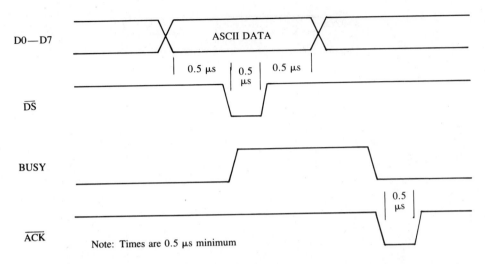

**Figure 9-17   The timing for the Centronics parallel printer interface.**

Two pointers are required to track the queue because there are two conditions that must be detected: empty and full. Empty is detected when the two pointers are equal. This is the condition that is initialized when the queue is first used. The other queue condition, full, is normally detected when the input pointer is one less than the output pointer.

As data enter the queue, they are placed at the location addressed by the input pointer; then there is a test to determine whether the queue is full and, if not, the input pointer is incremented. When data are to be removed from the queue, the pointers are first compared to test for an empty condition. If the queue is not empty, the contents of the memory location addressed by the exit pointer are removed from memory. After this, the exit pointer is incremented.

Figure 9-18 illustrates a queue with its entry and exit pointers initialized so that the queue is empty. This 64k byte queue is a substantial queue. As mentioned, the top location in the queue is adjacent to the bottom location. This condition is forced by software that controls incrementing the pointers. Both pointers are stored in memory locations above the queue.

E X A M P L E   9 - 9

```
                           ;
                           ;This subroutine increments the pointer value
                           ;in register A0 for the queue.
                           ;
015000   5288        INCPNT   ADD.L   #1,A0           ;increment pointer
015002   C188                 EXG     A0,D0           ;exchange
015004   02800030FFFF         AND.L   #$30FFFF,D0     ;keep in range
01500A   C188                 EXG     A0,D0           ;exchange
01500C   4E75                 RTS
```

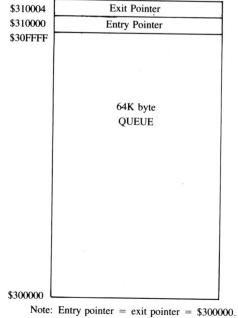

Note: Entry pointer = exit pointer = $300000.

**Figure 9-18** The queue, illustrating the locations of the entry and exit pointers.

Example 9-9 illustrates a subroutine that is used to increment a pointer stored in A0. Notice how the software detects an overflow and resets the address ($310000) to the bottom of the queue ($300000) if it overflows. This subroutine assumes that the queue is stored at memory locations $300000–30FFFF. The exchange instruction is used so that the address register can be ANDed with immediate data. There is no AND immediate data with an address register instruction in the 68000/68008 instruction set.

E  X  A  M  P  L  E      9 - 10

```
                          ;
                          ;This subroutine stores data into the
                          ;queue after the queue is first tested for
                          ;a full condition.
                          ;
01500E  207900310004  STORE  MOVE.L  EXIT,A0      ;get exit pointer
015014  61EA                 BSR     INCPNT       ;increment exit
015016  B1F900310000         CMP.L   ENTRY,A0     ;test for full
01501C  67F0                 BEQ     STORE        ;if full
01501E  207900310000         MOVE.L  ENTRY,A0     ;get entry pointer
015024  10B0                 MOVE.B  D0,(A0)      ;save data
015026  61D8                 BSR     INCPNT       ;increment entry
015028  23C800310000         MOVE.L  A0,ENTRY     ;save entry pointer
01502E  08F9000000400001     BSET    #0,$400001   ;enable CA1 interrupt
015036  4E75                 RTS
```

Example 9-10 illustrates a subroutine (STORE) that is used to place data into the queue. Notice how this subroutine first tests the queue to determine whether it is full. If the queue is full, the subroutine waits for it to become less than full. (Note that a character is removed from the queue by an interrupt. The interrupt changes the value in the exit pointer, making the queue less than full.)

If the queue is not full, the data located in the byte portion of D0 are stored in the queue. Next the entry pointer is incremented by the INCPNT subroutine of Example 9-9. The entry pointer is then stored in memory so that its new value may be used later. The software for the queue assumes that the entry pointer is stored in long-word memory location $310000 and the exit pointer is stored at long-word location $310004.

This subroutine also enables the interrupt used to remove data from the queue. This is required, as explained in connection with the subroutine to extract information from the queue (Example 9-11, below).

## Printer–Hardware Interface

Before the subroutine that removes data from the queue can be examined, the operation and structure of the hardware interface must be known. The hardware interface used in this example is the 6821 PIA.

Figure 9-19 illustrates the 6821 PIA connected to a Centronics parallel port. In this example, peripheral data register A (PDRA) is used to pass data to the interface. The 6821 is operated as an interrupting device, with the $\overline{ACK}$ triggering an interrupt. Here the CA1 input is connected to the $\overline{ACK}$ signal. The 6821 is programmed so that the $\overline{IRQA}$ pin goes low when $\overline{ACK}$ goes low. The $\overline{IRQA}$ pin is used to request an interrupt for each acknowledge. Recall that "acknowledge" is sent back from the printer when the printer is ready for additional data.

The data strobe signal ($\overline{DS}$) is generated by the CA2 pin, which is programmed to go low when control register bit $CRA_3$ is zero. It returns to a logic one level when $CRA_3$ is placed at a logic one level. In this manner software is used to generate the $\overline{DS}$ signal.

A PAL 10L8 is used to decode the I/O address. In this example, $\overline{O8}$ selects the 6821 and $\overline{O7}$ sends the $\overline{VPA}$ signal back to the 68008 microprocessor. The I/O addresses decoded for the 6821 are $400000–$400003.

This interface is buffered using 74ALS244 octal buffers. The buffers are important to prevent damage to the 6821 PIA. Notice that not all control signals on the parallel port are connected. In practice all other connections are made to PDRB. In this example we decided not to complicate the software with these connections.

## The Interrupt Service Subroutine

The interrupt service subroutine for this circuit (Figure 9-19) is responsible for taking data out of the queue and sending them to the printer. Example 9-11 illustrates this interrupt service subroutine, which is called each time the $\overline{IRQA}$ pin on the 6821 becomes a logic zero. $\overline{IRQA}$ is forced low each time that $\overline{ACK}$ is returned by the printer.

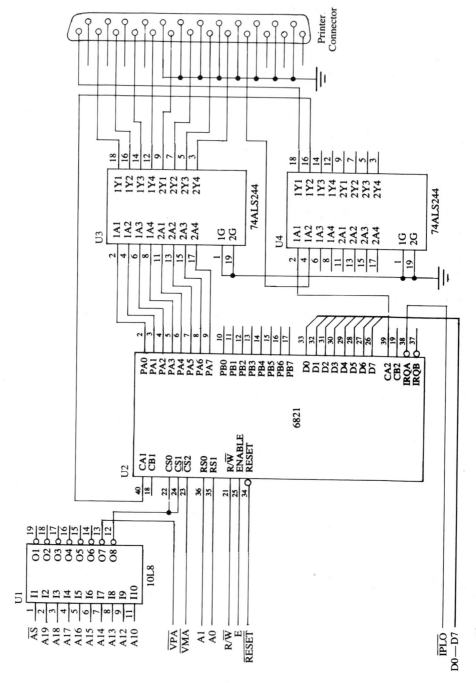

**Figure 9-19** The Centronics parallel printer interface connected to the 68008 microprocessor through a 6821 PIA.

**E X A M P L E    9 - 11**

```
                        ;
                        ;This is the interrupt service subroutine that is
                        ;activated each time the acknowledge signal is
                        ;returned by the printer.
                        ;
015038  2F08        ACKS    MOVE.L  A0,-(SP)        ;save A0
01503A  207900310004         MOVE.L  EXIT,A0         ;set exit pointer
015040  B1F900310000         CMP.L   ENTRY,A0        ;test for empty
015046  6600000E             BNE     ACKS1           ;if not empty
01504A  08B9000000400001     BCLR    #0,$400001      ;disable interrupt
015052  205F                 MOVE.L  (SP)+,A0        ;restore A0
015054  4E73                 RTE
015056  13D000400000 ACKS1   MOVE.B  (A0),$400000    ;send data to port A
01505C  61A2                 BSR     INCPNT          ;increment exit pointer
01505E  23C800310004         MOVE.L  A0,EXIT         ;save new exit pointer
015064  08B9000300400001     BCLR    #3,$400001      ;clear data strobe
01506C  08F9000300400001     BSET    #3,$400001      ;set data strobe
015074  205F                 MOVE.L  (SP)+,A0        ;restore A0
015076  4E73                 RTE
```

The first portion of the subroutine tests the queue to see whether it is empty. If empty, the interrupt is disabled until data are placed in the queue. Refer to the subroutine that places data into the queue (Example 9-10). It enables the interrupt each time it places data in the queue.

Next data are extracted from the queue and sent to PDRA and on to the printer through the buffers. Once data have been sent, the subroutine pulses the data strobe signal. This tells the printer that valid data appear on the data connections.

Finally a return from the interrupt service subroutine is made. This enables a future interrupt, which will occur when the printer sends back the $\overline{\text{ACK}}$ signal. The future interrupt again calls this subroutine so that the next data are sent to the printer.

## 9-4   The 68230 Parallel Interface and Timer

The 68230 parallel interface/timer (PI/T) is a versatile device that contains three parallel ports and a timer. The ports, labeled A, B, and C, are each 8 bits wide. Each of the port pins is individually programmable for maximum flexibility. Ports A and B can also be grouped together to form a 16-bit I/O port if desired. Bidirectional operation for ports A and B is available, as well as unidirectional operation.

A timer is found in the 68320 that is used as a programmable divider. The timer has a 5-bit prescaler and a 24-bit programmable timer. The output of the timer is either a continuous square wave, periodic interrupt, or a single interrupt. The 5-bit prescaler, which may or may not be used, divides the incoming clock signal by 32. Following the prescaler is the programmable timer, which divides by any value from 2 to 16,777,216. The maximum divide by number that can be programmed into the counter results when the prescaler is used with the count of 16,777,216. This maximum count is 32 times 16,777,216 or 538,870,912.

### 9-4.1    The 68230 Pinout

Figure 9-20 illustrates the pinout of the 68230 PI/T. Notice the three I/O ports. Ports A and B are general-purpose programmable I/O ports. Port C serves as a general-purpose I/O port or as a special port. Notice that six out of the eight pins of port C are dual purpose. The H1–H4 pins are handshaking connections that are used with certain interfaces and modes of operation. Generally, H1 and H2 are handshaking signals for port A, and H3 and H4 are used with port B.

On the system side there are eight data bus connections that make this device compatible with the 68000 and 68008. In the 68000 interface, these eight data connections are connected to either D0–D7 or D8–D15. The system side also contains RS pins, which are used for internal register selection. The PI/T has 23 internal registers that are selected with the RS pins. The PI/T is programmed through the internal registers. Finally, along with $\overline{\text{RESET}}$, R/$\overline{\text{W}}$, and $\overline{\text{CS}}$, is a $\overline{\text{DTACK}}$ output. This output is connected to the 68000 or 68008 $\overline{\text{DTACK}}$ connection. The $\overline{\text{CS}}$ connection is activated with a decoder that combines the I/O port address with the data strobe signal. A connection to the address strobe signal is optional with the decoder.

### 9-4.2    Interfacing the 68230 PI/T to the Microprocessor

Figure 9-21 illustrates the 68230 PI/T interfaced to the 68000 microprocessor. Notice that all the system connections to the 68230 are fairly direct. The 68230

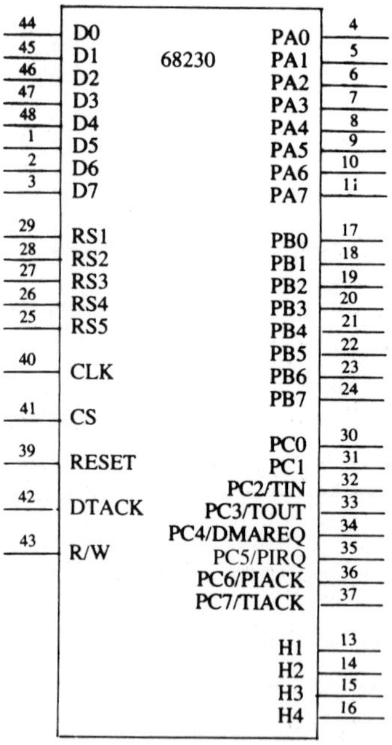

**Figure 9-20    The pinout of the 68230 parallel interface and timer (PI/T).**

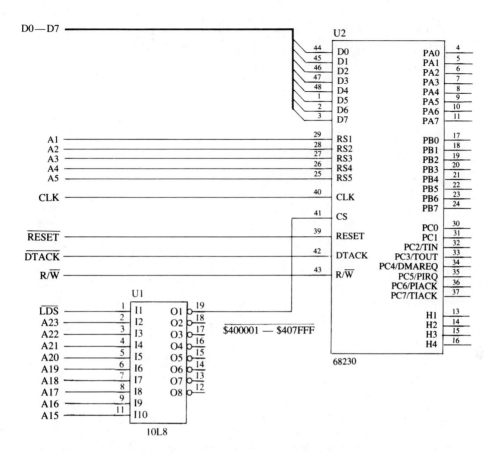

**Figure 9-21   The 68230 PI/T interfaced to the 68000 microprocessor at I/O addresses $4000001–$407FFF. Within this range of I/O addresses, only odd-numbered bytes are addressable because the 68230 is interfaced to the lower data bus half.**

internally includes a $\overline{\text{DTACK}}$ generator that allows it to be connected to any version of the 68000 at any clock speed. This interface will function properly even if the clock frequency is different from the microprocessor clock. Also notice that the register select inputs (RS) are connected to address connections A1–A5. On the 68008 microprocessor the RS connections are usually connected to A0–A4.

The decoder in this circuit selects the 68230 for the lower data bus at locations $400001–$407FFF. By connecting the 68230 to the lower data bus, access is provided to odd-numbered byte addresses only with the 68000 microprocessor.

To obtain access to even-numbered byte addresses, it is necessary to connect D8–D15 to the D0–D7 pins, with the upper data bus lines used as inputs of the PI/T. If this is done, the $\overline{\text{UDS}}$ signal is connected to the PAL decoder instead of $\overline{\text{LDS}}$. (If $\overline{\text{LDS}}$ is connected to the PAL decoder, only odd I/O addresses are available. If $\overline{\text{UDS}}$ is connected, only even addresses are available.) Note that a connection to the $\overline{\text{AS}}$ signal is not required for proper operation of the 68230. It is important that the data strobe signal be used to enable the 68230.

### 9-4.3   Programming the 68230

As mentioned, the 68230 contains 23 internal programmable registers, which direct the operation of the 68230, its ports, and its timer. Before programming is discussed, some definitions and an understanding of the different modes and submodes of operation for the 68230 are required.

#### Ports A and B

Ports A and B are programmed to operate in any of four different modes. Ports A and B are operated as 8-bit ports or combined to form one 16-bit port. When operated as a 16-bit port, port A is the most significant part and port B the least significant portion. In addition, the ports are operated as unidirectional or bidirectional ports. The four modes of operation appear in Table 9-6.

#### Nonlatched Input

One submode of operation for the I/O ports on the 68230 is called nonlatched input. The nonlatched submode, used for input data only, allows the data to be sampled from the input port at the exact time that the instruction used to read the port is executed. This is the same circuit configuration presented as the basic input port in the detailed discussion of I/O (Chapter 8).

#### Single-Buffered Output

The I/O ports on the 68230 can be operated in the single-buffered submode. The single-buffered submode is used for output data only. This term means that the data are output to an internal latch that holds the data at the I/O port pins until the next output. This is the same circuit presented as the basic output port in Chapter 8.

#### Double-Buffered Input and Output

Double-buffered ports are available as either inputs or outputs. The double-buffered input port uses a signal from the external I/O system to strobe data into the input port latch. The latch holds the data for the microprocessor.

**Table 9-6   Modes of Operation for Ports A and B of the 68230 PI/T**

| Mode | Operation |
|------|-----------|
| 0 | Unidirectional 8-bit mode |
| 1 | Unidirectional 16-bit |
| 2 | mode |
| 3 | Bidirectional 8-bit mode |
|   | Bidirectional 16-bit mode |

The input port holds 2 bytes of information before overflowing. This action is called double-buffering. The strobe usually generates an interrupt through the 68230 that calls attention to the data in the port. It may also generate a DMA request to transfer data through DMA techniques.

Double-buffered outputs hold data until the external I/O system strobes the data out of the port. As with double-buffered inputs, there is room for 2 bytes of data in the port operated in double-buffered mode. The strobe removes data from the port and signals the microprocessor that the port is empty, usually by means of an interrupt.

## Mode 0

Mode 0 has three possible submodes of operation: 00, 01, and 1X. Recall that mode 0 operation specifies that port A or B is to be operated as a unidirectional 8-bit port. The various submodes select between single-buffered, double-buffered, and non-latched functions for ports A and B. Table 9-7 lists the submodes of mode 0 operation, and Figure 9-22 illustrates them.

Submode 00 of mode 0 selects double-buffered inputs and single-buffered outputs. If port A or B is programmed as an input device, the H1 (port A) or H3 (port B) signal is used to clock the data into the port until the microprocessor removes it. If programmed as an output port, the data are held at the output pins until the next output instruction. Notice that the output is single buffered and requires no handshake from the external circuit.

Submode 01 of mode 0 selects double-buffered outputs and nonlatched inputs. If programmed as an output device, the H1 (port A) or H3 (port B) signal is used to strobe the data out of the port (i.e., to remove data from the port). If programmed as

**Table 9-7   Mode 0 Operation of the 68230 PI/T**

**Submode 00:   Double-buffered input or single-buffered output**

| | |
|---|---|
| H1 (H3) | Latches input data into port |
| H2 (H4) | Status/interrupt generating input, general-purpose output, or operated with H1 (H3) in the interlocked or pulsed handshake protocol |

**Submode 01:   Double-buffered output or nonlatched input**

| | |
|---|---|
| H1 (H3) | Strobes data out of port |
| H2 (H4) | Status/interrupt generating input, general-purpose output, or operated with H1 (H3) in the interlocked or pulsed handshake protocols |

**Submode 10 or 11:   Single-buffered output or nonlatched input**

| | |
|---|---|
| H1 (H3) | Status/interrupt generating input |
| H2 (H4) | Status/interrupt generating input or general-purpose output |

NOTE: These definitions apply to both ports A and B. Pins H1 and H2 are used with port A and (H3) and (H4) are used with port B.

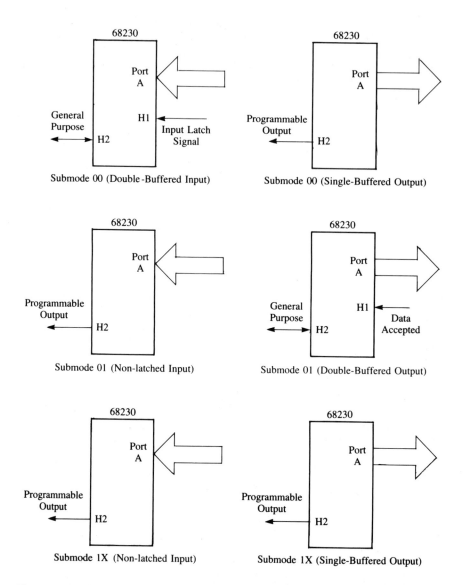

**Figure 9-22   Operation of port A in mode 0. When port B is operated in mode 0, H1 is H3 and H2 is H4.**

an input port, whatever is present on the port is input to the microprocessor at the time of the instruction that reads the port.

Submode 10 or 11 of mode 0 selects single-buffered output or nonlatched input. If programmed as an output port, a latch holds the data between output instructions. If programmed as an input port, the data are captured on the fly as the input instruction is executed. This submode is used when the direction of data flow on the port is split (e.g., for port A, pins PA0–PA2 are inputs and pins PA3–PA7 are outputs).

**Table 9-8   Mode 1 Operation of the 68230 PI/T**

**Port A (MSB) nonlatched input or single-buffered output**

| | |
|---|---|
| H1 | Status/interrupt generating input |
| H2 | Status/interrupt generating input or general-purpose output |

**Port B (LSB)**

Submode 00 or 10: Double-buffered input or single-buffered output

| | |
|---|---|
| H3 | Latches input data |
| H4 | Status/interrupt generating input, general-purpose output, or operated with H3 in the interlocked or pulsed handshake protocol |

Submode 01 or 11: Double-buffered output or nonlatched input

| | |
|---|---|
| H3 | Indicates data received by peripheral |
| H4 | Status/interrupt generating input, general-purpose output, or operated with H3 in the interlocked or pulsed handshake protocol |

## Mode 1

Mode 1 is operated as a unidirectional 16-bit I/O port. Port A is the most significant 8 bits and port B the least. If programmed as an input device, port A is a single-buffered output or a nonlatched input. Port B is programmed as a double-buffered output or as either a nonlatched input or a single-buffered input. Programming as a 16-bit unidirectional port is through two submodes for port B. Port A operates in only one submode. Refer to Table 9-8 for the submodes of mode 1 and Figure 9-23 for the operation and connection of the 68230.

## Mode 2

Mode 2 operation is a bidirectional mode that allows data to be sent or received from the ports. There are no submodes of operation for mode 2. Port A is used for bit I/O and port B is a double-buffered bidirectional port. Refer to Table 9-9 for a summary of the operation of the 68230 in mode 2 and to Figure 9-24 for an illustration of the connections of the 68230 when operated in modes 2 and 3.

## Mode 3

Mode 3 is almost identical to mode 2. The only difference is that it is used for 16-bit I/O instead of 8-bit I/O. The MSB is located at port A and the LSB at port B. The handshaking signals perform as with mode 2, illustrated in Table 9-9 and Figure 9-24.

## Port C

Port C is used as an 8-bit, general-purpose I/O port or any combination of six special functions. Each of these six dual-function port C pins operates indepen-

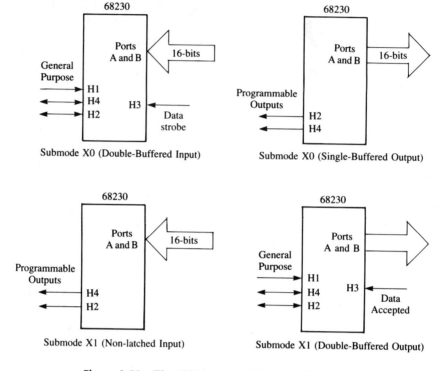

**Figure 9-23    The 68230 operated in the 16-bit mode 1.**

dently of other port C pins. The alternate functions for these six pins are used with the timer, interrupts, and DMA (direct memory access).

The TIN, TOUT, and $\overline{\text{TIACK}}$ pins are used with the timer. TIN provides the timer with its input clock signal. It also may be used to control whether the timer is running or not running. TOUT is used either to request an interrupt or to provide a square wave output from the timer. Finally, the $\overline{\text{TIACK}}$ pin is an input used for a timer interrupt acknowledge signal.

$\overline{\text{PIRQ}}$ and $\overline{\text{PIACK}}$ are interrupt pins. The $\overline{\text{PIRQ}}$ signal is an active low interrupt request signal. The $\overline{\text{PIRQ}}$ is programmed to function with both ports A and B. The $\overline{\text{PIACK}}$ is a port interrupt acknowledge input.

**Table 9-9    Mode 2 Operation of the 68230 PI/T**

| | |
|---|---|
| Port A | Bit I/O |
| Port B | Double-buffered bidirectional data |
| H1 | Enables port B output buffers |
| H2 | Indicates data are available at port B |
| H3 | Latches input data |
| H4 | Operates with H3 in the interlocked or pulsed input protocol |

NOTE: Applies also to mode 3.

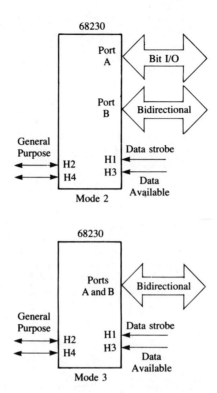

**Figure 9-24**   **The operation of the 68230 in modes 2 and 3. Mode 2 is an 8-bit bidirectional mode and mode 3 is a 16-bit bidirectional mode.**

The $\overline{\text{DMAREQ}}$ is used to request a direct memory access operation. This pin is compatible with the 68450 family of DMA controllers discussed in Chapter 10.

### 9-4.4   Internal Register Structure

The internal register structure (all 23 registers) is listed in Figure 9-25. Note that in this illustration, the internal register address uses the register selection bits (RS1–RS5) and the function of each bit of each register is given. The register selection pins are normally connected to the five least significant address connections.

Register 00000 is used to select the mode of operation, the sensitivity level of H4–H1, and whether H4–H1 are enabled. The port mode control bits select modes 0–3. If the sense bit for an H pin is programmed with a logic zero, the pin is an active low pin. If an H pin is programmed with a logic one, it is an active high pin. The port A or port B handshaking pins are enabled by placing a logic one in H12 for port A and H34 for port B.

Register 00001, the port service request register, is used to program DMA actions through SVCRQ and the operation of the interrupt structure of the 68230. A 00 on bits 6 and 5 programs PC4 as an I/O bit. If these bits are programmed with a 10, the PC4 pin becomes $\overline{\text{DMAREQ}}$, activated by the H1 pin (port A) for double-

| Register Select Bits 5 4 3 2 1 | 7 | 6 | 5 | 4 | 3 | 2 | 1 | 0 | Register Value RESET (Hex Value) | |
|---|---|---|---|---|---|---|---|---|---|---|
| 0 0 0 0 0 | Port Mode Control | | H34 Enable | H12 Enable | H4 Sense | H3 Sense | H2 Sense | H1 Sense | 0 0 | Port General Control Register |
| 0 0 0 0 1 | * | SVCRQ Select | | IPF Select | | Port Interrupt Priority Control | | | 0 0 | Port Service Request Register |
| 0 0 0 1 0 | Bit 7 | Bit 6 | Bit 5 | Bit 4 | Bit 3 | Bit 2 | Bit 1 | Bit 0 | 0 0 | Port A Date Direction Register |
| 0 0 0 1 1 | Bit 7 | Bit 6 | Bit 5 | Bit 4 | Bit 3 | Bit 2 | Bit 1 | Bit 0 | 0 0 | Port B Data Direction Register |
| 0 0 1 0 0 | Bit 7 | Bit 6 | Bit 5 | Bit 4 | Bit 3 | Bit 2 | Bit 1 | Bit 0 | 0 0 | Port C Data Direction Register |
| 0 0 1 0 1 | Interrupt Vector Number | | | | | | * | * | 0 F | Port Interrupt Vector Register |
| 0 0 1 1 0 | Port A Submode | | H2 Control | | | H2 Int Enable | H1 SVCRQ Enable | H1 Stat Ctrl | 0 0 | Port A Control Register |
| 0 0 1 1 1 | Port B Submode | | H4 Control | | | H4 Int Enable | H3 SVCRQ Enable | H3 Stat Ctrl | 0 0 | Port B Control Register |
| 0 1 0 0 0 | Bit 7 | Bit 6 | Bit 5 | Bit 4 | Bit 3 | Bit 2 | Bit 1 | Bit 0 | * * | Port A Data Register |
| 0 1 0 0 1 | Bit 7 | Bit 6 | Bit 5 | Bit 4 | Bit 3 | Bit 2 | Bit 1 | Bit 0 | * * | Port B Data Register |
| 0 1 0 1 0 | Bit 7 | Bit 6 | Bit 5 | Bit 4 | Bit 3 | Bit 2 | Bit 1 | Bit 0 | * * * | Port A Alternate Register |
| 0 1 0 1 1 | Bit 7 | Bit 6 | Bit 5 | Bit 4 | Bit 3 | Bit 2 | Bit 1 | Bit 0 | * * * | Port B Alternate Register |
| 0 1 1 0 0 | Bit 7 | Bit 6 | Bit 5 | Bit 4 | Bit 3 | Bit 2 | Bit 1 | Bit 0 | * * * * | Port C Data Register |
| 0 1 1 0 1 | H4 Level | H3 Level | H2 Level | H1 Level | H4S | H3S | H2S | H1S | * * * * | Port Status Register |
| 0 1 1 1 0 | * | * | * | * | * | * | * | * | 0 0 | (Null) |
| 0 1 1 1 1 | * | * | * | * | * | * | * | * | 0 0 | (Null) |

* Unused, read as zero
** Value before RESET
*** Current value on pins
**** Undetermined value

**Figure 9-25** The 68230 register set. (*Courtesy of Motorola, Inc.*)

buffered transfers. If programmed with a 11, PC4 becomes a $\overline{\text{DMAREQ}}$ signal for port B, using the H3 pin to request a DMA transfer for double-buffered operation. Table 9-10 illustrates the effect of bit positions 4 and 3 in the port service request register.

The right-most three bits of the port service request register (00001) determine the interrupt priority of the ports. Table 9-11 lists the different combinations of bits 2, 1, and 0 of the port service request register. Any H pin can be an interrupt source, depending on the mode and submodes of operation for the 68230 PI/T.

| Register Select Bits 5 4 3 2 1 | 7 | 6 | 5 | 4 | 3 | 2 | 1 | 0 | Register Value After RESET (Hex Value) | |
|---|---|---|---|---|---|---|---|---|---|---|
| 1 0 0 0 0 | TOUT/TIACK Control | | | ZD Ctrl | * | Clock Control | | Timer Enable | 00 | Timer Control Register |
| 1 0 0 0 1 | Bit 7 | Bit 6 | Bit 5 | Bit 4 | Bit 3 | Bit 2 | Bit 1 | Bit 0 | 0F | Timer Interrupt Vector Register |
| 1 0 0 1 0 | * | * | * | * | * | * | * | * | 00 | (Null) |
| 1 0 0 1 1 | Bit 23 | Bit 22 | Bit 21 | Bit 20 | Bit 19 | Bit 18 | Bit 17 | Bit 16 | ** | Counter Preload Register (High) |
| 1 0 1 0 0 | Bit 15 | Bit 14 | Bit 13 | Bit 12 | Bit 11 | Bit 10 | Bit 9 | Bit 8 | ** | Counter Preload Register (Mid) |
| 1 0 1 0 1 | Bit 7 | Bit 6 | Bit 5 | Bit 4 | Bit 3 | Bit 2 | Bit 1 | Bit 0 | ** | Counter Preload Register (Low) |
| 1 0 1 1 0 | * | * | * | * | * | * | * | * | 00 | (Null) |
| 1 0 1 1 1 | Bit 23 | Bit 22 | Bit 21 | Bit 20 | Bit 19 | Bit 18 | Bit 17 | Bit 16 | ** | Count Register (High) |
| 1 1 0 0 0 | Bit 15 | Bit 14 | Bit 13 | Bit 12 | Bit 11 | Bit 10 | Bit 9 | Bit 8 | ** | Count Register (Mid) |
| 1 1 0 0 1 | Bit 7 | Bit 6 | Bit 5 | Bit 4 | Bit 3 | Bit 2 | Bit 1 | Bit 0 | ** | Count Register (Low) |
| 1 1 0 1 0 | * | * | * | * | * | * | * | ZDS | 00 | Timer Status Register |
| 1 1 0 1 1 | * | * | * | * | * | * | * | * | 00 | (Null) |
| 1 1 1 0 0 | * | * | * | * | * | * | * | * | 00 | (Null) |
| 1 1 1 0 1 | * | * | * | * | * | * | * | * | 00 | (Null) |
| 1 1 1 1 0 | * | * | * | * | * | * | * | * | 00 | (Null) |
| 1 1 1 1 1 | * | * | * | * | * | * | * | * | 00 | (Null) |

\* Unused, read as zero
\*\* Value before RESET

**Figure 9-25 Continued.**

Registers 00010, 00011, and 00100 are used to program the direction of peripheral registers A, B, and C, respectively, and to function as data direction registers. Register 00101 is used to program the desired user interrupt vector number for an interrupt. Submodes are selected for ports A and B with registers 00110 and 00111.

The port data registers appear as registers 01000 for port A, 01001 for port B, and 01100 for port C. The remaining defined registers control the operation of the timer.

**Table 9-10** Interrupt Selection Through Bits 4 and 3 of the Port Service Request Register

| Bits | | Function |
|---|---|---|
| 4 | 3 | |
| 0 | 0 | The PC5/$\overline{\text{PIRQ}}$ and PC6/$\overline{\text{PIACK}}$ pins function as I/O bits (PC5 and PC6) for port C. |
| 0 | 1 | The PC5/$\overline{\text{PIRQ}}$ functions as an interrupt request that supports autovector interrupts. PC6/$\overline{\text{PIACK}}$ functions as an I/O bit (PC6) for port C. |
| 1 | 0 | The PC5/$\overline{\text{PIRQ}}$ functions as an I/O bit (PC5) for port C. The PC6/$\overline{\text{PIACK}}$ functions as an interrupt acknowledge signal. |
| 1 | 1 | Both PC5/$\overline{\text{PIRQ}}$ and PC6/$\overline{\text{PIACK}}$ function as interrupt request and interrupt acknowledge for user vectored interrupts. |

### 9-4.5  Timer Operation

Figure 9-26 illustrates the four basic modes of operation for the internal timer and its prescaler. The prescaler is a 5-bit counter that divides its input by a factor of 32. The timer is a 24-bit counter that is programmed to divide by any whole number between 2 and $FFFFFF. The timer is a down-counter that is loaded with a count. For example, if the timer is loaded with a count of 6, it counts down from 6 until it reaches 0. In one mode, when the timer hits 0, it is reloaded with the count. Here, the timer counts from 6 down to 0 and the count repeats. This causes the timer to divide the input by a factor of 7. If a divide by count of 306 is required, the programmed count is 305.

Registers 10011, 10100, and 10101 are the counter preload registers (refer to Figure 9-25) used to program the counter. Registers 10111, 11000, and 11001 are counter registers, which are read if the current count is desired. Data written to a

**Table 9-11**  Interrupt Priority Levels

| Bits | | | Priority levels | | | |
|---|---|---|---|---|---|---|
| | | | Highest | $\rightarrow$ | | Lowest |
| 0 | 0 | 0 | H1 | H2 | H3 | H4 |
| 0 | 0 | 1 | H2 | H1 | H3 | H4 |
| 0 | 1 | 0 | H1 | H2 | H4 | H3 |
| 0 | 1 | 1 | H2 | H1 | H4 | H3 |
| 1 | 0 | 0 | H3 | H4 | H1 | H2 |
| 1 | 0 | 1 | H3 | H4 | H2 | H1 |
| 1 | 1 | 0 | H4 | H3 | H1 | H2 |
| 1 | 1 | 1 | H4 | H3 | H2 | H1 |

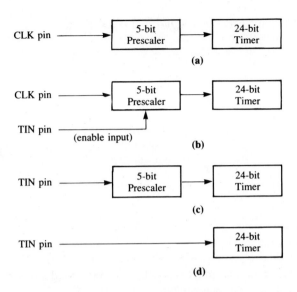

CLK pin → 5-bit Prescaler → 24-bit Timer

**(a)**

CLK pin → 5-bit Prescaler → 24-bit Timer
TIN pin — (enable input)

**(b)**

TIN pin → 5-bit Prescaler → 24-bit Timer

**(c)**

TIN pin → 24-bit Timer

**(d)**

**Figure 9-26**  The four modes of operation of the 68230 timer. (a) The clock pin as a timing source. (b) The clock pin as a timing source using TIN to enable counting. (c) The TIN pin as a timing source. (d) No prescaler, with TIN as the timing source.

counter register have no effect. The preload counter registers are used to change the count.

Two control registers (10000 and 10001) are associated with the timer. The timer control register (10000) is used to program the operation of the timer, and the timer interrupt vector register (10001) is used to program the interrupt vector for a timer user interrupt.

The timer control register bits 7, 6, and 5 program the configuration of the PC3/TOUT and PC7/$\overline{\text{TIACK}}$ pins. The functions of these pins, along with bits 7, 6, and 5 of the timer control register, are listed in Table 9-12. Notice that these bits select user or autovector interrupts.

Bit position 4 of the timer control register is used to program the zero detect control. If a zero is placed in this bit, the counter is reloaded with the preload count on each zero detect. If programmed with a logic one, the counter merely continues counting after a zero detect.

Bit positions 2 and 1 of the timer control register select the configuration of the prescaler and counter. Table 9-13 lists the functions of the clock for all four combinations of bits 2 and 1. The timer enable bit is used to enable the timer if it is a logic one. If it is a logic zero, the timer is disabled.

### 9-4.6 Example 68230 Keyboard/Display Interface

The 68230 is an extremely flexible interfacing component. Figure 9-27 illustrates this device connected to a keyboard and a display for a small system. Here an eight-digit display is interfaced to ports A and B. Port A is used to provide the display

**Table 9-12   The Function of PC3/TOUT and PC7/$\overline{\text{TIACK}}$**

| Bits | | | PC3/TOUT | PC7/$\overline{\text{TIACK}}$ |
|---|---|---|---|---|
| 7 | 6 | 5 | | |
| 0 | 0 | X | PC3 | PC7 |
| 0 | 1 | X | TOUT square wave | PC7 |
| 1 | 0 | 0 | TOUT timer interrupt request | No response |
| 1 | 0 | 1 | TOUT timer interrupt request | $\overline{\text{TIACK}}$ for user interrupt vectors |
| 1 | 1 | 0 | TOUT timer interrupt request | PC7 |
| 1 | 1 | 1 | TOUT timer interrupt request | $\overline{\text{TIACK}}$ for autovector interrupts |

with its seven-segment code. Port B selects one of the eight display positions and also columns on the keyboard.

The keyboard is organized as a matrix with 8 columns and 4 rows for a total of 32 keys. Port C is used to read the rows of the keyboard and also to provide a timer interrupt signal to the microprocessor.

The interrupt, which occurs 1000 times per second, is used to select a new display position, to send new data to the new display position, and to select a new column on the keyboard. This greatly eases the task of displaying data. This interrupt and its task are referred to as a *background program* because it functions without any attention from any program. In fact, it functions without user intervention as long as the system is powered.

### Initialization for the 68230

The 68230 is programmed with the software illustrated in Example 9-12. Notice that this software not only sets up the I/O ports, it also programs the timer. In this

**Table 9-13   The Clock Control**

| Bits | | Function |
|---|---|---|
| 2 | 1 | |
| 0 | 0 | The PC2/TIN pin is a port C I/O bit (PC3). The timer operates with the prescaler so that after every 32 clock pulses on the clock pin (CLK), the timer counts by one if enabled. |
| 0 | 1 | The PC2/TIN pin is used to enable the timer if the timer enable bit is also enabled. The timer operates with the prescaler, so that after every 32 clock pulses on the clock pin (CLK), the timer counts by one. |
| 1 | 0 | The PC2/TIN pin is used as a clock to the prescaler. The prescaler divides the TIN signal by 32 and applies it to the input of the timer. The timer enable bit enables the timer. |
| 1 | 1 | The PC2/TIN pin is used as a clock signal to the timer. The prescaler is not used. The timer enable bit enables the timer. |

program the MOVE.B instruction is used to move $00 into certain registers; CLR was not used to permit this software to serve as a model allowing different immediate data to be moved into any internal register.

E X A M P L E    9 - 12

```
                                    ;
                                    ;Software that initializes the 68230 for the
                                    ;Keyboard/display system of Figure 9-27,
                                    ;
016000  13FC000000040000  INIT  MOVE.B  #$00,$40000  ;select Mode 0
016008  13FC000000040001        MOVE.B  #$00,$40001  ;PC4, PC5, and PC6
016010  13FC00FF00040002        MOVE.B  #$FF,$40002  ;Port A = output
016018  13FC00FF00040003        MOVE.B  #$FF,$40003  ;Port B = output
016020  13FC000000040004        MOVE.B  #$00,$40004  ;Port C = input
016028  13FC000000040006        MOVE.B  #$00,$40006  ;Port A submode 0
016030  13FC000000040007        MOVE.B  #$00,$40007  ;Port B submode 0
016038  13FC000000040013        MOVE.B  #$00,$40013  ;program count of 8000
016040  13FC001F00040014        MOVE.B  #$1F,$40014
016048  13FC004000040015        MOVE.B  #$40,$40015
016050  13FC008000040011        MOVE.B  #$80,$40011  ;timer interrupt vector
016058  13FC00A700040010        MOVE.B  #$A7,$40010  ;program timer
016060  4E75                    RTS
```

The timer's user interrupt vector provides an interrupt vector number each time the timer reaches a count of zero. This vector is initialized to vector type $80 in this example. The interrupt is requested with the PC3/TOUT pin. This signal is connected to one of the active low $\overline{IPL}$ inputs of the 68008 microprocessor. Because the 68230 is programmed for user vectors, the 68230 issues the user vector number on the data bus and also a $\overline{DTACK}$ signal during the interrupt acknowledge cycle.

The source for the timer is the CLK signal connected to the PC2/TIN pin of the 68230 PI/T. Because an 8 MHz clock is attached, the timer is programmed to divide the clock by a factor of 8000 ($1F40) to produce a 1 kHz interrupting signal.

The software to program the 68230 first programs the I/O ports so that ports A and B are outputs and port C is an input port. Next, the timer count, interrupt vector number, and timer operation are programmed. The very last instruction before the return enables the timer, so that it begins counting and generating interrupts.

## Interrupt Service Subroutine

The interrupt service subroutine (vector $80) is called 1000 times a second by the timer. Example 9-13 lists this interrupt service subroutine. The subroutine itself uses a 10-byte section of RAM (locations $2000–$2009) to store the seven-segment codes for each position of the display, a selection code, and a pointer value. The selection code is used to select a display position, and the pointer locates the correct data for the display in the display RAM. This is almost identical to the display interfaced to the 6821 in Chapter 8.

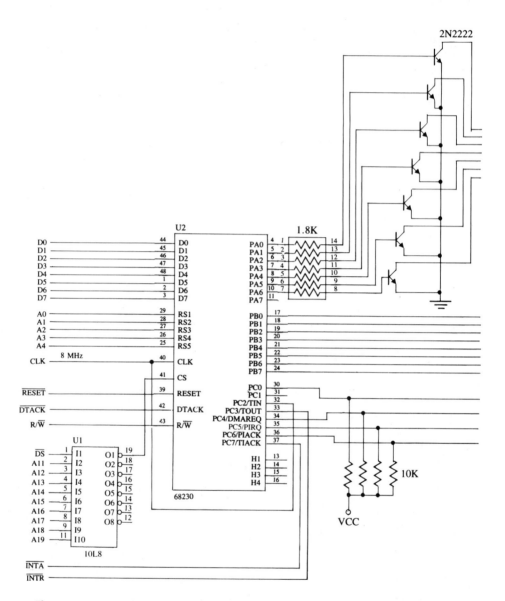

**Figure 9-27**    A keyboard and display interfaced through the 68230 to the 68008 microprocessor at I/O addresses $40000–$4001F.

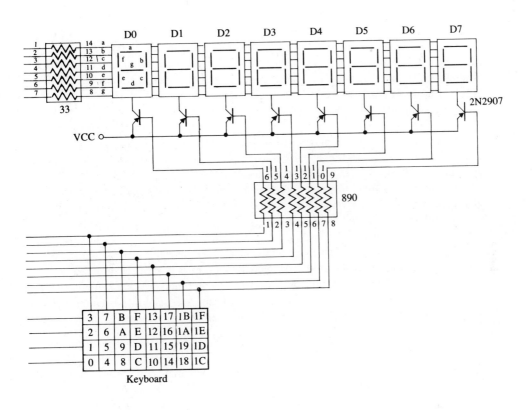

EXAMPLE    9 - 13

```
                              ;
                              ;Interrupt service subroutine that displays data from
                              ;the display RAM onto the eight displays.
                              ;
016062   48E7C080    INTRUP   MOVEM.L   D0-D1/A0,-(SP)       ;save registers
016066   307C2000             MOVE.W    #RAM,A0              ;address display RAM
01606A   4240                 CLR.W     D0
01606C   10280008             MOVE.B    8(A0),D0             ;get pointer
016070   12280009             MOVE.B    9(A0),D1             ;get select code
016074   E209                 LSR.B     #1,D1                ;adjust select code
016076   5300                 SUB.B     #1,D0                ;adjust pointer
016078   6A00000A             BPL       INT1                 ;if positive
01607C   123C007F             MOVE.B    #$7F,D1              ;reset select code
016080   103C0007             MOVE.B    #7,D0                ;reset pointer
016084   11400008    INT1     MOVE.B    D0,8(A0)             ;save new pointer
016088   11410009             MOVE.B    D1,9(A0)             ;save new select code
01608C   13C100040011         MOVE.B    D1,$40011            ;select display
```

```
016092  13F0000000040010        MOVE.B   0(A0,D0.W),$40010   ;send 7-seg code
01609A  4CDF0103                MOVEM.L  (SP)+,D0-D1/A0      ;restore registers
01609E  4E73                    RTE
```

Each time the interrupt occurs, the subroutine fetches the pointer and the selection code from the RAM. The values of both the pointer and the selection code are changed so that the next display position is selected. After the pointer and select code have been adjusted, the new display position is selected and the contents of a display RAM location (seven-segment code) is sent to port A for display. The location in the RAM is addressed by the pointer.

To display new information on this display, the user simply stores the seven-segment code into the display RAM memory locations. Display RAM location $2000 is display D0, and display RAM location $2007 is display D7. The interrupt service subroutine automatically displays the new data. The interrupt makes this type of display interface extremely easy to use.

Because the display position is changed 1000 times per second, all eight displays appear to light up at once. Your eyes retain the number displayed on each digit as they retain the individual frames in a motion picture. This is due to the persistence of visual data in the brain.

In addition to selecting a new display position, the interrupt service subroutine selects a new column on the keyboard. Notice that port B is connected to columns on the keyboard. The value located in the display pointer memory location indicates which column of the keyboard is currently selected. If display position D0 is selected, the keyboard column beginning with a zero is also selected.

### Keyboard Subroutine

The keyboard subroutine uses the pointer, modified each time an interrupt occurs, to test each column of the keyboard for a keystroke. In Example 9-14, which lists the subroutine that reads the keyboard, the data are returned in the D0 register as a number between 0 and 31. These numbers represent the 32 different keys on the keyboard, as illustrated. These codes are assigned other values if needed for a particular application. A table lookup subroutine can be added to this software for assigning other values to the keys.

**E  X  A  M  P  L  E    9 - 14**

```
                        ;
                        ;Subroutine that scans the keyboard and returns
                        ;with the code of the key in D0. This subroutine
                        ;must be branched to with a TRAP instruction
                        ;because of STOP.
                        ;
                        ;wait for release
                        ;
0160A0  48E76000  INKEY   MOVEM.L  D1-D2,-(SP)   ;save registers
0160A4  61000042  INKEY1  BSR      SCAN          ;test keyboard
0160A8  66FA              BNE      INKEY1        ;if key is pressed
0160AA  6100005E          BSR      DELAY         ;debounce key
```

```
0160AE  61000038                BSR     SCAN          ;test keyboard
0160B2  66F0                    BNE     INKEY1        ;if key is pressed
                          ;
                          ;wait for key
                          ;
0160B4  61000032        INKEY2  BSR     SCAN          ;test keyboard
0160B8  67FA                    BEQ     INKEY2        ;if no key
0160BA  6100004E                BSR     DELAY         ;denounce key
0160BE  61000028                BSR     SCAN          ;test keyboard
0160C2  67F0                    BEQ     INKEY2        ;if not key
                          ;
                          ;calculate key
                          ;
0160C4  10382008                MOVE.B  RAM+8,D0      ;get pointer
0160C8  E508                    LSL.B   #2,D0         ;multiply by 4
0160CA  E50A                    LSL.B   #2,D2
0160CC  64000014                BCC     INKEY3        ;if key found
0160D0  5200                    ADD.B   #1,D0         ;adjust key code
0160D2  E30A                    LSL.B   #1,D2
0160D4  6400000C                BCC     INKEY3        ;if key found
0160D8  5200                    ADD.B   #1,D0
0160DA  E30A                    LSL.B   #1,D2
0160DC  64000004                BCC     INKEY3        ;if key found
0160E0  5200                    ADD.B   #1,D0
0160E2  4CDF0006        INKEY3  MOVEM.L (SP)+,D1-D2   ;restore registers
0160E6  4E73                    RTE
                          ;
                          ;scan keyboard subroutine
                          ;
0160E8  323C0007        SCAN    MOVE.W  #7,D1         ;load counter
0160EC  4E722000        SCAN1   STOP    #$2000        ;wait for interrupt
0160F0  143900040014            MOVE.B  $40014,D2     ;read port C
0160F6  0002008E                OR.B    #$8E,D2       ;set unused bits
0160FA  0C0200FF                CMP.B   #$FF,D2       ;test for key
0160FE  66000008                BNE     SCAN2         ;if key found
016102  51C9FFE8                DBRA    D1,SCAN1      ;repeat 8 times
016106  4201                    CLR.B   D1
016108  4E75            SCAN2   RTS
                          ;
                          ;16 ms time delay
                          ;
01610A  323C000F        DELAY   MOVE.W  #15,D1        ;load count
01610E  4E722000        DELAY1  STOP    #$2000        ;wait 1 ms
016112  51C9FFFA                DBRA    D1,DELAY1
016116  4E75                    RTS
```

Notice that the keyboard subroutine contains two other subroutines. One is used as a time delay to debounce the keyboard. The time delay uses the STOP instruction to wait for an interrupt from the timer. Because the interrupt occurs once per millisecond, the STOP instruction causes a one-millisecond time delay. The time delay subroutine executes 16 STOP instructions for a time delay of 16 ms, which is used for debouncing the keyboard. Because the STOP instruction is used within the keyboard subroutine, the keyboard subroutine must be executed in the supervisor mode. This is accomplished by using one of the software interrupt (TRAP) instructions to access the keyboard subroutine.

The other subroutine is used to test all eight columns of the keyboard for activity. If no activity exists, the subroutine is called again and the keys are again tested. If a keystroke is detected, the subroutine returns and the code (position) of the key is calculated and placed in D0 for a return.

The position on the keyboard is calculated by using the pointer from the display RAM. The pointer contains a $00 for keys 0, 1, 2, and 3. It contains $01 for keys 4, 5, 6, and 7. This tracks up to pointer number $07, where keys $1C, $1D, $1E, and $1F are selected. If the pointer value is multiplied by 4, it indicates the first key code in a column. This is accomplished in the keyboard subroutine with a logical left shift.

Once the key code for the first key of a column has been determined, the software uses shifts and additions to modify the code to match the key closure. After the key code has been found, a return from this software interrupt is accomplished with the RTE instruction.

## Summary

1. Interrupts and exceptions are prioritized into three major groupings: 0, 1, and 2. Group 0 has the highest priority and contains exceptions for reset, bus error, and address error. Next in priority is group 1, which contains exceptions for trace, hardware interrupt, illegal exception, and privilege violation. Finally, with the lowest priority, are group 2 exceptions, entailing software, such as TRAP and TRAPV.

2. Whenever an interrupt or an exception is processed, the microprocessor places copies of the status register and program counter into the supervisor stack. A context switch occurs to the supervisor mode for all interrupt and exception processing. A return from the interrupt or exception handler is accomplished with the RTE instruction. RTE reinstates the prior contents of the status register and the state of the machine by retrieving this and the program counter from the supervisor stack.

3. The bus error and address error exceptions cause to be stored on the supervisor stack such additional information about the exception as the instruction and the access addresses. The other information indicates the function code bits of the operation that caused the bus or address error.

4. The exception/interrupt vector table occupies the first 1k bytes of the memory system from locations $000000 to $0003FF. The vector table contains 256 exception and interrupt vectors. Each vector is 4 bytes in length and contains the address of the interrupt service subroutine or the exception handler.

5. The hardware interrupt structure contains four interrupt input connections: $\overline{BERR}$, $\overline{IPL2}$, $\overline{IPL1}$, and $\overline{IPL0}$. The $\overline{BERR}$ input is used to request a bus error interrupt if asserted with $\overline{HALT}$ at a logic one level. If $\overline{HALT}$ is at a logic zero level when $\overline{BERR}$ is asserted, the 68000 reruns the current bus cycle. The $\overline{IPL}$ inputs are active low inputs used to request an autovector or a user interrupt.

**6.** The function code output connections indicate an interrupt acknowledge when all three pins are logic one. This condition is often labeled $\overline{\text{INTA}}$ for interrupt acknowledge and is decoded with a NAND gate.

**7.** Autovector interrupts are requested whenever the $\overline{\text{VPA}}$ input is asserted in response to the $\overline{\text{INTA}}$. Autovector interrupts are requested with the active low $\overline{\text{IPL}}$ inputs. For example, if $\overline{\text{IPL2}} = 1$, $\overline{\text{IPL1}} = 0$, and $\overline{\text{IPL0}} = 0$, autovector level 3 is requested.

**8.** User interrupts are requested if $\overline{\text{DTACK}}$ is asserted in response to $\overline{\text{INTA}}$. In addition, the system must provide the vector number on the data bus (D0–D7) for an interrupt acknowledge when user interrupts are desired.

**9.** The interrupt mask bits, in the status register, are used to enable and disable various interrupt levels. The number loaded into the mask bits determines which interrupt level is disabled. It also disables all lower priority level interrupts. For example, if a 100 is loaded into the interrupt mask bits, interrupt levels 4, 3, 2, and 1 are disabled. Interrupt level 7 has the special status of being nonmaskable.

**10.** There are 16 different software exception instructions available: TRAP 0–TRAP 15. Software exceptions are user definable and can be invoked for any purpose required.

**11.** The TRAPV instruction, a conditional exception instruction, tests the overflow CCR bit. If overflow is set, TRAPV causes an exception to occur. If overflow is cleared, this instruction performs a NOP and the program continues with the next instruction.

**12.** An interrupt service subroutine or exception handler is used to process the interrupt or an exception. It is a subroutine like any other except that it ends with the RTE instruction rather than RTS or RTR.

**13.** The primary purpose of the uninitialized interrupt vector (15) is to indicate that an external device has not been initialized. This interrupt is at times used for other purposes, however.

**14.** The spurious interrupt occurs when the external hardware does not respond with either a $\overline{\text{VPA}}$ or $\overline{\text{DTACK}}$ signal. The external hardware must respond with $\overline{\text{BERR}}$ in place of $\overline{\text{VPA}}$ or $\overline{\text{DTACK}}$ to cause this type of interrupt.

**15.** In daisy-chained interrupt expansion, multiple interrupting devices use one wire to signal the microprocessor of an interrupt request. Daisy-chained interrupting devices usually use a wired-AND connection to cause the interrupt request. Note that connections to the daisy chain must be with open-collector devices.

**16.** A queue is a first in, first out buffer memory used to interrupt low speed devices with high speed devices. In many cases keyboards and printers that are attached to a microprocessor use a queue.

17. The 68230 is a parallel interface/timer device that connects the microprocessor to 16 bits of I/O with handshaking in certain applications. The PI/T also contains a 24-bit programmable timer with a 5-bit prescaler.

## Questions

1. What is the difference between an exception and an interrupt?

2. What interrupt priority grouping contains software interrupts?

3. How many different interrupt vectors exist in the 68000 interrupt vector table?

4. What information is stored in an interrupt vector?

5. What registers are loaded whenever a hardware reset signal is applied to the 68000 microprocessor?

6. Explain the sequence of events for an interrupt or an exception.

7. What causes an address error exception to occur?

8. What is a bus error exception, and what causes it to occur?

9. Explain what causes a line emulator 1010 exception.

10. A privilege violation interrupt is caused by executing what instructions?

11. What instructions cause a privilege violation exception?

12. Describe how the CHK instruction functions.

13. The STOP instruction loads what register with immediate data at the time of its execution?

14. Describe the line emulator 1111 interrupt.

15. What instruction is used to end an interrupt service subroutine or an exception handler?

16. Which interrupt inputs are available on the 68008D microprocessor?

17. If $\overline{IPL2} = 0$, $\overline{IPL1} = 1$, and $\overline{IPL0} = 1$, what interrupt level is requested?

18. How is the interrupt acknowledge detected in the 68000 microprocessor?

19. Which 68000 pin is asserted in place of $\overline{DTACK}$ to generate an autovector interrupt?

20. What interrupt vector number is used with an autovector level 6 interrupt request?

21. Which interrupt autovector level is nonmaskable?

22. What interrupt autovector level has the lowest priority?

23. Describe how user interrupt vectors are enabled instead of autovector interrupts.

24. What is an uninitialized interrupt?

25. When does a spurious interrupt occur?

26. What is a daisy-chained interrupt?

27. With a daisy-chained interrupt scheme, how is the interrupting device determined?

28. What is a real-time clock?

29. The real-time clock uses a subroutine called UPDATE. How can this subroutine be changed so that time is in binary instead of BCD?

30. Determine how much microprocessor time is required to update the clock when only the 1/30 second counter is incremented.

31. Explain how a queue memory detects an empty condition.

32. Explain how a queue memory detects a full condition.

33. What is the purpose of the $\overline{DS}$ signal on the Centronics interface?

34. What is the purpose of the $\overline{ACK}$ signal on the Centronics interface?

35. Write a short sequence of instructions to place a pulse on the CB2 pin.

36. What is the PI/T?

37. How many bits is the timer in the 68230?

38. What is a prescaler?

39. What is meant by the term "single-buffered"?

40. What is meant by the term "double-buffered"?

41. How many 8-bit ports are found on the 68230?

42. What is the purpose of the H1 pin on the 68230?

43. Develop a sequence of instructions to program the 68030 so that port A is an output port and port B is an input port. Use mode 0 without any interrupts or handshakes on the handshaking pins.

# 10 Bus Arbitration (Direct Memory Access)

## OBJECTIVES

Upon completion of this chapter, you will be able to:

- Explain how data are transferred between I/O and memory using DMA techniques.

- Program the 68440 family of DMA controllers so that data are transferred between memory and I/O.

- Detail the various formats of digital data storage in disk memory systems. These formats include MFM and RLL.

- Compare MFM, RLL, ESDI, SCSI, and IDE interfaced disk memory systems.

- Explain the operation of and interface to the small computer system interface (SCSI).

- Describe the operation of an analog video display system.

- Explain how a coprocessor is connected to the microprocessor to perform functions concurrently with the microprocessor.

- Describe the coprocessor interrupt driven software interface between the microprocessor and the coprocessor.

## KEY TERMS

bus arbitration
bus master
direct memory access
  transfers
DMA transfer address
acknowledge or direct
  memory access
  acknowledge
DMA read, DMA
  write
memory-to-memory
  transfer
burst
non-DMA mode

DMA mode
implicitly, explicitly
  addressed
track
sector
index hole
modified frequency
  modulation
high density
non-return to zero
fixed disk
rigid disk
run-length limited

enhanced small disk
  interface
small computer
  system interface
integrated drive
  electronics
initiator
target
pixel
raster line
logical (memory)
  address
physical memory
  address

S o far we have discussed direct I/O using the PIA, and interrupt processed I/O using various techniques. The final I/O form is direct memory access (DMA). Direct memory access is sometimes also called bus arbitration. Bus arbitration is an I/O technique in which the microprocessor is disconnected from the system. In its place, another microprocessor, another bus controller, or a direct memory access controller is connected. The direct memory access controller takes over the bus controlling function of the microprocessor and transfers data directly between the memory and an I/O device. Many direct memory access controllers also transfer data between different memory locations. This type of DMA transfer is called a memory-to-memory transfer.

In providing detailed coverage of the bus arbitration process, as well as examples that illustrate its usefulness, this chapter uses the 68440 family of DMA controllers to transfer data directly between the memory and an I/O device. Note that DMA transfers require no software, other than programming the controller, which makes them extremely fast. A DMA transfer is strictly a hardware transfer.

As examples of DMA processed I/O, this chapter introduces video and disk systems. In both cases the DMA controller is normally used to transfer data between the memory and these high speed I/O devices.

Also introduced is the coprocessor connection between the microprocessor and coprocessor. A coprocessor is a device that operates concurrently with the microprocessor.

## 10-1    Basic Bus Arbitration with the 68000

This section explains the function of bus arbitration and the specific case of direct memory access in a microprocessor-based system. It also compares all I/O techniques available to the system designer to effect I/O operations.

### 10-1.1    Bus Arbitration

*Bus arbitration* applies the microprocessor system's ability to allow multiple bus masters to gain access, one at a time, to the system's memory and I/O spaces. Direct memory access is an example of bus arbitration, but not the only one. Other examples, such as coprocessors, are discussed later in this chapter and in Chapter 11, which is exclusive to the 68881/68882 floating-point coprocessor.

A *bus master* is any device that controls the memory and I/O connected to the system bus. The microprocessor itself is an example of a bus master. A DMA controller is another example of a bus master. A coprocessor is still another example. Microprocessors and DMA controllers are bus masters because they provide the memory and I/O with addresses and control signals. Only one bus master at a time exists on and controls a system. The orderly transfer of the control of the memory and I/O system from one bus master to another is designated bus arbitration. The 68000 family of microprocessors contains control signals that allow bus arbitration without the aid of a bus arbitration integrated circuit.

## 10-1.2 Direct Memory Access (DMA)

The direct memory access controller is responsible for transferring data directly between the memory and I/O or between two memory locations without the use of any software. *Direct memory access transfers* are strictly hardware transfers. The main functions asserted by the DMA controller are: providing the memory with its address and sometimes providing an address to an I/O device, selecting an I/O device, and providing control signals to both the memory and I/O.

The memory address that is provided by the DMA controller is stored within the controller through software from the microprocessor. Often called the *DMA transfer address,* this address is the starting location of the data that are transferred using DMA techniques. The DMA controller increments or decrements the DMA address if more than one byte, word, or long-word are transferred. This allows an entire block of data to be transferred with one programming of the DMA controller.

The DMA controller also selects the I/O device during the DMA transfer. This function is usually performed when an internally stored peripheral address is sent to the I/O device. Selection is also accomplished by a pin on the DMA controller that indicates that the DMA controller is in charge of the memory and I/O space. This pin or indicator signal is often called *acknowledge* ($\overline{\text{ACK}}$) or *direct memory access acknowledge* ($\overline{\text{DACK}}$). After the $\overline{\text{ACK}}$ signal or the internally programmed peripheral address has selected the I/O device, the transfer between memory and the I/O device of choice can occur.

Once the DMA controller has accessed the system buses, it causes data to be either read from memory and sent to the I/O device or written to memory from the I/O device. If data are read from the memory and transferred to I/O, the operation is called a *DMA read.* If data are transferred from the I/O device and written to memory, the operation is called a *DMA write.* It is also possible to use a DMA controller to transfer data between any two memory locations. This type of DMA transfer is called a *memory-to-memory transfer.*

Table 10-1, which compares all the I/O techniques available to the microprocessor system designer, illustrates the usefulness of direct memory access transfers. In this comparison of direct, interrupt, and DMA processed I/O techniques, notice that all three techniques are useful for certain applications. DMA is not suited for all I/O transfers, just as interrupts and direct I/O are not suitable for all I/O transfers. This doesn't mean that DMA transfers cannot be used for all types of I/O. The choice of which I/O technique to use is completely up to the system designer.

In general, direct I/O is suited to simple I/O devices such as switches and indicators or programmable devices such as the 6821 PIA or 68230 PI/T. Interrupt processed I/O is suited to devices that require the attention of the microprocessor only occasionally and at relatively low data transfer rates. DMA is suited to applications that require high speed data transfer rates. In fact, DMA is the only technique that allows truly high speed data transfer rates, approaching 5–10 mbps if high enough clock frequencies are used in the system. The DMA transfer is also suited to applications in which time lost to actual data transfer must be minimized. Mainframe computers, for example, use DMA exclusively for all I/O transfers to minimize the amount of time required for these transfers.

**Table 10-1  Comparison of I/O Data Transfer Methods Using an 8 MHz 68000 for Byte Transfers**

| Parameter | Technique | | |
| --- | --- | --- | --- |
| | Direct | Interrupt | DMA |
| Block transfer | 250 kbps | 50 kbps | 2 mbps |
| Cost | $ | $ | $$$$ |
| Instructions per byte | 2 | 4 (minimum) | None |
| Hardware requirements | Minimum | Minimum | Maximum |
| Purpose | Switches, displays | Printers, plotters | Video, disk memory, high speed I/O |

NOTES: kbps = kilobytes per second, mbps = megabytes per second.

The DMA transfer rate is also determined by the memory system speed. If memory devices that have a cycle time of 100 ns are in use, the DMA transfer rate approaches 10 mbps. This assumes that the clock frequency to the DMA controller is sufficient to support this transfer speed.

Figure 10-1 is a block diagram of a system that contains a microprocessor and two DMA controllers. Notice that although these devices coexist in the system on the same buses, only one is in control of the buses at any instant. The microprocessor OR one of the DMA controllers controls the memory and I/O. This allows any of these devices to gain access, through bus arbitration, to the memory and I/O spaces of the computer system.

### 10-1.3  Controlling the DMA Transfer

The 68000 microprocessor contains three pins for the purpose of controlling DMA transfers and performing bus arbitration. The microprocessor's bus request ($\overline{BR}$) pin is used by the DMA controller to request the system buses from the microprocessor to begin a DMA transfer. The bus grant ($\overline{BG}$) pin is used to grant a DMA action to the controller. The bus grant acknowledge ($\overline{BGACK}$) pin is used to signal the microprocessor that the DMA controller has taken control of the buses. The $\overline{BGACK}$ signal is also used to arbitrate the access to the bus system. Figure 10-2 represents the three pins used for bus arbitration and DMA.

The bus request input is asserted (logic zero) to request access to the system buses. The microprocessor normally notices the bus request signal within a clocking period. Upon receiving the logic zero on $\overline{BR}$, the microprocessor stops executing the program and issues the bus grant signal ($\overline{BG}$). Bus grant informs the requesting DMA controller or device that the microprocessor has recognized its request through the $\overline{BR}$ pin.

When the external DMA controller receives the $\overline{BG}$ signal from the microprocessor, it sends the microprocessor the bus grant acknowledge signal ($\overline{BGACK}$). The microprocessor, through the $\overline{BGACK}$ signal, allows the external DMA control-

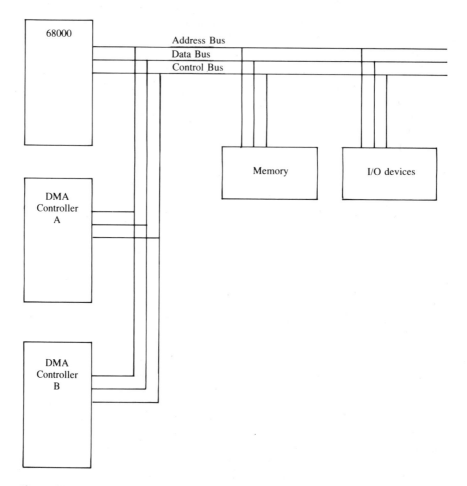

**Figure 10-1**    A system containing a microprocessor and two DMA controllers. Note that only one of these three devices controls the memory and I/O at any instant.

ler to gain access to the system buses. Bus grant acknowledge also prevents access by another bus master.

Access is provided to the buses because the microprocessor places its address, data, and control bus pins at their high impedance state. The DMA controller's access to the system buses continues until the external DMA request, applied to the $\overline{BR}$ pin, is terminated. The request is terminated when the DMA controller places a logic one on the $\overline{BR}$ pin of the microprocessor. It is important to note that the DMA controller waits for the microprocessor to send $\overline{BG}$ before it sends $\overline{BGACK}$ to the microprocessor. The timing diagram in Figure 10-3 illustrates the three DMA control signals and their actions during DMA transfers.

Bus arbitration is handled through the $\overline{BGACK}$ signal. Before requesting a DMA access, the DMA controller tests the $\overline{BGACK}$ line to determine whether another DMA controller has access to the system buses. If $\overline{BGACK}$ is a logic zero,

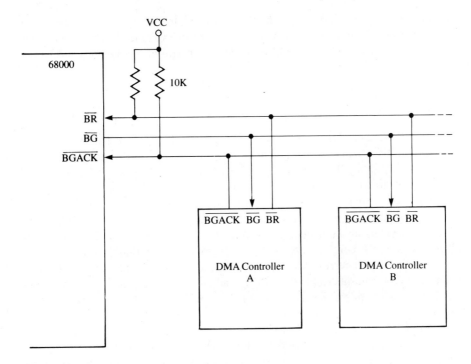

**Figure 10-2** The three control signals used by the DMA controller to gain access to the system buses.

the requesting controller waits until it becomes a logic one before requesting a DMA action.

DMA transfers occur a byte or word at a time or as a group of bytes or words. (Some DMA controllers can also transfer long-words.) A group of bytes or words transferred using DMA techniques is often called a *burst*. Burst mode operation is

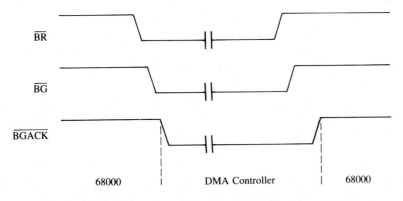

**Figure 10-3** The timing diagram of $\overline{BR}$, $\overline{BG}$, and $\overline{BGACK}$, illustrating which device has access to the bus system containing memory and I/O.

useful in systems such as video displays and disk memory. These devices often transfer or require more than one byte or word of data at a time. The burst continues unabated until the DMA controller relinquishes control of the memory and I/O to the microprocessor.

## 10-2   The 68440 Family of DMA Controllers

The 68440 family of DMA controllers includes the 68440, 68442, and 68450. The 68440 is a two-channel, programmable direct memory access controller that contains a 24-bit address bus. The 68442 is like the 68440 except that it contains a 32-bit address bus for microprocessors such as the 68020, 6830, and 68040. Finally, the 68450 is a four-channel DMA controller that contains a 24-bit address bus. These DMA controllers can transfer data between the memory and I/O directly. The DMA controllers also transfer data between two areas of memory. The number of data transferred is controlled by a 16-bit counter located within the controller.

Figure 10-4 illustrates the 68440 dual-channel DMA controller, the 68442 dual-channel DMA controller, and the 68450 quad-channel DMA controller. The 68440 and 68450 are both packaged in DIPs while the 68442 is packed in a PGA because of the number of pin connections on this device.

Notice from the pinouts that some of the address connections are multiplexed with data. Multiplexed address/data pins are found on all three versions as pins A8/D0–A23/D15 because the manufacturer decided not to use a larger integrated circuit for the DMA controller. Instead, to save pins, the address connections are multiplexed with data.

### 10-2.1   Pin Descriptions

Following is a listing of all pin connections on the 68440, 68442, and 68450 controllers, with a brief description of the purpose of each set of pins.

**A8/D0–A23/D15**   These multiplexed address and data connections provide address (A8–A23) and data (D0–D15) bus information during a DMA transfer and accept data during programming.

**A1–A7**   These address connections are used during programming to select an internal register of the DMA controller. During a DMA action, these pins provide a portion of the DMA address or I/O address. Each DMA channel uses a span of 64 bytes of register space for programming.

**A24–A31**   These pins (68442 only) provide the most significant address signals during a DMA action for a 32-bit address bus system such as on the 68020, 68030, or 68040 microprocessor.

**$\overline{\text{CS}}$ (chip select)**   This input is used to select the DMA controller for programming.

**$\overline{\text{AS}}$ (address strobe)**   This pin strobes the address of a programmable register into the DMA controller during programming. It is also used to provide the address strobe signal during a DMA action.

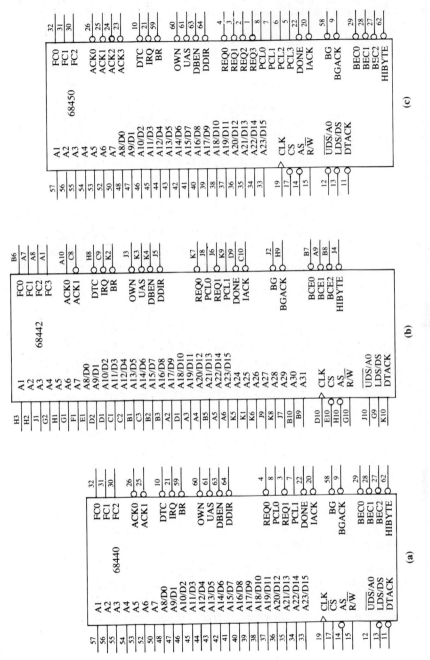

**Figure 10-4** The pinouts of the 68440 (a), 68442 (b), and 68450 (c) DMA controllers. Note that the 68440 and 68450 are dual in-line packages, while the 68442 is a pin grid array package.

385

**R/$\overline{\text{W}}$ (read/write)**   This signal is used during programming to read or write internal registers and during a DMA action to specify a read from memory or a write to memory.

**UDS/A0 (upper data strobe)**   This pin provides or accepts the upper data strobe if the controller is operated as a 16-bit device or functions as A0 if operated as an 8-bit device (for use with the 68008 microprocessor).

**$\overline{\text{LDS}}$/$\overline{\text{DS}}$ (lower data strobe)**   This pin provides or accepts the lower data strobe during 16-bit operations or functions as the data strobe signal for 8-bit operations with the 68008.

**$\overline{\text{DTACK}}$ (data transfer acknowledge)**   The $\overline{\text{DTACK}}$ signal is generated by the controller during programming and accepts a signal during a DMA action. This allows wait states to be inserted for the DMA controller during programming and also during a DMA transfer for the DMA memory system.

**FC2–FC0**   The function code bits are used as outputs during a DMA action. These lines can be used as additional address signals. This allows eight separate spaces to be defined in the memory along with the normal address signals.

**FC3**   Along with FC2–FC0, this extra function code bit (68442 only) allows 16 separate address spaces to be defined in the memory system.

**$\overline{\text{BEC2}}$–$\overline{\text{BEC0}}$ (bus exception control)**   These input functions are $\overline{\text{RESET}}$, $\overline{\text{HALT}}$, and $\overline{\text{BERR}}$, which are encoded on these three connections.

**$\overline{\text{OWN}}$**   The output during a DMA access enables the address latches that are used to demultiplex the address/data bus during a DMA action.

**$\overline{\text{UAS}}$ (upper address strobe)**   This signal is used to clock the address information from the address/data bus (A8–A23) into a set of latches used to hold the DMA address during a DMA action.

**$\overline{\text{DBEN}}$ (data bus enable)**   This signal is used to control the external bidirectional data bus buffers.

**$\overline{\text{DDIR}}$ (data bus direction control)**   This signal is used to control the direction of data bus flow through external data bus buffers. If this signal is high, data are transferred out of the DMA controller through the data bus.

**$\overline{\text{HIBYTE}}$ (high byte)**   This signal is used to control the enable connection on a bidirectional bus buffer during a DMA action. When this signal is a logic zero, the high part of the data bus can be transferred to the low part, or vice versa. During a reset, a ground or a +5.0 V on this connection configures the DMA controller as an 8- or a 16-bit data bus device, respectively.

**$\overline{\text{CLK}}$ (clock)**   This input is provided to time DMA transfers; usually it is the same frequency as the microprocessor clock, but it may be different.

**$\overline{\text{BR}}$ (bus request)**   This signal is connected to the microprocessor bus request input and is used to request the buses from the microprocessor.

$\overline{\text{BG}}$ **(bus grant)**   This input accepts the bus grant signal from the microprocessor, indicating that the microprocessor has granted a DMA action to the DMA controller.

$\overline{\text{BGACK}}$ **(bus grant acknowledge)**   This pin is placed at a logic zero when the 68440 begins to access the buses during the DMA. It is also tested prior to DMA access to assure that no other bus master has access to the system buses.

$\overline{\text{IRQ}}$ **(interrupt request)**   This output is used to request an interrupt under program control.

$\overline{\text{IACK}}$ **(interrupt acknowledge)**   This input causes the DMA controller to respond with a vector number (D0–D7) for user-vectored interrupts.

$\overline{\text{DTC}}$ **(data transfer complete)**   This signal is asserted when a data transfer is completed by the DMA controller.

**DONE**   This signal is activated by the DMA controller whenever a block of data has been completely transferred.

$\overline{\text{REQ1}}$**,** $\overline{\text{REQ0}}$   These inputs are used to request a DMA action for channels 1 and 0. ($\overline{\text{REQ3}}$ and $\overline{\text{REQ2}}$ on the 68442 request a DMA action for channels 3 and 2.)

**ACK1, ACK0**   The acknowledge outputs signal that a channel has access through the DMA controller. ($\overline{\text{ACK3}}$ and $\overline{\text{ACK2}}$ are available for channels 3 and 2 on the 68442.)

**PCL1, PCL0 (peripheral control)**   These lines are programmable to perform various operations, such as ready, abort, reload, status, or interrupt inputs. (Additional peripheral control lines, PCL3 and PCL2, are available on the 68442.)

### 10-2.2   Basic DMA Controller Interface

Figure 10-5 illustrates the basic circuitry required to demultiplex the address/data bus connections of any of the 68440 family of DMA controllers. This circuit in particular depicts the 68440. The circuit also allows the 68440 to connect itself to system address and data buses for programming and for DMA actions.

During a DMA action, latch circuits (U3 and U4) are used to capture the address from the DMA controller when clocked by the $\overline{\text{UAS}}$ (upper address strobe) signal. The $\overline{\text{UAS}}$ signal demultiplexes (captures) the upper address (A8–A23) and holds it in these two latches. The output pins of the latches are enabled by the $\overline{\text{OWN}}$ signal from the controller whenever the DMA controller has access to (owns) the memory and I/O system. The $\overline{\text{OWN}}$ signal becomes a logic zero during a DMA transfer.

Bidirectional buffers (U5 and U6) are controlled by the $\overline{\text{DBEN}}$ (data bus enable) signal from the DMA controller. This signal becomes a logic zero when the DMA controller is being programmed or read by the microprocessor. During a DMA transfer, the $\overline{\text{DBEN}}$ signal is a logic one so that data are directly transferred through the data bus between the memory and I/O device. The buffers are used during a memory-to-memory DMA transfer to allow the microprocessor to access data from one memory location and then output it to another.

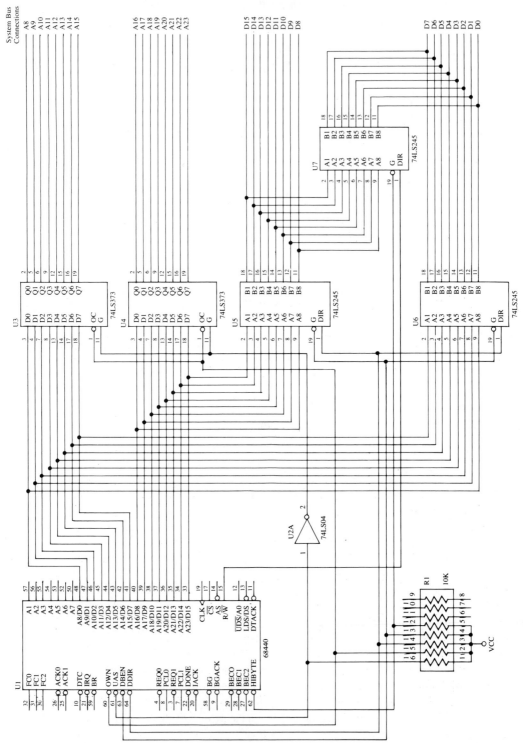

**Figure 10-5** The 68440 interface to the system bus, illustrating the latches and buffers required to demultiplex and drive the buses.

388

The $\overline{\text{DDIR}}$ signal from the controller selects whether the data bus buffers are inputting data to the controller or outputting data from the controller to the data bus. If this signal is a logic zero, data are input to the controller from the data bus.

The third bidirectional bus buffer (U7) is used during some DMA actions to exchange or steer the upper data bus half to the lower data bus half during byte-sized DMA transfers. If the transfer size is a byte operation from an even address, $\overline{\text{HIBYTE}}$ becomes a zero to gate the upper half of the data bus onto the lower half. This occurs so that the high byte is accessed. Eight-bit DMA devices are connected to the lower half of the data bus during a DMA for the 68008 microprocessor, which has only data connections (D0–D7). R/$\overline{\text{W}}$ controls the direction of data flow through U7.

## Bus Exception Control

Three connections on the 68440 DMA controller are used for bus exception control. Bus exceptions are system events such as reset, bus error, rerun, and halt. These exceptions are encoded as three bus exception inputs to the 68440 that are labeled $\overline{\text{BEC0}}$, $\overline{\text{BEC1}}$, and $\overline{\text{BEC2}}$. The microprocessor bus does not directly support these three inputs. Instead a circuit, discussed later, is used to generate the bus exception inputs to the DMA controller.

Table 10-2 depicts the bus exception inputs and their meaning to the 68440 DMA controller. These signals are developed through a circuit that uses the bus signals $\overline{\text{RESET}}$, $\overline{\text{BERR}}$, and $\overline{\text{HALT}}$ to develop the bus exception control inputs. This table defines four of the eight possible combinations of bus exception control inputs. The remaining combinations are undefined and reserved for future implementation.

Figure 10-6 illustrates a circuit that generates the bus exception control signals for the DMA controller. The $\overline{\text{RESET}}$ signal causes input 7 to generate a 000 on the outputs of the 74LS148. This causes the DMA controller to reset. The $\overline{\text{BERR}}$ and $\overline{\text{HALT}}$ signals connect to a 74LS139 decoder, which generates outputs for all four states of these two signals. If both signals are zero, the microprocessor is signaling a rerun. These zeros cause output zero of the decoder to ground pin 2 of NAND gate U2A. This forces the output of NAND gate U2B to go low, applying a logic zero to

**Table 10-2   The Bus Exception Control Inputs of the 68440 DMA Controller**

| $\overline{\text{BEC2}}$ | $\overline{\text{BEC1}}$ | $\overline{\text{BEC0}}$ | Definition |
|------|------|------|-------------|
| 0 | 0 | 0 | Reset |
| 0 | 0 | 1 | [undefined] |
| 0 | 1 | 0 | [undefined] |
| 0 | 1 | 1 | [undefined] |
| 1 | 0 | 0 | Rerun |
| 1 | 0 | 1 | Bus error |
| 1 | 1 | 0 | Halt |
| 1 | 1 | 1 | No exception |

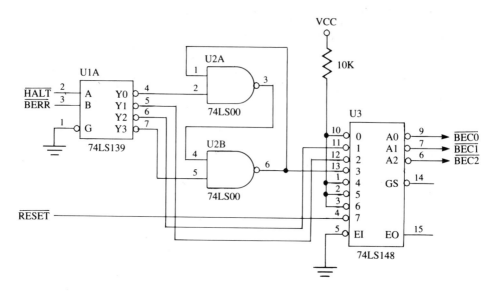

**Figure 10-6**   The circuit that generates the bus exception control signals for the 68440 family of DMA controllers.

input 3 of the 74LS148. Input 3 causes the outputs of the 74LS148 to apply a 100 to the bus exception control pins and forces a rerun. Likewise $\overline{\text{BERR}}$ by itself generates a bus error (101), and HALT by itself generates a halt (110). If both inputs are high, the NAND gate latch is forced to apply a logic one to input three of the 74LS148.

## The Interface

Figure 10-7 illustrates a complete interface between the 68000 microprocessor and the 68440 DMA controller. Notice that the same circuits illustrated in Figures 10-5 and 10-6 are used to interface the buses of these two devices and also provide the bus exception control signals. A PAL 16L8 selects the DMA controller for programming whenever the memory address is $400000–$403FFF. This address range activates the $\overline{\text{CS}}$ input for programming.

## 10-2.3   Operation of the DMA Controller

The DMA controller operates in two modes. One mode of operation causes the DMA controller to appear as a programmable I/O device to the microprocessor. This is the *non-DMA mode,* in which the DMA controller is programmed. As with any other programmable I/O device, the DMA controller has a $\overline{\text{CS}}$ (chip select) input that is decoded to select the device for programming. In Figure 10-7 a PAL 16L8 is used to decode the address and select the DMA controller for programming.

The other mode of operation is invoked when the DMA controller has been programmed to accomplish DMA transfers between I/O and memory or between two memory locations. The act of transferring the data with the DMA controller, called the *DMA mode* of operation, allows transfers to occur a single datum at a time or in groups called bursts.

## DMA Mode

During the DMA mode of operation, the DMA controller requests the system buses through its bus request ($\overline{\text{BR}}$) connection to the microprocessor. Once the microprocessor has recognized the request, it issues the bus grant ($\overline{\text{BG}}$) signal to the DMA controller. When the DMA controller has granted access to the bus, the DMA controller issues the bus grant acknowledge ($\overline{\text{BGACK}}$) signal. This indicates to the microprocessor, and more importantly to other DMA controllers, that the DMA controller is currently the bus master. Note that the DMA controller also monitors the $\overline{\text{BGACK}}$ connections before it requests a DMA action. This performs arbitration. If $\overline{\text{BGACK}}$ is a logic one, it can request a bus request. If $\overline{\text{BGACK}}$ is a logic zero, another DMA controller has access and it waits for $\overline{\text{BGACK}}$ to return to a logic one level. This daisy-chained connection prevents conflicts in systems that have more than one controller.

Once the DMA controller has gained access to the system buses, it begins transferring data. The methods used to transfer data differ depending on the type of I/O device used with the transfer. An I/O device is selected directly through its hardware select pin (chip select) or through a hardware decoder by an I/O address. A device that is selected directly through a hardware select pin is called *implicitly addressed*. An I/O device that is selected through a hardware address decoder is called *explicitly addressed*. Both types of I/O device exist in many systems.

## Implicit Addressed Operation

Devices that are implicitly addressed do not require any memory or I/O address during the DMA data transfer. Complete control and selection of the I/O device are handled through some or all of the DMA channel control signals. These channel control signals are $\overline{\text{REQ}}$ (request), $\overline{\text{ACK}}$ (acknowledge), PCL (peripheral control), $\overline{\text{DTC}}$ (data transfer complete), and $\overline{\text{DONE}}$ (data transfer finished).

Figure 10-8 illustrates a simple interface between a parallel printer and the DMA controller. It also shows the timing required for the printer.

The parallel printer interface has a BUSY connection that reveals a printer busy condition. If BUSY is a logic one, the printer is busy, and if a logic zero, the printer is not busy. Whenever the printer is not busy (BUSY = 0) the circuit requests a DMA action through the $\overline{\text{REQ0}}$ connection to the DMA controller. Notice that this input is conditioned with a data latch. The printer also requires a data strobe signal ($\overline{\text{DS}}$) to indicate that data are being sent to the printer for printing.

When the system is reset, and whenever the printer is not busy, the circuitry requests a DMA action. This is relayed to the DMA controller through U2, which is cleared when BUSY becomes a logic zero. Upon seeing that the $\overline{\text{REQ0}}$ input is a logic zero, the DMA controller requests the system buses with its $\overline{\text{BR}}$ pin. After a short time (a few clocks at most), the DMA controller is given access to the system

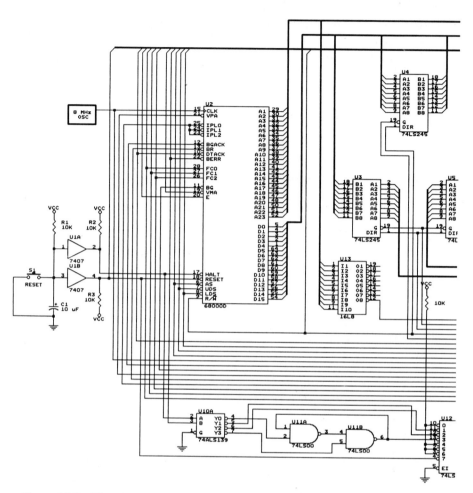

**Figure 10-7    The 68440 DMA controller interfaced to the 68000 microprocessor.**

address, data, and control buses. The controller is programmed with the memory address of the DMA transfer that it sends out on the address bus to access a memory location.

The contents of the selected memory location are passed on to the data bus and to the inputs of a latch that holds it for the printer. At this time the DMA controller also sends the $\overline{ACK}$ signal, to clear the request by setting U2. When the memory has been given time to access the data, the $\overline{DTC}$ pin becomes a logic zero. This generates a clock pulse for the latch (U3), which captures the ASCII character transferred from the memory.

The $\overline{DTACK}$ signal becomes a logic one before $\overline{DTC}$ becomes a logic one. This causes U4A to become a zero and U4B remains a logic one. On the next $\overline{DTACK}$ signal, the U4A becomes a logic one and U4B becomes a logic zero, developing the $\overline{DS}$ signal for the printer. The $\overline{DS}$ signal remains a logic zero until the next $\overline{DTACK}$

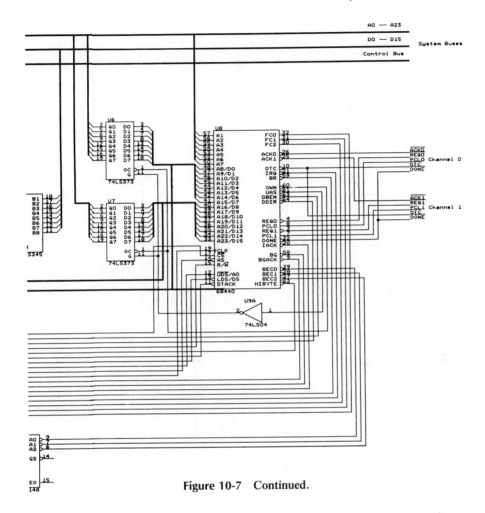

**Figure 10-7   Continued.**

pulse, whereupon it returns to a logic one level. The $\overline{DS}$ signal remains a logic one until the cycle is repeated and the BUSY signal returns to a logic zero.

### Explicit Addressed Operation

Explicit addressed devices require an I/O or memory address from the DMA controller for proper function. Memory-to-memory transfers are one example of a DMA transfer that requires an explicit address. One address is explicit while the other address is the normal DMA channel address. Likewise, DMA transfers to devices such as a 68230 PI/T also require an explicit address to select the 68230 during the DMA transfer.

Figure 10-9 illustrates the 68230 PI/T connected to the DMA controller so that it requests a DMA action from a keyboard interface. The 68230 is explicitly addressed because it is selected through an I/O address decoder by the DMA control-

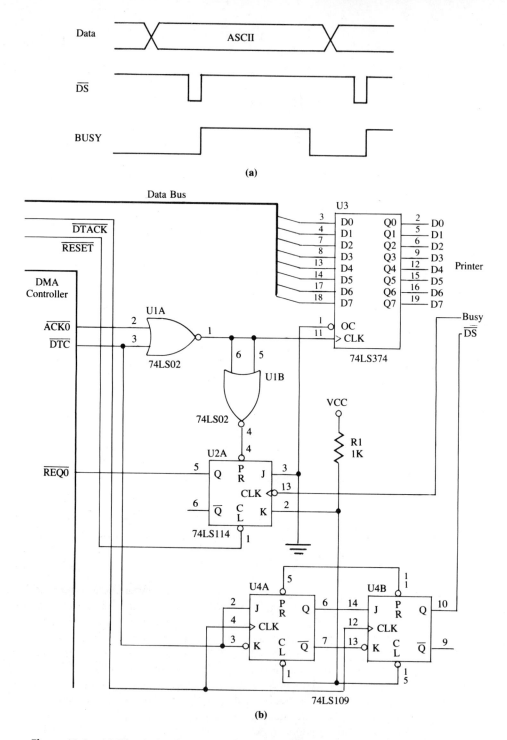

**Figure 10-8** (a) The timing for the parallel printer–DMA controller interface. (b) The circuit used to request a DMA action and to generate the data strobe signal for the printer.

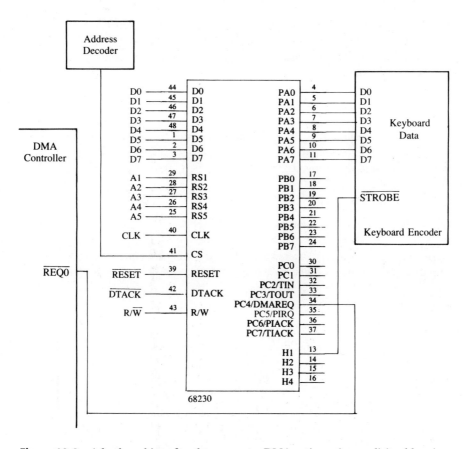

**Figure 10-9** A keyboard interfaced to request a DMA action using explicit addressing.

ler. The 68230 is also selected in the same manner from the microprocessor for programming or other data transfers.

In this system, every keystroke generates a $\overline{\text{STROBE}}$ signal from the keyboard interface. This signal is attached to the H1 input of the 68230. Because the 68230 is programmed in mode 0, submode 00 for port A, and H1 is programmed as an active low input latch input, $\overline{\text{STROBE}}$ causes port A to hold the keyboard data until read by a DMA access. H1 also activates the $\overline{\text{DMAREQ}}$ pin on the 68230 to request the DMA action that reads the keyboard character from port A.

Notice that explicit addressing uses only the chip selection and register selection inputs of the 68230 for accessing the keyboard data. This is possible because when explicit addressing is used for a DMA action, the DMA controller sends out the I/O address of the 68230 device and fetches the keyboard data from port A. The keyboard data are stored within the DMA controller for later transfer to the memory. Next the DMA controller issues a memory address and transfers the keyboard data through the data bus into memory from the DMA controller.

Explicit DMA transfers require two bus cycles, versus one for implicit transfers. Each datum transferred requires one bus cycle to execute. The implicit transfer requires a memory address to select a memory location and the $\overline{ACK}$ signal to select the I/O device. This requires one bus cycle.

The explicit transfer requires a memory address to select memory and an I/O address to select the I/O device. This requires two bus cycles, one for selection by the memory address and one for selection via the I/O address. This makes implicit transfers twice as efficient as explicit transfers. The only type of DMA transfer that cannot be implicitly addressed is memory-to-memory transfer. Memory-to-memory transfers always require two addresses for the transfer (source and destination) and two bus cycles. This is identical to an explicit transfer except that both the addresses provided are memory addresses.

### 10-2.4 Programming the DMA Controller

The DMA controller is programmed through a set of internal registers. Each channel is programmed via a set of 17 registers. The 68440 and 68442 each have two channels and two sets of registers, while the 68450 has four channels and four sets of registers. The various registers are selected through address inputs A1–A7.

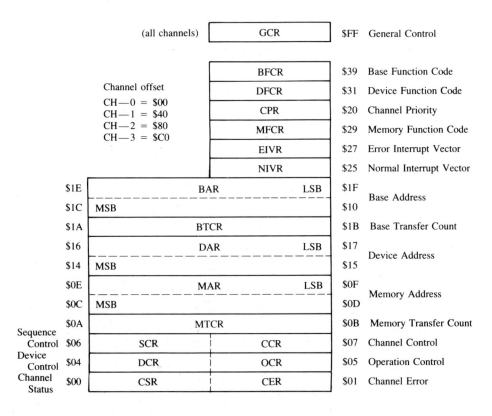

**Figure 10-10**  The internal register set for a channel of the 68440, 68442, or 68450 DMA controller.

Figure 10-10, which illustrates the internal register set for one DMA channel, also indicates that a different beginning offset address is used for each channel: channel 0 uses offset address $00, channel 1 uses offset address $40, channel 2 uses offset address $80, and channel 3 uses offset address $C0.

For example, if the DMA controller is decoded at memory locations $100000–$1000FF, then channel 1 is at location $100040–$10007F. The only register that is not addressed in this manner is the general control register (GCR), which is always located at address $FF. The general control register is a device-specific register, not a channel-specific register. The general control register programs the entire DMA controller, not a channel.

### The General Control Register

The general control register (GCR) programs the general operation of the DMA controller. Figure 10-11 illustrates the binary bit pattern of this register. Notice that only the right-most 4 bits of this register, which is located at address $FF, are programmable. This register selects the bus request bandwidth (BR) and the burst time (BT), which are used to limit the amount of time the DMA controller can transfer data. This prevents the DMA controller from using all the available bus time during a burst operation.

The bus request bandwidth bits program the controller bus access time. If BR is programmed for a 50% time, the DMA controller may access the system buses a maximum of 50% of the time. Other maximum times are also selectable through the BR bits of the GCR.

The burst time bits program the maximum number of clocks (duration) that can be used by any DMA burst transfer. This prevents the DMA controller from accessing the microprocessor bus continuously during a DMA burst. These bits are programmable for 16–128 clocks.

For example, suppose that BR is programmed for 50% and BT is programmed for 128 clocks. This means that out of every 256 bus clocks, the DMA controller can access the bus for a maximum of 128 clocks. If BR is programmed for 25% and BT is programmed for 128 clocks, the DMA controller has access to the bus for 128 out of every 512 clocks.

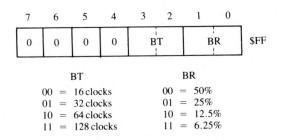

Figure 10-11  The general control register (GCR).

## Address Registers

The DMA controller has three address registers per channel: the memory address register (MAR), the device address register (DAR), and the base address register (BAR). Each address register is 32 bits in width, although only 24 bits are available on the 68440 and 68450 DMA controllers. All 32 bits are available on the 68442 DMA controller, which has a 32-bit address bus.

The memory address register normally specifies the address of the memory location involved in a DMA transfer. This could be the location written to with a DMA write or the location read with a DMA read. The device address register contains the explicit address of the I/O address or a memory location for a memory-to-memory transfer. The base address register is used when DMA actions are chained, as described later in this section. The base address register is also used to reload the memory address register for certain operations.

Associated with each of the three address registers are three function code registers that hold the function code of the memory or device accessed. The MAR register uses the memory function code register (MFCR) at location $29, the DAR register uses the device function code register (DFCR) at location $31, and the BAR uses the base function code register (BFCR) at location $39. The function code register contains a 3-bit (68440 and 68450) or 4-bit (68442) function code that is output on the FC pins of the DMA controller during the DMA action. The right-most bits of these registers specify the function code.

## Count Registers

Each of the two count registers specifies a 16-bit count. This means that the maximum transfer count is 64k. The memory transfer count register (MTCR) specifies the number of data transferred by the DMA controller. The base transfer count register (BTCR) indicates the number of base addresses (DMA actions) used with chaining or reloading into the MTCR for a continue or reload operation.

## Interrupt Vector Registers

The interrupt vector registers contain the user interrupt vector number associated with either a normal interrupt or an error interrupt. The normal interrupt vector register (NIVR) is located at address $25 and is used for a normal interrupt. A normal interrupt is at the end of a DMA transfer operation—that is, when the DMA controller has completed a DMA transfer as indicated by the MTCR.

The error interrupt vector register (EIVR) at address $27 is used for an error. Errors that cause an error interrupt are configuration error, operation timing error, address error, count error, external abort, and software error. These vectors are programmed with any available user interrupt vector in the system (vectors $40–$FF).

## Device Control Register

The device control register (DCR), illustrated in Figure 10-12, located at address $04, is used to program the operation of the device. The DCR contains four programmable fields of information. The XRM field is used to select the type of DMA

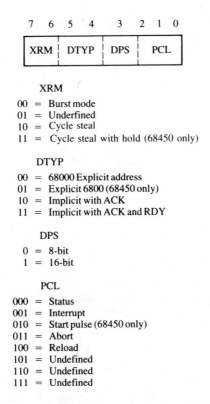

7   6   5   4   3   2   1   0

| XRM | DTYP | DPS | PCL |

XRM

00 = Burst mode
01 = Underfined
10 = Cycle steal
11 = Cycle steal with hold (68450 only)

DTYP

00 = 68000 Explicit address
01 = Explicit 6800 (68450 only)
10 = Implicit with ACK
11 = Implicit with ACK and RDY

DPS

0 = 8-bit
1 = 16-bit

PCL

000 = Status
001 = Interrupt
010 = Start pulse (68450 only)
011 = Abort
100 = Reload
101 = Undefined
110 = Undefined
111 = Undefined

**Figure 10-12    The device control register (DCR).**

transfer. The DTYP field is used to specify either explicit addressing or implicit addressing. The DPS field indicates the width of the device. The PCL field specifies the function of the PCL pin for the channel.

The peripheral control pin is programmed as an input to cause an interrupt, to abort the current DMA action, or to reload the MAR, MFCR, and MTCR from the BAR, BFCR, and BTCR. The PCL input is a negative (one-to-zero) edge-triggered input.

## Operation Control Register

The operation control register (OCR) is illustrated in Figure 10-13. The OCR, located at address $05, controls the operation of the controller during a DMA action; its four fields define the operation of the DMA controller for a particular channel. The DIR field specifies the direction of the DMA transfer. The SIZE field indicates the size of the transfer as byte or word unless the 68450 is used, in which case a long-word transfer may be specified. The CHAIN field applies only to the 68450 and must be disabled for the 68440 or 68442 to operate properly. Chaining for the 68450 is described later in this section.

The REOG field selects whether the transfer is to be initiated internally (via software) or externally (via hardware). If a limited internal rate is selected, the

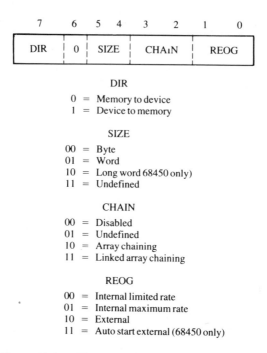

Figure 10-13    The operation control register (OCR).

number of clocks used for transfers is determined with the general control register (GCR). If the maximum internal rate is selected, the DMA transfers continue unabated until the transfer count is depleted. This overrides the general control register's limited rate and consumes all available bus time until the transfer is completed.

## Sequence Control Register

The sequence control register (SCR) is illustrated in Figure 10-14. The SCR, located at address $06, selects the operation of the MAR and DAR during a DMA action. Either address register can be incremented, decremented, or held constant for various types of DMA action. A memory-to-memory transfer might elect to

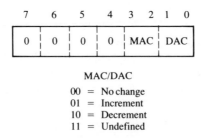

Figure 10-14    The sequence control register (SCR).

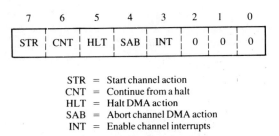

| 7 | 6 | 5 | 4 | 3 | 2 | 1 | 0 |
|---|---|---|---|---|---|---|---|
| STR | CNT | HLT | SAB | INT | 0 | 0 | 0 |

STR = Start channel action
CNT = Continue from a halt
HLT = Halt DMA action
SAB = Abort channel DMA action
INT = Enable channel interrupts

**Figure 10-15   The channel control register (CCR).**

increment both addresses, while a DMA read might increment the memory address but keep the device address constant.

### Channel Control Register

The channel control register (CCR) is illustrated in Figure 10-15. The CCR, located at address $07, controls the DMA channel. The channel can be started via software through this control register or aborted. It can also be stopped or halted and continued at some future time. The channel control register is also used to enable the channel interrupt if desired.

### DMA Channel Priority Register

The channel priority register (CPR) is illustrated in Figure 10-16. The CPR, located at address $20, programs the priority level of the channel. Any priority level may be selected for the channel. If given a priority level of 0, the channel will have the highest priority; if given a level of 3, it will have the lowest. If more than one channel are set for the same priority level, the channels will be serviced alternately.

### Channel Status Register

The channel status register (CSR) is illustrated in Figure 10-17. The CSR, located at address $00, indicates the status of the channel. This register indicates the operation of the channel and also the status of the PCL pin.

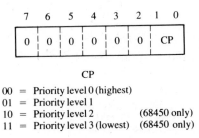

| 7 | 6 | 5 | 4 | 3 | 2 | 1 | 0 |
|---|---|---|---|---|---|---|---|
| 0 | 0 | 0 | 0 | 0 | 0 | CP | |

CP

00 = Priority level 0 (highest)
01 = Priority level 1
10 = Priority level 2        (68450 only)
11 = Priority level 3 (lowest)   (68450 only)

**Figure 10-16   The channel priority register (CPR).**

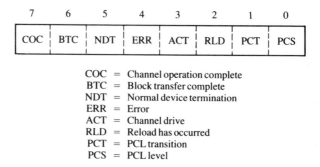

| 7 | 6 | 5 | 4 | 3 | 2 | 1 | 0 |
|---|---|---|---|---|---|---|---|
| COC | BTC | NDT | ERR | ACT | RLD | PCT | PCS |

COC = Channel operation complete
BTC = Block transfer complete
NDT = Normal device termination
ERR = Error
ACT = Channel drive
RLD = Reload has occurred
PCT = PCL transition
PCS = PCL level

**Figure 10-17   The channel status register (CSR).**

The RLD, PCT, and PCS bits are all affected by the operation of the PCL pin. These bits are set by PCL, but never cleared. To clear these bits either the DMA controller must be reset, or a zero must be written to each of these bits.

### Channel Error Register

The channel error register (CER) is illustrated in Figure 10-18. The CER, located at address $01, indicates any type of error that is detected during a DMA operation. This register is normally read during the interrupt service subroutine that occurs for an error. The error interrupt must be enabled, however. The CER may also be read after the error has been detected by the ERR bit in the channel status register. Notice that not all error codes are defined.

### 10-2.5   Memory-to-Memory DMA Transfer

One of the simplest applications of the DMA controller is the memory-to-memory DMA transfer. This type of operation requires explicit addressing because two addresses are used to perform a memory-to-memory transfer. A memory-to-memory

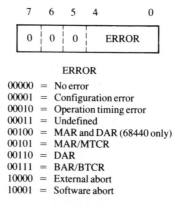

| 7 | 6 | 5 | 4 | | 0 |
|---|---|---|---|---|---|
| 0 | 0 | 0 | ERROR | | |

ERROR

00000 = No error
00001 = Configuration error
00010 = Operation timing error
00011 = Undefined
00100 = MAR and DAR (68440 only)
00101 = MAR/MTCR
00110 = DAR
00111 = BAR/BTCR
10000 = External abort
10001 = Software abort

**Figure 10-18   The channel error register (CER).**

DMA transfer is much faster than a transfer that is produced through software. The reason for the higher speed is that once the DMA controller has been programmed and started, no software is required for the transfer. This means that no instructions are fetched and the transfer occurs strictly through the hardware of the DMA controller. Each bus cycle is used to effect the transfer using the memory-to-memory DMA transfer.

E  X  A  M  P  L  E      10 - 1

```
                         ;
                         ;This subroutine programs a memory-to-memory DMA
                         ;transfer using channel 1 of the DMA controller.
                         ;When called, A0 = the source address, A1 = the
                         ;destination address, and D0 = the counts of bytes
                         ;transferred.
                         ;
015000  21C8054C    MEMS  MOVE.L   A0,MAR      ;load source address
015004  21C90564          MOVE.L   A1,DAR      ;load destination address
015008  31C0050A          MOVE.W   D0,MTCR     ;load byte count
01500C  103C0001          MOVE.B   #1,D0
015010  11C00569          MOVE.B   D0,MFCR     ;load user data function code
015014  11C00571          MOVE.B   D0,DFCR     ;load user data function code
015018  11FC000605FF      MOVE.B   #6,GCR      ;select burst bandwidth
01501E  11FC00050546      MOVE.B   $5,SCR      ;select increment
015024  11FC00010545      MOVE.B   #1,OCR      ;select memory-to-device
01502A  42380544          CLR.B    DCR         ;select explicit transfer
01502E  11FC00800547      MOVE.B   #$80,CR     ;start DMA
015034  4E75              RTS
```

The subroutine listed in Example 10-1 performs a memory-to-memory transfer using DMA channel 1. It is assumed that the decoded address of the DMA controller is $000500–$0005FF. The subroutine assumes that address registers A0 (source) and A1 (destination) are used to send the DMA source and destination addresses to the controller. The subroutine also assumes that D0 (count) is used to transfer the number of bytes to be transferred to the DMA controller. The subroutine further assumes that the addresses increment during the transfer and that no interrupt is used to signal the end of the transfer. Finally, it assumes that the channel is set at priority level 3, because this type of transfer usually has a low priority.

E  X  A  M  P  L  E      10 - 2

```
                         ;
                         ;This is the subroutine that tets for transfer
                         ;completeness after a channel 1 operation.
                         ;
016000  083800030540 END1  BTST    #3,CSR      ;test status register
016006  66F8              BNE      END1        ;if channel busy
016008  4E75              RTS                  ;if channel not busy
```

The subroutine of Example 10-2 illustrates how to test the channel for transfer completeness. In most cases this subroutine is called before the subroutine of

Example 10-1 so that no error can occur. If a channel is reprogrammed while transferring data, an error will ensue. This subroutine prevents reprogramming before a transfer is completed.

Here, the left-most bit of the channel status register is tested to determine whether the channel operation is complete. If complete, the subroutine terminates; if not, the subroutine continues to interrogate the channel status register.

### 10-2.6   DMA Transfer Using Implicit Addressing

A fairly common way to transfer data between memory and I/O is via an implicit DMA transfer. Figure 10-19 illustrates a circuit that interfaces a DAC0830 digital-to-analog converter to a 68000 microprocessor system. This circuit uses the lower data bus with a 68442 DMA controller to transfer data to the converter from the memory. No attempt is made to show all the interconnections between the microprocessor and the DMA controller: the only DMA controller connections illustrated are $\overline{REQ1}$ and $\overline{ACK1}$.

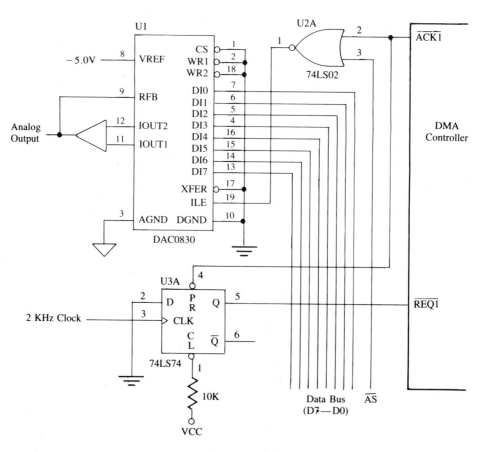

**Figure 10-19   The digital-to-analog converter interfaced to the DMA controller as an implicitly addressed device.**

Whenever a DMA transfer occurs, the $\overline{ACK1}$ output of the controller becomes a logic zero. This allows the address strobe signal through to the ILE input of the converter. The converter latches the contents of the data bus at this time and begins converting it into an analog voltage. The $\overline{ACK1}$ signal also deactivates the DMA request input by setting the request flip-flop (U3A). This causes one DMA request for each one of the clock pulses.

Once the DMA controller has been programmed, it transfers data to the converter each time the $\overline{REQ1}$ input is activated. In this system the request input is generated by a 2 kHz clock signal. The converter and software system are designed to output digital data through the converter to generate speech.

The software is in the form of a subroutine that is called each time speech is required. Example 10-3 lists the subroutine that causes the converter to utter speech. Of course this assumes that the correct binary bit patterns for speech are stored in the memory.

E X A M P L E    10 - 3

```
                         ;
                         ;This subroutine uses digitized memory data and DMA
                         ;channel 1 to cause the DAC to generate speech.
                         ;
                         ;A0 = the location of data and D0 = the number of bytes
                         ;sent to the DAC.
                         ;
017000   083800030540   SPEAK   BTST    #3,CSR      ;test for busy channel
017006   66F8                   BNE     SPEAK       ;if busy
017008   21C8054C               MOVE.L  A0,MAR      ;load address
01700C   31C0050A               MOVE.W  D0,MTCR     ;load count
017010   11FC00010569           MOVE.B  #1,MFCR     ;load user data function code
017016   11FC00040546           MOVE.B  #4,SCR      ;increment
01701C   11FC00020545           MOVE.B  #2,DCR      ;external request
017022   11FC00200544           MOVE.B  #$20,DCR    ;select implicit
017028   11FC00800547           MOVE.B  #$80,CR     ;start DMA
01702E   4E75                   RTS
```

In this subroutine, channel 1 is first tested to see whether it is busy. If it is not busy, the contents of a variable length block of memory are sent to the converter using implicit addressing. The subroutine requires that the address of the block of data be loaded into A0 and the length of the block be loaded into D0 before the subroutine is jumped to by the calling program. This subroutine allows messages of speech having a maximum length of 64k bytes or 32 seconds.

## 10-2.7   DMA Transfer Using Explicit Addressing

Although explicit addressing is less desirable because of the speed at which DMA transfers occur, this method is used with some of the programmable I/O devices found connected to the 68000 system. The hardware interface for explicit DMA control is identical to the interface required for normal I/O control. The reason is that the DMA controller addresses the I/O device just as any instruction would address it from the microprocessor. A little thought reveals that any I/O interface can be DMA controlled because of the explicit addressing feature of this DMA controller. Explicit addressing allows software to be rewritten to permit DMA control of any interface driven by any software.

Suppose that a simple stepper motor control system is to be operated as a DMA controlled device. Figure 10-20 illustrates the stepper motor controlled through a 68230 PI/T. Here the timer is varied to generate DMA requests at different rates to control the speed of the stepper motor. Each DMA request transfers one byte of data from an area of memory that contains the pattern to control energizing the coils in

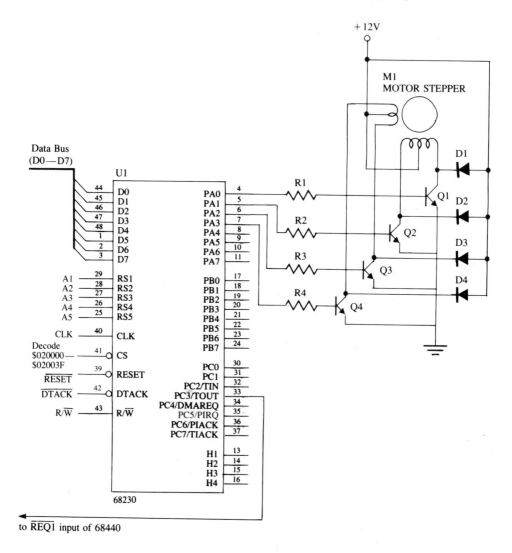

to $\overline{REQ1}$ input of 68440

**Figure 10-20   The 68230 interfaced to a stepper motor and the DMA controller using explicit addressing.**

the stepper motor. This pattern can rotate the stepper in the clockwise or counter-clockwise direction.

Software is written so that the DMA controller will transfer eight patterns to the stepper motor drivers through the 68230. After the eight patterns have been transferred, an interrupt occurs, indicating the end of the DMA action. The rate of transfer is controlled by the timer. Because eight patterns are transferred, the motor is operated in the half-step mode.

Each operation complete interrupt cycle accesses a 3-byte section of the memory, which holds the count for the timer. By changing the number in this 3-byte section of memory, we can change the speed of the motor. Each time an interrupt occurs, the 3 bytes are sent out to reprogram the timer and the DMA action is again started. If the count is changed, the speed of the motor changes.

E X A M P L E    10 - 4

```
                           ;
                           ;This subroutine programs the DMA controller and
                           ;68230 PI/T.
                           ;
                           ;Assume interrupt vectors for the DMA controller are
                           ;programmed elsewhere.
                           ;
018000  423900020000   START  CLR.B   PGCR           ;68230 mode 0
018006  423900020006          CLR.B   ACR            ;68230 port A submode 0
01800C  13FC00FF00020002      MOVE.B  #$FF,ADDR      ;port A = output
018014  21FC00000200054C      MOVE.L  #PATTERN,MAR   ;setup address
01801C  21FC000200080564      MOVE.L  #ADR,DAR       ;address port A
018024  31FC0008050A          MOVE.W  #8,MTCR        ;load count
01802A  11FC00020545          MOVE.B  #2,OCR         ;external request
018030  11FC00040546          MOVE.B  #4,SCR         ;increment MAR only
018036  42380544              CLR.B   DCR            ;explicit address
01803A  13FC00F100020010      MOVE.B  #$F1,TCR       ;program timer
018042  207C00000100          MOVE.L  #COUNT,A0      ;get count
018048  227C00020017          MOVE.L  #TIME,A1
01804E  10D9                  MOVE.B  (A1)+,(A0)+
018050  10D9                  MOVE.B  (A1)+,(A0)+
018052  10D9                  MOVE.B  (A1)+,(A0)+
018054  11FC00880547          MOVE.B  #$88,CR        ;start channel
01805A  4E75                  RTS
```

Example 10-4 lists a subroutine that programs the timer and also the DMA controller. As can be deduced, 3 bytes are transferred from memory and sent to the timer, changing its operating frequency. The DMA controller is programmed to transfer 8 bytes from a section of memory that holds the binary bit pattern required to half-step the stepper motor.

E X A M P L E    10 - 5

```
                           ;
                           ;Interrupt service subroutine for
                           ;reprogramming the DMA controller.
```

```
                    ;
019000   48E700C0   INTR   MOVEM.L   A0/A1,-(SP)
019004   6100EFFA          BSR       START         ;reprogram
019008   4CDF0300          MOVEM.L   (SP)+,A0/A1
01900C   4E73             RTE
```

Example 10-5 lists the interrupt service subroutine that is called whenever the DMA controller completes transferring the 8-byte, half-step pattern to the stepper motor. Notice that the timer is reprogrammed and then the DMA controller is reprogrammed and started. This process repeats itself until the system is turned off or the interrupt is disabled.

## 10-2.8   Chaining DMA Actions

Until this point, the purpose and function of the base address register (BAR) and the base transfer count register (BTCR) have been ignored except when necessary to reload a channel. These registers are also used to chain DMA controller actions. These registers and chaining operations are available with the 68450 DMA controller only, not the 68440 or 68442.

Two chain transfers are allowed: the array chain transfer and the linked array chain transfer. In both chain transfer techniques the BAR addresses an area of the memory that contains addresses and counts, and the BTCR controls how many events are chained together. The addresses and counts are used to reprogram the channel so that new DMA actions ensue.

### Array Chain Transfer

Figure 10-21 illustrates an area of memory containing an array chain that is used with an array chain transfer to reprogram the DMA controller three times. This array chain assumes that the implicit addressing mode is used for the DMA transfer.

The first address (address A) is accessed by loading the address of the top of the chain into the BAR. The BTCR register is loaded with the count of the number of array chain entries. Figure 10-21 uses a base count of 3 because there are three entries in the chain. As each address and count is fetched from the chain, it is loaded into the MAR and MTCR registers, and a DMA action is initiated.

The array chain transfer is controlled with two bits in the operation control register that select array chain transfers. The size of the chain entry depends on whether explicit or implicit addressing is chosen for the chained transfer. In Figure 10-21 implicit addressing is used, with the address of the device loaded into the device address register before a chain transfer is initiated. Once the array chain transfer has started, the DMA controller accesses the first entry in the chain to obtain the first address and count, which are loaded into the MAR and MTCR. Upon completion of the first transfer, the contents of the BTCR and the BAR are decremented and incremented, respectively, to the next entry in the chain. The next entry is fetched from the array and a new DMA transfer begins. This continues until the count in the BTCR reaches zero.

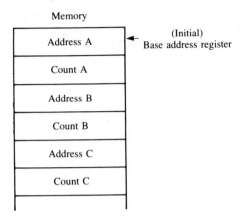

**Figure 10-21**   **The memory array containing addresses and counts for the DMA controller during an array chain transfer.**

## Linked Array Chain Transfer

Figure 10-22 illustrates the organization of the memory chain for a linked array chain. The operation of the linked array chain transfer is similar to the array chain transfer except that the memory array may be in noncontiguous sections of the memory.

If you look at any entry in this chain, you will notice that at the end of each one, a link address has been appended. The link address is a 32-bit address that is loaded into the base address register each time a DMA transfer is completed. This allows the next entry to be at any location in the memory. With the linked array chain transfer, the BTCR is not used. In place of the base count, the last entry in the linked array chain contains a zero, which indicates the end of the chain.

By using either of these chaining techniques, a queue can be set up for the DMA controller and its commands. This is useful in systems that make heavy use of DMA transfers between memory and I/O or even for memory-to-memory transfers. Note that one channel can be a chain and another channel can be a normal DMA transfer. This allows the most flexibility when using a DMA controller to perform I/O.

## 10-3   Disk Memory Systems

Disk memory is used to store data for the long term. Many types of disk storage system are available today. All types use magnetic media except the optical disk memory, which stores data on a plastic disk that is read or sometimes written with a laser beam. This section provides an introduction to disk memory systems so that they may be used with computer systems. It also provides operational details.

Memory

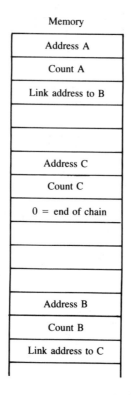

Figure 10-22    The memory map used with a linked array chain transfer.

### 10-3.1 Floppy Disk Memory

The most common and the most basic form of disk memory is the floppy or flexible disk. This magnetic recording medium is available in three sizes: the 8 inch standard, 5¼ inch mini-floppy, and the 3½ inch micro-floppy. Today the 8 inch standard version has all but disappeared, giving way to the mini- and micro-floppy disks. The micro-floppy disk is quickly replacing the mini-floppy in newer systems because of its advantages of size and durability.

All disks have several things in common. They are all organized so that data are stored in tracks. A *track* is a concentric ring of data stored on a surface of a disk. Figure 10-23 illustrates the surface of a 5¼ inch mini-floppy disk track and one (for the sake of clarity) sector. A *sector* is a common subdivision of a track that is designed to hold a reasonable amount of data. In many systems a sector often holds either 512 or 1024 bytes of data. Note the hole through the disk, labeled "index hole." The *index hole* is a design feature that permits the electronic system that reads the disk to find the beginning of a track and the first sector (00). Tracks are numbered from track 00 (the outermost track), in increasing value toward the center or innermost track.

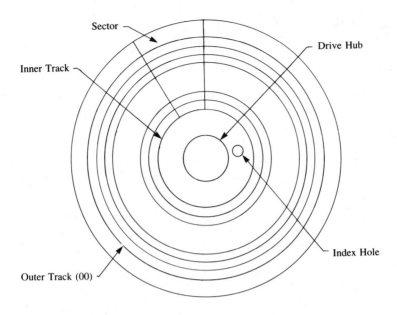

**Figure 10-23   The surface of a 5¹/₄ inch mini-floppy disk.**

## The 5¹/₄ Inch Mini-Floppy Disk

Today, the 5¹/₄ inch mini-floppy (Figure 10-24) is probably the most popular disk size used with older microcomputer systems. The disk is rotated at 300 rpm inside its semirigid plastic jacket. The head mechanism in the disk drive makes physical contact with the surface of the disk, which eventually causes wear and damage to the disk.

Most mini-floppy disks are double-sided. This means that data are written on both the top and bottom surfaces of the disk. A set of tracks is called a *cylinder* and consists of one top and one bottom track. Cylinder 00, for example, consists of the outermost top and bottom tracks.

Disk data are stored in double-density format, which uses a recording technique called *modified frequency modulation* (MFM) to store the information. Double-density disks normally are organized with 40 tracks of data on each side of the disk. A double-density disk track is typically divided into 9 sectors, with each sector containing 512 bytes of information. This means that the total capacity of a double-density, double-sided disk is 40 × 2 × 9 × 512 or 368,640 (360k) bytes of information.

Earlier disk memory systems used single-density and FM (frequency modulation) to store information in 40 tracks on one or two sides of the disk. Each of the 9 sectors on the single-density disk stored 256 bytes of data. This meant that a single-density disk stored 90k bytes of data per side. A single-density, double-sided disk stored 180k bytes of data.

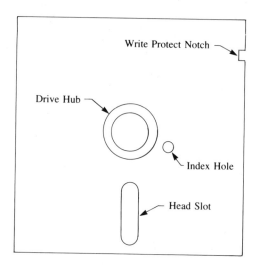

**Figure 10-24**   The 5¼ inch mini-floppy disk.

Also common today are *high density* mini-floppy disks. A high density mini-floppy disk contains 80 tracks of information per side, with 8 sectors each containing 1024 bytes of information. This gives the 5¼ inch high density mini-floppy disk a total capacity of 80 × 2 × 8 × 1024 or 1,310,720 (1.2M) bytes of information.

The magnetic recording technique used to store data on the surface of the disk is called *non-return to zero* (NRZ) recording. With NRZ recording, magnetic flux placed on the surface of the disk never returns to zero. Figure 10-25, which illustrates the information stored in a portion of a track, shows how the magnetic field encodes the data. Note that the polarity of the magnetic field stored on the surface of the disk is indicated by arrows.

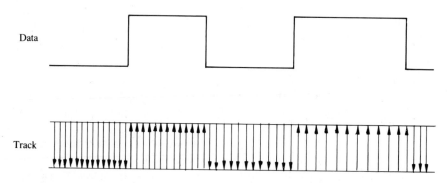

**Figure 10-25**   The non-return to zero (NRZ) recording technique used with disk memory data.

This form of magnetic encoding is chosen mainly because it automatically erases old information when new information is recorded. When another technique is used, a separate erase head is required. The mechanical alignment of a separate erase head and a separate read/write head is virtually impossible.

The magnetic flux density of the NRZ signal is so strong that it completely saturates (magnetizes) the surface of the disk, erasing all prior data. It also ensures that information will not be affected by noise because the amplitude of the magnetic field contains no information. The information is stored in the placement of the changes of magnetic field.

Data are stored in the form of MFM in modern floppy disk systems. The MFM recording technique stores data in the form illustrated in Figure 10-26. Notice that each bit time is 2 μs in width on a double-density disk. This means that data are recorded at the rate of 500,000 bits per second. Each 2 μs bit time is divided into two parts. One part is designated to hold a clock pulse, and the other holds a data pulse. If a clock pulse is present, it is 1 μs in width, like a data pulse. Clock and data pulses are never present at the same time in one bit period. (Note that high density disk drives halve these times, for a bit time of 1 μs and a clock or data pulse 0.5 μs in width.) This also doubles the transfer rate to 1 million bits per second.

If a data pulse is present, the bit time represents a logic one. If no data or no clock is present, the bit time represents a logic zero. If a clock pulse is present with no data pulse, the bit time also represents a logic zero. The rules that apply when data are stored using MFM are as follows.

1. A data pulse is always stored for a logic one.

2. No data and no clock are stored for the first logic zero in a string of logic zeros.

3. The second and subsequent logic zeros in a row contain a clock pulse, but no data pulse.

A clock is inserted as the second and subsequent zero in a row to maintain synchronization. The electronics used to recapture the data from the disk drive uses a phase-locked loop to generate a clock and a data window. The phase-locked loop needs a clock or data to maintain synchronized operation.

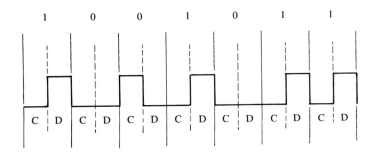

**Figure 10-26** Modified frequency modulation (MFM) used with disk memory.

*The 3¹/₂ Inch Micro-Floppy Disk*

Another very popular disk size is the 3¹/₂ inch micro-floppy disk. Recently this floppy disk size has begun to sell very well and in the future promises to be the dominant floppy disk. The micro-floppy disk is a much improved version of the mini-floppy described earlier. Figure 10-27 illustrates the 3¹/₂ inch micro-floppy disk.

Disk designers noticed several shortcomings of the mini-floppy. Probably one of the biggest problems associated with the mini-floppy is that its soft or semirigid plastic cover bends easily. The micro-floppy is packaged in a rigid plastic jacket that will not bend easily. This provides a much greater degree of protection to the disk inside the jacket.

Another problem with the mini-floppy is the head slot, which continually exposes the surface of the disk to contaminants. This problem is also corrected on the micro-floppy, which is constructed with a spring-loaded sliding head door. The head door remains closed until, when the disk is inserted into the drive, the drive mechanism slides it open. This provides a great deal of protection to the surface of the micro-floppy disk.

Yet another improvement is the sliding plastic write protection mechanism on the micro-floppy disk. On the mini-floppy disk a piece of tape was placed over a notch on the side of the jacket to prevent writing. This plastic tape easily became dislodged inside disk drives, causing problems.

On the micro-floppy, an integrated plastic slide has replaced the tape write protection mechanism. To write protect (prevent writing) the micro-floppy disk, the plastic slide is moved to open the hole though the disk jacket. This allows light to strike a sensor, which inhibits writing.

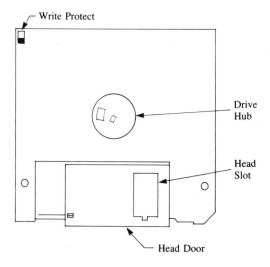

**Figure 10-27**   The 3¹/₂ inch micro-floppy disk.

Still another improvement is the replacement of the index hole with a different drive mechanism. The drive mechanism on the mini-floppy allows the disk drive to grab the disk at any point. This necessitates the index hole, to permit the electronics to find the beginning of a track. The micro-floppy has a drive mechanism that is keyed so that it fits only one way inside the disk drive, and the index hole is no longer required.

Two types of micro-floppy disk are widely available: double-sided, double-density and high density. The double-density micro-floppy disk has 80 tracks per side, with each track containing 9 sectors. Each sector contains 512 bytes of information. This allows $80 \times 2 \times 9 \times 512$ or 737,280 (720k) bytes of data to be stored on a double-density, double-sided floppy disk. Some systems pack up to 800k bytes on a disk of the same size by using 10 sectors instead of 9 sectors.

The high density, double-sided micro-floppy disk stores even more information. The high density version has 80 tracks per side, but the number of sectors is doubled to 18 per track. This format still uses 512 bytes per sector as did the double-density format. The total number of bytes on a high density, double-sided micro-floppy disk is $80 \times 2 \times 18 \times 512$ or 1,474,560 (1.44M) bytes of information.

## 10-3.2 Hard Disk Memory

Larger disk memory is available in the form of the hard disk drive. The hard disk drive is often called a *fixed disk* because it is not removable like the floppy disk. A hard disk is also often called a *rigid disk*. The term Winchester drive is also used to describe a hard disk drive. Hard disk memory has a much larger capacity than the floppy disk memory. Hard disk memory is available in sizes approaching 1G byte of data. Common, low cost sizes are presently 64M or 80M bytes.

There are several differences between the floppy disk and the hard disk memory. The hard disk memory uses a flying head to store and read data from the surface of the disk. A flying head does not touch the surface of the disk. Rather, it travels above the surface on a film of air that is carried with the surface of the disk as it spins. The hard disk spins at 3000 rpm, which is 10 times faster than the floppy disk. This higher rotational speed allows the head to fly (just as an airplane flies) just over the top of the surface of the disk. This is important because wear on the surface, encountered with the floppy disk, is eliminated.

Problems can arise because of flying heads, however. One problem is a head crash. If the power is interrupted or the hard disk drive is jarred, the head can crash onto the disk surface, damaging the disk surface or the head itself. To help prevent crashes, some drive manufacturers have included a system that automatically parks the head when power is interrupted. This type of disk drive has auto-parking heads. When the heads are parked they are moved to a safe landing zone (unused track) when the power is disconnected. Some drives are not auto-parking. This type of drive usually uses a program that parks the heads on the innermost track before power is disconnected. The innermost track is a safe landing area because it is the very last track filled by the disk drive. Parking is the responsibility of the operator with this type of disk drive.

Floppy disk and hard disk drives also differ in number of heads and disk surfaces. A floppy disk drive has two heads, one for the upper surface and one for the lower surface. The hard disk drive may have up to eight disk surfaces (four platters), with up to two heads per surface. Each time a new cylinder is obtained by moving the head assembly, 16 new tracks become available under the heads. Refer to Figure 10-28, which illustrates a disk system that uses two heads per surface.

Heads are moved from track to track, using either a stepper motor or a voice coil. The stepper motor is slow and noisy, while the voice coil mechanism is quiet and quick. To move the head assembly requires one step per cylinder in a system that uses a stepper motor. In a system that uses a voice coil, the heads can be moved many cylinders with one sweeping motion. This makes the disk drive faster when seeking new cylinders.

Another advantage of the voice coil system is that a servomechanism can monitor the signal as it comes from the read head and make slight adjustments in the position of the heads. This is not possible with a stepper motor, which relies strictly on mechanics to position the head.

Hard disk drives store information in sectors that are 1024 bytes in length. Data are addressed in clusters of four sectors, which contain 4096 bytes on most hard disk drives. Hard disk drives use either MFM or RLL to store information. MFM was described above in connection with floppy disk drives. *Run-length limited* (RLL) is described here.

The MFM hard disk drive uses 18 sectors per track, so that 18k bytes of data are stored per track. If a hard disk drive has a capacity of 40M bytes, it contains approximately 2280 tracks. If the disk drive has two heads, this means that it contains 1140 cylinders. If it contains four heads, then it has 570 cylinders. These specifications vary from disk drive to disk drive.

## RLL Storage

Run-length-limited (RLL) and MFM disk drives use different methods for encoding data. The term RLL means that the run of zeros is limited. A common RLL scheme in use today is RLL 2,7. This means that the run of zeros is always between 2 and 7. Table 10-3 illustrates the coding used with standard RLL.

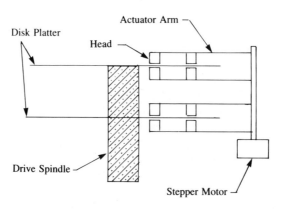

**Figure 10-28   A hard disk drive that uses four heads per platter.**

**Table 10-3   Standard RLL 2,7 Coding**

| Input data | RLL output |
|------------|------------|
| 000        | 000100     |
| 10         | 0100       |
| 010        | 100100     |
| 0010       | 00100100   |
| 11         | 1000       |
| 011        | 001000     |
| 0011       | 00001000   |

Data are encoded using Table 10-3 before being sent to the drive electronics for storage on the disk surface. Because of this encoding technique, it is possible to achieve a 50% increase in data storage on a disk drive when compared to MFM. The main difference is that the RLL drive often contains 27 tracks instead of the 18 found on the MFM drive. (Some RLL drives use 35 sectors per track.)

It is interesting to note that RLL encoding requires no change to the drive electronics or surface of the disk in most cases. The only difference is a slight decrease in the pulse width using RLL, which may require slightly finer oxide particles on the surface of the disk. Disk manufacturers test the surface of the disk and grade the disk drive as either an MFM-certified or an RLL-certified drive. Other than grading, there is no difference in the construction of the disk drive or the magnetic material that coats the disks.

Figure 10-29 compares MFM data and RLL data: a 101001011 is coded in both systems. Notice that the amount of time (space) required to store RLL data is

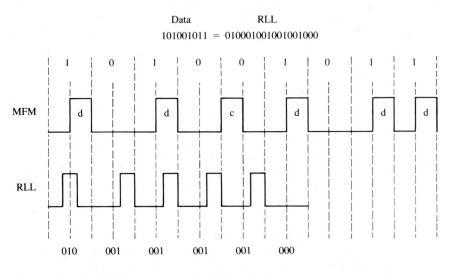

**Figure 10-29   A comparison of MFM with RLL using data 101001011.**

reduced compared to MFM and that the width of the RLL signal has been reduced so that 3 pulses fit in the same space as a clock and a data pulse for MFM. A 20M byte MFM disk can hold 30M bytes of RLL encoded data. Besides holding more information, the RLL drive can be written and read at a higher rate.

All hard disk drives use either MFM or RLL encoding. There are a number of disk drive interfaces in use today. The oldest and probably still the most common is the ST-506 interface, which uses either MFM or RLL data and is also called either MFM or RLL. Newer standards are also available. These include ESDI, SCSI, and IDE. All these newer standards use RLL, even though they normally do not call attention to it. The main difference is the interface between the computer and the disk drive.

The *enhanced small disk interface* (ESDI) system is capable of transferring data between itself and the computer at rates approaching 10M bytes per second. An ST-506 interface can approach a transfer rate of 860k bytes per second.

The *small computer system interface* (SCSI) system is also in use because it allows up to seven different disk or other interfaces to be connected to the computer through the same interface controller. SCSI is found in some PC-type computers and also in the Apple Macintosh system.

The newest system is *integrated drive electronics* (IDE), which incorporates the disk controller in the disk drive and attaches the disk drive to the host system through a small interface cable. This allows many disk drives to be connected to a system without worrying about bus conflicts. IDE drives are found in newer IBM PS-2 systems. The IDE interface is also capable of driving other I/O devices besides the hard disk. This interface also usually contains 32k bytes of cache memory for disk data, which speeds disk transfers.

### 10-3.3    Optical Disk Memory

Optical disk memory is commonly available in two forms: the ROM CD (read-only memory compact disk) and the WORM (write once/read mostly). The ROM CD is the lowest cost optical disk, but it suffers from lack of speed. It also suffers from lack of software applications at this time. The ROM CD is available for large volume data storage such as the Bible, encyclopedias, clip art, and magazine articles. None of these applications have wide appeal at the current prices. At some future date, if access times decrease and more applications are introduced, the ROM CD may become popular.

The WORM drive sees far more application than the ROM CD. The problem is that its application is very specialized due to the nature of the WORM. Because data may be written only once, the main application is in the banking and insurance industries, and other massive data storing operations. The WORM is normally used to form an audit trail of transactions that are spooled onto the memory and retrieved only during an audit. You might call the WORM an archiving device.

Many WORM and read/write optical disk memory systems are interfaced to the microprocessor by means of the SCSI or ESDI interface standards used with hard disk memory. The difference is that the current optical disk drives are no faster than the hard drives.

## 10-3.4   Small Computer System Interface (SCSI)

This section illustrates the small computer system interface (SCSI). It describes and explains the details of this interface standard, which finds widespread use with Apple Macintosh and IBM PC computers.

### The SCSI Interface Standard

The small computer system interface (SCSI) is a standard interface designated ANSI X3X3T9.2 (version 17B) by the Institute of Electrical and Electronics Engineers (IEEE). This standard is designed to allow transfer rates of up to 4M bytes per second through a 50-pin connector. The standard also allows up to eight devices such as disk memory, laser printers, and tape drives to be connected to the same bus. Other standards allow only one device to be connected to each interface cable. The standard is a parallel standard that allows 8 bits of data to be transferred at a time between the host and one of these I/O devices.

   Table 10-4 illustrates the SCSI bus control lines. All signals on this bus are active low. Active low signals are true if they are a logic zero. Devices connected to the bus fall into two categories, the *initiator* and the *target*. The initiator is a device that can begin actions on the bus and is typically the host computer system. The target is a device that performs services for the initiator and is usually a disk drive or laser printer.

   The SCSI standard allows cable lengths of up to 6 meters unless differential transmission is used on the bus. Differential transmission allows cable lengths of up to 25 meters. Single-ended signals are (TTL) zero volts for a true condition and +5.0 V for a false condition. This is why all the signals are active low signals.

**Table 10-4   The SCSI Bus Control Lines**

| Signal | Function |
|---|---|
| $\overline{\text{DB7}}$–$\overline{\text{DB0}}$ | Data lines that carry data between the bus device and host and also serve as selection lines during arbitration. |
| $\overline{\text{DBP}}$ | Data line parity bit. |
| $\overline{\text{BSY}}$ | Indicates that the bus is busy. |
| $\overline{\text{SEL}}$ | Select is active whenever the data lines contain a device address. |
| $\overline{\text{C/D}}$ | If this signal is a zero, the bus contains control information; if a one, it contains data. |
| $\overline{\text{MSG}}$ | Indicates that the data bus contains a message. |
| $\overline{\text{REQ}}$ | Signal asserted by a target I/O device to request a data transfer from the initiator. |
| $\overline{\text{ACK}}$ | Signal returned from the initiator to indicate that the data transfer is complete. |
| $\overline{\text{I/O}}$ | Indicates the direction of the data transfer. If $\overline{\text{I/O}}$ is a logic zero, data are input to the initiator from the target I/O device. |
| $\overline{\text{ATN}}$ | Attention is asserted by the initiator when it wishes to send a message to the I/O device. |
| $\overline{\text{RST}}$ | Reset. |

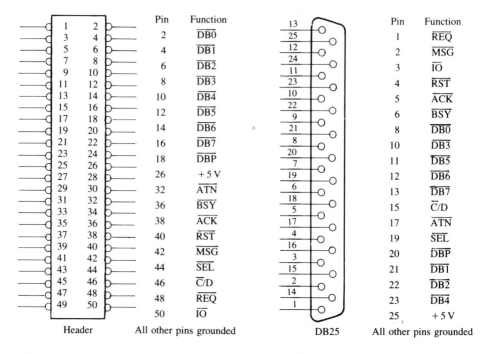

**Figure 10-30** The 50-pin SCSI connector and the Apple Macintosh external 25-pin DB25 connector.

Figure 10-30 illustrates the 50 pin-connector used for the SCSI interface. Also illustrated is a 25-pin connector used on the Apple Macintosh to connect to external SCSI devices. The Macintosh also uses a 50-pin internal connector to connect to internal SCSI devices.

### SCSI Interface Operation

When the system is reset, all devices on the bus enter the idle state. The bus is idle when both select ($\overline{SEL}$) and busy ($\overline{BSY}$) are in the inactive state. The inactive state of the bus occurs when $\overline{SEL} = 1$ and $\overline{BSY} = 1$. Whenever a device requests the bus, it activates the busy line ($\overline{BSY} = 0$) and its identification (ID) line, which is one of the data bus connections. For example, if the computer, connected as an initiator, requests the bus, it places a logic zero on $\overline{BSY}$ and $\overline{DB7}$ at the same time. The $\overline{DB7}$ data bus line has the highest priority and the $\overline{DB0}$ data bus line has the lowest priority. The data bus lines are used as device ID codes.

When a device sees a logic zero on the busy line, it may not itself place a logic zero on busy. In some cases more than one device can activate the busy line at the same time. If this occurs, the priority scheme whereby $\overline{DB7}$ has the highest priority and $\overline{DB0}$ has the lowest priority comes into play. If a higher priority device has access to the bus, the other devices disable themselves until the bus becomes free.

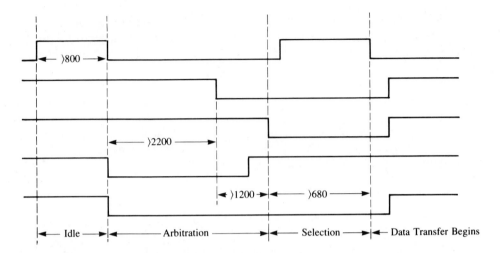

**Figure 10-31** Bus arbitration and device selection for the SCSI bus. Here device 7 selects device 5 for a data transfer.

Figure 10-31 illustrates the sequence of events required to arbitrate the SCSI bus and also to allow the initiator to select a target device. The idle state is by definition a logic one on both the $\overline{BSY}$ and $\overline{SEL}$ lines for greater than 800 ns. Once an idle state has been entered, any device on the system may assert the busy line along with its ID line. In the illustration, devices 6 and 7 both assert the busy line and their respective ID lines ($\overline{DB6}$ and $\overline{DB7}$). This begins the arbitration phase of bus operation.

During the first 2200 ns of the arbitration phase, devices that request the bus examine the ID lines to see whether they have won arbitration. This length of time is required to make sure that all devices have stopped changing the ID lines. At this time the winning device (device 7 in this example) asserts the $\overline{SEL}$ line, selecting the bus. The winning device now waits another 1200 ns for other devices to release their ID signals and $\overline{BSY}$ signals. At this time the winning device enters into the selection phase.

In the selection phase the winning device (device 7) selects a target. That is, the target is selected by the initiator by placing the target ID line at a logic zero level. Here the target is device 5 ($\overline{DB5}$). After waiting for at least 80 ns, the initiator releases the $\overline{BSY}$ line by placing it at a logic 1 level. When the target notices that the $\overline{BSY}$ line has been released, it asserts this line, to indicate that the target can now begin data transfer. It takes at least 680 ns from the time selection begins until the target begins transferring data.

## 10-4   Video Displays

Modern video displays are OEM (original equipment manufacturer) devices that are usually purchased and incorporated into a system. Today many different types of video displays are available, including color and monochrome versions.

Monochrome versions usually display information using amber, green, or paper-white displays. The paper-white display is becoming extremely popular for many applications, particularly desktop publishing and computer-aided drafting (CAD).

The color displays are more diverse. Color display systems are available that accept information as a composite video signal much as your home television does—as TTL voltage level signals (0–5 V) and as analog signals. Composite video displays are disappearing because the resolution available is low. Today many applications require high resolution graphics, which cannot be displayed on a composite display such as a home television receiver.

### 10-4.1   Video Signals

The signal sent to a composite video display (Figure 10-32) is composed of the several parts that are required for this type of display. The signals illustrated represent the signals sent to a color composite video monitor. Notice that these signals include not only video, but sync pulses, sync pedestals, and a color burst. Also notice that no audio signal is illustrated; this is because one often does not exist. Rather than being included with the composite video signal, audio is developed in the computer and output from a speaker inside the computer cabinet. The major disadvantages of the composite video display lie in the resolution and color limitations.

Most modern video systems use direct video signals that are generated with separate sync signals. In a direct video system, video information is passed to the monitor through a cable that uses separate lines for video and also synchronization pulses. Recall that these signals were combined in a composite video signal.

A monochrome (one color) monitor uses one line for video, one line for horizontal sync, and one line for vertical sync. Often these are the only signal lines found. A color video monitor uses three video signals. One signal represents red, another green, and the third blue. These monitors are often called RGB monitors for the video primary colors of light: red (R), green (G), and blue (B).

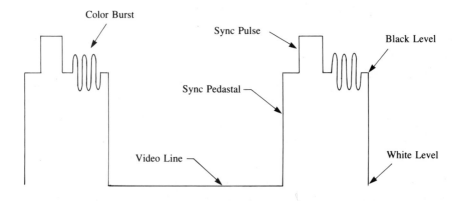

**Figure 10-32   The composite video signal.**

**Table 10-5**   The 16 Colors Available on a TTL Color RGB
Display

| Red | Green | Blue | Intensity | Color |
|-----|-------|------|-----------|-------|
| 0 | 0 | 0 | 0 | black |
| 0 | 0 | 0 | 1 | gray |
| 0 | 0 | 1 | 0 | light blue |
| 0 | 0 | 1 | 1 | blue |
| 0 | 1 | 0 | 0 | light green |
| 0 | 1 | 0 | 1 | green |
| 0 | 1 | 1 | 0 | light cyan |
| 0 | 1 | 1 | 1 | cyan |
| 1 | 0 | 0 | 0 | light red |
| 1 | 0 | 0 | 1 | red |
| 1 | 0 | 1 | 0 | light magenta |
| 1 | 0 | 1 | 1 | magenta |
| 1 | 1 | 0 | 0 | brown |
| 1 | 1 | 0 | 1 | yellow |
| 1 | 1 | 1 | 0 | white |
| 1 | 1 | 1 | 1 | intense white |

### 10-4.2   The TTL RGB Monitor

The RGB monitor is available in both analog and TTL forms. The RGB monitor
uses TTL level signals as video inputs and a fourth line called intensity to allow a
change in intensity value. The RGB video TTL display can display a total of 16
different colors.

Table 10-5 lists these 16 colors and also the TTL signals present to generate
them. Eight of the colors are generated at high intensity and the other eight at low
intensity. Red, green, and blue are primary colors; the secondary colors that are
generated include cyan, magenta, and yellow. Cyan is a blue-green combination of
blue and green. Magenta is purple, a combination of blue and red. Yellow and
brown are both combinations of red and green. If additional colors are desired, TTL
video is not normally used. A scheme was developed using low and medium color
TTL video signals, but it proved to have little application and never found widespread use in the field.

Figure 10-33 illustrates the 9-pin connector most often found on TTL RGB and
monochrome monitors. Two of the connections are used for ground, three for video,
two for synchronization or retrace signals, one for intensity, and one, pin 7, for
normal video. (Pin 7 is used on a monochrome monitor for the luminance or
brightness signal.) As indicated above, monochrome and RGB TTL monitors use
the same 9-pin connector.

### 10-4.3   The Analog RGB Monitor

An analog video display is required to display more than 16 colors. Such devices,
often called analog RGB monitors, still have three video input signals but lack an

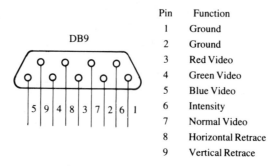

| Pin | Function |
|-----|----------|
| 1 | Ground |
| 2 | Ground |
| 3 | Red Video |
| 4 | Green Video |
| 5 | Blue Video |
| 6 | Intensity |
| 7 | Normal Video |
| 8 | Horizontal Retrace |
| 9 | Vertical Retrace |

**Figure 10-33    The 9-pin connector used with a TTL monitor.**

intensity input. Because the video signals are analog signals, they are any voltage level between 0.0 and 0.7 V. This allows an infinite number of colors to be displayed, because an infinite number of voltage levels between the minimum and maximum are generated. In practice, however, a finite number of levels are generated: usually either 256k or 16M colors, depending on the standard.

Figure 10-34 illustrates the connector used for an analog RGB or monochrome monitor. Notice that the connector has 15 pins and supports both RGB and monochrome analog displays. The data display format on an analog RGB monitor de-

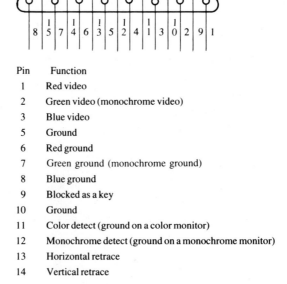

| Pin | Function |
|-----|----------|
| 1 | Red video |
| 2 | Green video (monochrome video) |
| 3 | Blue video |
| 5 | Ground |
| 6 | Red ground |
| 7 | Green ground (monochrome ground) |
| 8 | Blue ground |
| 9 | Blocked as a key |
| 10 | Ground |
| 11 | Color detect (ground on a color monitor) |
| 12 | Monochrome detect (ground on a monochrome monitor) |
| 13 | Horizontal retrace |
| 14 | Vertical retrace |

**Figure 10-34    The 15-pin connector used with an analog monitor.**

pends on the interface standard used with the monitor. Pin 9 is a key; that is no hole exists on the female connector for this pin.

Most analog displays use a digital-to-analog converter to generate each color video voltage. A common standard uses a 6-bit DAC for each video signal to generate 64 different voltage levels. There are 64 different red video levels, 64 different green video levels, and 64 different blue video levels. This allows 64 × 64 × 64 different colors to be displayed or 262,144 (256k) colors.

Other arrangements are possible, but the speed of the DAC is critical. Most modern displays require an operating conversion time of at least 25 ns (40 ns maximum). When converter technology advances, additional resolution at a reasonable price will become available. If 7-bit converters are used for generating video, then 128 × 128 × 128 or 2,097,152 (2M) colors are displayed. In this system a 21-bit color code is needed, so that a 7-bit code is applied to each DAC. Eight-bit converters also find applications and allow 256 × 256 × 256 or 16,777,216 (16M) colors.

Figure 10-35 diagrams the video generation circuit employed in many common video standards such as EGA (enhanced graphics adaptor) and VGA (variable graphics array), as used with the IBM-PC. The circuit illustrated generates VGA video. Notice that each color is generated with an 18-bit digital code: 6 of the 18 bits are used to generate each video color voltage.

A high speed palette SRAM (access time <40 ns) is used to store 256 different 18-bit codes representing 256 different hues. This 18-bit code is applied to the digital-to-analog converters. The address input to the SRAM selects one of the 256 colors stored as 18-bit binary codes. This system allows 256 colors out of a possible 256k colors to be displayed at one time. To select any of 256 colors, an 8-bit code is used to specify a color. If more colors are used in a system, the code must be wider. For example, a system that displays 1024 colors out of 256k colors requires a 10-bit code to address the SRAM, which holds 1024 locations, each containing an 18-bit color code.

The Apple Macintosh IIci uses a 24-bit binary code to specify each color in its color video adapter. Each DAC is 8 bits wide. This means that each converter can generate 256 different video voltage levels. There are 256 × 256 × 256 or 16,777,216 different possible colors. As with the IBM VGA standard, only 256 colors are displayed at a time. The SRAM in the Apple interface is 256 × 24 instead of 256 × 18.

Whenever a color is placed on the video display, provided RTC is a logic zero, the system sends the 8-bit code that represents a color to the D0–D7 connections. The PAL 16R8 then generates a clock pulse for U10, which latches the color code. After 40 ns (one 25 MHz clock) the PAL generates a clock pulse for the DAC latches (U7, U8, and U9). This amount of time is required for the palette SRAM to look up the 18-bit contents of the memory location selected by U10. Once the color code (18-bit) has been latched into U7–U9, the three DACs convert it to three video voltages for the monitor. This process is repeated for each 40 ns wide picture element (*pixel*) that is displayed. The pixel is 40 ns wide because a 25 MHz clock is used in this system. Higher resolution is attainable if a higher clock frequency is used with the system.

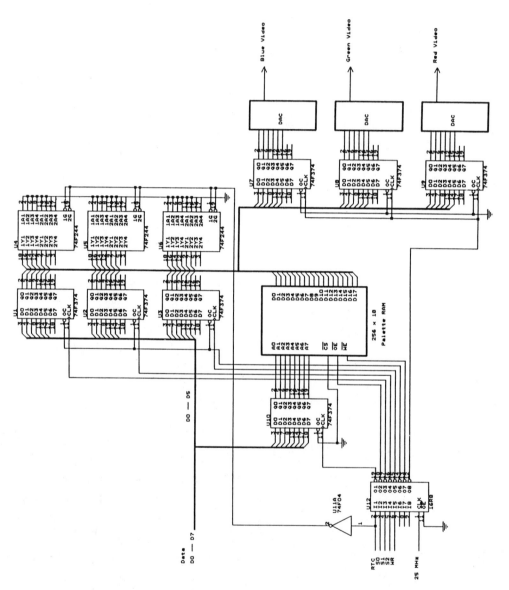

**Figure 10-35**  Generation of the VGA video signals.

The color codes (18 bits) stored in the SRAM are always changed during retrace, when RTC is a logic one, to prevent any video noise from disrupting the image displayed on the monitor.

To change a color, the system uses the S0, S1, and S2 inputs of the PAL to select U1, U2, U3, or U10. First the address of the color to be changed is sent to latch U10. This addresses a location in the palette SRAM. Next each new video color is loaded into U1, U2, and U3. Finally the PAL generates a write pulse for the $\overline{WE}$ input to the SRAM to write the new color code into the palette SRAM.

Retrace occurs 70.1 times per second in the vertical direction and 31,500 times per second in the horizontal direction for a 640 × 400 display. During retrace, the video signal voltage sent to the display must be 0 V. This causes black to be displayed during the retrace. Retrace itself is used to move the electron beam to the upper left-hand corner for vertical retrace and to the left margin of the screen for horizontal retrace.

The circuit illustrated causes U4–U6 buffers to be enabled so that they apply 00000 each to the DAC latch for retrace. The DAC latches capture this code and generate 0 V for each video color signal to blank the screen. By definition, 0 V is considered the black level for video and 0.7 V is considered full intensity on a video color signal.

The resolution of the display, for example, 640 × 400, determines the amount of memory required for the video interface card. If this resolution is used with a 256-color display (8 bits per pixel) then 640 × 400 bytes of memory (256,000) are required to store all the pixels for the display. Higher resolution displays are possible, but as you can imagine even more memory is required. A 640 × 400 display has 400 video raster lines and 640 pixels per line. A *raster line* is the horizontal line of video information that is displayed on the monitor. A pixel is a subdivision of this horizontal line.

In Figure 10-36, which illustrates the video display showing the video lines and retrace, the slant of each video line is greatly exaggerated, as is the spacing between lines. This illustration shows retrace in both the vertical and horizontal directions. In the case of a VGA display, as described, the vertical retrace occurs exactly 70.1 times per second and the horizontal retrace occurs exactly 31,500 times per second. (The Apple Macintosh IIci uses a vertical rate of 66.67 Hz and a horizontal rate of 35 kHz to generate a 640 × 480 color display.)

The time needed to generate 640 pixels across one line is 40 ns × 640 or 25.6 µs. A horizontal time of 31,500 Hz allows a horizontal line time of 1/31,500 or 31.746 µs. The difference between these two times is the retrace time allowed to the monitor. (The Apple Macintosh IIci has a horizontal line time of 28.57 µs.)

Because the vertical retrace repetition rate is 70.1 Hz, the number of lines generated is determined by dividing the vertical time into the horizontal time. In the case of VGA display, a 640 × 400 display, this is 449.358 lines. Only 400 of these lines are used to display information; the rest (49.358 lines) are lost during the retrace. Therefore the retrace time is 49.358 × 31.766 µs or 1568 µs. It is during this relatively large amount of time that the color palette SRAM is changed or the display memory system is updated for a new video display. The Apple Macintosh IIci computer (640 × 480) generates 525 lines, of which 45 are lost during vertical retrace.

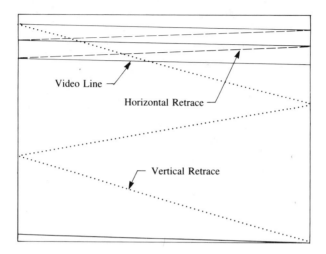

**Figure 10-36**   **A video screen illustrating raster lines and retrace.**

More recently video display systems are beginning appear that display graphics at a resolution of 1024 × 768 with 256 colors. This sounds like just a set of numbers, but realize that an average home television receiver has a resolution of approximately 400 × 300. The high resolution display available on computer systems is much clearer than that available as home television.

If a display system operates with a 60 Hz vertical time and a 15,600 Hz horizontal time, the number of lines generated is 15,600/60, or 260 lines. The number of usable lines in this system is most likely 240, where 20 are lost during vertical retrace. It is clear that the number of scanning lines is adjustable by changing the vertical and horizontal scanning rates.

The vertical scanning rate must be greater than 50 Hz or flickering will occur. The vertical rate must not be higher than about 75 Hz or problems with the vertical deflection coil may occur. The electron beam in a monitor is positioned by an electrical magnetic field generated by coils in a yoke that surrounds the neck of the picture tube. Since the magnetic field is generated by coils, the frequency of the signal applied to the coil is limited.

The horizontal scanning rate is also limited by the physical design of the coils in the yoke. Because of this, it is normal to find the frequency applied to the horizontal coils within a narrow range, usually 30,000–37,000 or 15,000–17,000 Hz. Some newer monitors are called multisync monitors because the deflection coil is taped so that it can be driven with different deflection frequencies.

## 10-5   Connecting Coprocessors

A coprocessor is a device that can process operations concurrently with the microprocessor. In other words, both the microprocessor and the coprocessor can be

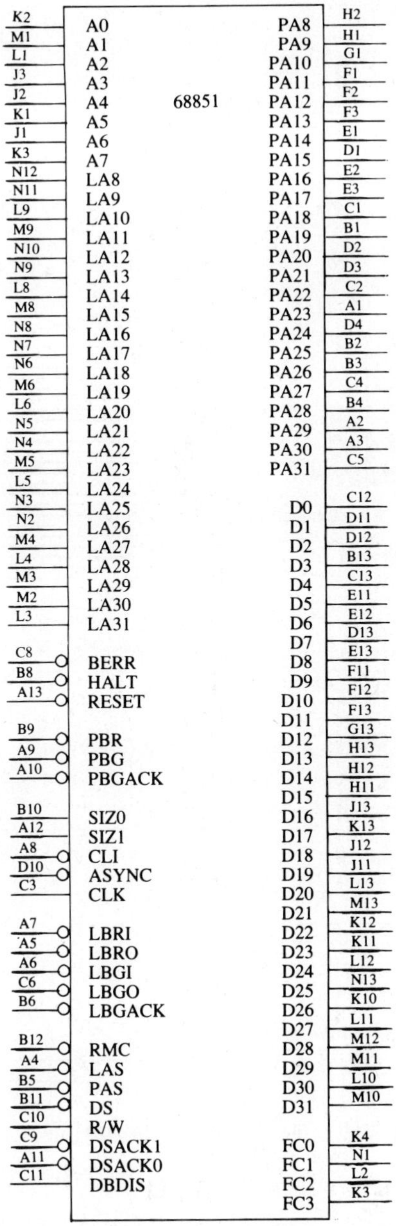

| | | 68851 | | |
|---|---|---|---|---|
| K2 | A0 | | PA8 | H2 |
| M1 | A1 | | PA9 | H1 |
| L1 | A2 | | PA10 | G1 |
| J3 | A3 | | PA11 | F1 |
| J2 | A4 | | PA12 | F2 |
| K1 | A5 | | PA13 | F3 |
| J1 | A6 | | PA14 | E1 |
| K3 | A7 | | PA15 | D1 |
| N12 | LA8 | | PA16 | E2 |
| N11 | LA9 | | PA17 | E3 |
| L9 | LA10 | | PA18 | C1 |
| M9 | LA11 | | PA19 | B1 |
| N10 | LA12 | | PA20 | D2 |
| N9 | LA13 | | PA21 | D3 |
| L8 | LA14 | | PA22 | C2 |
| M8 | LA15 | | PA23 | A1 |
| N8 | LA16 | | PA24 | D4 |
| N7 | LA17 | | PA25 | B2 |
| N6 | LA18 | | PA26 | B3 |
| M6 | LA19 | | PA27 | C4 |
| L6 | LA20 | | PA28 | B4 |
| N5 | LA21 | | PA29 | A2 |
| N4 | LA22 | | PA30 | A3 |
| M5 | LA23 | | PA31 | C5 |
| L5 | LA24 | | | |
| N3 | LA25 | | D0 | C12 |
| N2 | LA26 | | D1 | D11 |
| M4 | LA27 | | D2 | D12 |
| L4 | LA28 | | D3 | B13 |
| M3 | LA29 | | D4 | C13 |
| M2 | LA30 | | D5 | E11 |
| L3 | LA31 | | D6 | E12 |
| | | | D7 | D13 |
| C8 | BERR | | D8 | E13 |
| B8 | HALT | | D9 | F11 |
| A13 | RESET | | D10 | F12 |
| | | | D11 | F13 |
| B9 | PBR | | D12 | G13 |
| A9 | PBG | | D13 | H13 |
| A10 | PBGACK | | D14 | H12 |
| | | | D15 | H11 |
| B10 | SIZ0 | | D16 | J13 |
| A12 | SIZ1 | | D17 | K13 |
| A8 | CLI | | D18 | J12 |
| D10 | ASYNC | | D19 | J11 |
| C3 | CLK | | D20 | L13 |
| | | | D21 | M13 |
| A7 | LBRI | | D22 | K12 |
| A5 | LBRO | | D23 | K11 |
| A6 | LBGI | | D24 | L12 |
| C6 | LBGO | | D25 | N13 |
| B6 | LBGACK | | D26 | K10 |
| | | | D27 | L11 |
| B12 | RMC | | D28 | M12 |
| A4 | LAS | | D29 | M11 |
| B5 | PAS | | D30 | L10 |
| B11 | DS | | D31 | M10 |
| C10 | R/W | | | |
| C9 | DSACK1 | | FC0 | K4 |
| A11 | DSACK0 | | FC1 | N1 |
| C11 | DBDIS | | FC2 | L2 |
| | | | FC3 | K3 |

Figure 10-37 The pinout of the 68851 memory management unit (MMU).

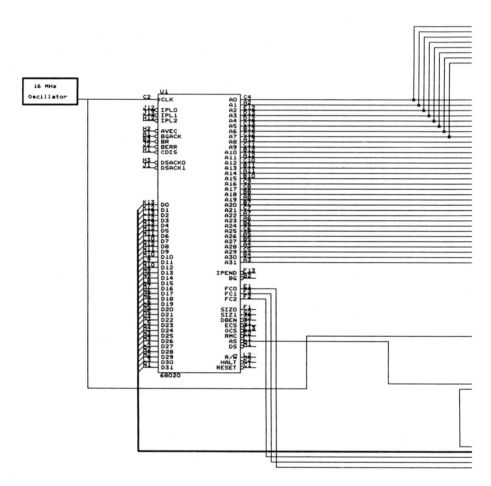

**Figure 10-38**   **The 68851 MMU interfaced to the 68020 microprocessor, illustrating the address interconnections.**

executing instructions at the same time. The 68000 system has two coprocessors that are commonly connected to the system: the arithmetic coprocessor (68881/68882), which is detailed in Chapter 11, and the memory management coprocessor (68851), which is detailed as part of the 68030 microprocessor in Chapter 13. Both devices use the 68000 family coprocessor interface.

Figure 10-37 illustrates the 68851 memory management unit that operates using the coprocessor interface of the 68020 microprocessor. The operation of the memo-

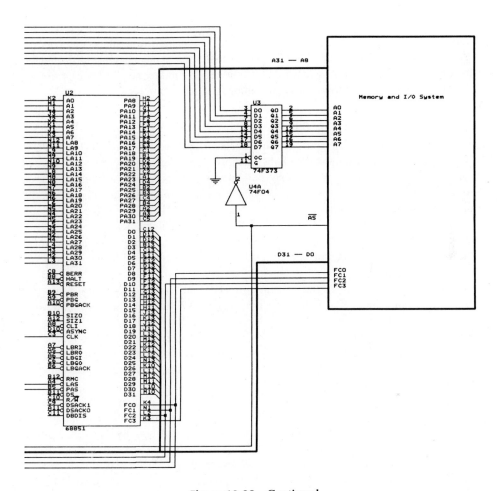

**Figure 10-38** Continued.

ry management unit that is incorporated in the 68030 microprocessor is described in Chapter 13. Two 68851 memory management units are also incorporated in the 68040 microprocessor. Here we are more concerned with explaining the coprocessor interface between the microprocessor and the coprocessor. The 68851 is illustrated, in case it is encountered in older designs that do not incorporate the 68030 microprocessor.

Figure 10-38, which illustrates the interface between the microprocessor and the 68851 memory management unit, shows where the physical and logical addresses appear in the system. The *logical (memory) address* consists of the addresses generated by a program, and the *physical memory address* is the actual memory location. The main purpose of the memory management unit is to remap the logical address to any desired physical address.

In Figure 10-38 the main emphasis is on the address bus interconnections. Notice that the logical address (A0–A7 and LA8–LA31) is connected to the logical address inputs of the memory manager. This is so that the memory manager can translate the logical address into a physical address. The physical address outputs (A0–A7 through the latch and PA8–PA31) are connected to the memory and I/O in the system. Notice the address latch that is required to capture the physical address signals A0–A7 during a physical address transfer.

## 10-5.1   The Coprocessor Concept

The 68000 microprocessor family coprocessor interface supports the 68881/68882 floating-point coprocessor and the 68851 memory management unit. The coprocessor interface allows the execution of special-purpose instructions that are designated for one of these two coprocessors. Instructions for both coprocessors are placed in a program just as 68000 instructions appear in a program. The difference is that the coprocessor instructions are actually FXXX line emulation instructions, which initiate a 68000 family exception. Some FXXX line emulation instructions are used with the floating-point coprocessor (FPCP), while others are used with the memory management unit.

Figure 10-39 illustrates the general format for all coprocessor instructions. Again notice that the coprocessor instruction is an FXXX line emulation exception. The first word of the instruction is an FXXX. Part of this first word identifies the coprocessor by ID number (000 to 111) and the remaining part is the effective address. The effective address portion is used for some coprocessor instructions to encode the effective addressing mode being requested by the instruction. The coprocessor ID codes for the 68851 and the 68881 are 001 and 000, respectively. Note that the address decoding for the coprocessor ID number is integrated into the 68851, which must use address 001. The FPCP uses an external chip selection logic that allows it to be selected as any coprocessor ID. Customarily the FPCP is decoded as coprocessor ID number 000.

Whenever a coprocessor instruction is executed, information is transferred through the memory system between the microprocessor and the coprocessor. Figure 10-40 illustrates the portion of the 68020 memory that is used for this coproces-

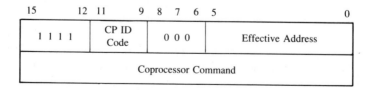

**Figure 10-39   The general format of a coprocessor instruction.**

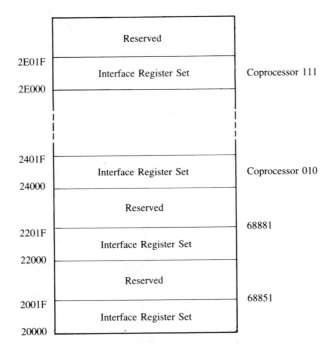

**Figure 10-40** The coprocessor interface memory map.

sor interface. Each coprocessor uses an 8k byte section of the memory for an interface register set and a reserved area. There are eight coprocessors allowed in the 68020 system. The area of memory designated for the interface is locations $00020000–$0002FFFF.

Figure 10-41 illustrates the interface register set for a coprocessor. Each register in the register set is 32 bits in width, with certain registers having two halves that are word-sized.

## Coprocessor Interface Registers (CIR)

The coprocessor interface registers are used to transfer information between the microprocessor and the coprocessor. The types of information transferred include addresses, operands, and coprocessor instructions. Following is a list of the coprocessor registers with a description of the function of each register.

The response register is a word-sized register located at address $00 in the interface address space for the coprocessor. The main processor reads this register to receive the coprocessor response during instruction execution.

The control register is a word-sized register located at address $02. The right-most two bits of the control register are accessed by the microprocessor to acknowledge a coprocessor exception or to abort a coprocessor instruction. If the right-most bit is a one, the operation is aborted. If bit position 1 is a logic one, the coprocessor is requesting an exception.

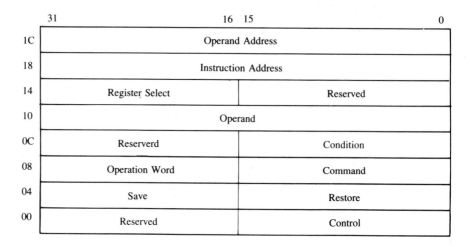

**Figure 10-41   The coprocessor interface register (CIR) set.**

The save register is located at address $04, and it too is a word-sized register, used by the coprocessor to initiate a coprocessor save instruction.

The restore register is similar to the save register because it initiates a restoration of the saved coprocessor registers. It also is a word-sized register, and it is located at address $06.

The operation word, located at address $08, is the site at which the microprocessor stores the FXXX line emulator instruction.

The command word, located at address $0A, is the site at which the second word of a coprocessor instruction is stored when executed.

The condition register is located at address $0E and contains the condition code for coprocessor conditional instructions. The right-most 6 bits of this word contain the coprocessor condition code.

The operand register is located at address $10, and it is here that the operand is stored (32-bit) when the coprocessor requests an operand transfer. Operands are transferred to and from the coprocessor through this register.

The select register, a word-sized register located at address $14, indicates the number and type of microprocessor registers transferred between the microprocessor and the coprocessor.

The instruction address register is located at address $18 and holds the address of the coprocessor instruction that is currently executing.

The operand address register, located at address $1C, holds the operand address of a transfer between the memory and the coprocessor.

## Summary

1. The term "bus arbitration" refers to the microprocessor system's ability to allow multiple bus masters to gain access, one at a time, to the system memory and

I/O. A bus master is any device that can control the memory and I/O connected to it. Only one bus master can exist and control the system at a time. The orderly transfer of control of the system from one bus master to another is called bus arbitration.

2. A direct memory access (DMA) occurs when the microprocessor is placed in wait states while a DMA controller takes over the function of the bus master and transfers data directly between the memory and the I/O system. DMA transfer can also occur between two areas of the memory system.

3. A DMA read occurs when data are read from the memory and transferred to an I/O device. A DMA write occurs when data are transferred from an I/O device and stored in the memory.

4. The DMA controller provides the memory address and selects the I/O device during a DMA transfer. It also provides both the memory and I/O with control signals to effect the DMA transfer.

5. All members of the 68000 family of microprocessors contain three pin connections that are associated with bus arbitration and DMA transfers. The $\overline{\text{BR}}$ (bus request) input is used to request a DMA transfer. The $\overline{\text{BG}}$ (bus grant) signal is an output that indicates that the microprocessor has granted the DMA transfer. The $\overline{\text{BGACK}}$ (bus grant acknowledge) input indicates to the microprocessor that the DMA controller has taken control of the system buses and a DMA action is occurring.

6. The 68440 family of DMA controllers consists of the 66440, the 68442, and the 68450. The 68440 and 68442 are both two-channel DMA controllers. The difference is that the 68440 has a 24-bit address bus and the 68442 has a 32-bit address bus. The 68450 has a 24-bit address bus and four DMA channels. All these devices are programmable DMA controllers that must be programmed before they can be used for a DMA transfer.

7. In implicit DMA addressing, the DMA controller sends the memory its address through the address connections and selects the I/O device through the $\overline{\text{ACK}}$ output pin. Explicit DMA addressing requires that the DMA controller execute two bus cycles. One bus cycle addresses memory or I/O and transfers data into the DMA controller temporarily. The second bus cycle transfers data out of the DMA controller to a memory location or an I/O device.

8. The 68450 is capable of performing array chaining and also linked array chaining. The former technique allows multiple DMA transfers to be pre-programmed in memory for later execution by the DMA controller. An array chain transfer uses a linear array of DMA commands, while the linked array chained transfers can use detached areas of memory that hold different commands for the DMA controller.

9. The most common forms of floppy disks include the 5¼ inch mini-floppy and the 3½ inch micro-floppy disks. The 5¼ inch mini-floppy is encoded as a double-density, double-sided disk holding 360k bytes of data or as a high

density disk holding 1.2M bytes of data. The $3^1/_2$ inch micro-floppy is either a double-density 720k byte disk or a high density 1.44M byte disk.

10. Two techniques are used for storing information on hard disks: MFM (modified frequency modulation) and RLL (run-length limited). The MFM technique stores a data pulse for a logic one, no pulse for the first logic zero in a run of zeros, and a clock pulse for the second and subsequent logic zeros in a row. The RLL technique encodes the data and achieves a 50% higher rate of data storage using the same media and electronics in most cases. Typically RLL 2,7 is used, which means that there are at least 2, but no more than 7 zeros in a row.

11. Hard disk interfaces include ST-506, which uses either MFM or RLL encoding. Newer interfaces, which primarily use RLL encoding, are ESDI (enhanced small disk interface), SCSI (small computer system interface), and IDE (integrated drive electronics).

12. The SCSI uses a 50-pin connector to connect up to eight devices. Devices that can control the bus are called initiators, and devices that are slaves to the initiators are called targets. Most systems contain one initiator and multiple slaves.

13. Video displays are available as TTL or analog. The TTL display uses TTL voltage signals to accept information for display from the computer. For this reason an RGB (red, green, and blue) TTL monitor can display only eight basic colors at two intensities. The analog display RGB can display an infinite number of colors because the video signals are analog voltages within the range of 0–0.7 V.

14. Coprocessor instructions are actually FXXX line emulation exceptions. Part of the word-wide FXXX line emulation instruction contains the coprocessor ID, which identifies the coprocessor and also locates a section of memory that is used for communications between the coprocessor and the microprocessor.

15. The coprocessor interface registers are located not within the coprocessor but in a section of memory. The coprocessor interface registers contain the coprocessor instruction, operand, operand address, instruction address, and other information about the operation of the coprocessor.

## Questions

1. Describe the term "bus arbitration."

2. What is a bus master?

3. What is a direct memory access?

4. When data are written to a memory location and read from an I/O device using DMA techniques, the process is known as a DMA _____.

5. When data are read from memory and written to I/O using DMA techniques, the process is known as a DMA _____.

6. What type of I/O interface is most suited to DMA transfers?

7. What three 68000 system bus signals are used to manage a DMA request?

8. What 68000 DMA control signal is placed at a logic zero to request a DMA action?

9. Compare the 68440, 68442, and 68450 DMA controllers.

10. The DMA controller has a multiplexed address/data bus. What address and what data pins are multiplexed?

11. What is the purpose of the $\overline{\text{DTC}}$ pin on the DMA controller?

12. What is the purpose of the $\overline{\text{ACK}}$ pins on the DMA controller?

13. Refer to Figure 10-5 and explain the purpose and operation of integrated circuits U3 and U4.

14. Again refer to Figure 10-5 and explain the purpose and operation of U7.

15. What is the difference between the non-DMA and DMA modes of operation of the DMA controller?

16. When implicit addressing is used, what supplies the DMA memory address, and where does it appear?

17. When implicit addressing is used, what selects the I/O device, and how is it selected?

18. During explicit addressing, how many bus cycles are required for a DMA data transfer?

19. What type of addressing must a memory-to-memory DMA transfer use for its operation?

20. Is the device address register used for an implicit DMA transfer? Explain your answer.

21. What registers hold interrupt vectors in the 68440 DMA controller?

22. What DMA controller register is common to all channels?

23. Develop a program that sets up the DMA controller so that an implicit DMA action is carried out through channel 1 using a DMA address of $200000 and a count of $30. Make sure that the DMA address is incremented.

24. Set up an array chain in memory so that four DMA actions will occur, starting at base address $100000. The transfer is to be an implicit transfer from address $30000 with a count of $12, then $40000 with a count of $33, then $70000 with a count of $2000, and finally $80000 with a count of $22.

25. What is the difference between an array chain and a linked chain?

**26.** How is a linked chain selected in the DMA controller?

**27.** Define the following terms:
  (a) mini-floppy disk
  (b) micro-floppy disk
  (c) track
  (d) sector
  (e) cylinder

**28.** If a floppy disk rotates at 300 rpm, how long does it take to rotate one time?

**29.** What importance is given to the calculation in question 28?

**30.** What is the difference between a double-density disk and a high density disk?

**31.** Explain how NRZ recording functions and describe its benefits.

**32.** What is MFM?

**33.** Draw the MFM waveform obtained for a data string of 1100010100.

**34.** What advantages does the $3^1/_2$ inch micro-floppy offer, compared to the $5^1/_4$ inch mini-floppy disk?

**35.** Explain the term "flying head."

**36.** Why should a head be parked in a hard disk memory system?

**37.** What type of disk drive may have more than two heads?

**38.** What is RLL?

**39.** What is meant by RLL 2,7?

**40.** Draw the RLL waveform obtained for the data 110001101010.

**41.** Compare MFM and RLL.

**42.** What type of encoding (MFM or RLL) is used with the ST-506 hard disk interface?

**43.** What type of encoding (MFM or RLL) is normally used with the SCSI interface?

**44.** Where is the disk controller in an IDE disk drive?

**45.** Compare the ROM CD with the WORM drive.

**46.** What is the purpose of the $\overline{BSY}$ signal on the SCSI bus?

**47.** Explain the sequence of events that occurs whenever an imitator accesses a device on the SCSI bus.

**48.** What is the maximum data transfer rate found on the SCSI bus?

**49.** Where is the device selection code found on the SCSI bus?

**50.** What is the difference between a TTL monitor and an analog monitor?

51. The TTL monitor uses a _____ -pin connector and the analog monitor uses a _____ -pin connector.

52. What are the three primary colors of light?

53. What are the three secondary colors of light?

54. Describe how an analog RGB monitor can display up to 256k colors, 256 at a time.

55. What is a pixel?

56. If a video display system uses a 60 Hz vertical scanning rate and a 31,500 Hz horizontal scanning rate, how many lines are generated?

57. In a display of 600 viewable scanning lines that has a vertical repetition rate of 56.2 Hz and a horizontal rate of 35.2 kHz, how much time is allowed for vertical retrace?

58. Why do you suppose that the number of colors displayed at one time is normally limited to 256?

59. What is the difference between a logical memory address and a physical memory address?

60. The 68851 memory management unit converts a _____ address into a _____ address.

61. What basic instruction is used as an instruction set for the 68851 and the 68881/68882?

62. How many different coprocessors can be connected to one system?

63. If a coprocessor is decoded as coprocessor ID 100, where are the interface registers stored in the memory system?

# 11

# The Floating-Point Coprocessor

**OBJECTIVES**

Upon completion of this chapter, you will be able to:

- Explain the purpose of the floating-point coprocessor and detail the operation of each of its instructions.
- Show how numbers are stored in floating-point, integer, and BCD forms for the floating-point coprocessor.
- Connect the floating-point coprocessor to any of the Motorola 680XX family of microprocessors.
- Develop programs and subroutines that utilize the floating-point coprocessor to solve complex arithmetic problems.

**KEY TERMS**

| | | |
|---|---|---|
| local connection | binary scientific | implicit, explicit one- |
| local buses | notation | bits |
| system buses | significand, mantissa | dyadic operations |
| coprocessor interface | biased exponent | monadic operations |
| registers | | aware conditions |

T HIS chapter explains how to program and connect the floating-point coprocessor to the 680XX microprocessor bus system. The floating-point coprocessor fully implements the standard binary floating-point arithmetic as specified by ANSI-IEEE 754-1985. The floating-point coprocessor functions with integers, binary floating-point numbers, and binary-coded decimal (BCD) floating-point numbers. Note that the 68040 microprocessor contains its own floating-point coprocessor that is upward compatible with the floating-point coprocessor discussed in this chapter.

A coprocessor is a device that, when connected to the microprocessor, can perform operations concurrently with the microprocessor. In the case of the floating-point coprocessor, these concurrent operations include addition, subtraction, multiplication, division, sine, cosine, tangent, and square-root.

## 11-1   Interfacing the 68881/68882 Floating-Point Coprocessor

We begin by detailing the interconnection of the microprocessor and the co-processor. This section also presents the pinout of both the 68881 and 68882 floating-point coprocessors. Each pin connection of the 68881/68882 is fully de-scribed, so that the significance of its operation and interconnection with the micro-processor can be understood.

### 1-1.1   Pinout

Figure 11-1 illustrates the pinout of the 68881/68882 floating-point coprocessor. Notice that this device is packaged in a 68-pin PGA (pin grid array) device. The pinout illustrates that most of the pin connections are used for the data bus connec-tions between the coprocessor and the microprocessor.

The pinouts for the 68881 and 68882 are identical. These coprocessors differ in execution speed. The 68882 is an enhanced version of the 68881 that executes multiple floating-point operations concurrently with the microprocessor. The 68882 also contains a special-purpose hardware circuit that allows it to convert between binary and extended floating-point numbers at a much higher speed than the 68881. The 68882 costs more than the 68881, so the 68881 still finds wide application in lower cost environments.

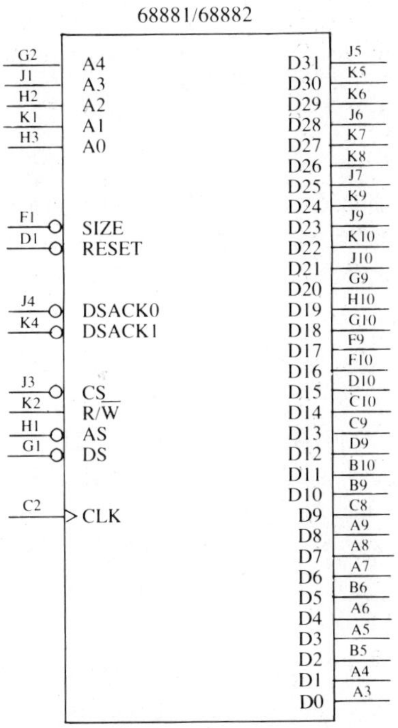

**Figure 11-1   The pinout of the 68881/68882 floating-point coprocessor.**

## Dc Characteristics of the 68881/68882

The 68881/68882 requires a +5.0 V power supply with a supply voltage tolerance of ±5%. The power supply is attached to PGA pins B1, B8, D2, D9, and H8. Power supply ground is attached to PGA pins A2, B2, B3, B7, C1, C3, E10, J8, and K3. For this device to function properly, all power and ground connections must be made. If a ground or power supply connection is missed, the coprocessor will not function properly. Power supply consumption is approximately 150 mW maximum, although it is usually less under normal operating conditions. Under temperature extremes and also during certain instructions, however, it approaches 150 mW.

The 68881/68882 is capable of driving the bus with a logic zero current of 5.3 mA (maximum) and a logic one current of 400 μA (maximum). If these currents are exceeded, no guarantee of proper operation is provided. Loading is seldom a problem because for most applications, the 68881/68882 is connected to the microprocessor before the system buffers. This type of coprocessor connection is often called a *local connection*.

## Ac Characteristics of the 68881/68882

The 68881 and 68882 are available in a wide range of clock operating frequencies. These include devices that operate at a low frequency of 12.5 MHz (68881RC12) to a high frequency of 25 MHz (68881RC25). Devices that operate at 33 MHz (68882RC33) will soon be available. Because the 68881 and 68882 are designed to connect to the 680XX family members, there is no need to investigate the remaining timing signals. All timing devices operate within the ranges allowed by the 680XX family members.

### 11-1.2   Pin Functions

Before the 68881/68882 is connected to the microprocessor, additional detail is required of each pin connection. Following is a list of descriptions for each grouping of pin connections on the 68881/68882.

**A4–A0 (address connections A4–A0)**   These address connections are used to select internal registers in the 68881/68882 for programming and data transfer. More detail on these pin connections is provided in Section 11-1.3.

**D31–D0 (data bus connections D31–D0)**   The data bus connections are used to transfer instructions, status, and data between the 68881/68882 and the microprocessor. The 68881/68882 can operate with any version of the 680XX microprocessor because the size of the data bus can be dynamically adjusted to 8, 16, or 32 bits in width.

**$\overline{\text{AS}}$ (address strobe)**   This connection indicates to the 68881/68882 that a valid address appears on the address bus connections and in particular A4–A0.

**R/$\overline{\text{W}}$ (read/write)**   This connection selects a read (1) or a write (0) operation.

**$\overline{\text{DS}}$ (data strobe input)**   This connection indicates that there are valid data on the data bus for the 68881/68882 coprocessor.

**Table 11-1**   Data Bus Widths as Selected by A0 and $\overline{\text{SIZE}}$

| $\overline{\text{SIZE}}$ | A0 | Data bus size | Microprocessor |
|------|-----|---------------|----------------|
| 0 | 0 | 8-bit | 68008 |
| 0 | 1 | 8-bit | 68008 |
| 1 | 0 | 16-bit | 68000/68010 |
| 1 | 1 | 32-bit | 68020/68030 |

$\overline{\text{CS}}$ **(chip selection input)**   This input is placed at a logic zero level to gain access to the internal register set of the 68881/68882 floating-point coprocessor. As with any I/O or memory device, a decoder is normally attached to this pin.

**CLK (clock input)**   The system clock signal is applied to the 68881/68882 at CLK. As mentioned, the clock can be any frequency from 12.5 to 25 MHz for currently available versions of this device.

$\overline{\text{SIZE}}$ **(size selection input)**   This input is used together with the A0 input to configure the data bus width. Table 11-1 illustrates the logic levels applied to the $\overline{\text{SIZE}}$ and A0 connections to select various data bus widths.

$\overline{\text{RESET}}$ **(reset input)**   The $\overline{\text{RESET}}$ input is used to initialize the 68881/68882. This input causes the data registers to be initialized to not-a-numbers (NANs) and clears the control, status, and instruction address registers within the 68881/68882. It also sets the null mode for the coprocessor.

$\overline{\text{SENSE}}$ **(sense output)**   This pin is sometimes used to signal the external hardware that the 68881/68882 is present. It basically is a ground connection that indicates the presence of this device when at a logic zero level. This connection is at a logic one level, with a pullup resistor, when the coprocessor is not present in the system.

$\overline{\text{DSACK1}}$, $\overline{\text{DSACK2}}$ **(data transfer and size acknowledge outputs)**   These signals indicate the completion of the bus cycle. Table 11-2 illustrates the operation of these pins for different sized data buses. These signals are also used to cause wait states when the coprocessor is not ready to accept or transfer data to the microprocessor.

**Table 11-2**   The $\overline{\text{DSACK}}$ Signals

| Bus width | A4 | $\overline{\text{DSACK1}}$ | $\overline{\text{DSACK0}}$ | Comment |
|-----------|-----|--------|--------|---------|
| 32-bit | 1 | 0 | 0 | Valid data on D31–D0. |
| 32-bit | 0 | 0 | 1 | Valid data on D31–D16. |
| 16-bit | X | 0 | 1 | Valid data on D31–D16 or D15–D0. |
| 8-bit | X | 1 | 0 | Valid data on D31–D24, D23–D16, D15–D8, or D7–D0. |
| All | X | 1 | 1 | Insert wait states in current bus cycle. |

### 11-1.3   Coprocessor Connections to the 680XX Microprocessor

The 68881/68882 is easily connected to the microprocessor. Most of the pins are connected directly to the microprocessor and require only a small amount of logic circuitry. When the coprocessor is connected directly to the microprocessor before the system bus buffers, the arrangement is called a local connection. The buses at this point are called the *local buses*. After the buses are buffered they are often called *system buses*. The main circuit required to interface the coprocessor is a decoder that selects the 68881/68882 for programming and data transfer.

Figure 11-2 illustrates a 68881 connected to the 68008 microprocessor. Notice how the data bus connections are made between the coprocessor and the microprocessor. This connection is required because the coprocessor uses all 32 bits of its data bus to transfer information. In the illustration, all 32 bits are placed on the 8-bit data bus of the 68008 microprocessor. The 32 bits of data are transferred 8 bits at a time through this type of interconnection.

A programmable logic device is used to select the 68881. Notice that the inputs to the PAL 16L8 are connected to address connections A19–A13 and also to FC2–FC0. These address and function code bits are used to select the coprocessor during coprocessor operations. Function code bits FC2–FC0 are 111 for the CPU space, which is where the coprocessor functions. Note that these are the same function code bits used for an interrupt acknowledge. The CPU space is used for the coprocessor because the coprocessor communicates using the 1111 line (F-line) emulation exception, which is an interrupt or exception.

Address connections A19–A16 contain a 0010 whenever the microprocessor communicates to the coprocessor. Address connections A15–A13 indicate the coprocessor identification number. This allows up to eight different coprocessors to be present in a system. By default, the assembler assumes that the floating-point coprocessor has ID number 001. This ID number should always be used when interfacing the first floating-point coprocessor to a system. Subsequent coprocessors may be interfaced with other ID numbers except 000, which is reserved for the 68851 memory management unit.

The PAL decodes this information with the program listed in Example 11-1. The program used for the PAL activates the $\overline{CS}$ pin of the coprocessor for binary bit pattern 0010001 on address connections A19–A13 only when the function code pins are a 111. This bit pattern occurs in response to line emulation exception 1111 for the coprocessor. The remaining bits (A12–A0) are used to pass an instruction and other information to the coprocessor. Note that all floating-point instructions begin with a 1111, causing the line emulation exception 1111 to occur when they appear in the flow of a program.

Also notice that the $\overline{DTACK}$ signal on the microprocessor is connected to the $\overline{DSACK0}$ output pin. Referring again to Table 11-2, notice that the $\overline{DSACK0}$ pin becomes a zero for valid data on the 8-bit data bus and a one for a wait state. The $\overline{DSACK1}$ pin has no function and is left unconnected in this circuit.

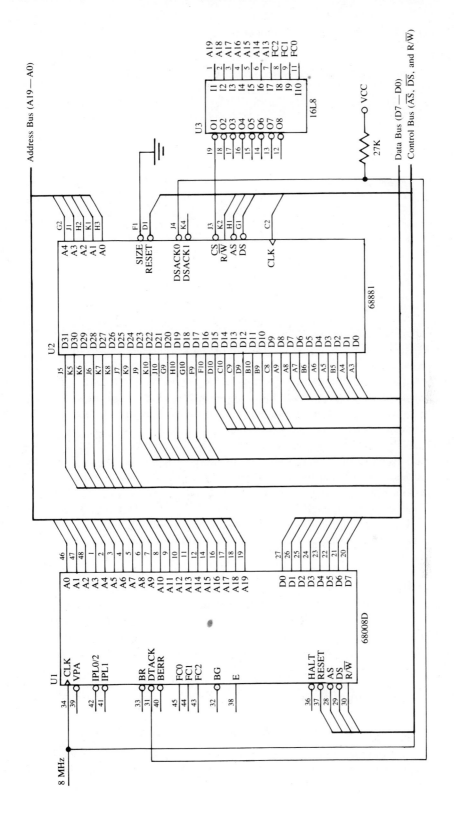

**Figure 11-2** The 68008D microprocessor interfaced to the 68881 floating-point coprocessor.

EXAMPLE   11-1

---

```
TITLE      Example
PATTERN    Test
REVISION   A
AUTHOR     BARRY BREY
COMPANY    DeVRY
DATE       2/7/91
CHIP Coproc PAL16L8

;PINS      1     2     3     4     5     6     7     8     9     10
           A19   A18   A17   A16   A15   A14   A13   FC2   FC1   GND

;PINS      11    12    13    14    15    16    17    18    19    20
           FC0   NC    NC    NC    NC    NC    NC    NC    CS    VCC

EQUATIONS
/CS = /A19*/A18*A17*/A16*/A15*/A14*A13*FC2*FC1*FC0
```

---

Figure 11-3 illustrates the 68000 microprocessor connected to the 68881 coprocessor. This interface is almost identical to the 68008 interface except for the data bus connections. Here the 16 data bus connections on the microprocessor are connected to the 32 data bus connections on the coprocessor. The PAL decoder is identical in these cases because the coprocessor's address is identical for both circuits. In fact, the only variation in the decoder from one interface to another is the coprocessor ID code.

The $\overline{\text{DSACK1}}$ pin is connected to the $\overline{\text{DTACK}}$ connection on the microprocessor. Refer to Table 11-2, and notice that when a microprocessor, with a 16-bit address bus, is connected to the 68881, the $\overline{\text{DSACK1}}$ connection indicates valid data or a wait state.

The data strobe input ($\overline{\text{DS}}$) must be activated if either $\overline{\text{UDS}}$ or $\overline{\text{LDS}}$ becomes active. This is accomplished in Figure 11-3 by using a 74F08 AND gate to generate a $\overline{\text{DS}}$ signal. If either $\overline{\text{UDS}}$ or $\overline{\text{LDS}}$ becomes a logic zero, $\overline{\text{DS}}$ becomes a logic zero.

The 68010 microprocessor is connected exactly the same as the 68000. This interface is not shown here for this reason. The 68020 and 68030 are connected to the 68881/68882 in Chapters 12 and 13, which illustrate these more powerful versions of the 68000 microprocessor. The main difference is that the 68020 and 68030 all have 32-bit data buses, which makes the coprocessor interface very straightforward. The 68040, as mentioned earlier, contains its own internal coprocessor and therefore does not use the 68881/68882.

## 11-2   Operation of the 68881/68882 Coprocessor

Before the floating-point coprocessor is programmed, an understanding of the data formats and internal structure of the 68881/68882 is required. This section of the text provides this background detail so that programming can be performed. It also provides detail on how communication between the microprocessor and coprocessor is conducted, as briefly introduced with the 68851 in Chapter 10 (Section 10-5).

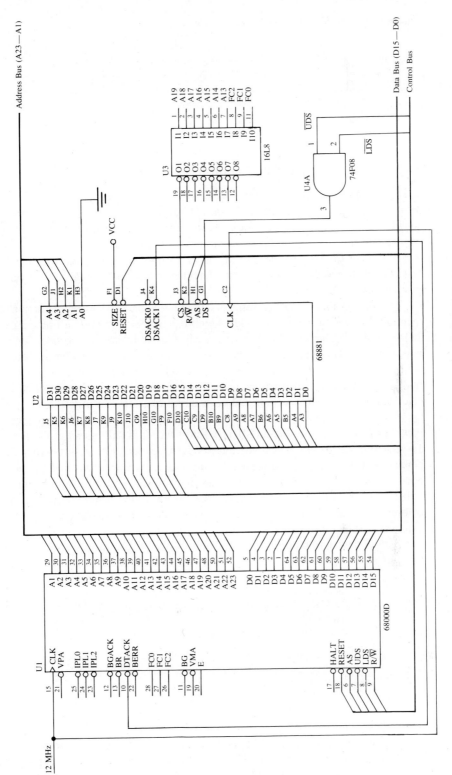

**Figure 11-3** The 68000 microprocessor interfaced to the 68881 floating-point coprocessor.

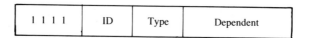

**Figure 11-4**   The floating-point coprocessor instruction format.

### 11-2.1   The Microprocessor/Coprocessor Interaction

A coprocessor instruction always begins with the binary code 1111. This code, recall from Chapter 9, is a line emulation 1111 exception. In response to a coprocessor instruction, the microprocessor executes exception processing. In the case of a coprocessor instruction, the coprocessor places the microprocessor in wait states as it executes bus transfers between itself and the memory system. These transfers also take place between the coprocessor and the microprocessor data registers for certain instructions.

Figure 11-4 illustrates the format of a floating-point coprocessor instruction. As mentioned, the first 4 bits are 1111, which makes the instruction a line emulator 1111 exception. The ID field specifies the coprocessor identification code, which is normally 001. The type field indicates the general type of instruction, as listed in Table 11-3. The dependent section (right-most 6 bits) indicates the mode and effective address for many instructions. The second word of the instruction often indicates the type of the instruction, although there are a few exceptions.

Coprocessor communication occurs through a set of interface registers called *coprocessor interface registers* (CIR). A list of the valid CIRs is provided in Table 11-4. Address connections A4–A0 are used to select one of the CIRs during a line emulation 1111 exception. Selection occurs whenever $\overline{CS}$ is activated by the decoder connected to it. These registers are not directly used when programming; rather, they are used by the microprocessor to control the coprocessor. The information about the CIRs is provided to promote a better understanding of the coprocessor–microprocessor interaction.

A brief description of each of the floating-point coprocessor interface registers follows.

**Table 11-3**   Coding of the Type Field in a Floating-Point Instruction

| Code | Type of instruction |
| --- | --- |
| 000 | General instructions such as arithmetic and moves |
| 001 | FDBcc, FScc, and FTRAPcc instructions |
| 010 | FBcc word-sized instruction |
| 011 | FBcc long-word-sized instruction |
| 100 | FSAVE instruction |
| 101 | FRESTORE instruction |
| 110 | [undefined] |
| 111 | [undefined] |

**Table 11-4   The Coprocessor Interface Registers (CIR)**

| Register | A4–A0 | Offset | Width (bits) | Type |
|----------|-------|--------|--------------|------|
| Response | 0000X | $00 | 16 | Read |
| Control | 0001X | $02 | 16 | Write |
| Save | 0010X | $04 | 16 | Read |
| Restore | 0011X | $06 | 16 | Read/write |
| Operation | 0100X | $08 | 16 | Read/write |
| Command | 0101X | $0A | 16 | Write |
| Condition | 0111X | $0E | 16 | Write |
| Operand | 1000X | $10 | 32 | Read/write |
| Register | 1010X | $14 | 16 | Read |
| Instruction address | 110XX | $18 | 32 | Write |
| Operand address | 111XX | $1C | 32 | Read/write |

**Response**   This register is read by the microprocessor for a response from the coprocessor to commands written to the command coprocessor interface register.

**Control**   An exception acknowledge or an abort is issued to the coprocessor through this register. Writing a $0001 aborts the current coprocessor operation and a $0002 acknowledges the exception.

**Save**   When this register is read by the microprocessor, the floating-point coprocessor suspends its current operation and saves the state of the coprocessor.

**Restore**   When the microprocessor writes to this register, the current operation of the coprocessor is suspended. Following the suspension, the coprocessor restores the internal state. This register is read by the microprocessor to verify that the format word written to the restore register is valid.

**Operation**   Writes to this location are ignored, and reads result in all ones. This register is not used by the floating-point coprocessor.

**Command**   A general coprocessor instruction dialog is initiated by a write to this register from the microprocessor. If a write occurs unexpectedly, it causes a coprocessor protocol exception.

**Condition**   This register is written to start a conditional coprocessor operation from the microprocessor.

**Operand**   This 32-bit register is used by the microprocessor to transfer data between the coprocessor and memory or a data register.

**Register**   The register mask for a floating-point multiple register MOVE instruction is transferred to the microprocessor through this register.

**Instruction Address**   This register is used to transfer the address of the coprocessor instruction to the microprocessor.

**Operand Address**   The operand address is transferred from the microprocessor through this register.

## 11-2.2   Data Formats

The 68881/68882 floating-point coprocessor is capable of functioning with integers, binary floating-point numbers, and packed floating-point BCD. These formats are used to represent data externally and are not used inside the 68881/68882. Internally, the coprocessor uses an 80-bit binary floating-point formatted number to represent all data. Data are converted between an 80-bit binary floating-point form and integer, binary floating-point, or BCD floating-point, when transferred between the coprocessor and the microprocessor or memory.

### Integer Form

The first numeric format for coprocessor data to be discussed is the integer format. Integers used with the coprocessor are byte, word, or long-word and are all signed integers. Just as with the signed data described in Chapter 1, a positive number is stored in true form and a negative number is stored in two's complement form. For reference, Figure 11-5 illustrates the three allowable forms of signed integers for the 68881/68882.

   A byte-sized signed integer stores values that range from $+127$ through $-128$. A word-sized signed integer stores values that range from $+32,767$ through $-32,768$. Long-word sized signed integers range in value between $+2,147,483,647$ and $-2,147,483,648$. These are integer values, and no support is provided for binary fractions. Fractions and mixed numbers must use either binary or BCD floating-point formats.

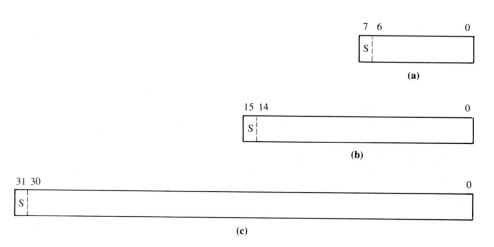

**Figure 11-5**   The three formats of binary integers for the 68881/68882 floating-point coprocessor: (a) byte, (b) word, and (c) long-word. In all cases S is the sign bit.

## Binary Floating-Point Form

Binary floating-point form is often called binary real form. Real numbers are similar to decimal scientific notation because the binary floating-point number is represented with a normalized fraction raised to a power of 2. Binary real or binary floating-point numbers are often correctly called *binary scientific notation*.

All binary floating-point numbers are formed with three distinct fields of information. Each number contains a sign, an exponent, and a fraction. The sign represents the sign of the fraction part. The exponent is a biased power of 2. The fraction is a number 1.XXXXXX, where XXXXXX is any fraction. This representation is not truly a fraction, because of the 1. The 1 is not stored with the fraction in the floating-point format. For this reason this portion of the floating-point number is often called a *significand* instead of a fraction. The significand is also often called a *mantissa*, but a true mantissa is a fraction, so this text does not use this term elsewhere.

Binary floating-point numbers are available in three sizes named single-precision (32 bits), double-precision (64 bits), and extended-precision (96 bits, of which 16 are not used). Figure 11-6 illustrates the forms of binary floating-point numbers. Notice that all three sizes use the left-most bit position as the sign of the significand. If the sign bit contains a zero, the significand is positive and if it contains a one, the significand is negative.

In addition to the sign bit, all three forms contain an exponent. The exponents vary in size from 8 bits (in the single-precision form) to 15 bits (in the extended-precision form). In each case, the exponent is biased by an integer.

A *biased exponent* is an exponent that has a number added. The single-precision form uses a bias of 127 ($7F), double-precision uses a bias of 1023 ($3FF), and extended-precision uses a bias of 16,383 ($3FFF). The bias is added to

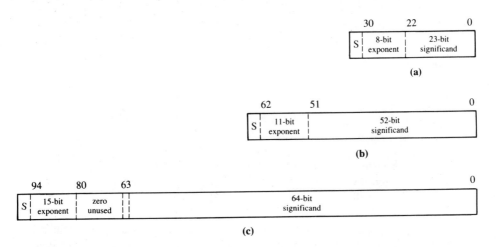

**Figure 11-6   Binary floating-point numbers are represented in three formats: (a) single-precision, (b) double-precision, and (c) extended-precision.**

the exponent before it is stored in this format and subtracted to convert to a true exponent when the number is interpreted.

For example, if the binary power of $2^4$ is represented in single-precision form, the biased exponent is $7F + 4 or $83. In other words, an $83 is stored to represent an exponent of +4. The same applies to the other forms of real numbers except that the bias is different. The same exponent represented in double-precision is $3FF + 4 or $403.

The significand for the single- and double-precision forms is stored without the logic one. For example, suppose that the binary significand is a 1.001101. The number stored as a significand for the single- and double-precision forms is 001101. The 1 followed by the point is not stored in these forms and is called an *implicit one-bit*. The extended-precision form of the real number is different because the 1. is stored and is called an *explicit one-bit*. In most cases systems work with single- or double-precision forms.

There are a few special cases that don't conform to floating-point form. The number zero is one example. A zero is represented with all bits of the exponent and significand cleared to zero. The sign may be a one or a zero to represent a +0 or a −0. The only other case is infinity, which has all bits of the exponent and significand set to logic ones. The sign may be plus or minus to represent positive and negative infinity.

## Converting from Decimal to Real Form

Conversion to real binary numbers is accomplished by first converting the decimal number to binary. Once in binary form, the number is normalized. In this case the normal form is a signed significand ($\pm1$.XXXXXX) raised to a binary power of 2. Once the binary number has been normalized, it is converted to floating-point format. To convert a decimal number to binary real form, perform the following steps.

1. Convert the decimal number to binary.

2. Normalize the binary number.

3. Code each part of the normalized number into real form:
   (a)   The sign bit of the significand.
   (b)   The biased exponent (by adding a $7F for single-precision, a $3FF for double-precision, and a $3FFF for extended-precision).
   (c)   The significand (with an implicit one-bit for single- and double-precision and an explicit one-bit for extended precision).

Example 11-2 illustrates a decimal −102.140625 converted to single-, double-, and extended-precision forms. Notice that the significand differs in the extended-precision version because of the explicit one-bit. Also notice that the exponents differ because the bias varies in all three forms.

E X A M P L E 11 - 2

1. $-102.140625 = -1100110.001001_2$

2. $-1.100110001001 \times 2^6$

3. *Single-precision*
   S exponent    significand (23 bits)
   1 10000101    10011000100100000000000

   *Double-precision*
   S exponent    significand (52 bits)
   1 10000000101    1001100010010000000000000000000000000000000000000000

   *Extended-precision*
   S exponent    significand (64 bits)
   1 100000000000101    1100110001001000000000000000000000000000000000000000000000000000

---

## Converting from Real Form to Decimal

Conversion from a real number to a decimal number is performed in the reverse order. That is, the number is first broken into its three parts (sign, exponent, and significand) and then converted to decimal. Follow the steps listed to convert from real to decimal.

1. Break the real number into sign, exponent, and significand.

2. Convert the exponent to its true value by subtracting the bias.

3. Write the normalized form of the binary number from the information in steps 1 and 2.

4. Convert the normalized form to a binary mixed number. (If the number is single- or double-precision, don't forget to add the implicit one-bit.)

5. Convert the binary mixed number to decimal.

   This conversion process is illustrated for a single-precision real number ($41640000) in Example 11-3.

E X A M P L E 11 - 3

1.                   S exponent    significand
   $41640000 = 0   10000010    11001000000000000000000

2. $82 - $7F = 3

3. $1.11001 \times 2^3$

4. 1110.01

5. $1110.01_2 = 14.25_{10}$

*Binary-Coded Decimal Floating-Point Form*

The binary-coded decimal floating-point form is able to represent a number in decimal (BCD) scientific notation. The number is represented as normalized significand raised to a power of 10. The significand ranges in value from 0.0000000000000000 to 9.9999999999999999. The exponent ranges in value from 000 to 999 decimal. Each decimal digit is stored in packed BCD form as two BCD digits per byte. The format for BCD floating-point is illustrated in Figure 11-7.

Notice from Figure 11-7 that this number is stored in 12 bytes of memory. The least significant 8 bytes of memory contain the 16-digit BCD fraction packed two BCD digits per byte. The next byte contains the whole number portion of the significand (0–9). The most significant 2 bytes contain the signs of the exponent and significand and also the BCD packed exponent (000–999).

Example 11-4 illustrates a decimal number stored in this format. Here the number +345.23 is stored in packed BCD floating-point form.

E  X  A  M  P  L  E    11 - 4

$$345.23 = 3.4523 \times 10^2$$

| Signs | exponent | zero | | fraction |
|---|---|---|---|---|
| 0000 | 000000000010 | 000000000000 | 0011 | 0100010100100011000000000000000000000000000000000000000000000000 |

### 11-2.3    Programming Model of the 68881/68882

Before software is developed for the floating-point coprocessor, the programming model and its operation must be introduced. Figure 11-8 illustrates the programming model for the floating-point coprocessor. The programming model includes eight floating-point data registers labeled FP7–FP0, a control register (FPCR), a status register (FPSR), and an instruction address register (FPIAR). This is the same programming model found in the 68040 microprocessor for its internal floating-point unit.

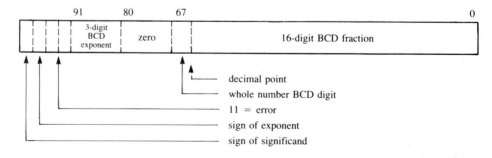

Figure 11-7    The format of the binary-coded decimal floating-point number.

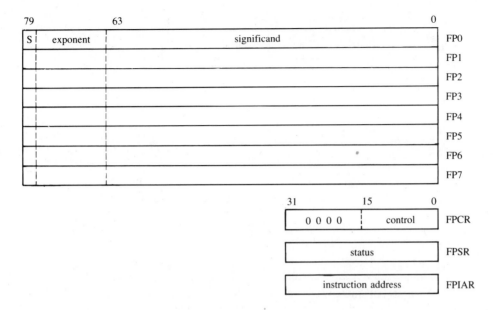

**Figure 11-8    The programming model of the 68881/68882 floating-point coprocessor.**

The general-purpose registers FP7–FP0 are each 80 bits in width and hold extended-precision floating-point numbers at all times. (These extended-precision floating-point numbers differ from the 96-bit format presented earlier because the 16 reserved bits are not stored in the registers.) The coprocessor interface allows these registers to be viewed as resident to the 680XX microprocessor when operated with a coprocessor.

When the instructions for the coprocessor are used, these registers are addressed as FP7–FP0. For example, the FMOVE.X FP2,FP3 instruction copies the extended-precision floating-point number from register FP2 to FP3. All internal transfers such as this are always in extended-precision format because the registers always hold extended-precision numbers.

### Control Register (FPCR)

The control register is a 32-bit register (see Figure 11-9) with the most significant word undefined at the present time. The least significant word contains the exception enable byte and the mode control byte. The exception enable byte is used to enable and disable coprocessor exceptions. The mode control byte selects rounding modes and rounding precisions.

### Mode Control Byte

The mode control byte selects the rounding mode and the rounding precision for the 68881/68882. Rounding precision can be selected for extended-, single-, or double-precision numbers. In most cases the extended-precision form is selected. Rounding

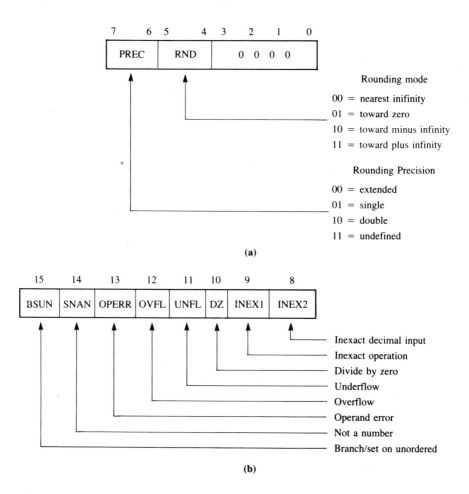

**Figure 11-9** (a) The mode control byte and (b) the exception enable byte for the floating-point control register (FPCR).

can be adjusted so that the number is rounded toward plus or minus infinity, toward zero, or toward the nearest infinity. In most cases the rounding selected is toward the nearest infinity.

Whenever the 68881/68882 is reset, the mode control byte is cleared to zero. This selects the default mode as specified by the IEEE standard for floating-point arithmetic. Default is specified as round to the nearest infinity, using extended-precision numbers. This mode is at times called the null mode. Most software normally uses the default mode of operation, to ensure compatibility with the IEEE standard.

### Exception Enable Byte

The exception enable byte allows various coprocessor exception requests to be enabled or disabled. When the 68881/68882 is reset, this byte is cleared to zero. A zero disables a corresponding exception so that on a reset all exceptions are disabled. A logic one enables the exception. Descriptions of the types of exception controlled by this byte follow.

**BSUN (branch/set on unordered)**    This exception occurs when a conditional test is made on a NAN (not-a-number). (A NAN is the result of such coprocessor operations as infinity divided by infinity or any other operation that doesn't have a mathematical representation. Hence the name, not-a-number.)

**SNAN (signaling not-a-number)**    This is a user-defined exception that occurs whenever a user writes a signaling NAN into a floating-point data register. A signaling NAN is different from a NAN. The NAN is created by an operation and the SNAN is created with a FMOVEM instruction as defined later.

**OPERR (operand error)**    An operation that creates a NAN will cause an operand error exception. Examples include 0/0 or $\infty/\infty$.

**OVFL (overflow)**    The overflow exception results when an arithmetic result is generated that is too large to store in a floating-point data register.

**UNFL (underflow)**    The underflow exception occurs when the arithmetic result is too small to store in a floating-point data register.

**DZ (divide by zero)**    This exception occurs whenever an attempt is made to divide by zero.

**INEX2 (inexact operation)**    An inexact operation exception occurs whenever an instruction attempts an operation on an inexact BCD floating-point number.

**INEX1 (inexact decimal input)**    An inexact decimal input exception occurs whenever the BCD floating-point number cannot be represented properly (too large or too small).

### Floating-Point Status Register (FPSR)

The floating-point status register contains four bytes of information: the floating-point CCR (condition code register), quotient byte, exception status byte, and accrued exception byte. Figure 11-10 illustrates all four bytes of the FPSR.

The floating-point CCR byte indicates negative, zero, infinity, and not-a-number (NAN). These four conditions can be used individually to test the output of an operation or together to detect more information. Table 11-5 illustrates additional conditions that are determined with the four CCR bits. The term "normalized" refers to all floating-point numbers except zero and infinity, which are considered to be denormalized. This term is applied to the N-CCR bit so that, if tested singly, it can indicate a normalized or a denormalized positive or negative number.

The floating-point quotient byte holds the sign and the least significant 7 bits of the quotient. These 7 bits can be used with transcendental functions to determine, for example, the quadrant of a circle.

The exception status byte holds exceptions that have occurred in the most recent arithmetic operation. This byte is tested by the exception handler to determine what caused the exception.

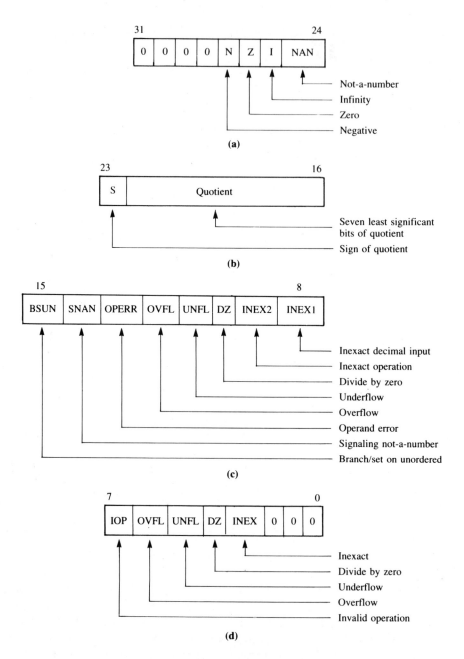

**Figure 11-10**    The 32-bit floating-point status register (FPSR) and its parts: (a) condition code register, (b) quotient byte, (c) exception status byte, and (d) accrued exception byte.

**Table 11-5   Condition Code Indications**

| N | Z | I | NAN | Condition |
|---|---|---|-----|-----------|
| 0 | 0 | 0 | 0 | positive normalized or denormalized |
| 0 | 0 | 0 | 1 | positive NAN |
| 0 | 0 | 1 | 0 | positive infinity |
| 0 | 1 | 0 | 0 | positive zero |
| 1 | 0 | 0 | 0 | negative normalized or denormalized |
| 1 | 0 | 0 | 1 | negative NAN |
| 1 | 0 | 1 | 0 | negative infinity |
| 1 | 1 | 0 | 0 | negative zero |

NOTE: The remaining codes indicate no conditions.

The accrued exception byte holds an history of all exceptions that have occurred since these interruptions were last cleared. This byte is cleared by a user instruction. It accrues exceptions because each bit of this register is set until cleared by a user instruction.

### Floating-Point Instruction Address Register

The floating-point instruction address register always contains the address of the most recent floating-point coprocessor instruction. This register is required whenever a coprocessor exception occurs, to permit the exception handler to locate the instruction that caused the exception. Without this register it may be impossible to locate the instruction that caused the exception.

## 11-3   The 68881/68882 Instruction Set

The 68881/68882 floating-point coprocessors perform operations using five distinct groupings of instructions. This section describes these five groups, explains the addressing modes allowed with each group, and illustrates the instructions provided in each group. These instructions groupings are moves, dyadic operations, monadic operations, program control, and system control. Additionally, Appendix C lists all the floating-point coprocessor instructions, in alphabetical order for easy reference.

### 11-3.1   Introduction to the Instruction Set

The instruction set uses many forms of data with each instruction. The forms are specified with an extension just as different data types are specified for the 680XX microprocessor instructions (.B, .W, and .L). The extensions allowed by the floating-point instructions are listed in Table 11-6.

Notice that the 68881/68882 allows seven different extensions to specify integer, binary floating-point, and BCD floating-point data. The additional extensions are required because of the various binary and BCD floating-point formats. It is important to note that all numbers are internally stored as extended-precision binary

**Table 11-6**   Extensions Allowed with the Floating-Point Coprocessor

| Extension | Description |
|-----------|-------------|
| .B | Byte integer |
| .W | Word integer |
| .L | Long-word integer |
| .S | Single-precision binary floating-point |
| .D | Double-precision binary floating-point |
| .X | Extended-precision binary floating-point |
| .P | BCD floating-point |

floating-point numbers. These other forms are used when the number is moved out of the internal floating-point registers between the memory or microprocessor and the floating-point coprocessor.

## 11-3.2   Floating-Point Data Movement Instructions

The coprocessor data movement instructions are FMOVE, FMOVECR, and FMOVEM. These instructions are used to control the flow of data inside the coprocessor, between the coprocessor and the microprocessor, and between the coprocessor and the memory.

The FMOVE instruction, which requires an extension, allows data to be moved from a data register, memory location, or a floating-point register to another floating-point register, memory location, or data register. For a complete listing of allowable addressing modes, refer to Appendix C, which lists each group of instructions along with the allowable addressing modes.

Some example FMOVE instructions are listed in Table 11-7. When data are moved into a floating-point register, they are converted by the coprocessor to an extended floating-point number. If a number is moved from a floating-point register, it is converted to whatever form is dictated by the extension associated with the instruction. As mentioned, numbers are always in extended-precision form in a floating-point register.

If the operand address, used with a floating-point instruction, uses the predecrement or postincrement mode of addressing, the address register is decremented or incremented by the appropriate value. For example, suppose that the FMOVE.D FP2,(A2)+ instruction is executed. This instruction takes the 8 byte-wide double-precision floating-point number from FP2 and stores it into the memory location addressed by A2. After the move, the contents of A2 are incremented by an eight. A double-precision number requires 8 bytes of memory. The size of the extension determines the number added or subtracted from the address register for the postincrement and predecrement forms of addressing.

The FMOVECR instruction fetches an extended-precision constant from a ROM located within the 68881/68882. The form of the instruction is FMOVECR.X #??,FPn. The ?? is the numeric value of the constant (see Table 11-8), and FPn is

**Table 11-7   Example FMOVE Instructions**

| Instruction | Comment |
|---|---|
| FMOVE.B DATA,FP0 | Moves a byte-sized integer from memory location DATA into FP0. |
| FMOVE.X FP0,FP1 | Moves the extended-precision floating-point number from FP0 to FP1. |
| FMOVE.S FP3,D2 | Moves a single-precision floating-point number from FP3 into D2. |
| FMOVE.P FP2,(A2) | Moves a BCD floating-point number from FP2 into 12 consecutive bytes of memory beginning at the location addressed by A2. |
| FMOVE.S FP2,MEM | Moves a single-precision floating-point number into memory location MEM. |
| FMOVE.X FP6,-(SP) | Subtracts 12 from SP and moves the extended-precision floating-point number from FP6 to the stack. |

**Table 11-8   The On-Chip ROM Constants Used with FMOVECR**

| Code | Constant |
|---|---|
| $00 | $\pi$ |
| $0B | $\log_{10}2$ |
| $0C | $e$ |
| $0D | $\log_2 e$ |
| $0E | $\log_{10}e$ |
| $0F | $0.0$ |
| $30 | $\log_e 2$ |
| $31 | $\log_e 10$ |
| $32 | $10^0$ |
| $33 | $10^1$ |
| $34 | $10^2$ |
| $35 | $10^4$ |
| $36 | $10^8$ |
| $37 | $10^{16}$ |
| $38 | $10^{32}$ |
| $39 | $10^{64}$ |
| $3A | $10^{128}$ |
| $3B | $10^{256}$ |
| $3C | $10^{512}$ |
| $3D | $10^{1024}$ |
| $3E | $10^{2048}$ |
| $3F | $10^{4096}$ |

any floating-point register. An example is the FMOVECR.X#$00,FP1 which moves the extended precision value of π into FP1.

The third type of data movement instruction is the FMOVEM instruction, which functions similarly to MOVEM. The main difference is that FMOVEM allows data to be transferred between the floating-point registers and memory. An example instruction is FMOVEM.X MEMORY,FP0/FP2-FP4, which loads extended floating-point registers FP0, FP2, FP3, and FP4 with data beginning at memory location MEMORY.

Example 11-5 shows a short sequence of instructions in which the FMOVEM instruction stores and then restores the floating-point data registers before and after a subroutine. In many cases the contents of the floating-point data registers must be saved before software in a new subroutine can be executed. At the end of the subroutine, they need to be restored. This is especially true when nesting coprocessor subroutines.

E  X  A  M  P  L  E     11 - 5

```
                       ;
                       ;Subroutine that uses the FMOVEM instruction
                       ;to save the floating-point data registers
                       ;before any operation. Before returning, the
                       ;registers are restored.
                       ;
000000   F227E0FF   SUBR   FMOVEM.X   FP0-FP7,-(SP)   ;save all
                                  .             .
                                  .             .
000030   F21FC0FF          FMOVEM.X   (SP)+,FP0-FP7   ;restore all
000034   4E75              RTS
```

## 11-3.3   Floating-Point Dyadic Operations

*Dyadic operations* are floating-point operations that require two input data elements to function. The term "dyadic" means having two parts or elements. Dyadic coprocessor functions include addition, subtraction, multiplication, and division. Each of these operations requires two elements or operands to properly execute. Table 11-9 illustrates all the dyadic operations allowed by the 68881/68882 coprocessor.

Dyadic operations are performed on integers and binary or BCD floating-point numbers. All dyadic instructions have two operands. The first is the source operand, which can be a memory location or a floating-point data register. The second operand (destination) must be a floating-point data register. The source operand can be of any data format, but the operation is performed at the extended-precision level by the coprocessor. The result will be in the extended-precision level except for FSGLDIV and FSGLMUL, which are single-precision instructions.

The single-precision division and multiplication instructions are included because they execute faster than extended-precision division and multiplication. Single-precision numbers are used in many applications that do not require a high

**Table 11-9    The Dyadic Operations**

| Instruction | Operation |
|---|---|
| FADD | addition |
| FCMP | compare |
| FDIV | division |
| FMOD | modulo remainder |
| FREM | IEEE remainder |
| FSCALE | scale exponent |
| FSGLDIV | single-precision division |
| FSGLMUL | single-precision multiplication |
| FSUB | subtraction |

degree of precision. Single-precision form is often the normal data storage form for higher level languages such as BASIC, C, and Pascal.

To illustrate the use of some of the dyadic instructions, Example 11-6 shows how the area of a circle is calculated with a subroutine. This subroutine assumes that the data are single-precision binary floating-point numbers. Upon entrance to the subroutine, D0 contains the radius of the circle. Upon exit from the subroutine, D0 contains the area of the circle.

E X A M P L E    11 - 6

```
004000                          ORG         $4000
                        ;Subroutine that calculates the area of a
                        ;circle.
                        ;
                        ;D0 is the radius upon entrance;
                        ;D0 is the area upon exit.
                        ;
                        ;No attempt is made to save any register.
                        ;
004000   F2004400   CIRCLE   FMOVE.S     D0,FP0      ;get radius
004004   F2000427            FSGLMUL.S   FP0,FP0     ;form radius²
004008   F2009C80            FMOVECR.X   #0,FP1      ;get pi
00400C   F2010427            FSGLMUL.S   FP1,FP0     ;form area
004010   F2006400            FMOVE.S     FP0,D0      ;area to D0
004014   4E75                RTS
```

## 11-3.4    Floating-Point Monadic Operations

Floating-point *monadic operations* have only one input operand. The term "monadic" means having one part or element. The coprocessor monadic functions include such operations as sine, cosine, tangent, arc sine, arc cosine, arc tangent, and square root. Table 11-10 contains a complete listing of all monadic operations available to the coprocessor.

The trigonometric functions are sine, cosine, tangent, arc sine, arc cosine, arc tangent, hyperbolic sine, hyperbolic cosine, hyperbolic tangent, hyperbolic arc sine, hyperbolic arc cosine, and hyperbolic arc tangent. For sine and cosine, the argument is automatically reduced to the range of $+2\pi$ to $-2\pi$ before the sine or cosine is calculated. Note that if the argument is greater than $10^{20}$, an error in accuracy may occur as a result of the scaling method employed. The results for sine and cosine are always within the range of $+1$ to $-1$.

Logarithmic functions include $\log_2$, $\log_{10}$, and $\log_e$. Example 11-7 illustrates the use of $\log_{10}$ and the equation required to find a voltage gain in decibels (dB). The equation is simple because the gain is equal to the $\log_{10}$ of the output voltage divided by the input voltage times 20.

**Table 11-10   The Monadic Operations**

| Instruction | Operation |
|---|---|
| FABS | absolute value |
| FACOS | arc cosine |
| FASIN | arc sine |
| FATAN | arc tangent |
| FATANH | hyperbolic arc tangent |
| FCOS | cosine |
| FETOX | $e^x$ |
| FETOXM1 | $e^x - 1$ |
| FGETEXP | extract exponent |
| FGETMAN | extract mantissa |
| FINT | extract integer portion |
| FINTRZ | extract integer portion, rounded-toward-zero |
| FLOGN | $\log_e X$ |
| FLOGNP1 | $\log_e (X + 1)$ |
| FLOG10 | $\log_{10} X$ |
| FLOG2 | $\log_2 X$ |
| FNEG | negate |
| FSIN | sine |
| FSINCOS | simultaneous sine and cosine |
| FSINH | hyperbolic sine |
| FSQRT | square root |
| FTAN | tangent |
| FTANH | hyperbolic tangent |
| FTENOX | $10^x$ |
| FTWOTOX | $2^x$ |

E  X  A  M  P  L  E    11 - 7

$$\text{Voltage gain (dB)} = 20 \log_{10} \frac{V_{out}}{V_{in}}$$

Example 11-8 illustrates a subroutine that determines the voltage gain in decibels. Here D0 and D1 are used to transfer the output and input voltages to the subroutine and the gain is returned at D2. The output voltage is in D0 and the input voltage is in D1. All three values are in single-precision binary floating-point format. Notice how the number 20 is defined in the multiply instruction (FSGLMUL). The 2E2 is an exponential form that represents a 2 raised to the power of $10^2$.

E  X  A  M  P  L  E    11 - 8

```
007000                          ORG         $7000
                        ;Subroutine that determines the voltage gain
                        ;in decibels (dB).
                        ;
                        ;D0 = output voltage
                        ;D1 = input voltage
                        ;D2 = resultant gain (dB)
                        ;
007000   F2004400       VGAIN   FMOVE.S     D0,FP0      ;get Vout
007004   F2014424               FSGLDIV.S   D1,FP0      ;divide by Vin
007008   F2000815               FLOG10.X    FP0         ;log10 of gain
00700C   F23C242741A00000       FSGLMUL.S   #2E2,FP0    ;multiply × 20
007010   F2026400               FMOVE.S     FP0,D2      ;get result
007014   4E75                   RTS
```

The last type of monadic instruction, exponentiation, allows us to raise 2, 10, or $e$ to a power. These functions are useful, but a close examination reveals that there is no function to raise any number to any power. This function, which is often useful, must be synthesized. Example 11-9 illustrates the equation that is used to find any number ($X$) raised to any power ($y$).

E  X  A  M  P  L  E    11 - 9

$$X^y = 2^y (\log_2 X)$$

This is made easier because the FTOTOX instruction allows 2 to be raised to any power and the FLOG2 instruction allows the $\log_2$ of a number to be calculated. Example 11-10 illustrates a subroutine that solves the equation of Example 11-9. This subroutine assumes that $X$ is placed in FP0, $y$ is placed in FP1, and the result is returned in FP2. All numbers are in extended floating-point format for this example subroutine.

E  X  A  M  P  L  E     11 - 10

```
00A000                          ORG         $A000
                        ;
                        ;Subroutine that finds Xʸ
                        ;
                        ;FP0 = X
                        ;FP1 = y
                        ;
                        ;FP2 = RESULT
                        ;
00A000  F20008016  EXPO  FLOG2.X     FP0       ;find log₂ X
00A004  F2010891          FTWOTOX.X  FP1       ;find 2 raised to y
00A008  F2010900          FMOVE.X    FP1,FP2
00A00C  F2000923          FMUL.X     FP0,FP2   ;form result
00A010  4E75              RTS
```

## 11-3.5   Floating-Point Program Control Instructions

The floating-point coprocessor program control instructions allow the flow of a program to be modified in response to the conditions present in the FPSR (floating-point status register). These instructions are similar to the program control instructions provided for the 680XX microprocessor.

Table 11-11 gives the program control instructions for the 68881/68882 coprocessor. Notice that these are the same basic program control instructions allowed by the 680XX microprocessor except that there is a letter F in front of them.

The main difference between the program control instructions for the coprocessor and the microprocessor is the conditions tested. Table 11-12 illustrates the condition codes that apply to the instructions in Table 11-11. Some are the same as for the microprocessor and some are new for the coprocessor. The floating-point conditions test the floating-point status register, not the microprocessor status register.

Notice, from the table, that many new conditions are defined. These conditions depend on the value of the zero (Z), negative (N), and NAN (not-a-number) floating-point CCR bits. The NAN bit indicates that the result of the most recent

**Table 11-11**   The Floating-Point Program Control Instructions

| Instruction | Operation |
| --- | --- |
| FBcc ⟨label⟩ | Branch on condition, where cc is a condition code. |
| FDBcc Dn ,⟨label⟩ | Decrement and branch until a condition, where cc is a condition code. |
| FNOP | Floating-point, no operation. |
| FScc ⟨ea⟩ | Set according to condition, where cc is a condition code. |
| FTST ⟨ea⟩ or FPn | Test register or effective address. |

**Table 11-12**   Condition Codes for the Instructions in Table 11-11

| Condition code | Test | Description |
|---|---|---|
| EQ | Z | equal |
| F | false | always false |
| GE | $Z + (\overline{NAN + N})$ | greater than or equal |
| GL | $\overline{NAN + Z}$ | greater than or less than |
| GLE | $\overline{NAN}$ | greater than or less |
| GT | $\overline{NAN + Z + N}$ | greater than |
| LE | $Z + (N \cdot \overline{NAN})$ | less than or equal |
| LT | $N \cdot (\overline{NAN + Z})$ | less than |
| NE | $\overline{Z}$ | not equal |
| NGE | $NAN + (N \cdot \overline{Z})$ | not greater than or equal |
| NGL | $NAN + Z$ | not greater than or less than |
| NGLE | $NAN$ | not greater than or less than or equal |
| NGT | $NAN + Z + N$ | not greater than |
| NLE | $NAN + (\overline{N + Z})$ | not less than or equal |
| NLT | $NAN + (Z + \overline{N})$ | not less than |
| OGE | $Z + (\overline{NAN + N})$ | ordered greater than or equal |
| OGL | $\overline{NAN + Z}$ | ordered greater than or less than |
| OGT | $\overline{NAN + Z + N}$ | ordered greater than |
| OLE | $Z + (N \cdot \overline{NAN})$ | ordered less than or equal |
| OLT | $N \cdot (\overline{NAN + Z})$ | ordered less than |
| OR | $\overline{NAN}$ | ordered |
| SEQ | Z | signaling equal |
| SF | signaling | signaling always false |
| SNE | $\overline{Z}$ | signaling not equal |
| ST | signaling | signaling always true |
| T | true | always true |
| UEQ | $NAN + Z$ | unordered or equal |
| UGT | $NAN + (\overline{N + Z})$ | unordered greater than |
| UGE | $NAN + Z + N$ | unordered or greater than or equal |
| ULE | $NAN + Z + N$ | unordered less than or equal |
| ULT | $NAN + (N \cdot \overline{Z})$ | unordered less than |
| UN | $NAN$ | unordered |

NOTE: + = logical OR and · = logical AND.

floating-point operation is not-a-number. NANs, as mentioned in connection with the floating-point CCR register, are results that have no mathematical interpretation. These results are generated by operations that multiply infinity by infinity, and so on.

If the 68881/68882 is reset, or if a restore operation occurs, all floating-point registers (FP0–FP7) are initialized as NANs. So if a number has not been loaded into a register, and an operation is performed with the register, the result will be a NAN.

An ordered condition occurs after a compare instruction when both numbers being compared are numbers. If one or both of the numbers compared are NANs, then the outcome of the comparison is considered to be unordered. Conditions available for both ordered and unordered results are called *aware conditions*. The standard IEEE tests use only GT, LE, etc. conditions, and if one of these tested conditions is made with a NAN, the coprocessor begins a BSUN (branch/set on unordered) exception. To prevent this exception, the ordered and unordered compare instructions are used in a program. These are considered to be aware conditions because the person developing the software is aware of ordered and unordered conditions. The IEEE standard does not support ordered and unordered conditions.

There are two different NANs: a signaling NAN (SNAN) and a nonsignaling NAN. The signaling NAN is a NAN with its leading significand bit equal to a zero. The nonsignaling NAN is a NAN that has a one in its leading significand bit. Notice that conditions tested in Table 11-12 can use SNANs and NANs. Signaling NANs are not created by the coprocessor. They are created by the person developing software. For this reason, SNANs are used as user signaling mechanisms if desired.

## 11-3.6   Floating-Point System Control Operations

The last instruction category consists of the system control instructions, such as instructions that save and store the invisible portion of the internal register set. (The invisible portion is everything except FP0–FP7.) There is also an instruction that is similar to the software TRAPV (trap on an overflow) conditional interrupt instruction in the 680XX microprocessor.

Table 11-13 illustrates the three forms of the system control instructions. These instructions are used to communicate with the operating system during context switches in virtual memory or other forms of context switching.

The FSAVE and FRESTORE instructions are used with the FMOVEM instruction to move all internal registers between the coprocessor and the memory. The FMOVEM instruction is used to move all the floating-point data registers (FP0–FP7). The FSAVE and FRESTORE instructions are used to move the flags, the address of the microprogram register, the temporary register, etc. These are considered to be programmer-invisible data. More detail on these instructions is provided in the next section on interrupts and exceptions.

Example 11-11 illustrates the software to store the entire state of the coprocessor onto a stack addressed by address register A6. It also illustrates software to retrieve the entire state of the coprocessor from the stack. Subroutine SAVE saves the state and subroutine LOAD reloads the state of the coprocessor.

**Table 11-13**   The Floating-Point System Control Instructions

| Instruction | Operation |
| --- | --- |
| FRESTORE | Restores the invisible portion of the coprocessor from memory. |
| FSAVE | Stores the invisible portion of the coprocessor into memory. |
| FTRAPcc | This conditional TRAP instruction uses the condition codes listed in Table 11-12 to determine whether an exception will be taken. |

EXAMPLE   11 - 11

```
00C000                     ORG        $C000
                       ;
                       ;This subroutine saves the state of the
                       coprocessor on the stack addressed by A6.
                       ;
00C000   F326      SAVE  FSAVE      -(A6)                          ;save state
00C002   F226E0FF         FMOVEM.X   FP0-FP7,-(A6)                ;save data
00C006   F226FC00         FMOVEM.X   FPCR/FPSR/FPIAR,-(A6)
00C00A   2D3CFFFFFFFF      MOVE.L     #-1,-(A6)
00C010   4E75             RTS
                       ;
                       ;This subroutine reloads the state of the
                       ;coprocessor from the stack addressed by A6.
                       ;
00C012   F21EDC00  LOAD  FMOVEM.X   (A6)+,FPCR/FPSR/FPIAR
00C016   F21EC0FF         FMOVEM.X   (A6)+,FP0-FP7
00C01A   F35E             FRESTORE
00C01C   4E75             RTS
```

## 11-4    Coprocessor Interrupts and Exceptions

The coprocessor may generate exceptions during processing of floating-point coprocessor instructions. Coprocessor exceptions are handled exactly like main microprocessor exceptions. A coprocessor-generated exception is the same as an exception caused by the microprocessor.

### 11-4.1   Exceptions and the Coprocessor

Exceptions detected by the coprocessor may occur as it executes instructions or as it communicates with the microprocessor. The microprocessor always coordinates these exceptions. This means that the coprocessor may have to wait until the microprocessor is ready to begin processing the exception. Exceptions are reported to the microprocessor through the coprocessor interface registers (CIRs). The coprocessor interface registers were described in Section 11-1 with the hardware for the coprocessor.

*Coprocessor Exception Vectors*

The coprocessor uses some of the 680XX main exception vectors for the exceptions that are detected. Table 11-14 shows these vectors with a brief description of each. These vectors, like the 680XX vectors, contain the addresses of the exception handlers responsible for servicing the exceptions.

Coprocessor exceptions are handled exactly like the microprocessor exceptions. When the exception is requested, the microprocessor stops executing instructions and places the program counter and status register on the supervisor stack (68000/68008). Next the exception vector is fetched from the vector table and a

**Table 11-14**   The Coprocessor Exception Vectors

| Vector type number | Function |
| --- | --- |
| $07 | FTRAP on condition |
| $0B | F-line emulator |
| $0D | Coprocessor protocol violation |
| $30 | Branch/set on unordered condition (BSUN) |
| $31 | Inexact result |
| $32 | Floating-point divide by zero |
| $33 | Underflow |
| $34 | Operand error |
| $35 | Overflow |
| $36 | Signaling NAN (SNAN) |

branch to the exception handler occurs. The exception does not store any of the coprocessor registers on the stack. This is the responsibility of the exception handler.

Vector type $07 is generated whenever the conditional FTRAP instruction is executed and the condition is true. If the condition tested by the conditional FTRAP instruction is false, no exception occurs. The FTRAPGT instruction, for example, will generate an exception if the condition tested is greater than (GT). Likewise, any of the 32 conditions presented in Table 11-11 can be tested by the conditional FTRAP instruction. In addition to the instruction, a word that is defined by the user can be appended to the opcode so that information about the exception is conveyed to the exception handler.

The F-line emulation exception occurs whenever an instruction exists that is not a valid coprocessor instruction. All 68881/68882 instructions begin with a $F. So do all F-line exceptions. The difference is that the F-line exception occurs only for instructions that are not coprocessor instructions. This exception is known as an illegal instruction coprocessor exception. We don't call it this, however, because at some future time additional $F instructions for other coprocessors may be added. (For example, the 68851 paged memory management unit uses some of the F-line exceptions.) It is possible for a second floating-point coprocessor to be added to the system or another coprocessor. The additional coprocessors use other coprocessor ID codes.

The coprocessor protocol violation exception occurs whenever there is a breakdown in communications between the coprocessor and the microprocessor. These protocol violations occur with unexpected accesses to the command, condition, register, or operand of the coprocessor interface registers. Serious programming errors can cause this type of exception. If serious enough, the 68882 will enter an unrecoverable protocol violation exception. This is not a problem with the 68881.

The branch/set on unordered condition (BSUN) exception is caused with a conditional test using the FBcc, FDBcc, or FTRAPcc instruction. This exception occurs whenever the compare instruction, which proceeds the test, compares not-

**Table 11-15  Other Causes of
Divide by Zero Exceptions**

| Instruction | Cause |
|---|---|
| FATANH | source operand = ± 1 |
| FLOG10 | source operand = 0 |
| FLOG2 | source operand = 0 |
| FLOGN | source operand = 0 |
| FLOGNP1 | source operand = −1 |

a-numbers (NANs). This type of exception will not occur if the ordered or unordered condition codes, described with Table 11-12, are used.

The inexact result exception occurs whenever the result of a coprocessor instruction has too many digits to be represented as a floating-point value with the selected rounding precision. This exception can also occur when a BCD floating-point number is converted to an extended-precision binary floating-point number. If the BCD floating-point conversion produces a binary extended-precision floating-point number that is inexact, the inexact result exception occurs.

A floating-point divide by zero exception occurs if an attempt is made to divide by zero. It also occurs for certain transcendental functions as listed in Table 11-15. To prevent these exceptions, one must test for the conditions in the "Cause" column before executing the instructions listed.

Underflows occur when the result of an operation is too small to be represented as a floating-point number. Underflows cause the underflow exception. Overflows occur when the result is too large to be represented as a floating-point number. Overflows cause the overflow exception.

Operand errors signal a result that has no specific arithmetic value—for example, the "result" of infinity divided by infinity. The $\infty/\infty$ operation has no specific arithmetic value and it causes the operand error exception. Operand error exceptions occur for many similar types of errors, including cosine of infinity, sine of infinity, any logarithm of infinity, and adding infinity to infinity.

A signaling NAN (SNAN) exception is a user-generated exception. The user must specifically create an SNAN and then execute an instruction that uses the SNAN. As mentioned earlier, an SNAN is a NAN that has a logic zero in the leftmost bit of the significand. A nonsignaling NAN has a logic one in the same bit.

## 11-4.2 The State Frame and Exceptions Using the Coprocessor

When an exception occurs, the current instruction may not be the instruction that caused the exception. This is because the coprocessor exception may not take effect at the time of the error. To determine exactly which coprocessor operation caused the exception, the FSAVE instruction is used to store the state of the coprocessor in the memory so that it can be examined. The FRESTORE instruction is used to reload the state of the coprocessor from the memory.

Figure 11-11 illustrates the state frames generated by the 68881 coprocessor whenever an FSAVE instruction is executed. The exact state frame stored in the memory depends on the state of the coprocessor. Notice that the first long-word of each of these state frames contains the same basic information. The first byte contains a zero or the version number of the coprocessor. A zero in this byte indicates a null state frame. The second byte indicates the size of the state frame.

The idle and busy state frames differ slightly for the 68882 coprocessor, as illustrated in Figure 11-12. Notice that the idle state contains register information that is not present in the idle state for the 68881. This is because the 68882 saves the control unit (CU) registers. The busy state for the 68882 is also larger because of these control unit registers.

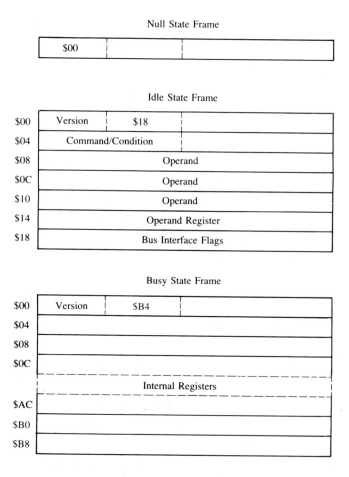

**Figure 11-11**   The state frames (null, idle, and busy) for the 68881 coprocessor when an FSAVE is executed.

## The Null State

The null state frame contains no information, as illustrated in Figures 11-10 and 11-11. A null state is stored by the FSAVE instruction if no floating-point coprocessor instructions have been executed since the last null state restore or hardware reset. The null state indicates that the internal register set of the coprocessor is empty.

## Idle State

The idle state is stored by the FSAVE instruction whenever the coprocessor is not executing an instruction. Located within the idle state frame are the contents of the

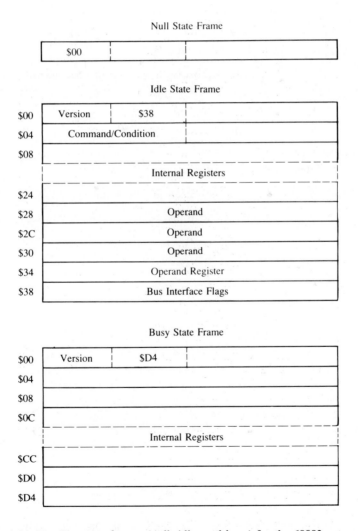

**Figure 11-12** The state frames (null, idle, and busy) for the 68882 coprocessor.

command/condition register: usually a valid image of the command register contents and condition codes for the coprocessor. The bus interface flags indicate whether the command/condition register is valid.

Following the command/condition register is the 12-byte operand. The operand can be tested if an error has caused the state to be saved with the FSAVE instruction. The operand register contains an image of the operand that was most recently used by the coprocessor.

The bus interface flags indicate conditions about the bus interface. Figure 11-13 depicts the contents of the bus interface flags. Notice that only the left-most 16 bits contain information about the bus interface. The right-most 16 bits are undefined, but reserved for future products.

The bus interface flags have the following meanings.

**Bit 31**    This bit (logic one) indicates that a protocol violation has been detected and is pending. It is a logic one for this condition when the microprocessor has not been able to begin processing this exception request.

**Bit 30**    This bit indicates that the coprocessor has received a new command but has yet to execute it.

**Bit 29**    This bit, along with bits 30 and 28, indicates the type of pending operand access, or type of pending operation alone.

**Bit 28**    This bit indicates that the coprocessor is expecting the next access to be the operand CIR. Refer to Table 11-16 for bits 30, 29, and 28.

**Bit 27**    This bit (logic zero) indicates that a floating-point exception is pending.

**Bit 26**    A logic zero on this bit indicates that an operand transfer to the memory is pending.

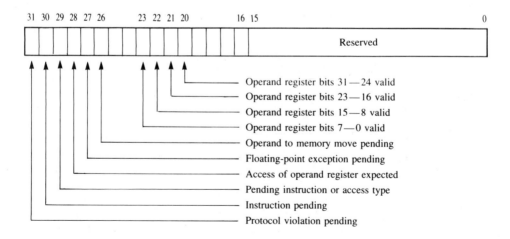

**Figure 11-13    The contents of the bus interface flag state frame.**

**Table 11-16**  Pending Operation

| 30 | Bits 29 | 28 | Definition |
|---|---|---|---|
| 0 | 0 | 0 | [undefined] |
| 0 | 0 | 1 | Conditional instruction pending |
| 0 | 1 | 0 | [undefined] |
| 0 | 1 | 1 | General instruction pending |
| 1 | 0 | 0 | Write of operand CIR pending |
| 1 | 0 | 1 | [undefined] |
| 1 | 1 | 0 | Read of operand CIR pending |
| 1 | 1 | 1 | No pending instruction or operand CIR access |

**Bits 20–23**  These bits indicate that the bytes of the data bus contain valid information.

*Busy State*

When the coprocessor is busy, the state frame is used to store all the internal registers: 180 bytes is required to store the registers of the 68881; 212 bytes is required for the 68882. The busy state frame contains no useful information for the programmer and should never be modified.

## 11-5  Programming Examples Using the Coprocessor

This section presents several short programming examples, to enhance understanding of the operation of the coprocessor. Each example illustrates a few groups of floating-point coprocessor instructions.

### 11-5.1  Quadratic Equation

The quadratic equation is a common mathematical formula for finding the roots of a polynomial. In Example 11-12, which illustrates the quadratic equation that is solved with a subroutine using the floating-point coprocessor, the equations for roots 1 and 2 are listed separately.

E  X  A  M  P  L  E      11 - 12

$$ROOT1 = \frac{-b + \sqrt{b^2 - 4ac}}{2a}$$

$$ROOT2 = \frac{-b - \sqrt{b^2 - 4ac}}{2a}$$

The subroutine that solves for the roots, listed in Example 11-13, assumes that *a, b,* and *c* are found in registers D0, D1, and D2 as single-precision floating-point numbers. Upon return from the subroutine, the roots are found in registers D3 and D4 as single-precision roots: D3 contains ROOT1 and D4 contains ROOT2. This subroutine solves for real roots only.

E  X  A  M  P  L  E    11 - 13

```
010000                          ORG       $10000
                         ;
                         ;Subroutine that solves the quadratic
                         ;equation.
                         ;
                         ;a = D0, b = D1, c = D2
                         ;
                         ;ROOT1 = D3
                         ;ROOT2 = D4
                         ;
010000  F2004400      ROOTS  FMOVE.S    D0,FP0          ;form 4ac in FP0
010004  F2024427             FSGLMUL.S  D2,FP0
010008  F27C442740800000     FSGLMUL.S  #2E1,FP0
010010  F2004480             FMOVE.S    D0,FP1          ;form 2a
010014  F27C44A740000000     FSGLMUL.S  #2E0,FP1
01001C  F2014500             FMOVE.S    D1,FP2          ;form b²
010020  F2000927             FSGLMUL.S  FP2,FP2
010024  F2000227             FSUB.X     FP0,FP2         ;form b² - 4ac
010028  F2000904             FSQRT.X    FP2             ;form square root
01002C  F2014400             FMOVE.S    D1,FP0          ;form ROOT1
010030  F200001A             FNEG.X     FP0
010034  F2000200             FMOVE.X    FP0,FP4
010038  F2000822             FADD.X     FP2,FP0
01003C  F2000424             FSGLDIV.S  FP1,FP0
010040  F2036400             FMOVE.S    FP0,D3          ;save ROOT1
010044  F2000A28             FSUB.X     FP2,FP4         ;form ROOT2
010048  F2000A24             FSGLDIV.S  FP1,FP4
01004C  F2046600             FMOVE.S    FP4,D4          ;save ROOT2
010050  4E75                 RTS
```

## 11-5.2   Resonant Frequency

An equation commonly used in electronics is the formula for determining the resonant frequency of an *LC* tank circuit. In the equation for the resonant frequency (Example 11-14), *L* is the inductance in henrys, *C* is the capacitance in farads, and $F_r$ is the resonant frequency in hertz.

E  X  A  M  P  L  E    11 - 14

$$F_r = \frac{1}{2\pi \sqrt{LC}}$$

The equation presented in Example 11-14 is used to write a subroutine for calculating the resonant frequency. The subroutine is listed in Example 11-15, where it is assumed that D0 contains the value of inductance and D1 the value of capacitance before the subroutine is called. Both numbers are in single-precision form. The resonant frequency is returned as a single-precision value found in register D2. Notice that the subroutine is very straightforward and very little data manipulation is required to solve the equation.

**E X A M P L E   11 - 15**

```
009000                          ORG       $9000
                             ;
                             ;Subroutine that calculates the
                             ;resonant frequency if D0 is loaded
                             ;with the value of inductance and D1
                             ;is loaded with the value of the
                             ;capacitance before branching to the
                             ;subroutine.
                             ;
                             ;Upon return, D2 contains the resonant
                             ;frequency.
                             ;
009000  F2005C00      RESON   FMOVECR.X  #0,FP0     ;get pi
009004  F23C82340000000       FMUL.X     #2E1,FP0   ;get 2 pi
00900C  F2004480              FMOVE.S    D0,FP1     ;form LC
009010  F20144A7              FSGLMUL.S  D1,FP1
009014  F2000485              FSQRT.X    FP1        ;square root
009018  F2018230              FMUL.X     FP1,FP0
00901C  F2005CB2              FMOVECR.X  #$32,FP1   ;get 1
009020  F20008A4              FSGLDIV.X  FP0,FP1
009024  F2026480              FMOVE.S    FP1,D2
009028  4E75                  RTS
```

## Summary

1. A coprocessor is a device that, when connected to the microprocessor, performs operations concurrently with the microprocessor. In the case of the floating-point coprocessor, concurrent operations include addition, subtraction, multiplication, division, sine, cosine, tangent, and square root. The 68881/68882 coprocessors fully implement the standard binary floating-point arithmetic as specified by ANSI-IEEE 754-1985.

2. The pinouts of the 68881 and 68882 are identical; these coprocessors differ mainly in speed. The 68882 is an enhanced version of the 68881 that can execute multiple floating-point operations concurrently with the microprocessor. The 68882 also contains special-purpose hardware that allows it to

convert between binary floating-point numbers and extended floating-point numbers at a much higher speed than the 68881. New designs normally use the 68882.

3. The 68881 and 68882 are available in a wide range of clock operating frequencies. These devices operate from a low frequency of 12.5 MHz (68881RC12) to a high frequency of 25 MHz (68882RC25). Both coprocessors operate with all versions of the 680XX microprocessor. This is accomplished with the $\overline{\text{SIZE}}$ and A0 pins, which indicate the size of the data bus.

4. The 68881/68882 floating-point coprocessor is capable of functioning with integers, binary floating-point numbers, and packed floating-point binary-coded decimal. These formats are used to represent data externally and are not used inside the 68881/68882. Internally the coprocessor uses an 80-bit binary floating-point format to represent all data. To store data, the coprocessor contains eight, 80-bit-wide registers called floating-point registers (FP0–FP7).

5. Integer data are signed whole numbers that are a byte, word, or long-word in width.

6. Binary floating-point data are 32 bits for single-precision, 64 bits for double-precision, and 80 bits for extended-precision. Each floating-point number is composed of three parts: sign bit, biased exponent, and significand. The sign bit contains the sign of the significand. The biased exponent contains a power of 2 that is biased by a constant. The significand contains a normalized fraction and either an explicit or implicit one-bit.

7. The binary-coded decimal floating-point form is able to represent a number in decimal scientific notation. The number is represented as normalized significand raised to a power of 10. The significand ranges in value from 0.0000000000000000 to 9.9999999999999999. The exponent ranges in value from 000 to 999 decimal.

8. The 68881/68882 floating-point coprocessors perform operations using five distinct groupings of instructions: moves, dyadic operations, monadic operations, program control, and system control.

9. The data movement instructions are: FMOVE, FMOVECR, and FMOVEM. These instructions are used to control the flow of data inside the coprocessor, between the coprocessor and the microprocessor, and between the coprocessor and the memory.

10. Dyadic operations are floating-point operations that require two input data elements to function. The term "dyadic" means having two parts or elements. Dyadic functions include addition, subtraction, multiplication, and division. Each of these operations requires two elements for proper execution.

11. Floating-point monadic operations have only one input operand. The term "monadic" means having one part or element. Monadic functions include operations such as sine, cosine, tangent, arc sine, arc cosine, arc tangent, and square root.

12. The floating-point coprocessor program control instructions allow the flow of a program to be modified in response to the conditions present in the FPSR (floating-point status register). These instructions are similar to the program control instructions provided for the 680XX microprocessor.

13. The system control instructions include instructions that save and store the invisible portion of the internal register set. (The invisible portion is everything except FP0–FP7.)

14. Exceptions can be detected by the coprocessor as it executes instructions or as it communicates with the microprocessor. Because the microprocessor always coordinates these exceptions, the coprocessor may have to wait until the 68XXX is ready to begin processing an exception. Exceptions are reported to the microprocessor through the coprocessor interface registers (CIRs).

## Questions

1. What is a coprocessor?

2. What are the differences between the 68881 and 68882 coprocessors?

3. Which speed versions are available for the 68881/68882 coprocessors?

4. Describe how the $\overline{\text{SIZE}}$ and A0 pins are used to select the data bus width for the coprocessor.

5. Which $\overline{\text{DSACK}}$ pin is used to insert wait states into the 68008 microprocessor timing?

6. Explain how the data bus is connected to the coprocessor for the 68000 microprocessor.

7. What is the significance of an instruction that begins with a 1111 binary in relation to the floating-point coprocessor?

8. Convert the following decimal numbers to 8-, 16-, and 32-bit signed binary integers for use with the floating-point coprocessor.
   (a) $-12$     (b) $+3002$     (c) $-68$     (d) $+100$

9. Convert the following decimal numbers to single-precision binary floating-point number.
   (a) $+34.625$     (b) $-200.5$     (c) $+800.1875$     (d) $-0.02$

10. Convert the following single-precision binary floating-point numbers (represented here in hexadecimal) into signed decimal numbers.
    (a) $40000000     (b) $44500000     (c) $FF000000

11. Convert the following decimal numbers into BCD floating-point form.
    (a) $-3000.4$     (b) $3.567 \times 10^{10}$     (c) $-3.6E2$

12. Floating-point registers (FP0–FP7) always contain what type of floating-point data?

13. Describe the purpose of the mode control byte in the floating-point control register.

14. List each exception controlled by the exception enable byte of the floating-point control register. Also briefly describe the purpose of each of these exceptions.

15. What bits are found in the floating-point CCR register, and what conditions are detected by these bits?

16. What is the purpose of the floating-point instruction address register?

17. What extensions are used with floating-point instructions?

18. Define the function performed by each of the following FMOVE instructions.
    (a)    FMOVE.W  D0,FP1
    (b)    FMOVE.P  MEMORY,FP7
    (c)    FMOVE.X  FL1,FP2
    (d)    FMOVE.S  FP2,D3

19. Indicate the functions performed by the following instructions.
    (a)    FMOVECR.X  #$33,FP2
    (b)    FMOVECR.X  #$00,FP1

20. Using the FMOVEM instruction, store the contents of FP0, FP2, FP3, and FP4 on the stack.

21. Using the FMOVEM instruction, load FP0, FP1, and FP2 from memory location WATER.

22. Choose floating-point instructions that add the extended floating-point numbers in registers FP1, FP2, and FP3. Save the result in FP4.

23. The perimeter of a rectangle is equal to the sum of all sides. Write a subroutine that finds the perimeter of a rectangle whose sides are stored as single-precision numbers in D0 and D1. Place the perimeter, also in single-precision form, in D3.

24. If the base and altitude of a right triangle are known, the hypotenuse is found by the following equation.

E  X  A  M  P  L  E      11 - 16

$$\text{hypotenuse} = \tan \frac{\text{altitude}}{\text{base}}$$

Use this equation to write a subroutine that calculates the hypotenuse of a triangle whose base is found in D0 and whose altitude is found in D1. Upon return from the subroutine, the hypotenuse must be left in D2. All dimensions are binary single-precision floating-point numbers.

25. Example 11-7 illustrated how the decibel voltage gain is calculated. If the decibel power gain is required, this equation is changed so that the logarithm is multiplied by 10 instead of 20. Knowing this, develop a subroutine that calculates the power gain when the input power is 10 mW and the output power is 50,000 W.

26. What is an aware condition?

27. What is a coprocessor protocol violation exception?

28. What causes an inexact result exception?

29. What is an underflow?

30. What is a null state?

31. What is a busy state?

# 12

## *Introduction to the 68010 and 68020 Microprocessors*

**OBJECTIVES**

Upon completion of this chapter, you will be able to:

- Contrast all the 68000 microprocessor family members.

- Interface memory and I/O to any 68000 family member.

- Explain the function of additional software as it applies to the 68010 or 68020 microprocessor.

- Explain the new addressing modes available with the 68020 microprocessor.

- Describe the operation of the 68020 instruction cache.

- Explain any difference in the exception vector tables and exception stack frame formats for the 68020 microprocessor.

**KEY TERMS**

loop mode operation
cache

cache disable input
bit field

THIS chapter provides a glimpse of the 68010 and 68020 micro-processors. These newer, more powerful versions are provided as an extension to the concepts learned earlier for the 68000 and 68008. The main differences between the older 68000/68008 and these newer microprocessors are higher speed, more efficient operation, wider bus widths (68020), and more memory (68020).

All software learned for the 68000/68008 functions without change on these newer microprocessors. (There are, however, a few changes in assembly language syntax.) Additional instructions for the 68010 and 68020 are added, and these are explained in this chapter. The hardware interface to memory and I/O is essentially the same for these newer microprocessors. This chapter clarifies the differences and presents schematics that illustrate buffering, memory interface, etc.

## 12-1 The 68010 Microprocessor

The 68010 microprocessor is an enhanced version of the 68000; its software is almost identical to the 68000, and its hardware interface is identical. This section illustrates all the differences between the 68000 and the 68010 microprocessors.

### 12-1.1 Pinout

Figure 12-1 illustrates the pinout of the 68010 microprocessor. Notice that the pin connections are identical to the 68000. The data bus is 16 bits in width and the address bus contains address connections A23 through A1, just as in the 68000. The 68010 is also available in a PGA version (not illustrated here); instead, Figure 12-1 shows the DIP version. A comparison of this pinout with the pinout of the 68000 would reveal no differences. All the differences between these microprocessors are at the software and register levels rather than at the hardware pin connection level.

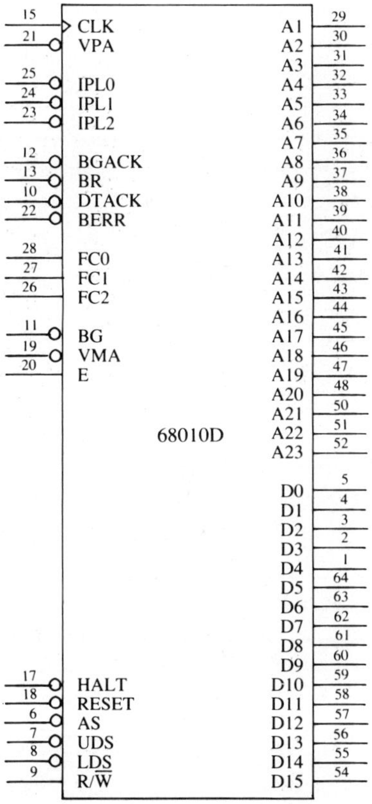

**Figure 12-1** The pinout of the 68010D microprocessor.

### 12-1.2    68010 Features

The features incorporated into the 68010 that are not present in the 68000 include additional instructions, a looping feature that enhances the speed performance for small loops, and a change in the programming model that allows expansion of the memory system beyond 16M bytes, as well as a change in the location of the interrupt vectors. Figure 12-2 illustrates the programming model of the 68010, which contains a vector base register and two alternate function code registers that are not found on the 68000/68008.

### The Vector Base Register

The vector base register is used by the microprocessor to relocate the exception vector table. The exception vector table in the 68000 and 68008 always started at memory location $000000 and extended to location $0003FF. In the 68010 this table

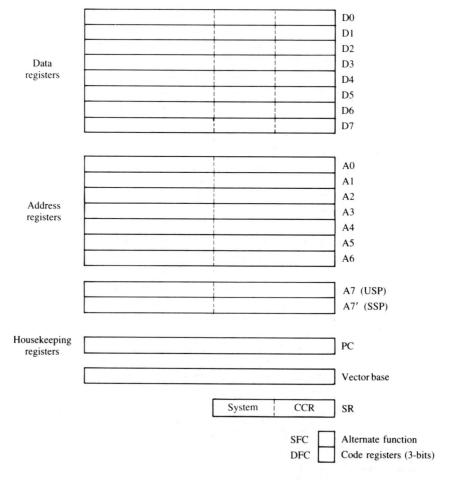

**Figure 12-2    The programming model of the 68010 microprocessor.**

may begin at any location, as dictated by the offset address stored in the vector base register.

For example, if the vector base register contains a $00001000, the exception vector table begins at location $001000 and ends at location $0013FF. Recall that the length of the vector table is $3FF bytes. In this relocated table, vector 0 is at memory location $001000, vector 1 is at location $001004, vector 2 is at location $001008, and so forth.

The vector base register allows different tasks to have different exception vector tables. This is important in multiuser systems, where each user might have different exception requirements. Note that the vector base register is cleared to $00000000 on a reset so that initially, the exception vectors are stored in memory locations $000000–$0003FF.

## The Alternate Function Code Registers

The alternate function code registers (SFC and DFC) allow the supervisor to access user memory and I/O space or to emulate CPU space cycles. Function code bits are also occasionally used to extend the amount of addressable memory beyond 16M bytes.

Emulation of CPU space is important if the hardware functions provided by a coprocessor are emulated with software in lieu of a coprocessor. The MOVEC instruction, which is new to the 68010, is used to load the SFC (source function code) and DFC (destination function code) registers. For example, a MOVEC #1,DFC is used to load a one into the destination function code register.

Another new instruction, MOVES, is used to transfer data between a data register and a memory location using the SFC and DFC function code registers. Both the MOVES and MOVEC instructions are privileged; that is, they may be executed only in the supervisor mode.

The MOVES instruction allows a supervisor program access to the user address space through the function codes specified by the SFC and DFC registers. Normally whenever data are accessed in the supervisor mode, the function control pins (FC2–FC0) specify supervisor data. This is changed if the MOVES instruction is used and SFC and DFC are loaded with the code for the user data memory (001) or user program space (010). Any other code may be used, but other codes are normally reserved for future Motorola products.

The function code bits may be thought of as additional memory address signals A24, A25, and A26. This allows more than 16M bytes of memory to be addressed by the microprocessor. In fact, by adding these three additional address bits, the supervisor software can access up to 128M bytes of memory.

## Prefetch Queue

The 68010 has a two-word prefetch queue. A queue is a first in, last out (FILO) memory that temporarily holds data. The queue inside the 68010 holds two words of an instruction from a program so that tight loops are executed at a much greater speed than possible without the queue. Operation and execution from the prefetch queue is called *loop mode operation*.

E  X  A  M  P  L  E     12 - 1

```
300000    207C00100000          MOVE.L   #BLOCKA,A0
300006    227C00200000          MOVE.L   #BLOCKB,A1
30000C    303C0063              MOVE.W   #COUNT,D0

300010    12D8          LOOP    MOVE.B   (A0)+,(A1)+    ;tight loop
300012    51C8FFFC              DBRA     D0,LOOP
```

Example 12-1 illustrates a short sequence of instructions that transfer the contents of memory BLOCKA into memory BLOCKB. Notice that this sequence contains a tight loop, the MOVE.B and the DBRA instructions. When this program is executed by a 68000 or 68008 microprocessor, each time the instructions within the loop are executed, the microprocessor must return to memory to fetch them. Because the same instructions are continually being fetched from memory, this wastes a vast amount of time.

In the 68010, these two instructions are fetched only once. The MOVE.B instruction is fetched into the internal instruction register and the two-word DBRA instruction is fetched into the prefetch queue. Because both instructions are stored inside the microprocessor, no further memory access for these instructions is required. This greatly increases the speed of execution of this tight loop.

Loop mode operation is transparent to the programmer, so no special provision is required to utilize it. Any program that uses a 2-byte opcode followed by one of the DBcc instructions automatically uses the loop mode and executes at a considerably higher speed than with the 68000 or 68008 microprocessor.

### Exception Stack Frames

The only other difference between the 68000 and the 68010 is the exception stack frame. The 68010 has two different exception stack frames: the short format (4 words) and the long format (29 words). Figure 12-3 illustrates both stack frames.

The short stack frame is used for all exceptions except bus error and address error, which use the long stack frame. The short stack frame uses a format code of 0000 and the long stack frame uses 1000. No other format codes are used with the 68010 microprocessor. Additional stack frames are found with more advanced family members such as the 68020, 68030, and 68040.

Figure 12-4 illustrates the special status word found in the long stack frame used with bus and address error exceptions. This word handles bus errors with software rather than having the microprocessor execute a rerun cycle. When software reruns the bus cycle, the RR bit is set so that the microprocessor does not execute a rerun cycle on the RTE instruction.

## 12-2    The 68020 Microprocessor

The 68020 is an enhanced version of both the 68000 and 68010. The 68020 is a true 32-bit microprocessor. Both the 68000 and 68010 are 32-bit microprocessors be-

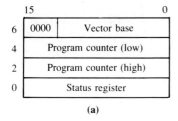

**(a)**

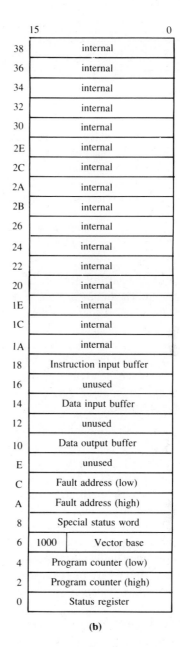

**(b)**

**Figure 12-3   The short (a) and long (b) stack frames for the 68010 microprocessor.**

| 15 | 14 | 13 | 12 | 11 | 10 | 9 | 8 | 7 | 6 | 5 | 4 | 3 | 2 | 1 | 0 |
|----|----|----|----|----|----|----|----|----|----|----|----|----|----|----|----|
| RR | | IF | DF | RM | HB | BY | RW | | | | | | FC2 | FC1 | FC0 |

$$
\begin{aligned}
RR &= \text{Re-run flag } (0 = \text{re-run and } 1 = \text{software re-run}). \\
IF &= \text{Instruction fetch to the instruction input buffer.} \\
DF &= \text{Data fetch to the data input buffer.} \\
RM &= \text{Read-modify-write cycle.} \\
HB &= \text{High byte transfer from the data output buffer or to the data input buffer.} \\
BY &= \text{Byte transfer flag.} \\
RW &= \text{Read/}\overline{\text{Write}} \\
FC2-FC0 &= \text{Function code used during the faulted access.}
\end{aligned}
$$

**Figure 12-4    The 68010 special status word.**

cause of internal register set, but not as far as the hardware pin connections are concerned. The 68020 is capable of addressing 4G bytes of memory through its 32-bit address bus. It addresses data as 8-bit bytes, 16-bit words, or 32-bit long-words through its 32-bit data bus. In addition to a much larger memory space, the 68020 supports more addressing modes than the 68000 and 68010 microprocessors. This section contrasts the 68020 with the 68000 and 68010 microprocessors and explains all the new features found on the 68020.

### 12-2.1    Pinout

Figure 12-5 illustrates the pinout of the 68020 microprocessor. Notice that this microprocessor is packaged in a PGA (pin grid array). The 68020 is available as the MC68020RC12, which is a 12.5 MHz version, and the MC68020RC16, which is a 16.7 MHz version.

The dc characteristics of the 68020 are similar to the 68000 because the input loading is $\pm 20$ $\mu$A maximum. The input voltage levels are TTL compatible, as are the output voltage levels. Table 12-1 gives the logic zero drive current available at each output pin. These currents are enough to drive a small system but must be increased with buffers for larger systems. The logic one output current in all cases is 400 $\mu$A. Buffers are more prevalent in a 68020-based system because of the large memory space available to this microprocessor.

### Pin Functions

Following are descriptions of the function of each pin or each grouping of pins of the 68020. Notice that many of the pins are the same as on the 68000 microprocessor.

**A31–A0 (address bus)**    The 32-bit address bus is used to access up to 4G bytes of memory. Each byte of this memory is numbered, just as the memory is numbered in the 68000 microprocessor.

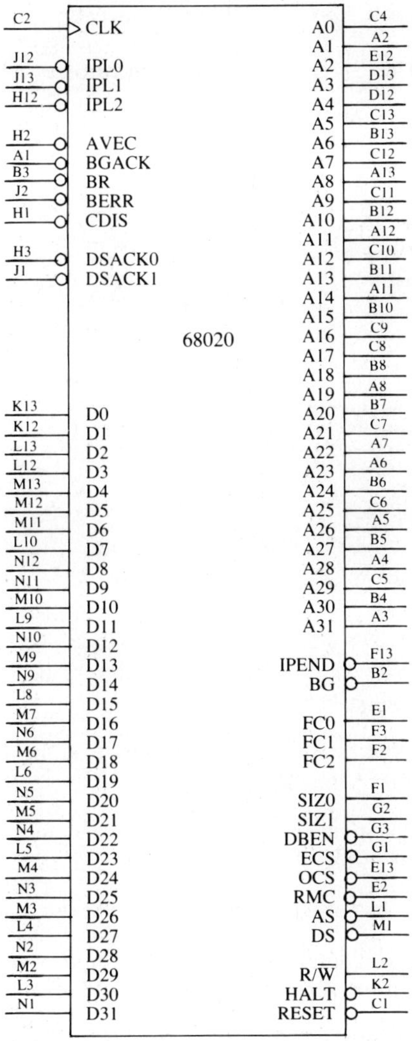

**Figure 12-5** The pinout of the 68020 microprocessor.

$\overline{\text{AS}}$ **(address strobe)** The address strobe output signals that the address bus contains a valid address. It also qualifies the following output signals: the function code bits, the memory size bits, and the R/$\overline{\text{W}}$ signal.

$\overline{\text{AVEC}}$ **(autovector)** This input is used to request the internal generation of an autovector interrupt. It performs the same function as $\overline{\text{VPA}}$ pin on the 68000 microprocessor. The difference is the peripheral control pins provided on the 68000 are missing on the 68020 microprocessor. This is because 6800 peripherals are far too slow to be useful with this microprocessor.

**Table 12-1    68020 Drive Currents**

| Pins | Logic zero current (mA) |
| --- | --- |
| A31–A0 | 3.2 |
| FC2–FC0 | 3.2 |
| SIZ1–SIZ0 | 3.2 |
| $\overline{BG}$ | 3.2 |
| D31–D0 | 3.2 |
| $\overline{AS}$ | 5.3 |
| $\overline{DS}$ | 5.3 |
| R/$\overline{W}$ | 5.3 |
| $\overline{RMC}$ | 5.3 |
| $\overline{DBEN}$ | 5.3 |
| $\overline{IPEND}$ | 5.3 |
| $\overline{ECS}$ | 2.0 |
| $\overline{OCS}$ | 2.0 |
| $\overline{HALT}$ | 10.7 |
| $\overline{RESET}$ | 10.7 |

$\overline{\text{BERR}}$ **(bus error)**   The bus error input is used to request a bus error interrupt or, if used in conjunction with the halt input, a rerun. As on the 68000, 68008, and 68010, this input is nonmaskable.

$\overline{\text{BG}}$ **(bus grant)**   The bus grant output indicates that the 68020 will release the system buses at the end of the current bus cycle.

$\overline{\text{BGACK}}$ **(bus grant acknowledge)**   This input indicates that an external DMA controller has taken access to the system buses. It is also tested for bus arbitration.

$\overline{\text{BR}}$ **(bus request)**   The bus request input is used to request a DMA action.

$\overline{\text{CDIS}}$ **(cache disable)**   This input disables the on-chip instruction cache memory. If this pin is placed at a logic zero, the cache is disabled.

**CLK (clock)**   The clock input provides the 68020 with its clock input signal. The clock frequency is either 12.5 or 16.7 MHz.

**D31–D0 (data bus)**   The 32-bit data bus is used to access bytes, words, or long-words from the memory system.

$\overline{\text{DBEN}}$ **(data buffer enable)**   This signal is used in a buffered system to enable data bus buffers.

$\overline{\text{DS}}$ **(data strobe)**   The data strobe output indicates that the data bus is available for a data transfer.

$\overline{\text{DSACK1}}$, $\overline{\text{DSACK0}}$ **(data transfer and size acknowledge)**   These signals indicate the size of a data transfer and also that a data transfer is complete. During a bus operation, the bus cycle is terminated with the $\overline{\text{DSACK}}$ signal as it was with $\overline{\text{DTACK}}$ in the 68000. Table 12-2 illustrates the coding for these two signals, which

**Table 12-2** $\overline{\text{DSACK}}$ Coding

| $\overline{\text{DACK1}}$ | $\overline{\text{DACK0}}$ | Function |
|---|---|---|
| 1 | 1 | Wait states inserted. |
| 1 | 0 | Cycle complete for an 8-bit transfer (D24–D31). |
| 0 | 1 | Cycle complete for a 16-bit transfer (D16–D24). |
| 0 | 0 | Cycle complete for a 32-bit transfer (D0–D31). |

are used to terminate a bus cycle. These inputs allow different sized memory and I/O components to be connected to the 68020 bus system through dynamic bus sizing.

**ECS (external cycle start)** This output becomes active during the first half clock of every bus cycle. This signal is used with address strobe to indicate a valid bus cycle.

**HALT (halt)** The halt pin is a bidirectional pin used as an output to indicate that the STOP instruction has executed. It is also an input to halt program execution.

**IPEND (interrupt pending)** This output indicates that the current interrupt request on the $\overline{\text{IPL}}$ pins is a higher priority than the current mask level in the status register.

**IPL2, IPL1, IPL0 (interrupt priority level)** These three inputs are used to request a level 1–7 interrupt. They are used for autovector interrupts with $\overline{\text{AVEC}}$ or user interrupts.

**OCS (operand cycle start)** This signal has the same timing as $\overline{\text{ECS}}$ and is used to indicate the first bus cycle of an operand transfer or an instruction prefetch.

**R/$\overline{\text{W}}$ (read/write)** The read/write signal indicates a read operation if at a logic one level and a write operation if at a logic zero.

**RESET (reset)** The reset connection is used as an input that causes a hardware reset and as an output whenever the reset instruction is executed.

**RMC (read–modify–write cycle)** This output indicates that the current bus cycle is a read–modify–write bus cycle. The $\overline{\text{RMC}}$ signal is used to lock the bus to ensure the integrity of a read–modify–write bus cycle. Locking the bus prevents a coprocessor or a DMA controller from gaining access in the middle of a read–modify–write cycle.

**SIZ1, SIZ0 (transfer size)** These three-state outputs are used with the dynamic bus sizing capabilities of the 68020 to indicate the number of bytes remaining to be transferred.

## 12-2.2 68020 Operation

The 68020 supports byte, word, and long-word transfers through its 32-bit-wide data bus to the memory and I/O system. Memory that is 32 bits wide is organized as four banks, each containing 1G byte of memory, for a total of 4G bytes. Figure 12-6

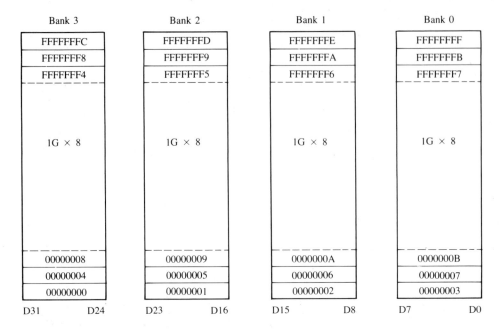

**Figure 12-6**   The 32-bit memory of the 68020 microprocessor. Note that the numbers shown in the memory are memory addresses.

illustrates the arrangement of the memory in a 32-bit memory system. This memory organization allows bytes, words, and long-words to be accessed through the 32-bit data bus of the 68020 microprocessor. Notice that each byte of memory is numbered, as in the 68000, 68008, and 68010.

The memory and I/O size is not limited to 32bits. Data bus widths of less than 32 bits are accommodated through a dynamic bus sizing arrangement within the 68020. Memory and I/O buses are 32, 16, or even 8 bits wide through the dynamic sizing feature. In fact, all three bus sizes (byte, word, and long-word) can coexist in the same memory and I/O system. This is advantageous because many I/O devices and even EPROM memory are 8 bits in width.

Memory and I/O bus width is determined by the organization of the memory and I/O system and also by the signals sent to the 68020 during a bus cycle. Size is determined by the response applied to the $\overline{\text{DSACK}}$ inputs of the microprocessor. (Refer back to Table 12-2.)

Figure 12-6 illustrates the organization of a 32-bit memory and I/O system using a 32-bit data bus. In a 32-bit bus system, both $\overline{\text{DSACK1}}$ and $\overline{\text{DSACK0}}$ are tied common and used like the $\overline{\text{DTACK}}$ signal on the 68000. Bank selection signals are generated with the A0, A1, SIZ0, and SIZ1 signals from the microprocessor. Table 12-3 illustrates these four signals in truth table form and also the banks selected by their combinations for memory transfers of different sizes.

The reason for all the unusual combinations is that the 68020 allows for misaligned addresses, whereas a misaligned transfer is not allowed on the 68000 when

**Table 12-3   Bank Selection Signal Generation for a 32-Bit Bus**

| Transfer | SIZ1 | SIZ0 | A1 | A0 | Active banks |
|----------|------|------|-----|-----|--------------|
| Byte | 0 | 1 | 0 | 0 | 3 |
|      | 0 | 1 | 0 | 1 | 2 |
|      | 0 | 1 | 1 | 0 | 1 |
|      | 0 | 1 | 1 | 1 | 0 |
| Word | 1 | 0 | 0 | 0 | 2 and 3 |
|      | 1 | 0 | 0 | 1 | 1 and 2 |
|      | 1 | 0 | 1 | 0 | 0 and 1 |
|      | 1 | 0 | 1 | 1 | 0 |
| 3-Byte | 1 | 1 | 0 | 0 | 1, 2, and 3 |
|        | 1 | 1 | 0 | 1 | 0, 1, and 2 |
|        | 1 | 1 | 1 | 0 | 0 and 1 |
|        | 1 | 1 | 1 | 1 | 0 |
| Long-word | 0 | 0 | 0 | 0 | 0, 1, 2, and 3 |
|           | 0 | 0 | 0 | 1 | 0, 1, and 2 |
|           | 0 | 0 | 1 | 0 | 0, 1 |
|           | 0 | 0 | 1 | 1 | 0 |

an address error occurs. For example, if a word is written to memory location XXXXXXX1, bank 1 and bank 2 are enabled to write data to the correct memory locations. The same transfer would cause an address error exception on earlier versions.

Some misaligned transfers require two bus cycles to complete. The 3-byte transfer occurs for some misaligned long-word transfers. An example of a misaligned transfer is a long-word transfer to memory location XXXXXXX1. For this transfer a byte is first written to bank 1, then a word is written to banks 2 and 3, and finally a byte is written to bank 0. This misaligned long-word transfer requires three bus cycles to accomplish. For this reason it is a good idea to place long-word data on 4-byte address boundaries. A 4-byte boundary allows all 32-bit data to be fetched or stored using one bus cycle. Likewise, word data should be stored on 2-byte boundaries to avoid misalignment.

Figure 12-7 illustrates the logic circuit required to generate active low bank selection signals for a 32-bit-wide memory system. In most cases, a PAL is used to generate these signals. The logic equations, for a PAL 16L8 used for bank selection, are illustrated in Figure 12-8. Note that Figure 12-8 uses active low bank selection signals instead of active high as in Figure 12-7.

Because the bus size can be 16 bits, the circuit in Figure 12-9 is used to generate bank selection signals if the memory size is 16 bits in width. The truth table used to generate 16-bit bank selection signals is located in Table 12-4. With a 16-bit-wide memory, bank 1 is connected to data bus connections D31–D24 and bank 0 is connected to data bus connections D23–D16.

A 68020 with a byte-wide memory system requires no special use of SIZ0, SIZ1, A0, and A1. These signals are not used to generate any bank selection signals

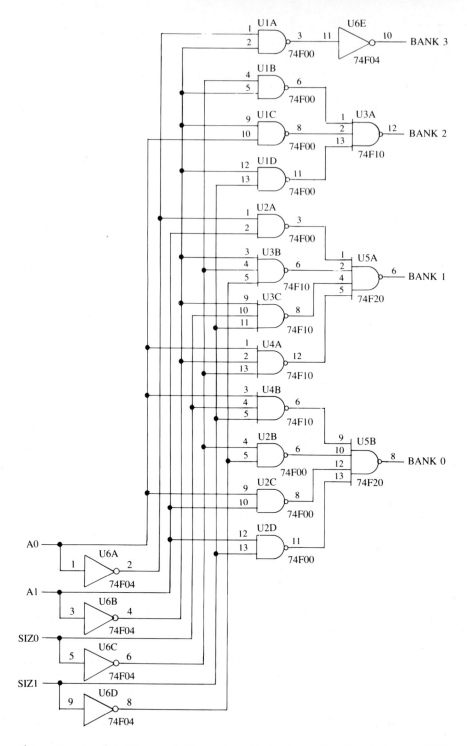

**Figure 12-7   A circuit for generating active high bank selection signals for the 68020 using a 32-bit data bus and memory.**

TITLE       Bank selection generator
PATTERN   P1
REVISION   1
AUTHOR    Barry B. Brey
COMPANY DeVry
DATE        2/7/91
CHIP         PAL16L8
;PINS

| ;1 | 2 | 3 | 4 | 5 | 6 | 7 | 8 | 9 | 10 |
|----|-----|-----|-----|-----|-----|-----|-----|-----|-----|
| S1 | S0 | A1 | A0 | NC | NC | NC | NC | NC | GND |
| ;11 | 12 | 13 | 14 | 15 | 16 | 17 | 18 | 19 | 20 |
| NC | B3 | B2 | B1 | B0 | NC | NC | NC | NC | VCC |

EQUATIONS

$/B3 = /A1 \times /A0$

$/B2 = /A1 \times A0$
$+ S1 \times /A1$
$+ /S0 \times /A1$

$/B1 = A1 \times /A0$
$+ S1 \times S0 \times /A1$
$+ /S1 \times /S0 \times /A1$
$+ S1 \times /A1 \times A0$

$/B0 = A1 \times A0$
$+ /S1 \times /S0$
$+ S1 \times A1$
$+ S1 \times S0 \times A0$

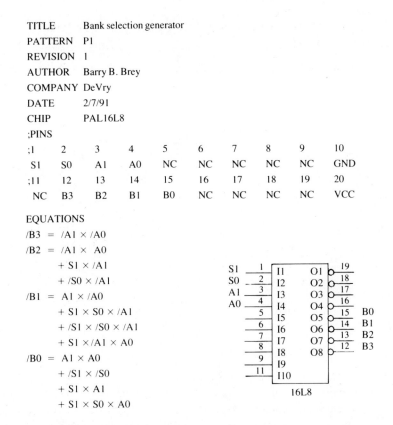

**Figure 12-8** A PAL 16L8 used to generate active low bank selection signals for a 68020 32-bit-wide memory system.

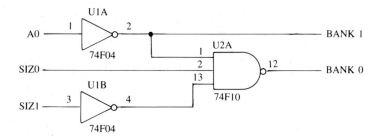

**Figure 12-9** Generation of active high bank selection signals for the 68020 for use with a 16-bit-wide memory system.

**Table 12-4**    Bank Selection Signal Generation for a 16-Bit-Wide Memory System

| Transfer | SIZ1 | SIZ0 | A1 | A0 | Active banks |
|----------|------|------|----|----|--------------|
| Byte | 0 | 1 | 0 | 0 | 1 |
| | 0 | 1 | 0 | 1 | 0 |
| | 0 | 1 | 1 | 0 | 1 |
| | 0 | 1 | 1 | 1 | 0 |
| Word | 1 | 0 | 0 | 0 | 0 and 1 |
| | 1 | 0 | 0 | 1 | 0 |
| | 1 | 0 | 1 | 0 | 0 and 1 |
| | 1 | 0 | 1 | 1 | 0 |
| 3-Byte | 1 | 1 | 0 | 0 | 0 and 1 |
| | 1 | 1 | 0 | 1 | 0 |
| | 1 | 1 | 1 | 0 | 0 and 1 |
| | 1 | 1 | 1 | 1 | 0 |
| Long-word | 0 | 0 | 0 | 0 | 0 and 1 |
| | 0 | 0 | 0 | 1 | 0 |
| | 0 | 0 | 1 | 0 | 0 and 1 |
| | 0 | 0 | 1 | 1 | 0 |

because there is only one bank in an 8-bit-wide memory system. It is doubtful that an 8-bit-wide memory system will ever be attached to the 68020; if it is, however, recall that data bus connections D31–D24 are attached to the memory data bus. The only 8-bit devices that are commonly attached to the 68020 are I/O devices.

### 12-2.3    A Buffered 68020 Using a 32-Bit Data Bus

A considerable number of buffers is required to fully buffer the 68020 with a full 32-bit data bus. Figure 12-10 illustrates a fully buffered 68020. The buffered system includes buffers on the address, control, and data buses. Compare this buffered system with a buffered 68000 system in Chapter 6 (Figure 6-4).

Two additional buffers are required for the data bus in the 68020 buffered system, because the bus is twice as wide. Likewise, the address bus requires additional buffers because it is 32 bits (30 bits buffered) instead of 24 bits (23 bits buffered) in the 68000. In addition to buffering the data and address buses, the function code bits, the data strobe signal, and the read/write signal are buffered.

Notice that this illustration also includes the 68881 floating-point coprocessor connected to the local bus. Compare this connection to the connections illustrated in Chapter 11 for the 16-bit bus of the 68000 and the 8-bit bus of the 68008 (Figures 11-3 and 11-2).

### 12-2.4    Cache Memory

The 68020 contains an internal 256-byte cache memory. A *cache* is a storehouse or a reserve of data. The cache found within the 68020 is an instruction cache, holding up to 64-long-word entries (256 bytes) that contain only instructions. This arrangement is a natural expansion of the cache (prefetch queue) found on the 68010. Data are not stored in the instruction cache on the 68020.

Recall that the 68010 could execute tight loops—an operation followed by a DBcc instruction—without returning to the memory to fetch the instructions. The same is true of the 68020 except the cache is much larger, which allows much longer loops.

In many program sequences, software is created that runs in loops. The cache memory accommodates these loops by allowing the microprocessor to fetch the instructions once. Once fetched, the entire sequence of instructions executes from the cache without any further instruction fetches. This greatly enhances the performance of the 68020 microprocessor when executing software from its instruction cache. The only possible improvement to this scheme would be to increase the size of the instruction cache.

Direct access to the instruction cache is not available to the user. Control of the instruction cache is available. The MOVEC instruction is used to access the cache control register (CACR). An example is the MOVEC D0,CACR instruction. Figure 12-11 illustrates the cache control register, which contains four bits that control the operation of the instruction cache.

The cache enable bit (E) is used to disable the cache when it is placed at a logic zero, permitting a software system to be debugged or emulated. Debugging cannot normally be accomplished with the cache enabled. Once debugging has been effected, the cache may be enabled by placing a logic one in this bit. Upon a hardware reset, the E bit is cleared, so the system software must set this bit to enable caching.

The freeze cache bit (F) causes the cache to retain all instructions that are already loaded. Any new instructions (cache misses) are not stored in the cache. This bit is at times used by debugging software to freeze the contents of the cache. It is also used in some systems to store a common sequence of instructions in the cache so that every time the sequence is called for execution, it is already in the cache.

The clear entry bit (CE) is used with the cache address register to invalidate an entry addressed by the cache address register. If CE is a logic zero, it has no effect on the operation of the cache. The CE bit, along with the cache addresses register, is used to disable an instruction in the cache for debugging.

The clear cache bit (C) is used to invalidate all entries in the cache. This effectively clears the cache. A logic one is written to the cache control register C bit to clear the cache.

The cache address register (CAAR), illustrated in Figure 12-12, is used to provide the address for the clear entry cache control register bit CE. Access to the cache address register is provided by the MOVEC instruction, as is access to the cache control register. An example is the MOVEC D0,CAAR instruction. The cache address register contains an address and an index. The index is the actual address of the instruction in the cache. The index is a 6-bit number that points to one of the 64 different long-words cached. The remaining part of the address corresponds to the external address of the instruction.

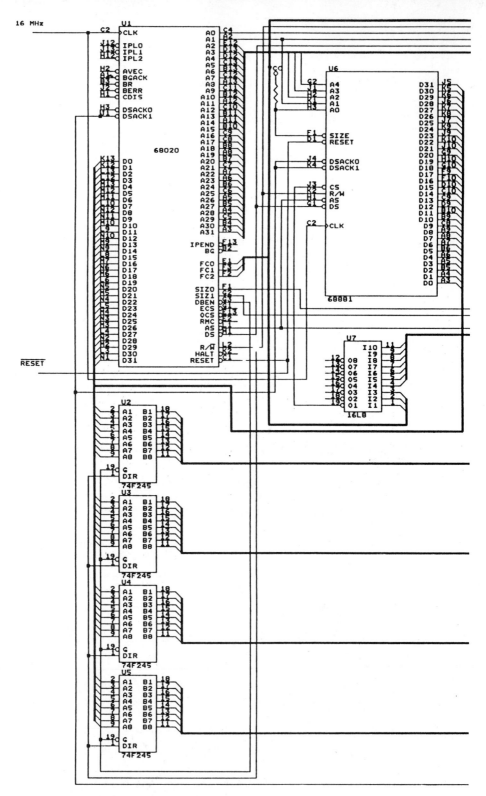

**Figure 12-10** A fully buffered 68020 microprocessor showing the placement of the 68881 floating-point coprocessor.

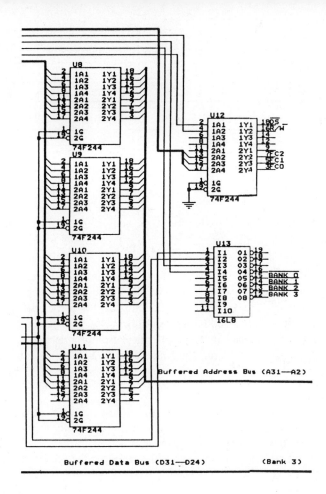

Buffered Address Bus (A31—A2)

Buffered Data Bus (D31—D24)          (Bank 3)

Buffered Data Bus (D23—D16)          (Bank 2)

Buffered Data Bus (D15—D8)          (Bank 1)

Buffered Data Bus (D7—D0)          (Bank 0)

$\overline{DTACK}$

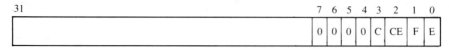

E  =  Enable Cache
F  =  Freeze Cache
CE  =  Clear Entry
C  =  Clear Cache

**Figure 12-11    The cache control register (CACR) of the 68020 microprocessor.**

The cache is disabled by the cache enable bit in the control register or by an external pin called the *cache disable input* ($\overline{\text{CDIS}}$). If a logic zero is placed on this pin, the cache is disabled regardless of the condition of the cache enable bit in the control register. If a one is placed on this pin, the cache is reenabled if the cache enable bit allows it to be reenabled. The $\overline{\text{CDIS}}$ pin is useful for debugging because it can be forced low with hardware. Hardware debuggers often use this input to disable the cache.

### 12-2.5    68020 Software

The 68020 is upward compatible with all previous 68000 family members. It does contain new instructions and addressing modes, but all instructions executed by earlier family members function without modification on the 68020.

### 68020 Programming Model

Figure 12-13 illustrates the programming model of the 68020 microprocessor. Notice that, as with earlier family members, the 68020 also contains data and address registers. In fact, the internal structure is almost identical to the 68010 except for the addition of the cache control register, the cache address register, and two supervisor stack pointers instead of one.

The supervisor stack pointer is missing in the programming model. In its place are two stack pointers: the interrupt stack pointer (ISP) and the master stack pointer (MSP).

The master stack pointer or the interrupt stack pointer is selected whenever the 68020 is operated in the supervisor mode. These two stack pointers replace the single supervisor stack pointer found in the earlier versions of this microprocessor. The difference between the 68020 and earlier family members is that a separate

**Figure 12-12    The cache address register (CAAR) of the 68020 microprocessor.**

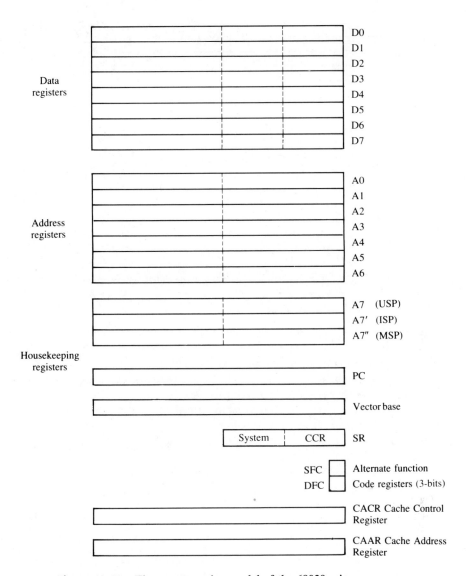

**Figure 12-13   The programming model of the 68020 microprocessor.**

stack pointer (ISP) is implemented for hardware interrupts. The MSP is used for all other supervisory software.

Exception processing sets the S status register bit, as it did on earlier family members. The S bit selects either the MSP or the ISP. If the exception is an interrupt, as requested through the $\overline{\text{IPL}}$ inputs, the ISP is selected. If the exception is not an interrupt, the MSP is selected.

Selection of either MSP or ISP is via a new status register bit called M (master/interrupt). If M is cleared, the ISP is selected and if M is set, the MSP is

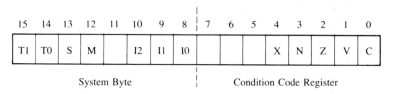

| 15 | 14 | 13 | 12 | 11 | 10 | 9 | 8 | 7 | 6 | 5 | 4 | 3 | 2 | 1 | 0 |
|----|----|----|----|----|----|---|---|---|---|---|---|---|---|---|---|
| T1 | T0 | S | M | | I2 | I1 | I0 | | | | X | N | Z | V | C |

System Byte                    Condition Code Register

T1, T0 = Trace enable bits
      S = Supervisor
      M = Master/interrupt
I2, I1, I0 = Interrupt masks
      X = Extend
      N = Negative
      Z = Zero
      V = Overflow
      C = Carry

**Figure 12-14    The status register (SR) of the 68020 microprocessor.**

selected. Figure 12-14 illustrates the status register of the 68020 microprocessor. Notice that there are also two trace status register bits instead of one. The trace bits aid in debugging a faulty program. Earlier versions of the 68020, such as the 68000 or 68010, had only one trace bit. In these earlier microprocessors, a trace exception occurred after each instruction if the T bit was set.

The trace bits, T1 and T0, allow a more refined approach to debugging; Table 12-5 states their effects. Notice that if both bits are cleared, normal program execution occurs. If T1 is cleared and T2 is set, tracing occurs only for a branch, jump, or any other change in the flow of a program. This is useful for detecting flaws in program flow. For general debugging, T1 is set and T0 is cleared so that a trace exception occurs after the execution of each instruction, as it did with earlier family members.

### New 68020 Addressing Modes

As mentioned, the 68020 contains new addressing modes not present in the 68000, 68008, or the 68010. In addition to the addressing modes presented for these microprocessors, the 68020 uses a base displacement with some of the prior indirect

**Table 12-5    Tracing Control Bits T1 and T0**

| T1 | T0 | Function |
|----|----|----------|
| 0 | 0 | No tracing |
| 0 | 1 | Trace on program flow change (JMP, BRA, etc) |
| 1 | 0 | Trace on every instruction |
| 1 | 1 | [undefined] |

modes and also postindexed and preindexed modes of indirectly addressing memory data. Scaling by a factor of 1, 2, 4, or 8 is also added to some addressing modes.

This section deals with the new addressing modes only. Refer to early chapters for a complete discussion of prior addressing modes and their syntax. Table 12-6 lists all addressing modes implemented for the 68020.

In Table 12-6, addressing syntax is changed from the 68000, 68008, and 68010 microprocessors. For example, the MOVE.B D2,10(A2) instruction of the 68000 is MOVE.B D2,(10,A2) on the 68020. Although such modifications are definitely a hindrance in learning the new machine, they are consistent from instruction to instruction and, with a little practice, fairly easy to learn. The major disadvantage of the new syntax is that software written for earlier versions must be changed at the source code level unless the assembler you are using accommodates both forms of addressing syntax.

Scaling is applied to any index register by using a scaling factor of 1, 2, 4, or 8. The scaling factor multiplies the index register by the scaling factor. For example, MOVE.B D2,(10,A1,D2.L*4) is an instruction that uses a scaling factor of 4. Here the contents of the long-word portion of D2 are multiplied by a factor of 4 before being added to A1 and 10 to form the effective address.

Suppose that you are using the index register to address long-words of data. The scaling factor allows the value in D2 to be adjusted to long-word data bound-

**Table 12-6   68020 Addressing Modes**

| Syntax | Mode |
|---|---|
| Dn | data register |
| An | address register |
| (An) | address register indirect |
| (d16,An) | address register indirect with displacement |
| (An)+ | address register indirect with postincrement |
| −(An) | address register indirect with predecrement |
| (d8,An,Xn) | address register indirect with index (8-bit displacement) |
| (bd,An,Xn) | address register indirect with index (base displacement) |
| ([bd,An],Xn,od) | memory indirect postindexed |
| ([bd,An,Xn],od) | memory indirect preindexed |
| (d16,PC) | program counter indirect with displacement |
| (d8,PC,Xn) | program counter indirect with index (8-bit displacement) |
| (bd,PC,Xn) | program counter indirect with base displacement |
| ([bd,PC],Xn,od) | program counter memory indirect postindexed |
| ([bd,PC,Xn],od) | program counter memory indirect preindexed |
| (xxx).W | absolute short address |
| (xxx).L | absolute long address |
| #⟨data⟩ | immediate |

NOTES: Dn = any data register, An = any address register, Xn = any address or data register, d8 = 8-bit displacement, d16 = 16-bit displacement, bd = base displacement of 16 or 32 bits, and od = 16- or 32-bit outer displacement.

aries in this example, because long-word data lie on 4-byte boundaries. Likewise, we have scaling factors of 2 to scale the index register to word boundaries, 1 (which is implied) for byte boundaries, and 8 64-bit boundaries. A scaling factor of 8 is often used with double-precision floating-point numbers that are 64-bits wide.

Address register indirect with index (base displacement) functions as address register indirect with index (8-bit displacement). The only difference is that the value of the displacement can be either 16 or 32 bits. If a 16-bit base displacement is used, it is sign-extended into a 32-bit value. This addressing mode also allows a 32-bit displacement if required.

The MOVE.B D2,(D3) instruction is an example of this addressing mode. The base displacement is zero and, since the address register is omitted, none is added. This allows data register indirect addressing if required, which is a significant new feature.

The MOVE.B D2,(DATA,A2,D4.L*2) instruction is another example of this addressing mode. Suppose that A2 is $00001000 and D4 is $00000200. This instruction stores the byte contents of D2 into memory location DATA+$1800. All DATA with a short address are sign-extended to a full 32-bit address.

Memory indirect addressing is indicated with brackets [ ] in assembly language. The value located within the brackets points to a long-word memory address that contains an address that is used to select another memory location. You might call this form of addressing indirect-indirect addressing or double-indirect addressing. This addressing mode is probably the most radically different of the new addressing modes that are added to the 68020 microprocessor.

Memory indirect addressing postindexed fetches the operand address from the memory location addresses by the bracketed portion of the instruction and then adds the contents of the index register to that address to form the effective address. For example, a MOVE.B D2,([A0],A1.L) instruction stores the byte contents of D2 in memory. Suppose that A0 = $00001000 and A1 = $00000001. Memory location $00001000 contains a $00002000. If these facts are true, this instruction stores the data at memory location $00002001. Why location $00002001? First, the bracketed portion of the instruction addresses memory location $00001000. This location contains a $00002000. The $00002000 is added to the contents of A1 (a 1 in this example) to form the memory address used as the effective address in this instruction.

The MOVE.B D2,([10,A0],A1.L*4,5) instruction is another example. If the same values are used for A0 and A1, this instruction references memory location $0000100A for the indirect memory address. The contents of $0000100A then are added to A1 times 4 plus 5 to generate the effective address. If $0000100A contains a $00004000, the actual address at which D2 is stored is location $00004000 + 1*4 + 5 or location $00004009.

Memory indirect preindexed is similar to memory indirect postindexed except the contents of the index register are added before the indirect memory address is fetched. The syntax is clearly different, if you refer back to Table 12-6. For example, notice that the index is located within the brackets for this type of addressing. This differs from the memory indirect postindexed form, which places the index register outside the brackets. The MOVE.B D2,([A0,A1.L]) instruction is an example. Here the contents of A0 and A1 are added to point to a memory location. This long-word location holds the effective address in this example.

Program counter addressing also uses a base displacement, and postindexed and preindexed addressing modes. The addition of these modes vastly expands the options available to the programmer when compared to the 68000 microprocessor.

### New 68020 Instructions

In addition to the new addressing modes, the designers of the 68020 have added instructions that often prove useful in solving certain programming problems. Table 12-7 lists all instructions that are new to the 68020, along with brief descriptions.

The *bit field* instructions allow an operation on a group of bits in an effective address. The bit field location is specified by the starting bit and the width of the field. The bit field is designated as {bit:width}, where "bit" identifies the starting bit position and "width" determines how many bits comprise the bit field.

For example, {2,4} represents a bit field starting at bit position 2 and extending through bit position 5. That bit field contains bit positions 2, 3, 4, and 5 for a total of 4 bits.

The bit field instructions encompass most of the new 68020 instructions. If Table 12-7 is examined, all instructions beginning with the letters BF are seen to be bit field instructions. All bit field instructions test the contents of the designated bit

**Table 12-7   New 68020 Instructions**

| Instruction | Function |
| --- | --- |
| BFCHG | Tests bit field and changes. |
| BFCLR | Tests bit field and clears. |
| BFEXTS | Extracts bit field and sign-extends. |
| BFEXTU | Extracts bit field and zero-extends. |
| BFFFO | Finds first one in bit field. |
| BFINS | Inserts bit field. |
| BFSET | Sets bit field. |
| BFTST | Tests bit field. |
| BKPT | Breakpoint. |
| CALLM | Call module. |
| CAS, CAS2 | Compares and swaps operands. |
| CHK2 | Checks register against bounds. |
| CMP2 | Compares register against bounds. |
| DIVSL | Divides signed long-word. |
| DIVUL | Divides unsigned long-word. |
| EXTB | Extends byte to long-word. |
| PACK | Packs BCD. |
| RTM | Returns from module. |
| TRAPcc | Conditional TRAP. |
| UNPK | Unpacks BCD. |

field before performing an operation. The N- and Z-CCR bits are affected by all bit test instructions.

If the most significant bit of the bit field is set, then the N-CCR bit is set. If it is cleared, N-CCR is cleared. The Z-CCR bit indicates a zero condition ($Z = 1$) if all the bits in the bit field are a logic zero. The V- and C-CCR bits are always cleared by bit field instructions, and the X-CCR bit is not affected.

The four basic bit field instructions, BFTST, BFCLR, BFSET, and BFCHG, are used to test, clear, set, and invert the bits specified in the bit field. For example, the BFSET D2{8:24} sets the most significant 24 bits of the D2 register. The BFCLR D1{16:16} instruction clears the most significant 16 bits of D1. Likewise, bits are complemented or inverted with the BFCHG instruction or merely tested with the BFTST instruction.

Bit field instructions that prove useful before a division are BFEXTS and BFEXTU. The BFEXTS instruction sign-extends a number and the BFEXTU instruction zero-extends a number. For example, suppose that signed word division is performed and the number in D1 must be sign-extended to a long-word. This is accomplished with the BFEXTS D1{16:16} instruction. If the same number is to be zero-extended for unsigned division, the BFEXTU D1{16:16} instruction is used to zero-extend the number in register D1.

The bit field insert instruction BFINS is used to copy a specified bit field within a data register into an effective address. For example, the BFINS D1,D2{8:8} instruction copies bit positions 8–15 from D1 into D2. This allows access to any grouping of bits in a data register. This operation requires more than one instruction before the inclusion of the BFINS instruction.

The bit field find-first-one instruction BFFFO is useful for scanning a bit field to search for a logic one. For example, the BFFFO D1{2:2},D2 instruction scans bit positions 2 and 3 of D1, looking for a logic one. The result found in D2 is either a 2 or a 3. If bit position 2 is a logic one, then D2 contains a 2. If bit position 3 is a logic one, then D2 contains a 3. This instruction finds the first set bit, so that if they are both set, it can be concluded that D2 contains a 2. Finally if no bits are set, D2 contains a 3, but the Z-CCR bit indicates a zero condition. If Z-CCR indicates a non-zero condition, a bit is found within the bit field.

Division is modified on the 68020 compared to earlier family members. There are now four signed and four unsigned division instructions. Table 12-8 illustrates the eight divide instructions with a comment about the operation of each. Notice that the dividend is either 32 or 64 bits and the divisor is either 16 or 32 bits. Earlier family members allow only the DIVS.W ⟨ea⟩,Dn or the DIVU.W ⟨ea⟩,Dn instruction, both of which require that the dividend be a 32-bit number located in Dn and the divisor a 16-bit number located in ⟨ea⟩.

The DIVU.L ⟨ea⟩,Dn or DIVS.L ⟨ea⟩,Dn instruction performs 32-bit division. The 32-bit contents of Dn are divided by the 32-bit contents of ⟨ea⟩. The 32-bit quotient is found in Dn after this division. The remainder is not saved by this form of division. Note that the quotient is truncated.

If the remainder is important, the DIVU.L ⟨ea⟩,Dx:Dy or DIVS.L ⟨ea⟩, Dx:Dy instruction is used in place of DIVU.L ⟨ea⟩,Dn or DIVS.L ⟨ea⟩,Dn. Here the same division occurs except the 64-bit contents of Dx:Dy are divided by the 32-bit

**Table 12-8   Signed and Unsigned Division on the 68020**

| Instruction | Function |
|---|---|
| DIVS.W ⟨ea⟩,Dn | Signed division 32/16, where both the quotient and remainder are 16 bits found in Dn. |
| DIVS.L ⟨ea⟩,Dn | Signed division 32/32, where the 32-bit quotient is found in Dn, the remainder is lost. |
| DIVS.L ⟨ea⟩,Dx:Dy | Signed division 64/32, where the 32-bit quotient is found in Dy and the 32-bit remainder in Dx. |
| DIVSL.L ⟨ea⟩,Dx:Dy | Signed division 32/32, where the 32-bit quotient is found in Dy and the 32-bit remainder in Dx. |
| DIVU.W ⟨ea⟩,Dn | Unsigned division 32/16, where both quotient and remainder are 16 bits found in Dn. |
| DIVU.L ⟨ea⟩,Dn | Unsigned division 32/32, where the 32-bit quotient is found in Dn and the remainder is lost. |
| DIVU.L ⟨ea⟩,Dx:Dy | Unsigned division 64/32, where the 32-bit quotient is found in Dy and the 32-bit remainder in Dx. |
| DIVUL.L ⟨ea⟩,Dx:Dy | Unsigned division 32/32, where the 32-bit quotient is found in Dy and the 32-bit remainder in Dx. |

contents of ⟨ea⟩. Dx contains the most significant part of the 64-bit dividend and Dy contains the least. The quotient is found in Dy and the remainder in Dx.

The final form of division, DIVUL.L ⟨ea⟩,Dx:Dy or DIVSL.L ⟨ea⟩, Dx:Dy, divides the 32-bit contents of Dy by the 32-bit contents of ⟨ea⟩. This division leaves the remainder in Dx and the quotient in Dy.

A breakpoint instruction (BKPT) is added to the 68020 instruction set. The instruction's syntax is BKPT #⟨data⟩, and its operation depends on the hardware attached to a system for debugging.

The instruction itself places the immediate data (value 0–7) on address lines A2, A3, and A4 during a breakpoint acknowledge cycle. The interpretation of this number is left completely to the hardware attached to the system. The hardware interprets any of eight different breakpoints using the value placed on the address bus during the breakpoint acknowledge cycle. Note that the breakpoint acknowledge cycle is usually a user-supplied exception vector number generated by the external hardware.

The call (CALLM) and return (RTM) from module instructions are new to the 68020 microprocessor. The CALLM and RTM are different from the normal subroutine BSR and RTS instructions in that they use module descriptors to control entry into a new module. These instructions are missing from the 68030 and 68040 instruction sets. Therefore the author has not provided additional information regarding the modules or the CALLM and RTM instructions. Such information may be located in the 68020 data book if desired, but it is not recommended that these instructions be used in software because they are not upward compatible to newer versions of this microprocessor.

The compare and swap operands instructions (CAS and CAS2) are normally used at the system software level. These instructions allow the system programmer to update counter, pointer, and other information in a secure fashion. Both instructions compare the destination operand with the source operand. If the operands match, the destination operand is updated with the update operand. This instruction is particularly useful when pointers are used in FIFO memory or queues.

Table 12-9 illustrates the CAS and CAS2 instructions along with their addressing modes. Notice the difference between these instructions. The CAS instruction functions with a single operand while CAS2 functions with dual operands.

The CHK2 instruction is similar to the CHK instruction presented with discussion of the 68000 microprocessor instruction set. The difference is that CHK2 compares an address or data register and an upper and lower boundary. The CHK instruction compares a data register with only a single boundary. The CHK2 instruction compares the data or address register against both a lower boundary at the location addressed by ⟨ea⟩ and an upper boundary at the location following the lower boundary. If Rn is less than the lower boundary or is greater than the upper boundaries, a TRAP exception ensues. The CMP2 instruction, which uses exception vector 6, functions in the same manner as the CHK2 instructions except that no TRAP occurs. Instead of a TRAP, the condition code registers indicate the outcome of the comparison.

PACK and UNPK are used to pack and unpack BCD numbers. The PACK instruction converts unpacked BCD data (one character per byte) into packed BCD (two characters per byte) data. In addition to packing the number, an adjustment may be added if desired. The 16-bit source register contains two unpacked BCD digits that are packed into one of the 16-bit destination registers with an adjustment added. Note that the adjustment is added before the unpacked data are packed.

For example, if D1 = $0203 and a PACK D1,D2,#1 instruction is executed, the contents of D1 are adjusted by adding a $0001. After adjustment, the packed result found in D2 is $0024.

The UNPK instruction converts packed BCD data into unpacked BCD data and also adds an adjustment if desired. UNPK will unpack the contents of the source operand and add the adjustment before storing the result into the destination operand. For example, if D1 = $0046, the UNPK D1,D2,#$0303 instruction will place a $0709 into D2.

The TRAPcc instruction is a conditional TRAP instruction. This instruction

Table 12-9    The CAS and CAS2 Instructions

| Instruction | Operation |
| --- | --- |
| CAS Dc,Du,⟨ea⟩ | Compares Dc with ⟨ea⟩; if equal, updates ⟨ea⟩ with Du. |
| CAS2 Dc1:Dc2,Du1:Du2,Rn1:Rn2 | Compares Dc1:Dc2 with Rn1:Rn2; if equal, updates Rn1:Rn2 with Du1:Du2. |

uses all the conditional codes allowed for the Bcc or DBcc instructions. For example, the TRAPNE instruction performs a NOP if the condition is equal (not true), and exception processing begins if a not equal condition (true) exists. The exception vector used by a conditional TRAPcc is the same as for the TRAPV instruction, or vector 7.

### 12-2.6   68020 Exception Processing

The 68020 processes exceptions and interrupts in the same manner as the 68000, 68008, and 68010. Table 12-10 illustrates the exception vector assignments for the 68020. You may wish to refer back to Chapter 9 and compare this table with the exception vector table for the 68000 (Table 9-2). Most notably different are extra exceptions that are in use for the new 68020 microprocessor instructions. Many of the extra exception vectors listed are for the floating-point coprocessor (68881/68882) or the paged-memory management coprocessor (68851).

The vector table of the 68020 is relocatable by changing the vector base address. This is also true as described for the 68010 microprocessor. For example, if the vector base address is changed with the MOVEC A2,VBR, the contents of A2 will be copied into the vector base register (VBR). If A2 contains a $00001000, the vector table will begin at location $00001000 and extend to location $000013FF. Upon a hardware reset, the vector base register is cleared to zero placing the vector table at location $00000000–$000003FF.

Exception processing on the 68020 is nearly identical to the 68000 case. Following is a list of the steps that occur for an exception or hardware interrupt.

1. Status register is saved.

2. The S bit is set, placing the microprocessor in the supervisor mode.

3. T1 and T0 are cleared to terminate tracing.

4. Vector number is determined.

5. Processor context is now saved in the supervisor stack frame. This includes the status register. If the exception is a hardware interrupt, the M bit is set; if it is not a hardware interrupt, the M bit is cleared.

6. The exception vector's address is determined and the vector is fetched from the vector table. Once fetched, a JMP to the vector address occurs.

The main difference between the 68000 and the 68020 is the stack frame saved by an exception. Of the six different stack frames used by the 68020 and its coprocessors, the most common is the normal four-word frame illustrated in Figure 12-15. This frame is used with hardware interrupts, format errors, TRAP instructions, illegal instructions, A- and F-line emulator traps, privilege violations, and coprocessor preinstruction exceptions. The vector offset is the vector number times 4, which is used to fetch the vector for the exception. For example, if the stack frame is due to a privilege violation, the vector offset will be $020. This is vector number 8 times 4, or 32 decimal, which is $020.

**Table 12-10     68020 Exception Vectors**

| Vector number | Assignment |
| --- | --- |
| 0 | Reset: Initial interrupt stack pointer |
| 1 | Reset: Initial program counter |
| 2 | Bus error |
| 3 | Address error |
| 4 | Illegal instruction |
| 5 | Divide by zero |
| 6 | CHK, CHK2 instructions |
| 7 | TRAPcc, TRAPV, and coprocessor TRAP |
| 8 | Privilege violation |
| 9 | Trace |
| 10 | Line A emulator |
| 11 | Line F emulator |
| 12 | [unassigned] |
| 13 | Coprocessor protocol violation |
| 14 | Format error |
| 15 | Uninitialized interrupt |
| 16–23 | [unassigned] |
| 24 | Spurious interrupt |
| 25 | Level 1 autovector interrupt |
| 26 | Level 2 autovector interrupt |
| 27 | Level 3 autovector interrupt |
| 28 | Level 4 autovector interrupt |
| 29 | Level 5 autovector interrupt |
| 30 | Level 6 autovector interrupt |
| 31 | Level 7 autovector interrupt |
| 32–47 | TRAP 0–TRAP 15 instructions |
| 48 | FPCP branch/set on unordered condition |
| 49 | FPCP inexact result |
| 50 | FPCP divide by zero |
| 51 | FPCP underflow |
| 52 | FPCP operand error |
| 53 | FPCP overflow |
| 54 | FPCP signaling error |
| 55 | [unassigned] |
| 56 | PMMU configuration |
| 57 | PMMU illegal operation |
| 58 | PMMU access level violation |
| 59–63 | [unassigned] |
| 64–255 | User-defined vectors |

NOTES: FPCP = 68881 floating-point coprocessor and PMMU = 68851 paged memory management unit.

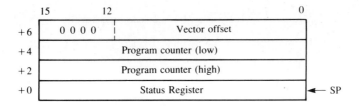

**Figure 12-15   The normal four word stack frame for the 68020 microprocessor.**

| 15 | 12 | | 0 |
|---|---|---|---|
| +10 | Instruction address (low) | | |
| +8 | Instruction address (high) | | |
| +6 | 0 0 1 0 | Vector offset | |
| +4 | Program counter (low) | | |
| +2 | Program counter (high) | | |
| +0 | Status Register | | ←— SP |

**Figure 12-16   The normal six word stack frame for the 68020 microprocessor.**

| 15 | 12 | | 0 |
|---|---|---|---|
| +18 | Internal Coprocessor register | | |
| +16 | Internal Coprocessor register | | |
| +14 | Internal Coprocessor register | | |
| +12 | Internal Coprocessor register | | |
| +10 | Instruction address (low) | | |
| +8 | Instruction address (high) | | |
| +6 | 1 0 0 1 | Vector offset | |
| +4 | Program counter (low) | | |
| +2 | Program counter (high) | | |
| +0 | Status Register | | ←— SP |

**Figure 12-17   The 68020 coprocessor midinstruction stack frame.**

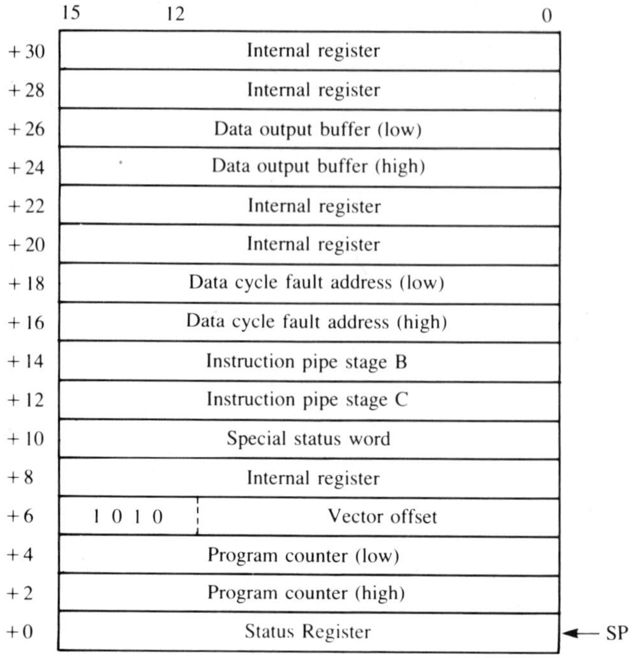

**Figure 12-18**   The short bus cycle fault stack frame for the 68020 microprocessor.

Another stack frame, called the throwaway four-word stack frame, looks just like the frame of Figure 12-15 except that the format code is 0001 instead of 0000. The throwaway stack frame is created on the interrupt stack during exception processing for an interrupt when a transition from the master state to the interrupt state occurs.

A six-word stack frame (Figure 12-16) occurs for coprocessor postinstruction exceptions, CHK, CHK2, TRAPcc, TRAPV, coprocessor TRAPcc, trace, and divide by zero. The difference is that the address of the instruction that caused the exception is also stored in the stack frame.

The coprocessor midinstruction stack frame is created whenever the coprocessor takes a midinstruction exception. Figure 12-17 illustrates the stack frame created by this type of exception. A midinstruction exception occurs for a primitive read while the coprocessor is processing an instruction, or while there is a protocol violation during processing an instruction or an interrupt pending during a coprocessor instruction.

A short bus cycle fault stack frame (Figure 12-18) is created for a bus cycle fault if the microprocessor detects the fault at an instruction boundary.

A long bus cycle fault stack frame (Figure 12-19) occurs when an exception takes effect not on an instruction boundary. This stack frame stores the complete state of the microprocessor at the time of the exception.

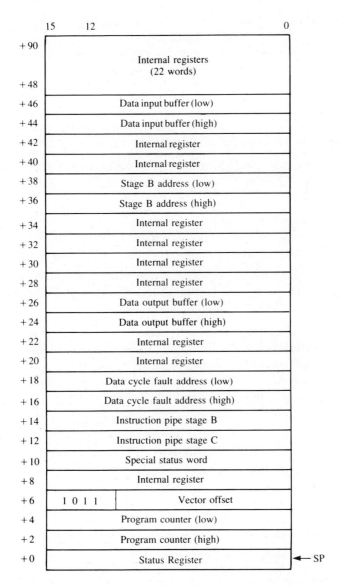

**Figure 12-19   The long bus cycle fault stack frame for the 68020 microprocessor.**

## Summary

1. The 68010 microprocessor is almost identical to the 68000 microprocessor except for a few additional registers. The vector base register (VBR) allows the interrupt vector table to be located at any point in the memory system. The SFC (source function code) and DFC (destination function code) registers are used by the MOVEC and MOVES instructions.

2. The 68010 has a small prefetch queue of 4 bytes that helps to speed up programs that contain tight loops. This mode of operation is called the loop mode. In loop mode, one 2-byte instruction is stored in the instruction register and the next instruction (usually a DBcc instruction) is stored in the queue. This allows the instructions in the instruction register and prefetch queue to execute at a higher speed because they are fetched from memory only once.

3. The 68010 has a few new stack frames that are not present on the 68000. This can cause software incompatibilities for some operating systems.

4. The 68020 is a full 32-bit microprocessor. It contains a full 32-bit address bus and also a full 32-bit data bus. This allows the 68020 to address 4G bytes of memory.

5. The 68020 contains an instruction cache that holds 256 bytes of instructions. This cache allows larger loops to execute within the 68020 when compared to the queue of 4 bytes in the 68010.

6. Dynamic bus sizing is added to the 68020 microprocessor. This allows the memory or I/O bus to be 8, 16, or 32 bits in width. A system can actually contain all three bus sizes simultaneously using this feature.

7. Some addressing modes are added to the 68020 microprocessor. These include a base displacement with some of the prior indirect modes and also postindexed and preindexed modes of indirectly addressing memory data. Scaling by a factor of 1, 2, 4, or 8 is also added to some addressing modes. Scaling is useful for adjusting an address to word, long-word, or 64-bit boundaries.

8. New instructions added to the 68020 microprocessor include bit field instructions, a breakpoint instruction, call and return from module instructions, compare and swap operand, divide long-word, pack and unpack BCD, and conditional TRAP instructions.

## Questions

1. Compare the pinouts of the 68000 and 68010 microprocessors.

2. The 68010 addresses how many bytes of memory?

3. If the vector base register is loaded with a $000A0000, the exception vector table begins at location _____ and ends at location _____.

4. List the two alternate function code registers.

5. What instruction uses the alternate function code registers?

6. Describe the 68010 prefetch queue.

7. What is loop mode operation of the 68010, and what advantage does it furnish?

8. The 68020 microprocessor addresses _____ bytes of memory.

9. The 68020 data bus is _____ bits wide.

10. What is the purpose of the $\overline{\text{AVEC}}$ pin connection on the 68020 microprocessor?

11. What 68020 input pins are used to control dynamic memory sizing?

12. What is the purpose of the SIZ1 and SIZ0 pins on the 68020 microprocessor?

13. How large is the instruction cache in the 68020 microprocessor?

14. Are data ever stored in the 68020 instruction cache?

15. What function is provided by the $\overline{\text{CDIS}}$ pin on the 68020 microprocessor?

16. List the stack pointer registers available on the 68020 and explain the purpose of each.

17. List the different modes of tracing available in the 68020.

18. What is a base displacement in the 68020 instruction set?

19. What is an outer displacement in the 68020 instruction set?

20. What is meant by the terms postindexed and preindexed?

21. What is a scaling factor, and how is it applied to the 68020 instruction set?

22. The 68020 bit field instructions operate on a group of bits. How is this grouping defined in a bit field instruction?

23. Use bit field instructions to perform the following:
    (a) Set bit positions 1, 2, 3, 4, and 5 of register D2.
    (b) Clear bit positions 23 and 24 of register D6.
    (c) Test bit positions 19, 20, and 21 of register D1.
    (d) Invert bits 2, 3, and 4 of register D7.

24. What 68020 instruction is used to sign-extend a number, and what instruction is used to zero-extend a number?

25. Describe the new forms of division found in the 68020 microprocessor.

26. What is a breakpoint, and how does the 68020 microprocessor process it?

27. Describe how the 68020 CAS and CAS2 instructions function.

28. What are packed and unpacked BCD numbers, and which 68020 instructions are used to convert between these two forms of BCD data?

29. Generally, what new exception vectors have been added to the 68020 exception vector table?

30. Describe the events that occur for an exception in the 68020 microprocessor.

# 13

# *Introduction to the 68030 and 68040 Microprocessors*

**OBJECTIVES**

Upon completion of this chapter, you will be able to:

- Contrast the 68030 and 68040 with the 68020, 68010, 68008 and 68000 microprocessors.
- Explain the operation of the data and instruction caches.
- Explain and program the operation of the paged memory management unit.
- Describe and use the new instructions found in both the 68030 and 68040 microprocessors.
- Explain the operation and interface of asynchronous and synchronous memory systems.
- Describe the differences between the 68881/68882 and the floating-point instructions available to the 68040 microprocessor.
- Explain how the output buffers in the 68040 are programmed.

**KEY TERMS**

| | | |
|---|---|---|
| hit | memory management | short format page |
| miss | unit (MMU) | descriptor |
| write-through | demand system | short format invalid |
| flushing | page frames | descriptor |
| asynchronous and | pages | short format indirect |
| synchronous | virtual memory | descriptor |
| transfers | short format table | snooping |
| zero wait states | descriptor | |

T HIS chapter introduces the 68030 and 68040 microprocessors. The 68030 microprocessor is an enhanced version of the 68020 that includes a 256-byte data cache in addition to the 256-byte instruction cache. It also includes a paged memory management unit that controls access to virtual memory.

The 68040 microprocessor is a combination of the 68030 and a modified version of the floating-point coprocessor (68881/68882) discussed in Chapter 11. In the 68040, both the instruction cache and the data cache are increased in size, to 4k bytes each. This represents a prominent improvement over the caches found in the 68020 and 68030. Two memory management units are also included inside the 68040. Finally, the output buffers in the 68040 have been improved and are programmable to provide up to 50 mA of current for large systems. The 68040 is indeed a powerful microprocessor.

## 13-1   The 68030 Microprocessor

The main difference between the 68030 and the 68020 microprocessors is that the 68030 includes a paged memory management unit (PMMU). The PMMU is an ancillary with the 68020 in the form of a coprocessor (the 68851 paged memory management unit coprocessor). In addition to the instruction cache introduced in the 68020, the 68030 contains a data cache. The 68030 also offers better bus operation with an improved bus interface system.

### 13-1.1   Pinout

A comparison of Figure 13-1, the pinout of the 68030 microprocessor, with Figure 12-5, the pinout of the 68020, reveals only minimal differences between these two microprocessors as far as pin connections are concerned.

The 68030 is available in a PGA package as two versions: the MC68030RC16, which operates with a 16.7 MHz clock and the MC68030RC20, which operates with a 20 MHz clock. Power supply current consumption is only slightly greater than the 68020. Currents available at the output pin connections are comparable to the 68020 as listed in Table 12-1. The $\overline{\text{STATUS}}$, $\overline{\text{REFILL}}$, and $\overline{\text{CIOUT}}$ pins, which are new to the 68030, will drive up to 2.0 mA of current. The $\overline{\text{CBREQ}}$ pin, also new, will drive up to 5.3 mA of current.

### Pin Functions

Following is a description of the function of each pin or each grouping of pins on the 68030 microprocessor. Many of the pins are identical to the pin connections on the 68020 microprocessor.

**A31–A0 (address bus)**   The 32-bit address bus accesses 4G bytes of memory. Each location is numbered in bytes, as the memory is numbered in all other 68000 family members.

$\overline{\text{AS}}$ **(address strobe)**   The address strobe output indicates that the address bus contains a valid address. It also qualifies the following output signals: the function code bits, the size bits, and R/$\overline{\text{W}}$.

$\overline{\text{AVEC}}$ **(autovector)**   This input is used to request the internal generation of an autovector interrupt. It performs the same function as $\overline{\text{VPA}}$ on the 68000 microprocessor.

$\overline{\text{BERR}}$ **(bus error)**   The bus error input is used to request a bus error interrupt or, if used in conjunction with the halt input, a rerun.

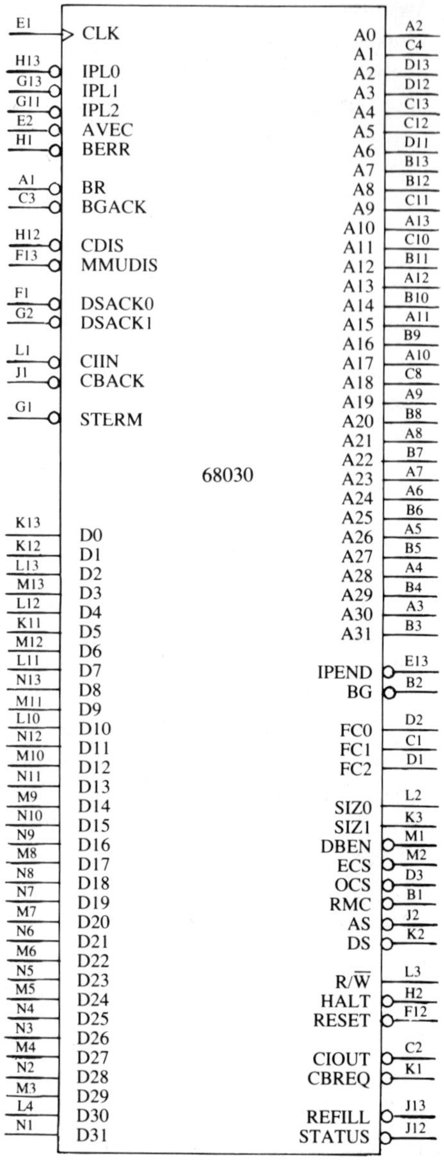

| | | |
|---|---|---|
| E1 | CLK | A0 — A2 |
| | | A1 — C4 |
| H13 | IPL0 | A2 — D13 |
| G13 | IPL1 | A3 — D12 |
| G11 | IPL2 | A4 — C13 |
| E2 | AVEC | A5 — C12 |
| H1 | BERR | A6 — D11 |
| | | A7 — B13 |
| A1 | BR | A8 — B12 |
| C3 | BGACK | A9 — C11 |
| | | A10 — A13 |
| H12 | CDIS | A11 — C10 |
| F13 | MMUDIS | A12 — B11 |
| | | A13 — A12 |
| F1 | DSACK0 | A14 — B10 |
| G2 | DSACK1 | A15 — A11 |
| | | A16 — B9 |
| L1 | CIIN | A17 — A10 |
| J1 | CBACK | A18 — C8 |
| | | A19 — A9 |
| G1 | STERM | A20 — B8 |
| | | A21 — A8 |
| | | A22 — B7 |
| | 68030 | A23 — A7 |
| | | A24 — A6 |
| K13 | | A25 — B6 |
| K12 | D0 | A26 — A5 |
| L13 | D1 | A27 — B5 |
| M13 | D2 | A28 — A4 |
| L12 | D3 | A29 — B4 |
| K11 | D4 | A30 — A3 |
| M12 | D5 | A31 — B3 |
| L11 | D6 | |
| N13 | D7 | IPEND — E13 |
| M11 | D8 | BG — B2 |
| L10 | D9 | |
| N12 | D10 | FC0 — D2 |
| M10 | D11 | FC1 — C1 |
| N11 | D12 | FC2 — D1 |
| M9 | D13 | |
| N10 | D14 | SIZ0 — L2 |
| N9 | D15 | SIZ1 — K3 |
| M8 | D16 | DBEN — M1 |
| N8 | D17 | ECS — M2 |
| N7 | D18 | OCS — D3 |
| M7 | D19 | RMC — B1 |
| N6 | D20 | AS — J2 |
| M6 | D21 | DS — K2 |
| N5 | D22 | |
| M5 | D23 | R/W — L3 |
| N4 | D24 | HALT — H2 |
| N3 | D25 | RESET — F12 |
| M4 | D26 | |
| N2 | D27 | CIOUT — C2 |
| M3 | D28 | CBREQ — K1 |
| L4 | D29 | |
| N1 | D30 | REFILL — J13 |
| | D31 | STATUS — J12 |

**Figure 13-1   The pinout of the 68030 microprocessor.**

$\overline{\text{BG}}$ **(bus grant)**   The bus grant output indicates that the 68030 will release the system buses at the end of the current bus cycle.

$\overline{\text{BGACK}}$ **(bus grant acknowledge)**   This input indicates that an external DMA controller has taken access to the system buses. It is also tested for bus arbitration.

$\overline{\text{BR}}$ **(bus request)**   The bus request input is used to request a DMA action.

$\overline{\text{CBACK}}$ **(cache burst acknowledge)**   This input signal indicates that the device accessed by the microprocessor is capable of operating in the burst mode.

$\overline{\text{CBREQ}}$ **(cache burst request)**   This output requests a burst mode operation to fill a line (4 long-words) in either the instruction or the data cache.

$\overline{\text{CDIS}}$ **(cache disable)**   This input disables the on-chip cache memories. If this pin is placed at a logic zero, both caches are disabled.

$\overline{\text{CIIN}}$ **(cache inhibit input)**   This input prevents data from being loaded into the internal instruction and data caches.

$\overline{\text{CIOUT}}$ **(cache inhibit output)**   This signal indicates to the external bus that it should ignore the current bus cycle.

**CLK (clock)**   The clock input provides the 68030 with its clock input signal. The 68030 uses either a 16.7 or 20 MHz clock.

**D31–D0 (data bus)**   The 32-bit data bus is used to access bytes, words, or long-words from the memory and I/O system.

$\overline{\text{DBEN}}$ **(data buffer enable)**   This signal is used in a buffered system to enable data bus buffers.

$\overline{\text{DS}}$ **(data strobe)**   The data strobe output indicates that the data bus is available for a data transfer.

$\overline{\text{DSACK1}}$, $\overline{\text{DSACK0}}$ **(data transfer and size acknowledge)**   These signals indicate the size of a data transfer and also that a data transfer is complete. During a bus operation, the bus cycle is terminated with the $\overline{\text{DSACK}}$ signal as with $\overline{\text{DTACK}}$ in the 68000. Refer back to Table 12-2, which illustrates the coding for these two signals used to terminate a bus cycle.

$\overline{\text{ECS}}$ **(external cycle start)**   This output becomes active during the first half clock of every bus cycle. This signal is used with the address strobe signal to indicate that a bus cycle is valid.

$\overline{\text{HALT}}$ **(halt)**   The halt pin is a bidirectional pin that acts as an output to indicate that the STOP instruction has executed and as an input to halt program execution.

$\overline{\text{IPEND}}$ **(interrupt pending)**   This output indicates that the current interrupt request on the $\overline{\text{IPL}}$ pins is a higher priority than the current mask level in the status register.

$\overline{\text{IPL2}}$, $\overline{\text{IPL1}}$, $\overline{\text{IPL0}}$ **(interrupt priority level)**   These three inputs are used to request level 1–7 interrupts.

$\overline{\text{MMUDIS}}$ **(MMU disable)**   This input disables the address translation feature provided by the memory management unit.

$\overline{\text{OCS}}$ **(operand cycle start)**   This signal has the same timing as $\overline{\text{ECS}}$ and indicates the first bus cycle of an operand transfer or an instruction prefetch.

**R/$\overline{\text{W}}$ (read/write)**   The read/write signal indicates a read operation if a logic one level, or a write operation if a logic zero.

$\overline{\text{REFILL}}$ **(pipeline refill)**   This signal indicates that the 68030 is beginning to refill its instruction pipeline.

$\overline{\text{RESET}}$ **(reset)**   The reset connection is used as an input that causes a hardware reset and as an output whenever the reset instruction is executed.

**RMC (Read–Modify–Write Cycle)**   This output indicates the current bus cycle is a read–modify–write bus cycle. The $\overline{\text{RMC}}$ signal is typically used to lock the bus to ensure the integrity of a read–modify–write bus cycle.

**SIZ1, SIZ0 (transfer size)**   These three-state outputs are used with the dynamic bus sizing capabilities of the 68030 to indicate the number of bytes remaining to be transferred.

$\overline{\text{STATUS}}$ **(internal microsequencer status)**   This output indicates the state of the internal microsequencer.

$\overline{\text{STERM}}$ **(synchronous termination)**   This input is a bus handshake signal that indicates an addressed port size of 32 bits. It also indicates that on the next falling edge of the clock, data will be latched for a read cycle.

### 13-1.2   68030 Operation

The operation of the 68030 microprocessor is similar to the 68020 microprocessor. Both machines have on-chip cache memory. The difference is that the 68030 has two caches—one for data and one for instructions. The instruction cache is identical to the instruction cache of the 68020. The size of the data cache (64 long-words or 256 bytes) is also identical to the size of the instruction cache on the 68020. Often, the 68030 executes software completely from its internal instruction cache and also references data from its internal data cache. This allows the 68030 to execute from the instruction cache software that references data in the data cache at extremely high speeds.

### Data Cache

The data cache functions similarly to the instruction cache as explained in connection with the 68020 microprocessor in Chapter 12. The difference is that instead of storing instructions, the data cache stores data referenced by the program using any of the addressing modes.

During normal operations, data are read from the data cache whenever there is a hit. A *hit* occurs if the data, in the cache, have been read from the memory during a prior instruction. If a *miss* occurs, the 68030 executes a bus cycle to retrieve the data from memory. Data retrieved from memory are placed into the cache for future access and also into the destination operand, as specified by the instruction. When a line in the cache is filled, the microprocessor reads four consecutive long-words from the memory and places them into the cache.

When data are written to the memory, they are written into the data cache as well as the memory in what is called *write-through* cache operation. This places the written data in the cache so that another instruction, which may read data from the same memory location, can access the data from the cache. It is possible for another instruction to access the written data in the cache while they are still being written to memory. This causes no adverse effects, because memory and cache will match in a few clocks.

Operation of the data cache during a write is adjusted through the write alloca-tion bit (WA) in the cache control register. If WA = 0, write cycles that miss (cache misses) do not change the data cache. A miss occurs whenever data are written to an address that is not currently stored in the cache. If WA = 1, the 68030 will write data to the cache along with its memory address for future reference.

Why would WA = 0 ever be chosen? Suppose a program references the same memory locations many times for read data. The data cache eventually contains such read data. Suppose the same program stores a few results, but each result is stored only once and never again referenced. In this case it is wise to set the WA bit to a logic zero. Caching the write data in this example would be wasteful. Note that many programs function in this manner. So being able to disable the data cache for a write operation is an important feature of the 68030 microprocessor.

The 68030 has two registers associated with the cache: the cache control regis-ter (CACR) and the cache address register (CAAR). Both registers are also present in the 68020. The 68020 cache address register (see Figure 12-12) is identical to the 68030 cache address register and is not discussed here.

The cache control register for the 68030, however, is different (Figure 13-2). For comparison, refer again to the cache control register for the 68020, illustrated in Figure 12-11. Notice that many more bits are defined in the 68030 CACR because the 68030 contains two caches. As with the 68020, the CACR and CAAR are loaded and read with the MOVEC instruction, using either CACR or CAAR as operands.

| 31 | | 14 | 13 | 12 | 11 | 10 | 9 | 8 | | 5 | 4 | 3 | 2 | 1 | 0 |
|---|---|---|---|---|---|---|---|---|---|---|---|---|---|---|---|
| 0 0 0 0 0 0 0 0 0 0 0 0 0 0 0 0 0 0 | | WA | DBE | CD | CED | FD | ED | | 0 0 0 | | IBE | CI | CEI | FI | EI |

WA  = Write allocate
DBE = Data burst enable
CD  = Clear data cache
CED = Clear entry in data cache
FD  = Freeze data cache
ED  = Enable data cache
IBE = Instruction burst enable
CI  = Clear instruction cache
CEI = Clear entry in instruction cache
FI  = Freeze instruction cache
EI  = Enable instruction cache

**Figure 13-2   The 68030 cache control register (CACR).**

The right-most 4 bits of the CACR are identical in function to the 68020, except for the I that is appended to each abbreviation to indicate the instruction cache. The remaining bits are new to the 68030 and are discussed at this point.

**CI (clear instruction cache)**    This control bit is used to clear all the entries in the instruction cache. Clearing all entries is sometimes called *flushing* the cache. This bit is set to clear the cache by operating systems and other software prior to performing a context switch.

**IBE (instruction burst enable)**    The IBE bit is set to enable instruction bursts to fill the instruction cache. When bursting is enabled, the microprocessor reads or writes an entire cache line. A cache line always contains 4 long-words.

**ED (enable data cache)**    The data cache is enabled when the ED bit is set and disabled when it is cleared. A hardware reset also clears the ED bit to disable data caching. When the data cache is disabled it is not flushed, so that when reenabled, the data remain valid.

**FD (freeze data cache)**    When this bit is set, the data cache is frozen in its current state. Any write will update the contents of the cache. Setting this bit forces the microprocessor to maintain current read data in the cache for program use.

**CED (clear entry in data cache)**    This bit is used with the cache address register to clear an entry in the data cache. If CED is set, the entry indicated by the address in the cache address register is cleared. If CED is cleared, no entry is cleared.

**CD (clear data cache)**    This bit flushes the data cache when it is set. If cleared, the cache operates as dictated by the other cache control bits.

**DBE (data cache burst enable)**    Setting DBE causes the data cache to fill with a burst. When DBE is cleared, normal filling occurs if dictated by the other control bits.

**WA (write allocation)**    If this bit is cleared, writes that miss do not change the contents of the data cache. If this bit is set, any miss will cause the data to be written to the cache and the memory.

In addition to the cache control register, some of the external pin connections on the 68030 microprocessor are used to control the cache. To enable the instruction and/or data cache, three steps must be followed:

1. The appropriate cache control register enable bits must be set to enable either or both caches. The instruction cache is enabled by the EI bit and the data cache is enabled by the ED bit.

2. The $\overline{\text{CDIS}}$ signal must be placed at a logic one level. This allows the CACR register bits EI and ED to effect the operation of the caches. If $\overline{\text{CDIS}}$ is placed at a logic zero level, both caches are disabled.

3. The $\overline{\text{CIIN}}$ signal is placed at a logic one level. Note that this input is dynamic and must be active for each bus cycle whenever data or instructions are to be stored in either cache.

If a burst transfer is to occur, the $\overline{\text{CBACK}}$ (cache burst acknowledge) signal is activated to indicate that the memory system can supply at least one more long word. If $\overline{\text{CBACK}}$ is not active, a burst transfer cannot occur.

### 13-1.3   Memory Interface and the 68030 Microprocessor

Memory is connected to the 68030 using either an *asynchronous transfer* or a *synchronous transfer*. Asynchronous transfers, which are presented with the 68020 using the $\overline{\text{DSACK}}$ connections, are also presented with the 68000 microprocessor using the $\overline{\text{DTACK}}$ connection. Asynchronous transfers occur in systems with data bus widths of 8, 16, and 32 bits. Synchronous transfers may occur only in systems that have 32-bit data buses. If a system requires wait states for slower memory or I/O, asynchronous transfers are almost always chosen.

Asynchronous transfers are used when external I/O and memory components require a considerable amount of time to access. Such components include EPROM, and many I/O devices. All asynchronous transfers require at least three clocking periods to transfer up to one long-word.

Synchronous transfers are possible when only the memory or I/O device is 32 bits. The memory device must also function so quickly that no wait states are required. All synchronous cycles require two clocks to transfer up to one long-word. This makes a synchronous transfer faster than an asynchronous transfer.

Another form of synchronous transfer is the burst. A synchronous burst transfers 4 long-words in five clocking periods. This type of transfer is used for filling the internal instruction or data caches.

Memory access time requirements are different for asynchronous and synchronous memory systems. Access time is identified as the time needed by the memory to fetch data, once an address has been provided. Table 13-1 illustrates the access time allowed memory using different clocking frequencies for the two different versions of the 68030. Note that the times in this table are worst-case times for each microprocessor. If additional access times are needed, wait states are inserted in the asynchronous timing or the clock frequency can be reduced.

### Asynchronous Memory Operation

Asynchronous operation of the 68030 is almost identical to the 68020 because the $\overline{\text{DSACK}}$ inputs are used to acknowledge a memory transfer. Figure 13-3 illustrates the read timing diagram for an asynchronous bus transfer. Notice that this is equivalent to the timing for a transfer on the 68000 microprocessor except only three clocking periods are needed in the 68030, instead of four as in the 68000.

**Table 13-1   68030 Memory Access Times (ns) Under Various Clocking Frequencies Without Wait States**

| Type | 68030RC16 at 16.7 MHz | 68030RC20 at 20 MHz |
| --- | --- | --- |
| Synchronous | 55 | 45 |
| Asynchronous | 115 | 95 |

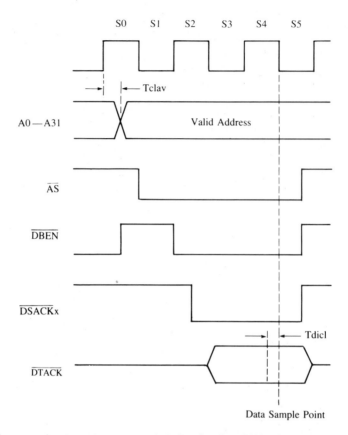

**Figure 13-3   Asynchronous read timing for the 68030 microprocessor.**

The asynchronous read cycle is developed with six states or three clocking periods. During the first state, the microprocessor issues the address and the R/$\overline{W}$ signal to the memory. This is the starting point of a memory access calculation, as it was with the 68000 or any other microprocessor.

The address appears $T_{clav}$ time after the start of S0. This $T_{clav}$ time is 30 ns for the 16.7 MHz version of the 68030 and 25 ns for the 20 MHz version. Data are sampled by the microprocessor at the end of S4. This sample point has a setup time, as it did on the 68000, called $T_{dicl}$. The $T_{dicl}$ time is 5 ns for both speed versions of the 68030. Access time is calculated by subtracting $T_{clav}$ and $T_{dicl}$ from five states. This is the maximum access time allowed the memory from the address inputs.

For example, if the 68030 is operated with a 20 MHz clock, a state is 25 ns. Here the access time is 125 ns − 25 ns − 5 ns, or 95 ns. In the 68030 operated with a 16.7 MHz clock, each state is 30 ns, so access time is 150 ns − 30 ns − 5 ns, or 115 ns. Access time may be increased by lowering the clock frequency, but this is uncommon in a 68030-based system.

Wait states are inserted in the timing by delaying the application of the $\overline{DSACK}$ signals beyond the end of S2. Note that $\overline{DSACK}$ inputs are sampled at the end of S2.

If $\overline{\text{DSACK}}$ goes low by the end of S2, no wait states are inserted, provided it goes high again within 60 ns (50 ns for the 20 MHz version) after $\overline{\text{AS}}$ has gone high. If $\overline{\text{DSACK}}$ is held high beyond the end of S2, the wait states appear and delay S4, which is where the data are sampled. This allows more time for the memory to access data.

Figure 13-4 illustrates an asynchronous memory interface using the same PAL that is developed for the 68020 in Figure 12-8. Note that this circuit looks very similar to the interfaces discussed earlier for the 68000 microprocessor. The main difference is that the 68030 uses 32-bit-wide memory and has four banks of memory instead of two banks, as in the 68000 memory system.

### Synchronous Memory Operation

Synchronous memory operation differs from asynchronous operation in several ways. The main difference is that instead of using the $\overline{\text{DSACK}}$ signal to terminate the read, a synchronous read operation uses the $\overline{\text{STERM}}$ signal for termination. In addition, a synchronous read requires two clocking periods instead of three and does not allow wait state insertion. This means that a system using synchronous memory operation operates at a higher effective speed than one that uses asynchronous memory.

Figure 13-5 illustrates the timing for a synchronous read operation. Notice that the address appears during state S0, just as it does for an asynchronous read operation. The time required for the address to appear after the start S0 is $T_{\text{clav}}$. The data bus is sampled at the end of S4 for an asynchronous transfer. For a synchronous transfer it is sampled at time $T_{\text{dicl}}$ before the end of S2. This is a full clocking period earlier than with an asynchronous transfer.

If the 68030RC20 is operated with synchronous data transfer, the time allowed for the memory access is 75 ns $-$ 25 ns $-$ 5 ns or 45 ns. This is such a short time that static RAM is required for operation at this speed. Dynamic RAM, at present, operates at speeds of 60 ns or higher.

A static RAM synchronous memory interface appears in Figure 13-6 for the 68030 operating at 20 MHz. This memory system uses 32 static RAMs, 64k $\times$ 1. Each SRAM has an access time of 25 ns. The SRAM allows operations with *zero wait states*. Because 32 SRAMs are used in this system, the memory size is 256k bytes.

A PAL is used to decode the memory and also to generate the $\overline{\text{STERM}}$ signal immediately if the address is correct. This allows the memory to operate with zero wait states. If the $\overline{\text{STERM}}$ signal is delayed, wait states are inserted as in the asynchronous system, but this feature is rarely used in practice.

Figure 13-7 illustrates the program for the PAL16L8 used in the circuit of Figure 13-6. Here the PAL partially decodes the 256k bytes of memory at locations \$EXXXXXXX. In many applications a second PAL is used to further decode the memory so that it functions in a unique 256k byte section of memory. The PAL decoder also generates the $\overline{\text{STERM}}$ signal, the bank selection signals, and a signal to enable the data output bus from the memory devices.

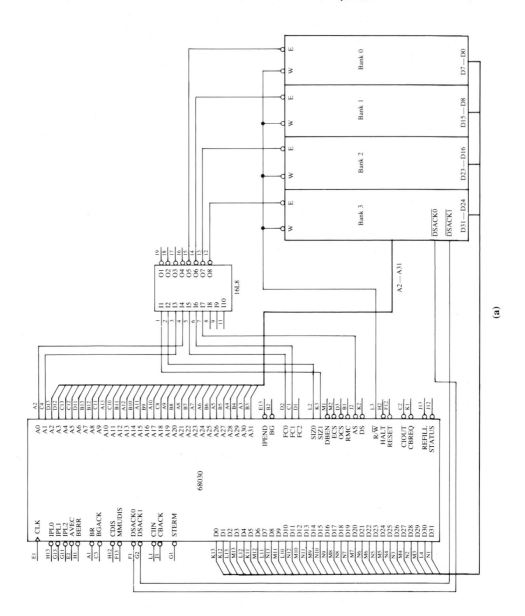

**Figure 13-4    (a) The 68030 interfaced to an asynchronous memory system. (b) The program for the PAL 16L8 used to select the banks of memory.**

TITLE          Bank selection generator
PATTERN        P1
REVISION       1
AUTHOR         Barry B. Brey
COMPANY        DeVry
DATE           11/01/90
CHIP           PAL16L8
;PINS

| ;1 | 2 | 3 | 4 | 5 | 6 | 7 | 8 | 9 | 10 |
|----|----|----|----|----|----|----|----|----|----|
| S1 | S0 | A1 | A0 | FC0 | FC1 | AS | NC | NC | GND |
| ;11 | 12 | 13 | 14 | 15 | 16 | 17 | 18 | 19 | 20 |
| NC | B3 | B2 | B1 | B0 | NC | NC | NC | NC | VCC |

EQUATIONS

$/B3$ = $/A1$ = $/A0$ = FC0 =   FC1 = $/AS$

$/B3$ = $/A1$ =  A0 = FC0 = FC1 = $/AS$
     + S1 = $/A1$ = FC0 = FC1 = $/AS$
     + $/S0$ = $/A1$ = FC0 = FC1 = $/AS$

$/B1$ =  A1 = $/A0$ = FC0 = FC1 = $/AS$
     + S1= S0 = $/A1$ = FC0 = FC1 = $/AS$
     + $/S1$ = $/S0$ = $/A1$ = FC0 = FC1 = $/AS$
     + S1 = $/A1$ =  A0 = FC0 = FC1 = $/AS$

$/B0$ =  A1 =  A0 = FC0 = FC1 = $/AS$
     + $/S1$ = $/S0$ = FC0 = FC1 = $/AS$
     + S1 =  A1 = FC0 = FC1 = $/AS$
     + S1 = S0 =  A0 = FC0 = FC1 = $/AS$

**(b)**

**Figure 13-4    Continued.**

## Burst Mode Memory Operation

Burst mode operation is by far the most efficient method of operating a memory system with the 68030 microprocessor. It is also the most costly. Figure 13-8 illustrates a 256k byte burst mode memory system that allows both the instruction cache and the data cache to be filled with a burst transfer. Burst filling of the caches is very efficient because a synchronous burst cycle transfers 4 long-words in five clocking periods. It is also very efficient because most software operates from the instruction cache and often data exist in the data cache.

The burst mode circuit differs from the synchronous circuit because a burst generator is added. The burst generator provides address bus signals A2 and A3 for the memory interface. (Remember that A2 is connected to memory pin A0 and A3 is connected to memory pin A1.) These address lines are not provided by the

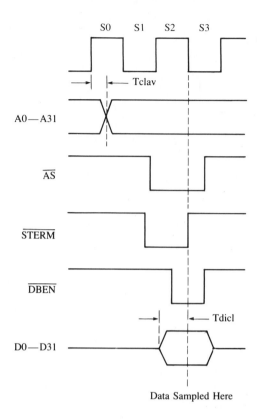

**Figure 13-5    Synchronous read timing for the 68030 microprocessor.**

microprocessor during the burst. Each burst transfers four 32-bit numbers during five clocking periods.

### 13-1.4    The Memory Management Unit (MMU) within the 68030

The *memory management unit (MMU)* supports a paged demand virtual memory environment. The management is considered to be a *demand system* because programs do not specify memory areas in advance for the MMU. Instead, programs request memory areas on access. Any instruction that accesses memory will demand an access through the memory management unit. This also includes any opcode fetches accessed via the program counter.

The memory is divided into small physical areas of equal size that are called *page frames*. The operating system has the task of assigning page frames to tasks as they are required for the execution of programs and the acquisition of data. The page frame system allows the operating system to dynamically assign memory to tasks as they execute. *Pages* allow a system having a limited memory size to be utilized by programs requiring much larger memory than actually available. This is because

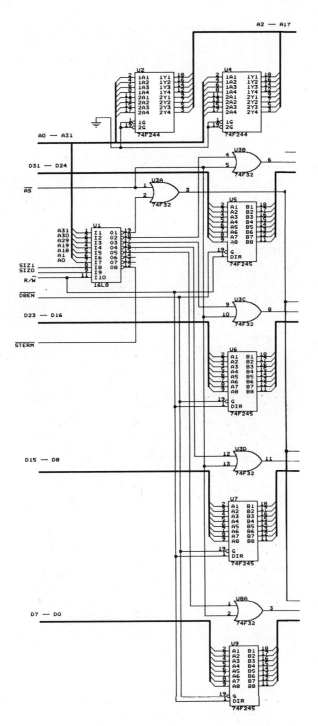

**Figure 13-6**   A fully buffered synchronous memory system for the 68030 micro-processor.

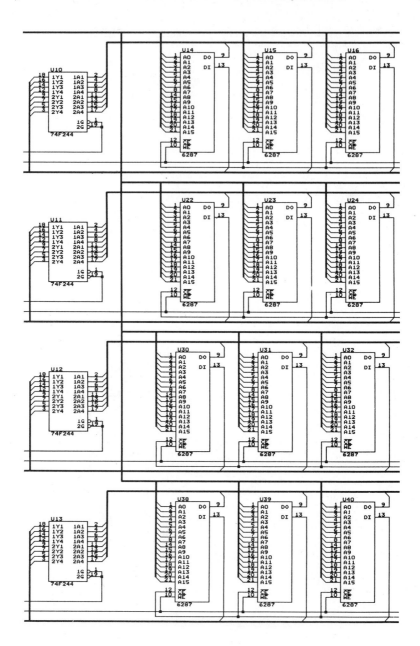

Figure 13-6   Continued.

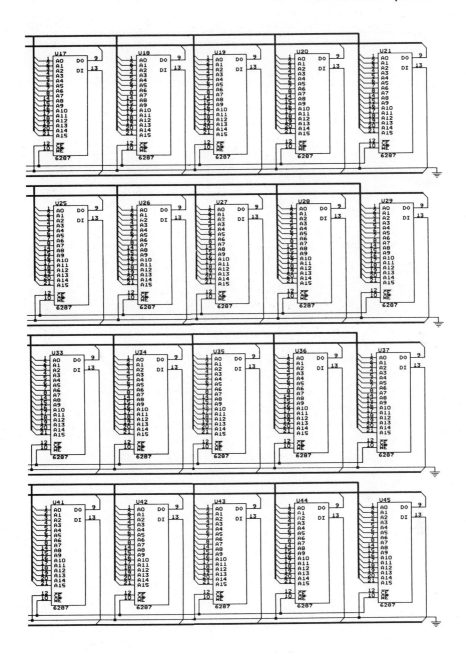

Figure 13-6 Continued.

TITLE        Synchronous Decoder
PATTERN      P1
REVISION     1
AUTHOR       Barry B. Brey
COMPANY      DeVry
DATE         11/01/90
CHIP         PAL16L8

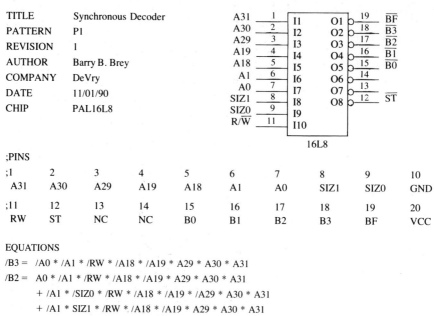

;PINS

| ;1 | 2 | 3 | 4 | 5 | 6 | 7 | 8 | 9 | 10 |
|---|---|---|---|---|---|---|---|---|---|
| A31 | A30 | A29 | A19 | A18 | A1 | A0 | SIZ1 | SIZ0 | GND |

| ;11 | 12 | 13 | 14 | 15 | 16 | 17 | 18 | 19 | 20 |
|---|---|---|---|---|---|---|---|---|---|
| RW | ST | NC | NC | B0 | B1 | B2 | B3 | BF | VCC |

EQUATIONS

/B3 =  /A0 * /A1 * /RW * /A18 * /A19 * A29 * A30 * A31
/B2 =   A0 * /A1 * /RW * /A18 * /A19 * A29 * A30 * A31
       + /A1 * /SIZ0 * /RW * /A18 * /A19 * /A29 * A30 * A31
       + /A1 * SIZ1 * /RW * /A18 * /A19 * A29 * A30 * A31
/B1 =  /A0 * A1 * /RW * /A18 * /A19 * A29 * A30 * A31
       + /A1 * /SIZ0 * /SIZ1 * /RW * /A18 * /A19 * A29 * A30 * A31
       + /A1 * SIZ0 * SIZ1 * /RW * /A18 * /A19 * A29 * A30 * A31
       + /A1 * A0 * /SIZ0 * /RW * /A18 * /A19 * A29 * A30 * A31
/B0 =   A0 * A1 * /RW * /A18 * /A19 * A29 * A30 * A31
       + A0 * SIZ1 * SIZ0 * /RW * /A18 * /A19 * A29 * A30 * A31
       + /SIZ0 * /SIZ1 * /RW * /A18 * /A19 * A29 * A30 * A31
       + A1 * SIZ1 * /RW * /A18 * /A19 * A29 * A30 * A31
/BF =   RW * /A18 * /A19 * A29 * A30 * A31
/ST =  /A18 * /A19 * A29 * A30 * A31

**Figure 13-7    The program for the PAL 16L8 used in Figure 13-6.**

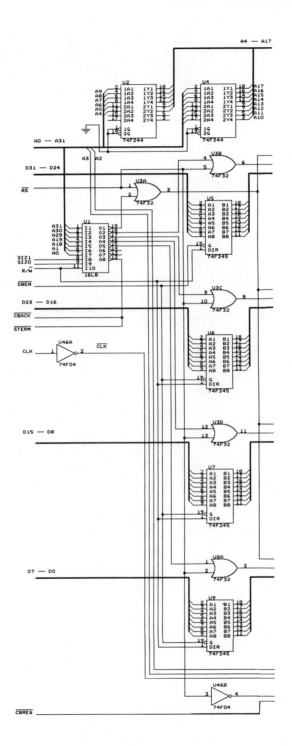

**Figure 13-8** A burst mode memory interface for the 68030 microprocessor.

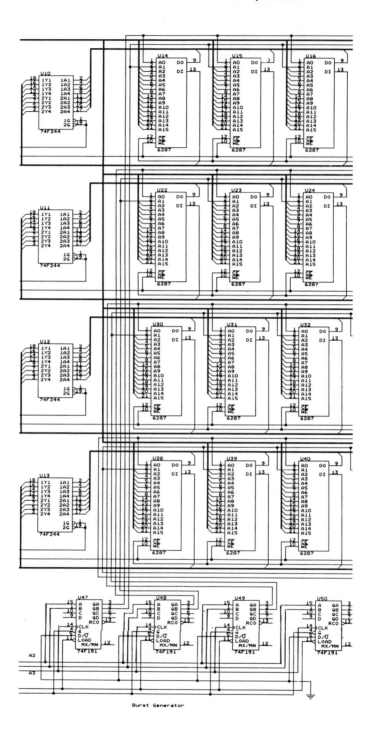

Figure 13-8    Continued.

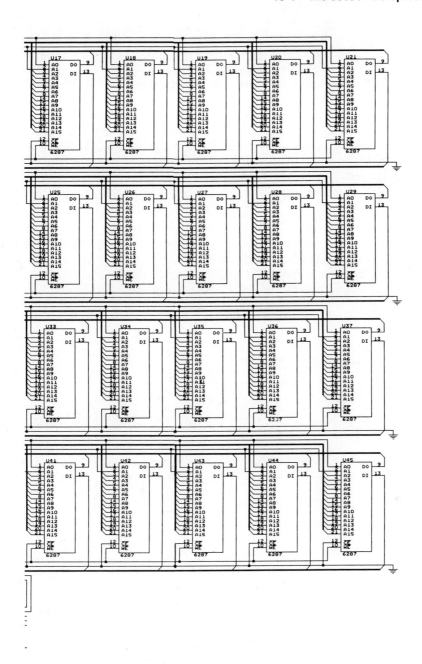

Figure 13-8 Continued.

any logical address can be mapped to any physical address. This is what is called a *virtual memory.* The term "virtual" is defined as existing in effect, but not real.

Translation of a logical address, as it is generated by a program, into a physical address is accomplished by the MMU via page translation tables. Whenever an address is generated by a program, the microprocessor searches an address translation cache for the physical address of the reference. If the address is in the cache, the translation is complete. If the address is not in the cache, the microprocessor searches an address translation table for the physical page address and stores it in the cache for future reference. If the same page address is accessed in the future, it is already in the cache, which reduces translation time.

The structure of a two-level address translation table appears in Figure 13-9. Here the logical address, as it appears in an instruction, is divided into three parts. The first (most significant) 12 bits are used to select one of 4096 level A table entries. The next 10 bits are used to select one of 1024 entries in the level B page table. This location in table B addresses an actual page of memory data through the page frame address stored in table B. The right-most 10 bits select a byte, word, or long-word location in the physical (1024-byte) page of memory.

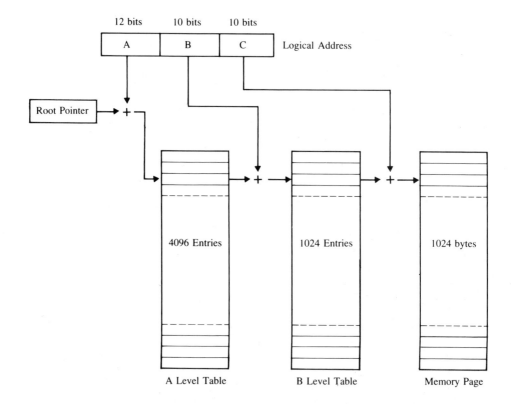

**Figure 13-9   A two-level translation table that addresses a 1024-byte memory page for the 68030 microprocessor.**

By using this translation technique, it is possible to map any logical address to any physical address. Operating systems do this so that any program may be operated at any location of the memory. This makes the computer system's memory totally independent of the software. Translation tables also allow data to be stored in any location. The storage occurs regardless of the actual address requested by the program and regardless of the actual memory size.

The page table translation unit of the MMU is flexible enough to support different page sizes. A page may be 256, 512, 1k, 2k, 4k, 8k, 16k, or 32k bytes in length. The MMU is also programmable for up to four levels of translation tables. The example illustrated in Figure 13-9 uses two levels of translation tables. The number of bits in the logical address that are used for indexing each translation table can be programmed from zero to 15 bits.

### Translation Control Register (TC)

The translation control register (TC) is used to program the number of translation tables used in a search, the size of the final memory page, and other information. Figure 13-10 illustrates the 32-bit translation control register of the 68030. A PMOVE ⟨ea⟩,TC is instruction is used to load the TC.

Following is a description of each bit or field in the translation control register.

**E (enable)**   This bit controls whether a logical address is translated into a different physical address through the translation process. If E is a zero, translation is blocked; if E is a one, translation occurs. A hardware reset will always clear this bit, preventing translation.

**SRE (supervisor root pointer enable)**   When this bit is disabled (a logic zero), the 68030 accesses memory in both the supervisor and the user modes through the CPU

| 31 | 30 | 29 | 28 | 27 | 26 | 25 | 24 | 23 | 20 19 | 16 15 | 12 11 | 8 7 | 4 3 | 0 |
|---|---|---|---|---|---|---|---|---|---|---|---|---|---|---|
| E | 0 | 0 | 0 | 0 | 0 | SRE | FCL | | PS | IS | TIA | TIB | TIC | TID |

$$
\begin{aligned}
E &= \text{Enable translation} \\
SRE &= \text{Supervisor root pointer enable} \\
FCL &= \text{Function code lookup enable} \\
PS &= \text{Page size} \\
IS &= \text{Initial shift} \\
TIA &= \text{Table A size} \\
TIB &= \text{Table B size} \\
TIC &= \text{Table C size} \\
TID &= \text{Table D size}
\end{aligned}
$$

**Figure 13-10   The 68030 MMU translation control register (TC).**

root pointer (CRP). If SRE is enabled (a logic one), supervisor accesses use the SRP (supervisor root pointer) and user accesses use the CRP.

**FCL (function code lookup)**    This bit enables the function code lookup when a one and disables it when a zero.

**PS field (page size)**    The page size field is a 4-bit field that selects the size of the memory page. Table 13-2 illustrates the binary bit patterns required to program the translation unit for various page sizes; if other values are placed in this field, the microprocessor will execute an MMU configuration error exception.

**IS field (initial shift)**    These four bits specify how many bits of the logical address are ignored during translation. If this field contains a 0000, then all address bits are used during translation. The field may contain any number between 0000 and 1111, which allows up to the left-most 15 bits of the address to be ignored.

**TIA, TIB, TIC, and TID fields (table index)**    Each of these 4-bit fields defines how many bits of the logical address are used in the translation. Each field can indicate between 0 and 15 bits. If a field contains a zero, the MMU stops looking to other fields for translation table size.

In Figure 13-9, which used a two-level translation table, the level A pointer was 12 bits in width, level B was 10 bits, and the page size was 1k bytes. To set the TC register for this specification, TIA is loaded with a 1100, TIB with a 1010, and both TIC and TID are loaded with a 0000. The IS field is also loaded with a 0000 because all 32 bits of the logical address are used in the translation. The PS field is loaded with a 1010 for a 1k byte page size. The PMOVE ⟨ea⟩,TC instruction is used to enable translation and to load the remaining fields with $80A9CA00, which is stored in memory (⟨ea⟩) and loaded to the TC register.

Suppose that the logical address is divided as illustrated in Figure 13-11. Here a four-level translation is used to access 256-byte pages of memory: the first 2 bits are ignored, table level A is 4 bits, and table levels B, C, and D are all 6 bits. This means that the level A table has 16 entries, and each of the tables for levels B, C, and D has 64 entries. Since the first two bits of the logical address are ignored, they must be the same as the physical addresses used to access the level tables.

**Table 13-2    Selection of Page Size Using the PS Field of the TC Register**

| Bits | Size (bytes) |
|------|--------------|
| 1000 | 256 |
| 1001 | 512 |
| 1010 | 1k |
| 1011 | 2k |
| 1100 | 4k |
| 1101 | 8k |
| 1110 | 16k |
| 1111 | 32k |

| 2-bits | 4-bits | 6-bits | 6-bits | 6-bits | 8-bits |
|---|---|---|---|---|---|
| IS | A | B | C | D | offset |

**Figure 13-11** **The logical address used to access a four-level translation table.**

## *Root Pointer Register Formats*

The 68030 microprocessor has two root pointer registers: the supervisor root pointer (SRP) and the CPU root pointer (CRP). Each root pointer register is a 64-bit register that contains address of the root translation table and also related control bits. Figure 13-12 illustrates the format for both the SRP and the CRP.

Following is a description of each bit and field in a root pointer.

**L/U (lower or upper page range)** If this bit is a 1, it specifies that the limit is an unsigned lower limit of the indexes in the root page table. If this bit is cleared, it indicates that the limit is the unsigned upper limit of the indexes in the root page table.

**Limit field** This field indicates the upper or lower limit of the index used for the next page table entry. If no limit is desired, the limit field is placed at $7FFF and the L/U bit is cleared.

**DT (descriptor type)** There are four descriptor types. Type 00 is not allowed in the root pointer. If used, the MMU executes an MMU configuration error exception. Type 01 is a page descriptor, which sets a direct offset using the table address. If this descriptor is selected, all the physical addresses are the logical address plus the unsigned table address. Type 10 is a valid 4-byte descriptor, meaning that all translation table entries are 4 bytes wide. Type 11 is a valid 8-byte descriptor, meaning that all translation table entries are 8 bytes wide.

L/U = Lower or upper page range
Limit = Limit on table index for the root table
DT = Description type (2-bits)
Table address = Address of root table

*BREY*

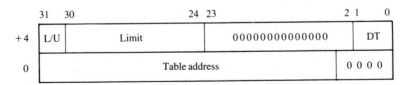

**Figure 13-12** **The root pointer for the MMU of the 68030 microprocessor.**

**Table address**   The table address indexes the start of the root translation table. If the DT field contains a 01, 10, or 11, the table address is the actual physical address of the root translation table. If DT = 00, this address is an offset added to all logical addresses to generate a physical address.

### Descriptor Types (4- and 8-byte)

As mentioned in connection with the descriptor type field (DT) of the root pointer register, there are different descriptor types. The 4-byte and 8-byte descriptors are used as entries in the root and level translation tables.

There are four different short format descriptors, as shown in Figure 13-13: short format table descriptor, short format page and early termination descriptor, short format invalid descriptor, and short format indirect descriptor.

The *short format table descriptor* is used to address a table of descriptors and contains the physical base address of a descriptor table. The right-most 4 bits of this descriptor contain status information and the remaining 28 bits contain the physical address of a descriptor table. Bit position U (used) is set by the 68030 whenever it is fetched from the translation table. The 68030 never clears this bit. The WP bit is the write protection bit. If this bit is set, the 68030 will not allow a write to the logical address mapped by this descriptor. The DP bits are used to identify the descriptor type. These bits have the same meanings as defined with the root pointer register.

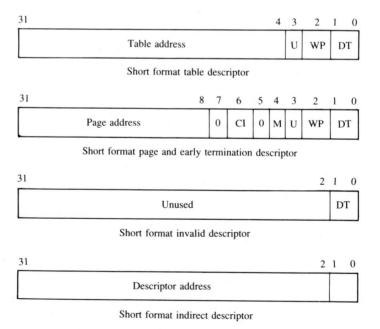

**Figure 13-13   The four different forms of the 4-byte short format descriptor.**

The *short format page descriptor* stores the page address. Note that this descriptor may be at any page translation table level. If it is present before the final page translation table, it causes an early termination of the translation process. The M bit indicates a modified page. That is, a page that is written to by the 68030 will have this bit set in the descriptor. The 68030 never clears this bit. The CI bit is set to inhibit caching of data within the page; if this bit is cleared, caching will occur for any access to this page.

The *short format invalid descriptor* can be used at any level of the translation tree except at the root level. This descriptor indicates that the entry refers to an invalid section of the memory. This may be a section that is assigned to an external I/O device or other use, as the operating system sees fit.

The *short format indirect descriptor* resides at the bottom level of the page translation table. The descriptor address portion contains the physical address of a page descriptor.

Descriptors may also be 8 bytes in length. There are four different 8-byte descriptors that function in basically the same manner as the 4-byte descriptors. Figure 13-14 illustrates the four long format (8-byte) descriptors.

The long format descriptors are identical to the short format except that they contain a limit and an L/U bit. The limit is a 15-bit field that contains the lower or upper limit of the translation table. If the L/U bit is a logic 1, the limit is a lower limit. If L/U is set, the limit is an upper limit. The limit specifies the upper or lower limit of the index. If the boundary is exceeded, an out-of-bounds exception occurs.

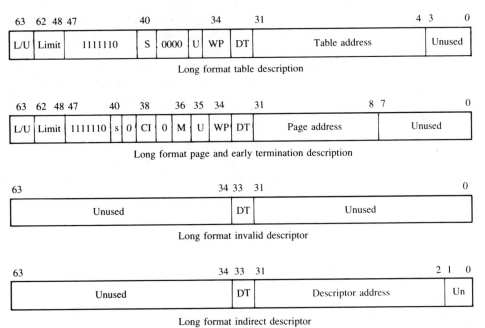

**Figure 13-14** The long format (8-byte) descriptor.

## Function Code Lookup

One way of protecting the spaces of the user and supervisor is through the function code lookup bit in the TC register. This feature segments the supervisor program space, supervisor data space, user program space, and the user data space. When the function code lookup is enabled, each segment has its own translation table.

When function code lookup is enabled, another level of translation is added to all translation trees. Figure 13-15 illustrates the addition of the function code lookup before translation of a logical address into a physical address via translation tables. This feature allows a five-level translation using the function code lookup and levels A through D.

## The Address Translation Cache and Transparent Translation

The address translation cache (ATC) is a 22-entry cache that contains the most recent 22-page address translations. As long as the cache contains a prior translation from a logical address to a physical address, the translation process is transparent and instant. If the cache becomes full, the least recently used entry is discarded and replaced by a new entry. Hit rates for the ATC are 98% or greater for many applications.

In addition to the 22 cache entries, there are two transparent translation registers (TT1 and TT0). These registers optionally define two blocks of logical address space that are directly mapped to physical address spaces. Each TTx register defines a 16M byte or larger block of logical address space that is to be mapped as a physical address space. These blocks may overlap if desired.

Figure 13-16 illustrates the bit pattern of the TTx register. The TTx register is composed of a logical address base, logical address mask, and some control bits.

The logical address base defines the first 8 bits (A31–A24) of the logical address that is to be mapped as a physical address. This defines a 16M byte section of the memory system. If the logical address base is a $90, then locations $90000000–$90FFFFFF are defined as physical addresses $90000000–$90FFFFFF.

This space may be increased in size by using the logical address mask portion of the TTx register. If any bit is masked off with a logic one in the logical address mask portion, the address space becomes larger. Suppose that the logical address mask is $03. This masks off the least significant bits of the logical address base register, increasing the size of the address space.

Suppose that the logical base address is $10 and the logical address mask is $03. This means that only the first 6 bits of the logical address are used in the translation. The logical addresses mapped as physical address space are now $10000000–$13FFFFFF. This range of addresses represents a 64M byte block of memory.

The remaining bits of the TTx register are defined as follows.

**E (enable)**    This bit disables translation when cleared and enables it when set. The E bit is always cleared with a reset.

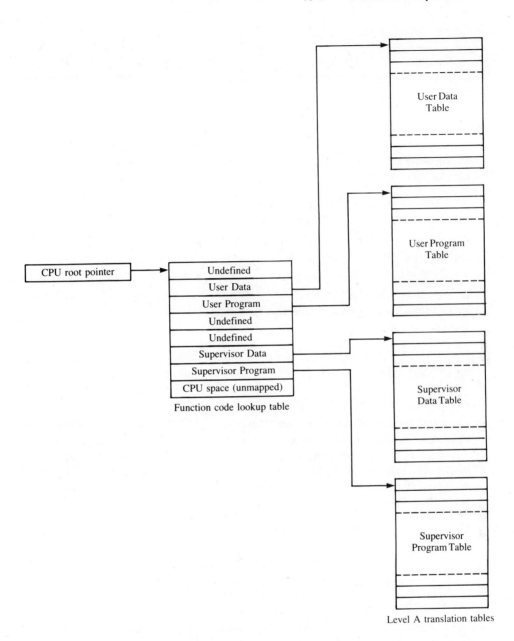

**Figure 13-15** Page translation using the function code lookup feature of the 68030 microprocessor's memory management unit.

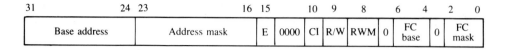

**Figure 13-16**    The transparent translation register (TTx) format.

**CI (cache inhibit)**    The CI bit inhibits caching if it is set and allows caching if it is cleared.

**R/W (read/write)**    This bit selects the type of operation that is transparent: if R/W is set, read accesses are transparent; if it is cleared, write accesses are transparent.

**RWM (read/write mask)**    This bit selects whether the R/W bit is to be ignored or enabled. If RWM is a logic one, the R/W bit is ignored, with the result that all read and write accesses are transparent. If RWM is a logic zero, only read or write accesses are transparent, as defined by the R/W bit.

**FC base (function code base)**    This 3-bit field defines the function code accesses that will be transparent.

**FC mask (function code mask)**    Setting a bit in this 3-bit field causes a corresponding function code base bit to be ignored.

### The MMU Status Register

The status register located within the MMU, the MMUSR, indicates the status of a translation if read with the either of the two PTEST instructions. Figure 13-17 illustrates the binary bit pattern of the MMU status register. The two PTEST instructions, which test the MMU status register, are listed in Table 13-3, which describes how the PTEST instructions test the MMU status register. The PTEST

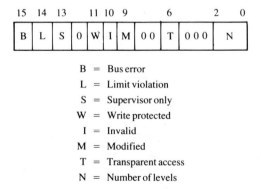

**Figure 13-17**    The status register of the 68030 memory management unit.

**Table 13-3** The Purpose of Each Bit in the MMU Status Register

| Bit | PTEST, level 0 | PTEST, levels 1–7 |
|---|---|---|
| Bus error, B | This bit is set if the bus error bit is set in the ATC entry for the specified logical address. | This bit is set if a bus error is encountered during the table search for the PTEST instruction. |
| Limit, L | This bit is cleared. | This bit is set if an index exceeds a limit during the table search. |
| Supervisor, S | This bit is cleared. | This bit is set if the S bit of a format table descriptor or long format page descriptor encountered during the search is set and the FC2 bit of the function code specified by the PTEST instruction is not equal to one. The S bit is undefined if the I bit is set. |
| Write protected, W | This bit is set if the WP bit of the ATC entry is set. It is undefined if the I bit is set. | This bit is set if a descriptor or page descriptor is encountered with the WP bit set during the table search. The W bit is undefined if the I bit is set. |
| Invalid, I | This bit indicates an invalid translation. The I bit is set if the translation for the specified logical address is not resident in the ATC, or if the B bit of the corresponding ATC entry is set. | This bit indicates an invalid translation. The I bit is set if the DT field of a table or a page descriptor encountered during the search is set to invalid, or if either the B or L bit of the MMU status register is set during the table search. |
| Modified, M | This bit is set if the ATC entry corresponding to the specified address has the modified bit set. It is undefined if the I bit is set. | This bit is set if the page descriptor for the specified address has the modified bit set. It is undefined if the I bit is set. |
| Transparent, T | This bit is set if a match occurred in either transparent register or in both (TT0 or TT1). | This bit is set to zero. |
| Number of levels, N | This 3-bit field is cleared to zero. | This 3-bit field contains the actual number of tables accessed during the search. |

instruction is used in bus error exceptions so that information about the bus error can be determined.

### 13-1.5 68030 Software

Figure 13-18 illustrates the programming model for the 68030 microprocessor. You may wish to compare this to the 68020 or earlier versions. The programming model for the 68020 is almost identical to the 68030 except that the 68030 programming model contains registers that are used with the memory management unit, namely CRP, SRP, TC, TT0, TT1, and MMUSR. A description of these registers was given above, with the description of the MMU.

Four new instructions are added to the 68030. The CALLM and RTM instructions, introduced with the 68020, have been removed from the 68030 instruction set and should be considered obsolete. Table 13-4 lists the new 68030 instructions, with a comment about the operation of each.

### Flushing an Entry in the Address Translation Cache

The PFLUSH instruction is used to flush (erase) all entries in the address translation cache or selected entries. The PFLUSHA instruction will flush all entries, while the PFLUSH ⟨fc⟩,#mask,⟨ea⟩ instruction will flush selected entries. The ⟨fc⟩ field selects the function code as SFC or DFC for these two registers or as immediate data indicating the function code. The mask field is a 1, 4, or 6. A mask of 1 flushes all entries, a 4 flushes all entries by function code, and a 6 flushes all entries by function code and the effective address ⟨ea⟩.

### Loading an Entry into the Address Translation Cache

The PLOAD instruction is used to load an entry into the ATC. Two forms of this instruction are available: PLOADR (read) and PLOADW (write). The PLOADR instruction causes U bits in the translation table to be set as if a read access had occurred. The PLOADW instruction causes the U and M bits in the translation table to be set as if a write had occurred. The U bit indicates that the descriptor has been used by the operating system.

Both forms of this instruction have two operands. The first specifies the function code and the second the effective address. The PLOAD instruction searches the translation table for a descriptor that contains the specified effective address. A new entry is created by PLOAD just as if the 68030 had attempted to access the effective address.

### Loading the CRP, SRP, and Other MMU Registers

The PMOVE instruction is used to transfer data between the effective address and an MMU register. The valid MMU registers are CRP, SRP, TC, TT0, TT1, and MMUSR. The valid forms of this instruction are listed in Table 13-5. Notice that the PMOVE instruction allows transfers to or from the MMU registers, while the PMOVEFD instruction allows only moves from an effective address into an MMU register. The PMOVEFD is used to load MMU register with the flush disabled, while PMOVE enables flushing the ATC.

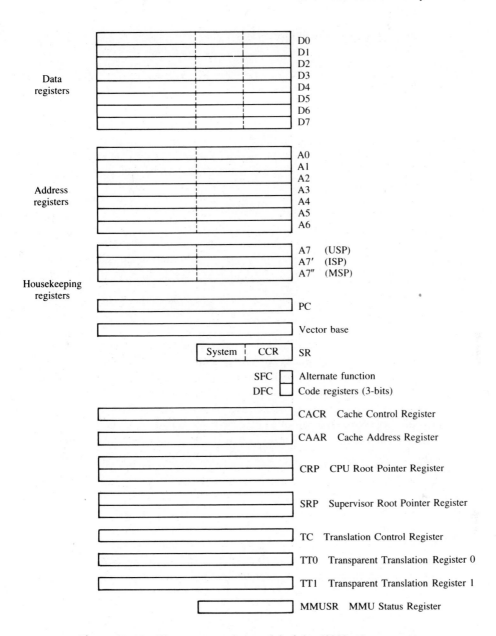

**Figure 13-18   The programming model of the 68030 microprocessor.**

Table 13-4   New 68030 Instructions

| Instruction | Comment |
| --- | --- |
| PFLUSH | Flushes an entry in the address translation cache (ATC). |
| PLOAD | Loads an entry into the ATC. |
| PMOVE | Moves to and from the MMU registers. |
| PTEST | Tests a logical address. |

### Testing a Logical Address

The PTEST instruction searches the translation tables to a specified level for the translation descriptor that corresponds to the effective address. This search changes the MMUSR (MMU status register) according to the status of the descriptor. An option exists that stores the physical address of the descriptor in an address register. Refer to Figures 13-3 and 13-14 for descriptors and Table 13-3 for the MMUSR.

## 13-2   The 68040 Microprocessor

The 68040 microprocessor contains more than 1.2 million transistors. The lowest speed version of the 68040 operates at 25 MHz, but it will also be made available in 33 and 50 MHz versions. The 68040 is an enhanced version of the 68030 that averages 1.3 clock cycles per instruction, versus 3.4 for the 68030.

In addition to the extensive speed improvement, the 68040 incorporates a floating-point coprocessor, a pair of memory management units, a snoop controller, and instruction and data caches that are each 4k bytes in size. New instructions also appear in the 68040 instruction set, to further increase the efficiency of this microprocessor.

### 13-2.1   Pinout

The 68040 is packaged in a 179-pin PGA device as illustrated in Figure 13-19. Although there are similarities between the pinouts of the 68030 and 68040, there are also quite a few differences. The most striking difference is that the 68040 has snoop control and other bus control signals that are not present on the 68030. In

Table 13-5   The 68030 PMOVE Instructions

| Instruction | Comment |
| --- | --- |
| PMOVE MMUreg,⟨ea⟩ | Copies the contents of an MMU register into an effective address. |
| PMOVE ⟨ea⟩,MMUreg | Copies the contents of an effective address into an MMU register. |
| PMOVEFD ⟨ea⟩,MMUreg | Copies the contents of an effective address into an MMU register with the flush disabled. |

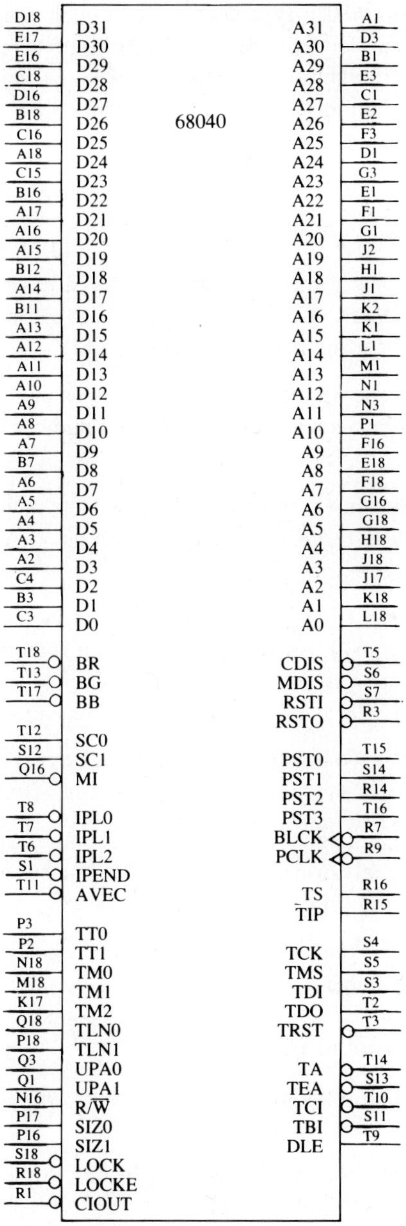

| | | | |
|---|---|---|---|
| D18 | D31 | A31 | A1 |
| E17 | D30 | A30 | D3 |
| E16 | D29 | A29 | B1 |
| C18 | D28 | A28 | E3 |
| D16 | D27 | A27 | C1 |
| B18 | D26 | A26 | E2 |
| C16 | D25 | A25 | F3 |
| A18 | D24 | A24 | D1 |
| C15 | D23 | A23 | G3 |
| B16 | D22 | A22 | E1 |
| A17 | D21 | A21 | F1 |
| A16 | D20 | A20 | G1 |
| A15 | D19 | A19 | J2 |
| B12 | D18 | A18 | H1 |
| A14 | D17 | A17 | J1 |
| B11 | D16 | A16 | K2 |
| A13 | D15 | A15 | K1 |
| A12 | D14 | A14 | L1 |
| A11 | D13 | A13 | M1 |
| A10 | D12 | A12 | N1 |
| A9 | D11 | A11 | N3 |
| A8 | D10 | A10 | P1 |
| A7 | D9 | A9 | F16 |
| B7 | D8 | A8 | E18 |
| A6 | D7 | A7 | F18 |
| A5 | D6 | A6 | G16 |
| A4 | D5 | A5 | G18 |
| A3 | D4 | A4 | H18 |
| A2 | D3 | A3 | J18 |
| C4 | D2 | A2 | J17 |
| B3 | D1 | A1 | K18 |
| C3 | D0 | A0 | L18 |

68040

| | | | |
|---|---|---|---|
| T18 | BR | CDIS | T5 |
| T13 | BG | MDIS | S6 |
| T17 | BB | RSTI | S7 |
| | | RSTO | R3 |
| T12 | SC0 | | |
| S12 | SC1 | PST0 | T15 |
| Q16 | MI | PST1 | S14 |
| | | PST2 | R14 |
| T8 | IPL0 | PST3 | T16 |
| T7 | IPL1 | BLCK | R7 |
| T6 | IPL2 | PCLK | R9 |
| S1 | IPEND | | |
| T11 | AVEC | $\overline{TS}$ | R16 |
| | | $\overline{TIP}$ | R15 |
| P3 | TT0 | | |
| P2 | TT1 | TCK | S4 |
| N18 | TM0 | TMS | S5 |
| M18 | TM1 | TDI | S3 |
| K17 | TM2 | TDO | T2 |
| Q18 | TLN0 | TRST | T3 |
| P18 | TLN1 | | |
| Q3 | UPA0 | TA | T14 |
| Q1 | UPA1 | TEA | S13 |
| N16 | R/$\overline{W}$ | TCI | T10 |
| P17 | SIZ0 | TBI | S11 |
| P16 | SIZ1 | DLE | T9 |
| S18 | LOCK | | |
| R18 | LOCKE | | |
| R1 | CIOUT | | |

Figure 13-19  The pinout of the 68040 microprocessor.

fact, most of the familiar 68000-type control bus signals are missing or redefined. Another significant change is that the 68040 can be powered up to provide eight different output buffer configurations that allow various levels of drive currents for the memory and I/O system. The 68040 also supports the IEEE 1149.1 test access port, for boundary scan testing of board interconnections.

### Pin Functions

Following are descriptions of the function of each pin or grouping of pins on the 68040 microprocessor. Many of the pins are the same as on the 68030 and earlier family members except for the bus control signals.

**A31–A0 (address bus)** The 32-bit address bus accesses 4G bytes of memory. Each location is numbered in bytes just as the memory is numbered in the 68000 microprocessor.

**$\overline{\text{AVEC}}$ (autovector)** This input is used to request the internal generation of an autovector interrupt. It performs the same function as $\overline{\text{VPA}}$ on the 68000 microprocessor.

**$\overline{\text{BB}}$ (bus busy)** The bus busy pin is a bidirectional signal indicating that the bus is currently owned by the 68040. As an input, this signal is monitored by the 68040 to determine whether the bus is owned by another device. $\overline{\text{BB}}$ is used during bus arbitration much as $\overline{\text{BGACK}}$ is used with earlier family members.

**BCLK (bus clock)** The bus clock input is a TTL level signal that is used to generate all bus-related timing signals.

**$\overline{\text{BG}}$ (bus grant)** This input signal indicates that the bus is available for use by the microprocessor. This signal normally is generated by the bus arbiter. Notice that this signal functions differently on earlier family members.

**$\overline{\text{BR}}$ (bus request)** The bus request is an output pin on the 68040, which is opposite from all other family members. This signal is used by the microprocessor to gain access to the bus system. The $\overline{\text{BR}}$ pin normally connects to a bus arbiter that arbitrates bus requests from multiple bus masters.

**$\overline{\text{CDIS}}$ (cache disable)** This input disables the on-chip cache memories. If this pin is placed at a logic zero, both caches are disabled.

**$\overline{\text{CIOUT}}$ (Cache Inhibit Output)** This signal indicates to the external bus that the 68040 will not cache the current bus cycle.

**D31–D0 (data bus)** The 32-bit data bus transfers bytes, words, or long-words from the memory and I/O system.

**$\overline{\text{DLE}}$ (data latch enable)** The data latch enable input is used to latch read data from the data bus.

**$\overline{\text{IPEND}}$ (interrupt pending)** This output indicates that the current interrupt request, on the $\overline{\text{IPL}}$ pins, is a higher priority than the current mask level in the status register.

**IPL2, IPL1, IPL0 (interrupt priority level)** These three inputs are used to request a level 1–7 interrupt.

**LOCK (lock output)** The $\overline{\text{LOCK}}$ signal becomes a logic zero for a read/modify/write cycle, thus blocking an external bus arbiter from accessing the bus during the locked interval.

**LOCKE (lock end)** The $\overline{\text{LOCKE}}$ signal indicates that the current bus transfer is the last in a sequence of locked bus transfers.

**MDIS (memory disable)** This input disables memory address translation by the MMU. It is often used during debugging operations by an external debugging circuit.

**MI (memory inhibit)** This output line prevents memory from responding during a snoop.

**PCLK (processor clock)** The processor clock is a TTL level input that generates internal 68040 timing. The PCLK frequency is twice the frequency of the BCLK signal. The PCLK and BCLK signals are locked together in phase by an internal phase-locked loop.

**PST3–PST0 (processor status bits)** The processor status bits indicate the status of the 68040 microprocessor. Processor status encoding is listed in Table 13-6.

**R/$\overline{\text{W}}$ (Read/Write)** The read/write signal indicates a read operation if at a logic one level and a write operation if at a logic zero.

**RSTI (reset input)** This input signal is used to reset the 68040 microprocessor.

**Table 13-6 Processor Status Bit Encoding**

| PST3 | PST2 | PST1 | PST0 | 68040 status |
|------|------|------|------|--------------|
| 0 | 0 | 0 | 0 | User start/continue current operation |
| 0 | 0 | 0 | 1 | User end current instruction |
| 0 | 0 | 1 | 0 | User branch not taken and end current instruction |
| 0 | 0 | 1 | 1 | User branch taken and end current instruction |
| 0 | 1 | 0 | 0 | User table search |
| 0 | 1 | 0 | 1 | Halted state (double bus fault) |
| 0 | 1 | 1 | 0 | [reserved] |
| 0 | 1 | 1 | 1 | [reserved] |
| 1 | 0 | 0 | 0 | Supervisor start/continue current instruction |
| 1 | 0 | 0 | 1 | Supervisor end current instruction |
| 1 | 0 | 1 | 0 | Supervisor branch not taken and end current instruction |
| 1 | 0 | 1 | 1 | Supervisor branch taken and end current instruction |
| 1 | 1 | 0 | 0 | Supervisor table search |
| 1 | 1 | 0 | 1 | Stopped state (supervisor instruction) |
| 1 | 1 | 1 | 0 | RTE executed |
| 1 | 1 | 1 | 1 | Exception stacking |

$\overline{\text{RSTO}}$ **(reset output)**   This output signal is used to reset peripheral devices connected to the 68040 microprocessor.

**SC1, SC0 (snoop control lines)**   These input lines specify the snoop operation for an alternate bus transfer. Table 13-7 illustrates the encoding and snoop modes requested by these two input lines.

**SIZ1, SIZ0 (transfer size)**   These three-state outputs are used with the dynamic bus sizing capabilities of the 68040 to indicate the number of bytes remaining to be transferred.

$\overline{\text{TA}}$ **(transfer acknowledge)**   This bidirectional pin is used to indicate the completion of a bus transfer. It is also used as an input to determine whether a bus slave has completed a bus transfer.

$\overline{\text{TBI}}$ **(transfer burst inhibit)**   This input prevents the microprocessor from using the burst transfer mode for data storage or retrieval.

$\overline{\text{TCI}}$ **(transfer cache inhibit)**   This input prevents data read from the memory system from being stored in the instruction or data caches.

**TCK (test clock)**   This is a TTL level clock input that is used during testing.

**TDI (test data input)**   This input is used to enter serial test data into the test access port (TAP).

**TDO (test data output)**   This output connection provides output data from the test access port.

$\overline{\text{TEA}}$ **(transfer error acknowledge)**   This input is placed at a logic zero level whenever a slave detects an error condition.

$\overline{\text{TIP}}$ **(transfer in progress)**   This output signal becomes a logic zero whenever the microprocessor is transferring data. At the completion of the transfer, $\overline{\text{TIP}}$ returns to a logic one level and then to its high impedance state.

**TLN1, TLN0 (transfer line number)**   These output pins indicate which set of lines is active for the internal data and instruction caches. These lines are used in a high

**Table 13-7   Snoop Control Line Encoding**

| SC1 | SC0 | Requested operation | |
| --- | --- | --- | --- |
| | | Read access | Write access |
| 0 | 0 | Inhibits snooping. | Inhibits snooping. |
| 0 | 1 | Supplies dirty data and leaves dirty data. | Sinks byte, word, or long-word data. |
| 1 | 0 | Supplies dirty data and marks line invalid. | Invalidates line. |
| 1 | 1 | [reserved] | [reserved] |

**Table 13-8** Transfer Line Number Encoding

| TLN1 | TLN0 | Transfer line number |
|------|------|----------------------|
| 0 | 0 | zero |
| 0 | 1 | one |
| 1 | 0 | two |
| 1 | 1 | three |

performance system to build an external set of snoop filters. Table 13-8 illustrates the encoding found on these pins.

**TM2–TM0 (transfer modifier)** The transfer modifier output connections provide supplemental information for each transfer type as specified by the TT1 and TT0 signals. Tables 13-9 and 13-10 illustrate this supplemental information.

**TMS (test mode select)** This input is used to select a test mode.

**TRST (test reset input)** This input is used to reset the test access port controller.

**TS (transfer start)** The 68040 places this signal at a logic zero level at the start of each bus transfer. The duration of the pulse is equal to one clock cycle. This signal is monitored by the 68040 during alternate bus master accesses to detect the start of each transfer to be snooped.

**TT1, TT0 (transfer type)** The transfer type connections are new to the 68040 microprocessor. These pins are encoded as illustrated in Table 13-11. Note that acknowledge access is used for both interrupts and breakpoints.

**UPA1, UPA0 (user programmable attributes)** These output connections are programmable attribute bits.

**Table 13-9** Normal and MOVE16 Access as Specified by TT1 = 0

| TM2 | TM1 | TM0 | Transfer function |
|-----|-----|-----|-------------------|
| 0 | 0 | 0 | Data cache push access |
| 0 | 0 | 1 | User data access (MOVE16 only) |
| 0 | 1 | 0 | User code access |
| 0 | 1 | 1 | MMU table search data access |
| 1 | 0 | 0 | MMU table search code access |
| 1 | 0 | 1 | Supervisor data access (MOVE16 only) |
| 1 | 1 | 0 | Supervisor code access |
| 1 | 1 | 1 | [reserved] |

**Table 13-10    Alternate Logical Function Code Access**

| TM2 | TM1 | TM0 | Transfer function |
|-----|-----|-----|-------------------|
| 0 | 0 | 0 | Logical function code 0 |
| 0 | 0 | 1 | [reserved] |
| 0 | 1 | 0 | [reserved] |
| 0 | 1 | 1 | Logical function code 3 |
| 1 | 0 | 0 | Logical function code 4 |
| 1 | 0 | 1 | [reserved] |
| 1 | 1 | 0 | [reserved] |
| 1 | 1 | 1 | Logical function code 7 |

### 13-2.2    68040 Operation

The 68040 operates in a fully synchronous mode that uses the BCLK signal to time transfers between the microprocessor and memory. It also uses a PCLK signal to time internal operations. The 68040 supports byte, word, and long-word transfers and also supports line burst transfers through its 32-bit data bus. A line burst transfer fills or empties a 4-long-word section (line) of the instruction or data cache.

The 68040 does not incorporate dynamic bus sizing as did the 68020 and 68030. The 68040 expects to see 32-bit memory. If 8- or 16-bit I/O devices are used with this microprocessor, they must be interfaced to the low order data bus connections. Note this difference from earlier family members. Any interrupt vector must be passed to the microprocessor through data bus connection D7–D0.

### Basic Clock Timing

Basic timing is provided by the BCLK (bus clock) and PCLK (processor clock) inputs. The PCLK signal is twice the frequency of the BCLK signal. If the microprocessor is operated at 25 MHz, the PCLK signal frequency is 50 MHz and the BCLK signal is 25 MHz. Internally, the BLCK signal is synchronized to the PCLK signal with a phase-locked loop.

### Reset Operation

Reset operation is initiated whenever the $\overline{\text{RSTI}}$ input is placed at a logic zero level. Motorola recommends that the $\overline{\text{RSTI}}$ input be grounded for at least 10 BCLK

**Table 13-11    Transfer Type Pin Encoding**

| TT1 | TT2 | Transfer type |
|-----|-----|---------------|
| 0 | 0 | Normal access |
| 0 | 1 | MOVE16 access |
| 1 | 0 | Alternate logical function code access |
| 1 | 1 | Acknowledge access |

periods after the initial application of power. After $\overline{\text{RSTI}}$ has returned to a logic one level, the 68040 internally holds reset active for an additional 128 clocking periods. This assures that external and internal components are properly reset.

As long as the $\overline{\text{RSTI}}$ input is a logic zero, the $\overline{\text{RSTO}}$ output pin is a logic zero. The $\overline{\text{RSTO}}$ pin generates a reset signal for peripherals that require a reset operation for proper initialization. Whenever the RESET instruction is executed, the $\overline{\text{RSTO}}$ pin also becomes a logic zero. The length of time this occurs for the RESET instruction is 512 BCLK periods.

An $\overline{\text{RSTI}}$ input initializes a variety of internal states as follows.

1. Both T1 and T0 are cleared to disable tracing.

2. The S bit is set and the M bit is cleared, placing the microprocessor in the interrupt mode of the supervisor mode.

3. The priority mask is set to 111, which disables all levels of interrupt except interrupt level 7. The interrupt priority inputs are read by the microprocessor during the reset to program the output buffers.

4. The vector base register is initialized to $00000000, placing exception vectors at memory addresses $00000000–$000003FF.

5. Both data and instruction caches are disabled because reset clears the cache enable bits in the cache control register.

6. Translation is disabled because the translation enable bit is cleared.

7. Vectors 0 and 1 are generated, which contain the initial values of the interrupt stack pointer and the program counter.

8. The first long-word of the reset exception vector (vector 0) is loaded into the interrupt stack pointer (ISP).

9. The second long-word of the reset exception vector (vector 1) is loaded into the program counter (PC).

10. The first four long-words addressed by the program counter are fetched.

The output buffers, as mentioned, are programmed during the reset operation by placing a code on the three $\overline{\text{IPL}}$ inputs. Programming allows the user to select either the large or small buffers. Large buffers have a 4 $\Omega$ output impedance and can sink up to 50 mA of current. Large buffers are often used for large systems. Small buffers have an output impedance of 30 $\Omega$ and can sink 5 mA of current. Small buffers are often used for small systems. Table 13-12 illustrates the effect of these three $\overline{\text{IPL}}$ inputs at the time of a reset.

In addition to selecting the mode of operation for output buffers, the hardware reset operation also selects the multiplexed bus mode and the data latch enable mode. The multiplexed bus mode is chosen by placing a logic zero on the $\overline{\text{CDIS}}$ pin during the reset. The data latch enable mode is selected by placing a logic zero on the $\overline{\text{MDIS}}$ input during a reset. Figure 13-20 illustrates a reset circuit that allows the application of the $\overline{\text{IPL}}$, $\overline{\text{CDIS}}$, and $\overline{\text{MDIS}}$ signals during a reset operation.

**Table 13-12    Output Buffer Selection via the Interrupt Priority Inputs During a Reset**

| Pin | Buffers controlled |
| --- | --- |
| $\overline{IPL2}$ | Data bus buffers (D31–D0) |
| $\overline{IPL1}$ | Address bus and transfer attribute buffers (A31–A0, $\overline{CIOUT}$, $\overline{LOCK}$, $\overline{LOCKE}$, R/$\overline{W}$, SIZ1–SIZ0, TLN1, TLN0, TM2–TM0, TTI, TTO, UPA1, and UPA0) |
| $\overline{IPL0}$ | Miscellaneous control buffers ($\overline{BB}$, $\overline{BR}$, $\overline{IPEND}$, $\overline{MI}$, $\overline{PST3}$–$\overline{PST0}$, $\overline{RSTO}$, $\overline{TA}$, $\overline{TIP}$, and $\overline{TS}$) |

NOTE: A logic one selects small buffers and a logic zero selects large buffers.

In the multiplexed bus mode, the address and data bus connections are wired together to form a single 32-bit bus. In this mode, the combination address/data bus contains address information during the assertion of $\overline{TS}$ (transfer start) and data at other times. This connection is used when the number of bus connections in a system must be reduced.

The data latch enable mode allows data to be latched into the microprocessor by

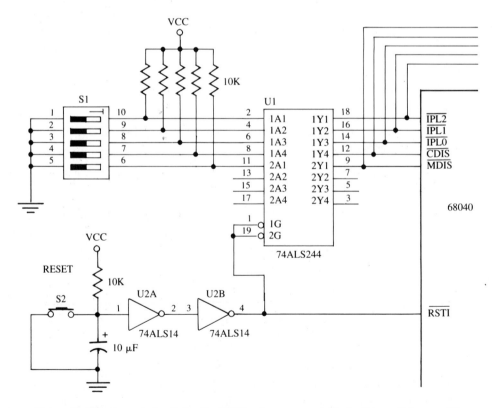

**Figure 13-20    A reset circuit for the 68040 microprocessor illustrating switches used to select different buffers, data latch mode operation, and multiplexed bus operation.**

the DLE (data latch enable) signal. Latching is normally accomplished by the BCLK signal at the end of each transfer.

## Cache Operation

The cache memory sizes are increased on the 68040 microprocessor. The instruction cache is increased from the 256 bytes found in the 68020 and 68030 to 4k bytes in the 68040. The 256-byte data cache in the 68030 is also increased to 4k bytes on the 68040 microprocessor. In addition to changing the sizes of the caches, Motorola changed the composition of the cache control registers (CACR) and the operation of the caches. A snoop controller also has been added to the 68040.

The snoop controller allows the 68040 to monitor bus activity when another bus controller (DMA controller or another microprocessor) has access to the buses. The snoop controller allows the 68040 to update its internal caches when the alternate master has control of the buses. This allows the 68040 to keep current information in its caches even though it is not controlling the system buses. This operation is called *snooping*.

Each location in either cache stores 4 long-words of data. This means that each cache contains 64 locations of 128 bits each. Whenever new information (a cache miss) is stored in either cache, 4 long-words are fetched into a cache location. The rationale behind this is that programs are sequential and so are data. By filling 4 long-words, the amount of memory access tends to be less.

The bus operates in the burst mode whenever a cache location is filled. Recall from the 68030 that it took five clock periods to read 4 long-words of data during a burst. The 68040 also fills a cache location in five clocks. This is probably the most efficient possible use of the system buses.

Figure 13-21 illustrates the cache control register (CACR) for the 68040 microprocessor. If you compare this register to the CACR of the 68030, you will notice that it is greatly simplified. There are only two bits in this register that control the cache: the DE bit, which enables the data cache, and the IE bit, which enables the instruction cache. A logic one placed in either DE or IE will enable the associated cache. A logic zero will disable it.

Another difference between the 68030 and the 68040 is that the 68040 has instructions that apply to the cache. These instructions are CINV and CPUSH. The CINV instruction allows selective invalidation of cache entries. The CPUSH instruction pushes all the dirty selected cache locations to memory and then invalidates all selected cache locations. These instructions are covered in more detail in Section 13-2.7 which explains all the new instructions for the 68040 microprocessor.

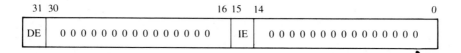

**Figure 13-21   The cache control register (CACR) of the 68040 microprocessor.**

### 13-2.3  68040 Memory Interface

Memory interface to the 68040 is different from any earlier family members because of new control signals that are added to this microprocessor. The control signals used for data transfer are R/$\overline{\text{W}}$, SIZ1, SIZ0, A1, A0, $\overline{\text{TS}}$, and $\overline{\text{TA}}$.

Table 13-13 illustrates the SIZ1, SIZ0, A1, and A0 signals that are used to validate different size bus transfers. They are similar in function to the same bits in the 68030 microprocessor. The main difference is the last case in the table, for a line transfer, which for the 68040 is a 32-bit transfer that is used to fill one of the internal caches.

As with the 68030 or 68020, the bus transfer size is important only for write operations. A read operation may always apply 32-bit memory or I/O data to the data bus even if only a byte is read. During a write operation only the correct sections of the memory or I/O are enabled to transfer data. The sections enabled are indicated in Table 13-13 and are implemented with a simple combinational logic circuit as depicted in Figure 13-22.

### Bus Cycles

Bus cycles in the 68040 bus system appear in two forms: synchronous and burst bus cycles. There are no asynchronous transfers in the 68040 system. Before memory or I/O is interfaced, the operation of these bus cycles must be understood. A synchronous transfer requires two system BCLK clocks, while a burst transfer requires five BCLK clocks to transfer 4 long-words of data. This is identical to the synchronous and burst operations of the 68030, although the control signals are different in the 68040 system.

Figure 13-23 illustrates the timing diagram for a nonburst synchronous transfer. The first clocking period is used to send the address and control signals to the memory. In the second clock, the data are transferred between the microprocessor and the memory or I/O connected to the buses.

**Table 13-13   Bus Activity for Byte, Word, and Long-Word Transfers**

| Size | A1 | A0 | SIZ1 | SIZ0 | Data Bus Selection | | | |
|------|----|----|------|------|---------|---------|--------|-------|
| | | | | | D31–D24 | D23–D16 | D15–D8 | D7–D0 |
| Byte | 0 | 0 | 0 | 1 | V | — | — | — |
| Byte | 0 | 1 | 0 | 1 | — | V | — | — |
| Byte | 1 | 0 | 0 | 1 | — | — | V | — |
| Byte | 1 | 1 | 0 | 1 | — | — | — | V |
| Word | 0 | 0 | 1 | 0 | V | V | — | — |
| Word | 1 | 0 | 1 | 0 | — | — | V | V |
| Long-word | X | X | 0 | 0 | V | V | V | V |
| Line | X | X | 1 | 1 | V | V | V | V |

NOTES: X = don't care and V = valid information.

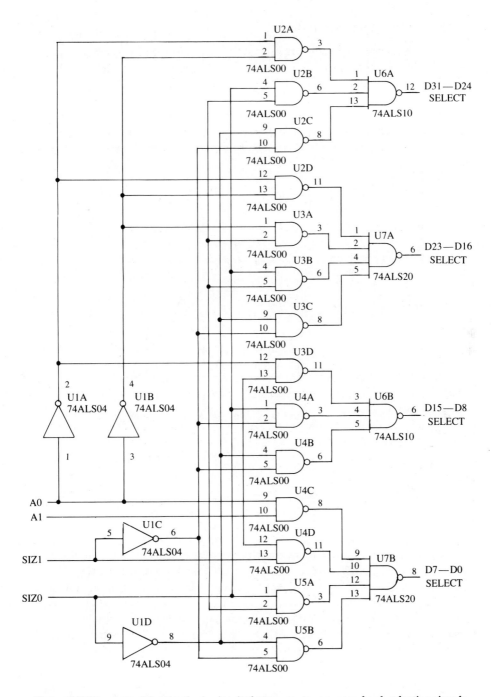

**Figure 13-22** A combination logic circuit that generates memory bank selection signals for the 68040 microprocessor.

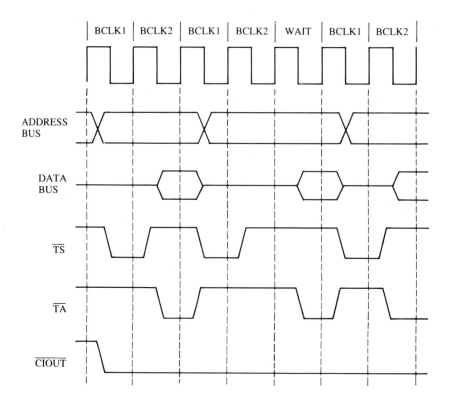

**Figure 13-23**    The synchronous bus operation timing diagram of the 68040 microprocessor.

During BCLK1 the microprocessor outputs the transfer attribute information (LOCK, LOCKE, SIZ1, SIZ0, TT1, TT0, CIOUT, TM2–TM0, TLN1, TLN0, UPA1, and UPA0), the R/W̄ signal, TS (transfer start), TIP (transfer in progress), and the memory address on the address bus. If large buffers are selected, the transfer attribute information, the R/W̄ signal, the memory address, and all other signals mentioned appear, assuming a 25 MHz BLCK signal, within 21 ns after the start of BCLK1. If small buffers are selected, this time is within 30 ns. The CIOUT (cache inhibit output) is asserted to indicate to the external system that the transfer is a synchronous transfer rather than a burst transfer.

The BCLK2 period allows the memory to access data and transfer information. At the end of BCLK2, the data bus is sampled with a setup time of 5 ns and a hold time of 4 ns. This presents a memory data valid window of 9 ns in duration at the end of BCLK2. The data write window is substantially larger, although measured differently. Write data appear within 23 ns (large buffer) or 32 ns (small buffer) after the start of BCLK2. Data are held on the data bus connection until 9 ns after the end of BCLK2.

Read access times for a BLCK frequency of 25 MHz (40 ns) are then equal to two clocks minus the time it takes for the address to appear on the address bus minus the setup time requirement at the end of BCLK2. Two clock cycles require 80 ns. Read access time is then 80 ns − 21 ns − 5 ns, or 54 ns for large buffers. Small buffers allow slightly less access time (45 ns).

Access time is stretched by inserting wait clocking periods (see Figure 13-23) as with other family members. If the $\overline{\text{TA}}$ transfer access signal is delayed beyond the end of BLCK2, wait states are inserted as illustrated in the timing diagram of Figure 13-23. The $\overline{\text{TA}}$ signal must become a logic zero at least 10 ns before the end of BCLK2 to prevent the insertion of any wait clocks. It must be held low at least 2 ns after BCLK2 before returning to a logic one level.

Burst mode operation is similar to synchronous operation. With burst mode, four 32-bit long-words of data are transferred in five clocking periods. This is considerably faster than synchronous transfer. Bursts are used to fill or unload the internal cache memory within the microprocessor.

Figure 13-24 illustrates the burst mode timing diagram for the 68040 micro-processor. Notice that burst mode, as mentioned, transfers 4 long-words of data in

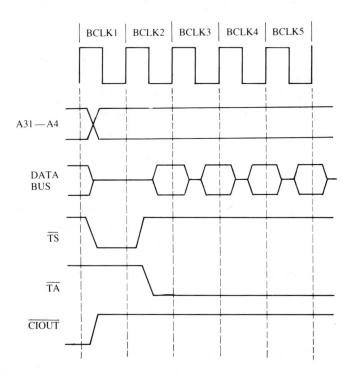

**Figure 13-24  The burst mode bus operation timing diagram of the 68040 micro-processor.**

five clocking periods. Burst mode is used to fill a line of 4 long-words in either the instruction or data cache.

During the first clocking period, the address, transfer attributes, and control signals appear in the 68040 timing. The microprocessor also places a logic zero on the $\overline{\text{TS}}$ line to indicate the start of the transfer. The $\overline{\text{CIOUT}}$ signal is placed at a logic one to indicate a burst transfer.

During the second clock, the microprocessor places a logic one on the $\overline{\text{TS}}$ signal. The contents of the first long-word data are pair placed on the data bus, and the memory or I/O device places a logic zero on the $\overline{\text{TA}}$ line. If a burst transfer is not supported, the external device places a logic zero on the $\overline{\text{TBI}}$ line to abort the burst. Although $\overline{\text{TBI}}$ is not illustrated, its timing is identical to the $\overline{\text{TA}}$ signal if a burst is inhibited.

The 68040 holds all attributes including the address constant during clocks BCLK3, BCLK4, and BCLK5. The external system is responsible for selecting the address and placing data from the next three long-word memory locations on the data bus during these three clocks. This causes 4 long-words of data to be transferred to the microprocessor in five clocking periods. Address connections A2 and A3 are changed by the external system so that four long-words of data are transferred in burst mode.

Figure 13-25 illustrates a memory system connected to the 68040 microprocessor. This memory system supports either synchronous transfers or burst transfers. Burst transfer addresses are generated by a circuit depicted in this illustration. Compare this illustration with Figure 13-8, which contains the burst mode memory system for the 68030 microprocessor. In this circuit, the $\overline{\text{CIOUT}}$ signal initiates a burst transfer.

### 13-2.4    68040 Memory Management

Memory management is handled by two independent memory management units (MMUs) within the 68040. The 68030 contained one MMU. A separate MMU exists for the instruction and date caches in the 68040. The MMUs within the 68040 perform the same function as the MMU within the 68030. That is, the MMU translates a logical address into a physical address.

Figure 13-26 illustrates the programming model for the memory management unit within the 68040 microprocessor. If this model is compared to the 68030 MMU programming model, one notices that there are two sets of transparent translation registers: one for the instruction cache and one for the data cache. Other differences also exist.

The MMU in the 68030 had more translation table levels available. The 68030 could have up to five levels of address translation. The 68040 supports no more than three levels of translation. The width of the fields used to address translation tables is variable in the 68030. In the 68040 it is fixed except for the TIC field, which is either 5 or 6 bits.

Page sizes are also fixed in the 68040, at either 4k bytes or 8k bytes. In the 68030, page sizes are variable, from 256 bytes up to 32k bytes. Apparently the flexibility offered with the 68030 page structure is not required in practice. It is important that any new software developed use only 4k and 8k byte page sizes.

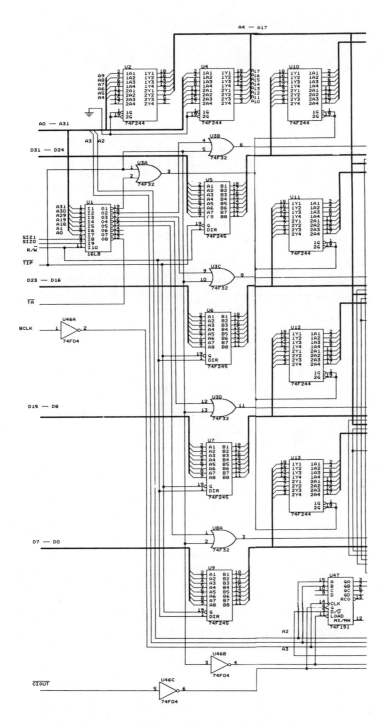

**Figure 13-25** A 256k byte memory system for the 68040 microprocessor that supports both synchronous and burst mode operation.

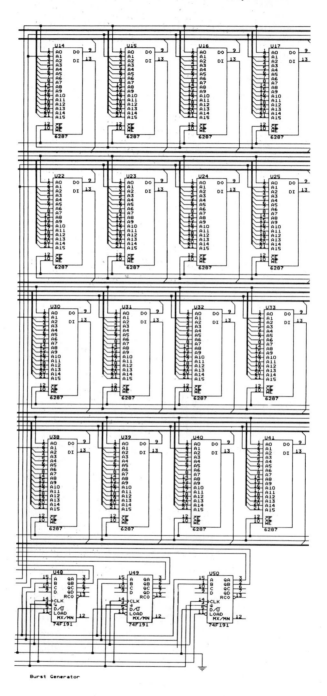

Figure 13-25    Continued.

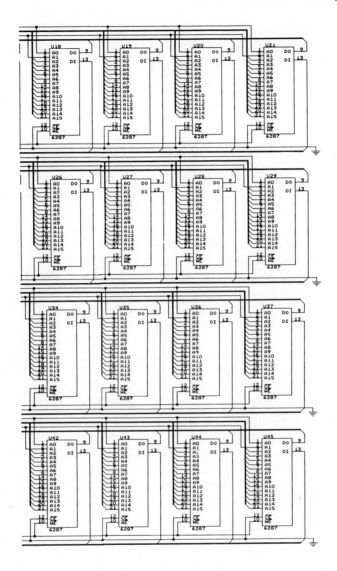

Figure 13-25 Continued.

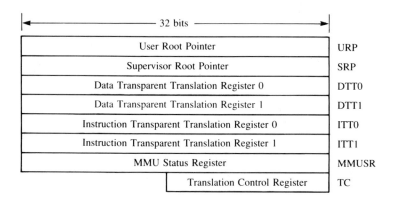

**Figure 13-26   The memory management unit (MMU) programming model for the 68040 microprocessor.**

Figure 13-27 illustrates a logical address in the 68040 microprocessor and depicts how this logical address is translated into a physical address via the translation tables. Here the logical address is $932A1100 and it is translated into physical address $30000100. This example assumes that the page size is 4k bytes, as indicated by the 12-bit offset address of $100.

Notice how the first 7 bits of the logical address are used to index the root table addressed by the root pointer. There are actually two root pointers, one for the supervisor mode root table and one for the user mode root table. In this example the $49 at level TIA is used to address entry $49 in the root table. Because the root pointer is loaded with a $00001000, the root table begins at location $00001000 and extends to location $000011FF.

Entry $49, of the level A table, addresses the level B table plus the contents of the TIB field of the logical address. The level B table entry, $4A, is addressed by the $4A in field TIB of the logical address. The contents of the $4A entry in the level B table address the level C table.

Here a 6-bit code from TIC is used to locate entry $21 in the level C table. Although not shown in the illustration, this entry contains $30000000, which is added to the offset of the logical address ($100) to generate physical memory location $30000100.

Notice from this example that if all logical addresses are translated into physical addresses, quite a bit of memory is required for the translation tables. The level A table contains 128 entries of 4 bytes each, so it requires 512 bytes of memory. There are up to 128 different level B tables, each requiring 512 bytes of memory to store 128 different entries. This means that 128 × 512 bytes (64k bytes) of memory is required to store all 128 level B tables.

Finally there are a maximum of 16k different level C tables. Because each level C table has 64 entries in this example, and each entry is 4 bytes, each level C table requires 256 bytes of memory. Because there are a maximum of 16k level C tables,

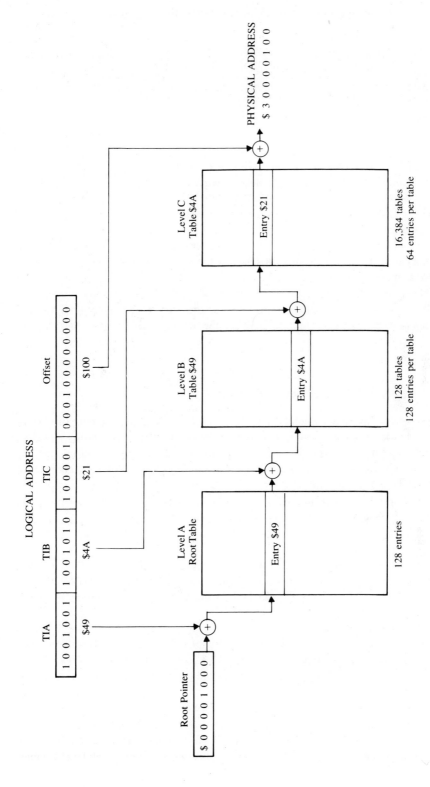

**Figure 13-27** Translation of a logical address into a physical address by the 68040 memory management unit.

this means that all level C tables require 16k × 256 (4M bytes) of memory. Together, the three tables require up to 4M + 64k + 512 bytes of memory. Because there are separate tables for the user and supervisory modes, more than 8M bytes of memory is required to store tables for complete address translation. The maximum number of tables is usually required because there is no way to prejudge what logical addresses will be required by software. This is true only in a system that expects to see a logical address that ranges in value from $00000000 to $FFFFFFFF. If software is written to limit the address range to something less than the maximum, fewer translation tables are required.

The entire idea of address translation is to allow a software system of any size to be executed in a memory system of any size. How is this possible? It is possible because each of the table entries indicates whether a memory page exists. If it does not, pages are swapped between the disk and actually memory to provide a virtual memory system. This gives the illusion that the computer contains all 4G bytes of physical memory even though it does not.

This same idea (virtual memory) allows each of multiple users to see a memory system of 4G bytes even though the computer addresses only a total of 4G bytes of memory space. Through spooling, between the main memory and the disk memory system, a memory system of virtually any size can be made to appear to be present in the system.

### 13-2.5   68040 Floating-Point Arithmetic Unit

Unlike the earlier family members, which require an external floating-point arithmetic coprocessor to accomplish floating-point arithmetic, the 68040 contains an internal floating-point unit that executes a subset of the floating-point instructions found in the 68881/68882 floating-point coprocessor. Please review the contents of Chapter 11 if you have not already studied the 68881/68882 floating-point coprocessor. Also review Appendix C, which contains a complete listing of floating-point coprocessor instructions; an asterisk (*) appears next to the instructions that apply to the 68040 microprocessor's floating-point unit.

Floating-point instructions that are not implemented by the 68040 microprocessor cause an F-line exception that must be dealt with by an exception handler. Typically, this exception handler is responsible for emulating the unimplemented floating-point instructions. Table 13-14 lists the unimplemented floating-point instructions that require emulation for full compatibility with the 68881/68882 floating-point coprocessor.

As indicated in Table 13-14, many of the trigonometric functions and logarithmic instructions are not implemented. Also note that the single-precision multiply and divide instructions are not implemented by the 68040. Software is written either so that these instructions are not used or so that the 68040 will emulate them when they are used by a program. Emulation drastically reduces execution time for the instructions not implemented by the 68040 floating-point unit.

The packed real decimal format for data (P) is not implemented in the 68040 floating-point unit. If packed real decimal numbers are used, the unimplemented

**Table 13-14    68881/68882 Instructions That Are Not Implemented
in the 68040 Microprocessor**

| Type | Instructions |
|---|---|
| Monadic | FACOS, FASIN, FATAN, FATANH, FCOS, FCOSH, FETOX, FETOXM1, FGETEXP, FGETMAN, FINT, FINTRZ, FLOG10, FLOG2, FLOGN, FLOGNP1, FSIN, FSINCOS, FSINH, FTAN, FTANH, FTENTOX, FTWOTOX |
| Dyadic | FMOD, FREM, FSCAL, FSGLDIV, FSGLMUL |
| Miscellaneous | FMOVECR |

data type exception occurs. In this case, the packed real decimal data format must be supported by software emulation. Other floating-point unit data types that must be supported are denormalized and unnormalized data types.

### 13-2.6    68040 Exceptions and Interrupts

Exceptions and interrupts on the 68040 microprocessor are similar to those for earlier family members. Like earlier versions of this microprocessor, the 68040 supports 256 different interrupt vectors using a vector table 1024 bytes in length. This table is initially assigned to memory locations $00000000–$000003FF, as it is on earlier family members. As introduced with the 68020, the 68040 also contains a vector base register (VBR) that allows the vector table to be placed in any area of the memory system.

Table 13-15 lists all the interrupt vectors available in the 68040 microprocessor, along with any dedicated usage. Notice that many of the exception and interrupt vectors are identical to those for earlier family members.

The bus error exception (vector 2) is called an access fault on the 68040 microprocessor. This exception occurs for an external bus error or an internal MMU address translation fault. External logic can signal a bus error through the $\overline{\text{TEA}}$ (transfer error acknowledge) input line. On earlier family members, a bus error was signaled through the $\overline{\text{BERR}}$ input line. Processing a transfer error is almost the same as processing a bus error. In fact, the main change is the nomenclature.

A major change in the exception/interrupt structure is the way that multiple exceptions are processed. Table 13-16 gives the priority of the exceptions. Notice that there are quite a few more priority groupings. These are added so that multiple exceptions can be processed in a pragmatic manner. In the 68040, the exception with the highest priority level (lowest number) is processed first. The remaining exceptions are regenerated after the exception has been processed and the current instruction restarted. Because of this, multiple levels of exceptions are processed without loss.

Suppose that a data access error and an interrupt occur simultaneously. In this example, the microprocessor would process the data access error. Upon return from the data access exception handler, the interrupt would take effect.

**Table 13-15    The 68040 Exception/Interrupt Vector Table**

| Vector number | Address | Function |
|---|---|---|
| 0 | 000 | Initial value of the ISP upon reset |
| 1 | 004 | Initial value of the PC upon reset |
| 2 | 008 | Access fault |
| 3 | 00C | Address error |
| 4 | 010 | Illegal instruction |
| 5 | 014 | Integer divide by zero |
| 6 | 018 | CHK and CHK2 instructions |
| 7 | 01C | FTRAPcc, TRAPcc, and TRAPV instructions |
| 8 | 020 | Privilege violaton |
| 9 | 024 | Trace |
| A | 028 | Line 1010 emulation (A-line) |
| B | 02C | Line 1111 emulation (F-line) |
| C | 030 | [reserved] |
| D | 034 | [unused by 68040] |
| E | 038 | Format error |
| F | 03C | Uninitialized interrupt |
| 10–17 | 040–05C | [reserved] |
| 18 | 060 | Spurious interrupt |
| 19 | 064 | Level 1 autovector interrupt |
| 1A | 068 | Level 2 autovector interrupt |
| 1B | 06C | Level 3 autovector interrupt |
| 1C | 070 | Level 4 autovector interrupt |
| 1D | 074 | Level 5 autovector interrupt |
| 1E | 078 | Level 6 autovector interrupt |
| 1F | 07C | Level 7 autovector interrupt |
| 20–2F | 080–0BC | TRAP #0–TRAP #15 instructions |
| 30 | 0C0 | Floating-point branch/set on unordered condition |
| 31 | 0C4 | Floating-point inexact result |
| 32 | 0C8 | Floating-point divide by zero |
| 33 | 0CC | Floating-point underflow |
| 34 | 0D0 | Floating-point operand error |
| 35 | 0D4 | Floating-point overflow |
| 36 | 0D8 | Floating-point signaling NAN |
| 37 | 0DC | Floating-point unimplemented data type |
| 38–3A | 0E0–0E8 | [unused by 68040] |
| 3B–3F | 0EC–0FC | [reserved] |
| 40–FF | 100–3FC | User-defined vectors |

Exception processing occurs in the same manner as it did for other family members. That is, when the exception is recognized, the microprocessor performs the following steps as it processes the exception.

**1.** An internal copy of SR is made and temporarily saved.

**2.** The S bit is set, selecting supervisor mode.

**Table 13-16**  The Priorities of the Exception/Interrupts Structure
of the 68040 Microprocessor

| Priority | Type | Comment |
|---|---|---|
| 0 | Reset | Aborts all processing and saves nothing. |
| 1 | Access error | Aborts current instruction. Can have pending trace, floating-point post-instruction, or unimplemented floating-point instruction exceptions. |
| 2 | Floating-point preinstruction | Exception processing begins before current floating-point instruction is executed. Instruction is restarted upon return from exception. |
| 3 | BKPT #n, CHK, CHK2, divide by zero, FTRAPcc, RTE, TRAP #n, TRAPV | Exception processing is part of the instruction. |
|  | Illegal instruction; line A, line F privilege violation | Exception processing begins before the instruction is executed. |
|  | Unimplemented floating-point instruction | Exception processing begins after memory operands have been fetched and before the instruction is executed. |
| 4 | Floating-point postinstruction | Reported for FMOVE to memory only. Exception processing begins when the FMOVE instruction and previous exception processing have been completed. |
| 5 | Address error | Reported after all previous instructions and associated exceptions have been completed. |
| 6 | Trace | Exception processing begins when current instruction or previous exception processing has been completed. |
| 7 | Instruction access error | Reported after all previous instructions and associated exceptions have been completed. |
| 8 | Interrupt | Exception processing begins when current instruction or previous exception processing has been completed. |

**3.** Tracing is inhibited by clearing both T1 and T0.

**4.** The exception vector number is calculated.

**5.** The current processor context is saved as an exception stack frame. If the exception is an interrupt, the processor clears the M bit and builds a second stack frame on the interrupt stack.

**6.** The microprocessor uses the exception vector to access the exception handler.

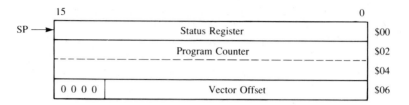

**Figure 13-28**    The two-long-word stack frame for the 68040 microprocessor. Note that the stack frame may contain number 0000, as illustrated, or number 0001.

### 68040 Stack Frames

As with earlier family members, the 68040 builds different stack frames for different types of exception. Stack frames are used for all exceptions. These frames vary in length from 2 to 25 long-words.

Figure 13-28 illustrates the two-long-word stack frame. This is the shortest and the most common of all stack frames. Events that cause this stack frame to be stored are interrupts, format errors, TRAP instructions, illegal instructions, A- and F-line instructions, privilege violations, and floating-point preinstruction exceptions. This stack frame includes the status register, the program counter, and the vector offset. The type number is 0000 or 0001 for this shortest of all stack frames. Type 0000 is saved on the master stack, and type 0001 is a copy used during an interrupt, which is saved on the interrupt stack.

A three-long-word stack frame exists for processing the following exception types: CHK, CHK2, TRAPcc, FTRAPcc, TRAPV, trace, divide by zero, unimplemented floating-point instruction, floating-point postinstruction, and address error. Figure 13-29 illustrates the contents of this stack frame, whose type number is 0010 or 0011. All exceptions listed are type 0010 except for the floating-point postinstruction exception, which is type 0011.

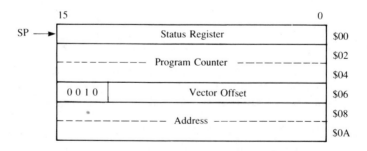

**Figure 13-29**    The three-long-word stack frame for the 68040 microprocessor. Note that this stack frame is numbered either 0010 or 0011.

The three-long-word stack frame contains the status register, the program counter, and the vector offset, like the two-long-word stack frame. The difference is that the third long-word contains the address of the instruction that caused the error or the effective address of a floating-point instruction.

Access error stack frames are much larger, as indicated in Figure 13-30. Notice that this stack frame contains 15 long-words of information. This type of stack frame has type number 0111 and occurs for an access fault exception (vector type number 2). On earlier family members, this stack frame is called a bus error stack frame.

One of several registers saved as part of an access error stack frame is the special status word (SSW). Figure 13-31 depicts the bit pattern of the SSW and the definition of each bit. This special status word indicates whether the access fault was caused by access to the instruction stream, the data stream, or both.

In addition to the SSW, the access error stack frame includes three writeback status bytes, which have the format illustrated in Figure 13-32. The writeback status bytes identify three possible writebacks that might be pending after the faulted access.

The floating-point unit within the 68040 generates several different state frames. Figure 13-33 illustrates the state frame generated for a busy state. A state frame is not to be confused with a stack frame. The state frame is created whenever the FSAVE instruction is executed and stored in memory. State frames are usually stored in memory in response to an exception. Notice that this state frame contains 25 long-words of information and is the largest state frame generated by the FSAVE instruction in the 68040 microprocessor. This state frame is stored by the FSAVE instruction, which saves the current floating-point context. The busy state frame is reloaded by the FRESTORE instruction.

The busy state frame contains many areas that are reserved for internal storage by the 68040 floating-point unit. Areas that are not reserved are defined in the following paragraphs.

The CU_SAVEPC field contains the internal microprogram counter for the floating-point unit. This number represents the program location in the microcoded sequence within the floating-point unit.

The WBTS, WBTE, WBTM, and SBIT fields contain an internal data format that represents an exceptional operand. This is generated for an E3 exception.

The FPIARCU, the floating-point instruction address register, contains the address for the conversion unit.

The CMDREG1B and CMDREG3B fields are command words. A type E1 exception uses CMDREG1B and a type E3 exception uses CMDREG3B.

The STAG and DTAG fields contain a 3-bit code that indicates the data type of the source and destination operands, respectively. Table 13-17 illustrates the coding of the three bits.

The E1 bit is set for an E1-type exception. This occurs whenever the floating-point unit is operating in the conversion unit pipeline stage of an instruction.

The E3 bit is set for an E3-type exception. This occurs whenever the floating-point unit is operating in the normalization unit pipeline stage of an instruction.

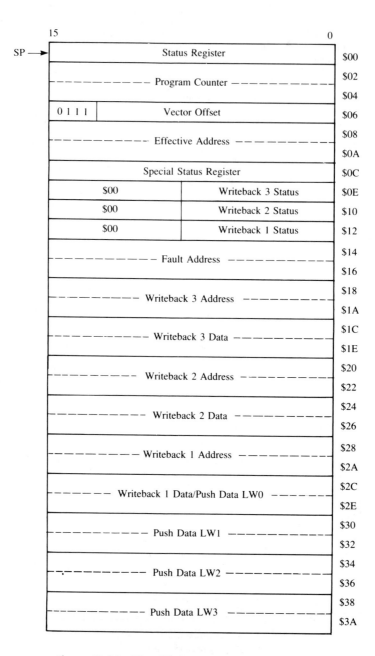

**Figure 13-30   The 68040 access error stack frame.**

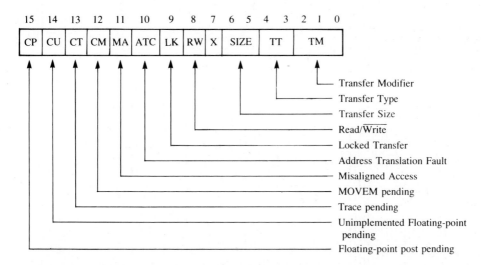

**Figure 13-31** The special status word (SSW) from the access error stack frame of Figure 13-30.

The ETS, ETE, and ETM fields contain the source operand in extended-precision form. The FPTS, FPTE, and FPTM fields contain the destination operand in extended-precision form.

Other state frames that occur for the floating-point unit appear in Figure 13-34. Note that this illustration contains three state frames. Two (null and idle) are generated with the FSAVE instruction; the third (unimplemented) is generated by an unimplemented floating-point unit instruction and also saved in memory by the FSAVE instruction.

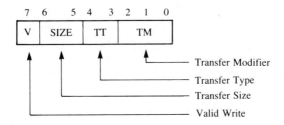

**Figure 13-32** A writeback status byte from the access error stack frame in Figure 13-30.

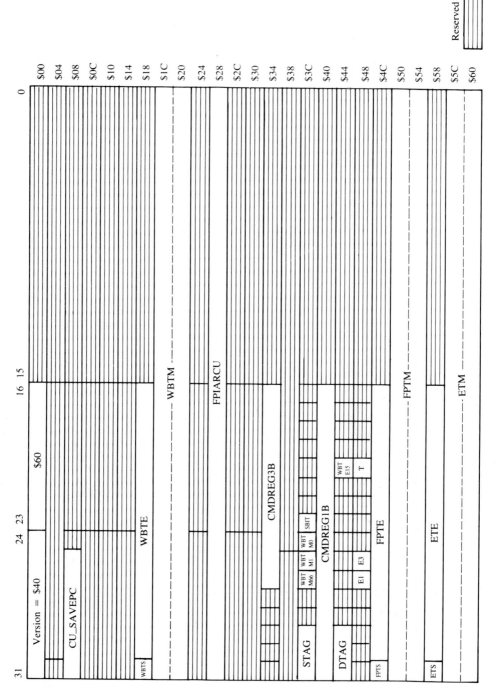

**Figure 13-33** The 68040 floating-point unit's busy state frame.

**Table 13-17**  The Coding for the STAG and DTAG
Fields of the 68040 Floating-Point Unit Busy State Frame

| Code | Type |
|------|------|
| 000 | normalized |
| 001 | zero |
| 010 | infinity |
| 011 | NAN |
| 100 | extended-precision, denormalized or unnormalized |
| 101 | single- or double-precision, denormalized |

### 13-2.7  68040 Software

The instruction set for the 68040 is comparable to the 68030 using a companion 68881/68882 floating-point coprocessor except for a few additional instructions. Also recall that some of the floating-point instructions for the 68881/68882 have been deleted from the floating-point unit within the 68040.

Before the changes in the instruction set are discussed, let us view the programming model for the 68040 microprocessor (Figure 13-35). To see that it is basically a combination of the 68030 microprocessor with the 68881/68882 floating-point coprocessor, compare this illustration with Figures 13-18 and Figure 11-8, the programming models for the 68030 microprocessor and the 68881/68882 floating-point coprocessor, respectively.

### New 68040 Instructions

Instructions that are new to the 68040 microprocessor appear in Table 13-18. Notice that there are only three new instructions added to the 68040 microprocessor instruction set. Two of these three new instructions are used with the cache system, namely the data, instruction, and address translation caches. The third instruction is radically new and allows 16 bytes of information to be moved from a source address into a destination address.

For example, the MOVE16 (A2)+,(A3)+ instruction moves 16 bytes of data from the area of memory addressed by A2 into the area of memory addressed by A3. Both pointers are incremented by a factor of 16. This instruction is very efficient because it uses burst mode to accomplish the 16-byte transfer. This means that all 16 bytes are transferred in 10 BCLK periods. Five BCLKs are required to read source data and another five to store the 16 bytes. Other forms of the MOVE16 instruction are given in Table 13-19.

### 13-2.8  68040 Test Access Port

The 68040 incorporates a test access port that is fully compatible with IEEE 1149.1 (Standard Test Access Port and Boundary Scan Architecture). The 68040 hardware uses five pin connections, two test registers, and a 16-state controller to implement the test access port (TAP).

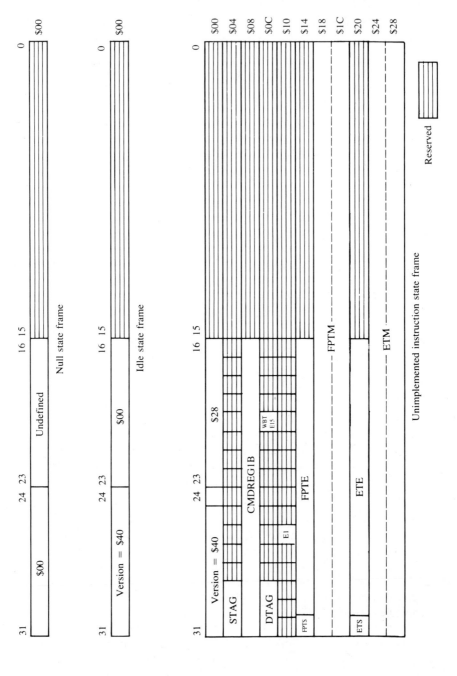

**Figure 13-34** The null, idle, and unimplemented state frames of the 68040 floating-point unit.

Table 13-20 lists the TAP signals with a brief description of the function of each. Inside the 68040, the TAP contains an instruction register and a boundary scan register, which implement testing via the test access port.

Figure 13-36 illustrates the internal construction of the test access port. As mentioned, the structure of the TAP includes an instruction register that is 3 bits wide and a boundary scan register that is 184 bits wide. The instruction register allows the TAP to perform five different instructions, of which three are not used at this time. Table 13-21 presents the five instructions performed by the TAP.

### The EXTEST Instruction

The external test instruction (EXTEST) selects the 184-bit boundary scan register that includes cells for all device signals and clock pins on the 68040 microprocessor. Each cell activates a pin on the microprocessor so that electrical continuity can be tested on the external circuit board. The results of these tests on all microprocessor pins are shifted into the boundary scan register for later access. This allows the microprocessor interface to be tested.

### The Sample/Preload Instruction

The sample/preload instruction is used to obtain a copy of the contents of the boundary scan register. This allows the system control and data signals to be sampled and output after the EXTEST instruction has been executed.

The sample/preload instruction also allows all the cells in the boundary scan register to be initialized prior to the execution of the EXTEST instruction. Initialization assures that the cells in the boundary scan register contain known data for the boundary scan test.

### The Shutdown Instruction

The shutdown instruction disables the PCLK and BCLK signals on the 68040. This allows these pins to be clocked at any rate so that the interfaces to the microprocessor can be tested.

### The BYPASS Instruction

The BYPASS instruction connects the TDI pin to the TDO pin through a one-clock time delay. This effectively bypasses the boundary scan register so that other system tests can be performed.

### 13-2.9   68040 Bus Arbitration

Bus arbitration for the 68040 is totally different from earlier family members. In the earlier versions of the 68040, bus arbitration was handled by the $\overline{\text{BGACK}}$ pin. On the 68040 microprocessor, bus arbitration is handled by an external arbiter. Even though some of the control pins are labeled the same as earlier family members, they do not function in the same manner.

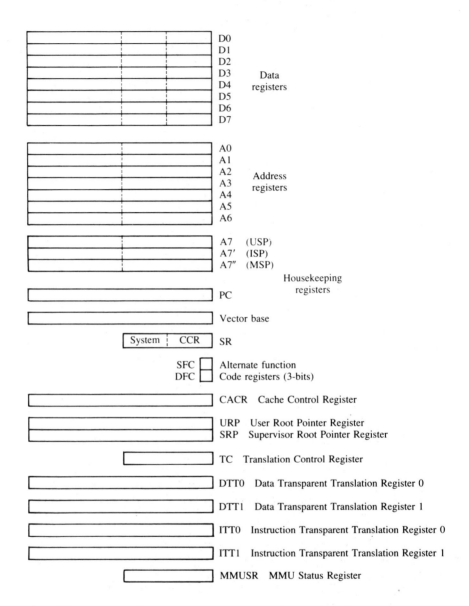

Figure 13-35    The programming model of the 68040 microprocessor.

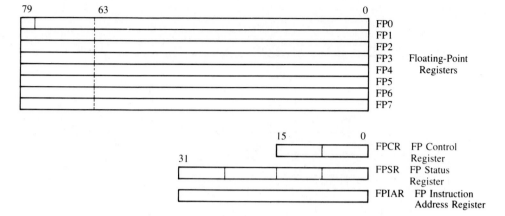

Figure 13-35   Continued.

Table 13-18   New 68040 Instructions

| Instruction | Function |
|---|---|
| CINV | Invalidates cache entries. |
| CPUSH | Pushes and invalidates cache entries. |
| MOVE16 | Moves a 16-byte block. |

Table 13-19   The Allowable Forms
of the MOVE16 Instruction

| Form | Example |
|---|---|
| (Ax)+,(Ay)+ | MOVE16 (A2)+,(A4)+ |
| xxx.L,(An) | MOVE16 $30000,(A2) |
| xxx.L,(An)+ | MOVE16 $44000,(A5)+ |
| (An),xxx.L | MOVE16 (A2),$340000 |
| (An)+,xxx.L | MOVE16 (A3)+,$A0000 |

Table 13-20   The TAP Signals

| Signal | Description | Function |
|---|---|---|
| TCK | Tests clock signal. | Synchronizes the test logic. |
| TDI | Tests data input. | Inputs serial test data to the TAP. |
| TDO | Tests data output. | Outputs serial data from the TAP. |
| TMS | Tests mode select. | Sequences the TAP controller's state machine. |
| TRST | Tests reset. | Resets the TAP controller. |

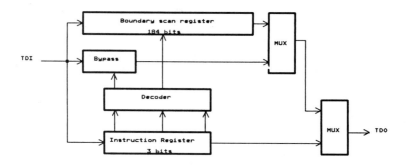

**Figure 13-36    The internal structure of the test access port (TAP).**

The 68040 has three pins devoted to bus arbitration or DMA: $\overline{BR}$ (bus request), $\overline{BG}$ (bus grant), and $\overline{BB}$ (bus busy). The 68040 requests access to the system buses by placing a logic zero on the bus request line. This signal line continues to be activated until it is recognized by the arbiter.

The arbiter, upon noticing the $\overline{BR}$ signal, returns the bus grant signal to the 68040 when the bus is available. When the $\overline{BG}$ signal becomes a logic zero, the microprocessor begins to monitor the $\overline{BB}$ (bus busy) line. It does this to determine when the prior master has relinquished control of the buses. If $\overline{BB}$ is a logic zero, the microprocessor waits for it to become a logic one, indicating that the bus is available. Next the 68040 places a logic zero on the $\overline{BB}$ line to indicate that it is now in control of the system buses.

When the microprocessor has completed a bus transfer, it returns the $\overline{BR}$ line to a logic one level. This allows the arbiter to regain control of the buses so that they can be passed to another bus master. Figure 13-37 illustrates the timing signals for a bus request and subsequent arbitration.

In the bus arbitration circuit illustrated in Figure 13-38, a 74F148 priority encoder determines which of the two bus request inputs ($\overline{BR1}$ or $\overline{BR2}$) is active. If

**Table 13-21    The TAP
Instruction Set**

| Code | Instruction |
| --- | --- |
| 000 | EXTEST |
| 001 | High impedance |
| 01X | Sample/preload |
| 10X | Shutdown |
| 110 | [reserved] |
| 111 | BYPASS |

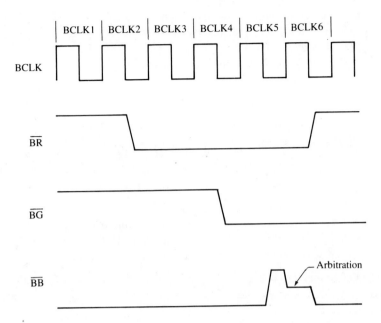

**Figure 13-37    Timing for a bus request and arbitration for the 68040 microprocessor.**

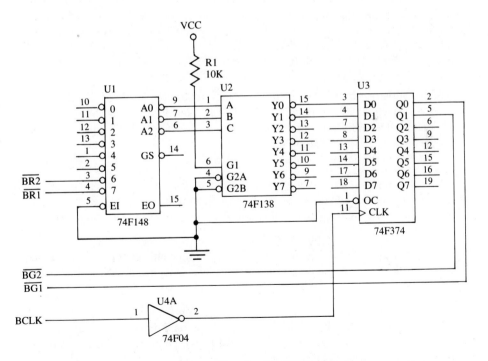

**Figure 13-38    A simple bus arbiter for the 68040 microprocessor system.**

$\overline{BR1}$ is active, a 000 is generated at the outputs of the encoder; if $\overline{BR2}$ is active, a 001 is generated. The BR1 input has the highest priority, so if both requests are active, BR1 takes effect.

The output of the priority generator is connected to a 74F138 decoder. The decoder connects to a latch. If $\overline{BR1}$ is active output, $\overline{Y0}$ becomes active on the 74F138. At the negative edge of the bus clock, $\overline{BG1}$ becomes active, granting the bus request.

This system is expanded by using additional input to the 74F148 as bus request inputs. The bus grant signals are available at the outputs of the 74F374 latch.

## Summary

1. The 68030 microprocessor is basically a 68020 microprocessor that contains a memory management unit (MMU). In addition to the instruction cache, as introduced with the 68020, the 68030 contains a data cache.

2. The 68030 memory management unit (MMU) supports a paged demand virtual memory environment. The memory is divided into small physical areas of equal size that are called page frames. The operating system has the task of assigning page frames to tasks as they are required for programs.

3. Translation table registers are used to directly map logical memory to physical memory. In the 68030 microprocessor there are two TTx registers for this purpose, and they may specify a translation of any size.

4. The 68030 address translation cache (ATC) contains 22 entries so that the last 22 logical address pages, which are converted to physical addresses by the MMU, are stored in the ATC within the microprocessor.

5. New instructions are added to the 68030 to control the MMU. These instructions include PFLUSH, PLOAD, PMOVE, and PTEST. The 68030 incorporates all the 68020 instructions except for CALLM and RTM, which are deleted from the 68030 instruction set. For this reason, it is suggested that CALLM and RTM not be incorporated into any software.

6. The 68040 is a much improved version of the 68030 microprocessor. This device contains two 4k byte caches, a floating-point arithmetic coprocessor, two memory management units, a new control bus structure, and a test access port.

7. The 68040 microprocessor transfers data using either synchronous or burst transfers. Synchronous transfers require two clocking periods, while a burst transfers 4 long-words of data in five clocking periods.

8. The floating-point unit within the 68040 microprocessor is compatible with the 68881/68882 floating-point coprocessor. The only difference is that the 68040 floating-point unit does not execute all floating-point instructions and does not support decimal floating-point format.

9. A few new instructions (CINV, CPUSH, and MOVE16) are added to the 68040 instruction set. The most useful, the MOVE16 instruction, which moves 16 bytes of data using burst techniques, is very efficient.

10. The 68040 includes a test access port (TAP) that is used to test the components connected to the microprocessor by having the test port activate all the microprocessor pin connections. A history of this is made and output, so that the information can be examined.

11. The bus error stack frame is now called an access error stack frame. Also changed on the 68040 is a priority structure for multiple exceptions/interrupts.

12. The 68040 memory management unit has a three-level translation structure that uses memory page sizes of either 4k or 8k bytes. This is a change from the MMU on the 68030 microprocessor. In addition, two MMUs have been incorporated, one for the data cache and the other for the instruction cache.

13. Bus arbitration is totally different on the 68040 microprocessor and earlier versions of this microprocessor. The bus request ($\overline{BR}$) signal is used to request access to the bus through an arbiter. Once the arbiter has recognized the request and the bus has become available, the arbiter returns the bus grant ($\overline{BG}$) signal. The bus busy ($\overline{BB}$) signal is next tested by the microprocessor to determine whether the bus is busy; if it is not, the 68040 asserts the $\overline{BB}$ line to take control of the bus.

## Questions

1. In general, the 68030 contains what new (compared to the 68020) major processing units?

2. Describe the purpose of the 68030 data cache.

3. What is the purpose of the data cache WA control bit?

4. What is the purpose of the $\overline{CIIN}$ pin on the 68030 microprocessor?

5. How many clocks are used to transfer data using asynchronous techniques with no wait states in the 68030 microprocessor?

6. What is the memory access time allowed by the 68030 when operated at 20 MHz in the asynchronous mode?

7. How many clocks are required to transfer a long-word of data using synchronous data transfer techniques?

8. The 68030 operated synchronously at 16 MHz requires a memory with an access time of _____ ns.

9. How many clocks are required to burst four 32-bit long-words of data?

**10.** Briefly describe what is accomplished by the memory management unit (MMU).

**11.** What is a page?

**12.** What are the available sizes of memory pages?

**13.** Define the term "logical address."

**14.** Define the term "physical address."

**15.** The MMU within the 68030 supports _____ levels of translation tables.

**16.** What does the translation control (TC) register program?

**17.** How many root pointers are available in the 68030, and what is their purpose?

**18.** What is a descriptor, and where are descriptors stored?

**19.** What is the purpose of function code lookup by the MMU?

**20.** How many entries are stored within the address translation cache?

**21.** What is the purpose of the address translation cache?

**22.** What is the purpose of TT0 and TT1?

**23.** Is there any limit to the size of memory specified by the TTx registers?

**24.** What is the purpose of the MMUSR?

**25.** How are the contents of the MMUSR changed?

**26.** What new instructions have been added to the 68030 instruction set?

**27.** What 68020 instructions have been deleted from the 68030 instruction set?

**28.** What new features are found on the 68040 microprocessor and not on the 68030?

**29.** Explain the relation between the 68040 microprocessor's BCLK and PCLK signals.

**30.** Given a BCLK frequency of 25 MHz, what frequency signal is applied to the PCLK pin on the 68040 microprocessor?

**31.** A synchronous transfer requires _____ BCLK periods in the 68040 microprocessor.

**32.** A burst transfer requires _____ BCLK periods in the 68040 microprocessor.

**33.** What is the purpose of the $\overline{\text{TS}}$ signal on the 68040 microprocessor?

**34.** Wait states are inserted in the timing for a synchronous transfer in the 68040 system using which control pin?

**35.** Which 68040 pin signals either a synchronous transfer or a burst transfer?

**36.** The 68040 memory management unit allows memory page sizes of _____ or _____ bytes.

**37.** How many levels of address translation are allowed by the 68040 memory management unit?

**38.** How many transparent translation registers are found in the 68040 microprocessor?

**39.** What is the maximum number of entries in the level A translation table of the 68040 microprocessor memory management unit?

**40.** What basic types of floating-point instruction are missing from the 68040 floating-point unit when compared to the 68881/68882 floating-point coprocessor?

**41.** What 68881/68882 floating-point coprocessor data type is missing from the floating-point unit within the 68040 microprocessor?

**42.** Which 68040 exception vector is used for an unimplemented floating-point unit instruction?

**43.** Is there any difference in the sequence of events for an interrupt in the 68040 microprocessor when compared to the 68030 microprocessor?

**44.** Explain how buffer size is selected in the 68040 microprocessor.

**45.** Explain how the multiplexed address/data bus is selected in the 68040 microprocessor.

**46.** What is accomplished by the MOVE16 instruction?

**47.** What is the purpose of the TDI pin on the test access port of the 68040 microprocessor?

**48.** Explain the purpose of the EXTEST instruction in the test access port of the 68040 microprocessor.

**49.** Explain the purpose of the bus request ($\overline{\text{BR}}$) pin on the 68040 microprocessor.

**50.** What device generates the $\overline{\text{BG}}$ signal in the 68040 system?

**51.** Compare bus arbitration on the 68000 microprocessor with bus arbitration on the 68040 microprocessor.

# Assembly Language Instruction Summary

This appendix lists all the 68000 instructions in alphabetical order, along with their effect on the condition code register bits N, Z, X, C, and V. If an effective address ⟨ea⟩ is allowed with an instruction, each mode used in the 68000 is designated yes (y) or no (n).

## The 68000 Assembly Language Instruction Summary

| Opcode | Ext | Operand | N | Z | X | C | V |
|---|---|---|---|---|---|---|---|
| ABCD | | Dx,Dy | U | * | * | * | U |
| | | −(Ax),−(Ay) | U | * | * | * | U |

Add binary-coded decimal with extend. This instruction adds the source to the destination with extend. Note that both numbers are assumed to be bytes that contain two packed BCD digits.

| Opcode | Ext | Operand | N | Z | X | C | V | Dn | An | (An) | (An)+ | −(An) | d(An) | d(An,Rn) | xxx.W | xxx.L | d(PC) | d(PC,Rn) | #xxx |
|---|---|---|---|---|---|---|---|---|---|---|---|---|---|---|---|---|---|---|---|
| ADD | B,W,L | ⟨ea⟩,Dn | * | * | * | * | * | y | y | y | y | y | y | y | y | y | y | y | y |
| | B,W,L | Dn,⟨ea⟩ | * | * | * | * | * | n | n | y | y | y | y | y | y | y | n | n | n |
| | B,W,L | #xxx,⟨ea⟩ | * | * | * | * | * | y | n | y | y | y | y | y | y | y | n | n | n |
| | W,L | ⟨ea⟩,An | – | – | – | – | – | y | y | y | y | y | y | y | y | y | y | y | y |

Add binary adds the source data to the destination data. Note that this instruction is byte, word, or long-word sized. Variations such as ADDA and ADDQ are not shown because they are seldom used with assembly language programming.

| Opcode | Ext | Operand | N | Z | X | C | V |
|---|---|---|---|---|---|---|---|
| ADDX | B,W,L | Dx,Dy | * | * | * | * | * |
|  | B,W,L | -(Ax),-(Ay) | * | * | * | * | * |

Add binary with extend adds the source data to the destination data with extend. Note that only two forms of addressing are allowed for this instruction.

| Opcode | Ext | Operand | N | Z | X | C | V | An | Dn | (An) | (An)+ | -(An) | d(An) | d(An,Rn) | xxx.W | xxx.L | d(PC) | d(PC,Rn) | #xxx |
|---|---|---|---|---|---|---|---|---|---|---|---|---|---|---|---|---|---|---|---|
| AND | B,W,L | ⟨ea⟩,Dn | * | * | – | 0 | 0 | n | y | y | y | y | y | y | y | y | y | y | y |
|  | B,W,L | Dn,⟨ea⟩ | * | * | – | 0 | 0 | n | n | y | y | y | y | y | y | y | n | n | n |
|  | B,W,L | #xxx,⟨ea⟩ | * | * | – | 0 | 0 | n | y | y | y | y | y | y | y | y | n | n | n |
|  | B | #xxx,CCR | * | * | * | * | * |  |  |  |  |  |  |  |  |  |  |  |  |
|  | W | #xxx,SR | * | * | * | * | * |  |  |  |  |  |  |  |  |  |  |  |  |

This byte-, word-, or long-word-sized instruction logically multiplies (ANDs) the contents of the source with the destination.

| Opcode | Ext | Operand | N | Z | X | C | V | An | Dn | (An) | (An)+ | -(An) | d(An) | d(An,Rn) | xxx.W | xxx.L | d(PC) | d(PC,Rn) | #xxx |
|---|---|---|---|---|---|---|---|---|---|---|---|---|---|---|---|---|---|---|---|
| ASL | B,W,L | Dx,Dy | * | * | * | * | * |  |  |  |  |  |  |  |  |  |  |  |  |
|  | B,W,L | #xxx,Dy | * | * | * | * | * |  |  |  |  |  |  |  |  |  |  |  |  |
|  | W | ⟨ea⟩ | * | * | * | * | * | n | n | y | y | y | y | y | y | y | n | n | n |

The arithmetic shift left instruction shifts the contents of the destination data left. The left-most bit is shifted into both the carry and extend CCR bits. A zero is moved into the right-most bit for each bit shifted. There are two forms of this instruction. One form (one operand) allows data to be shifted one place, and the other form (two operands) allows data to be shifted multiple places. In the two-operand version, the source data specify the number of bits shifted.

| Opcode | Ext | Operand | N | Z | X | C | V | An | Dn | (An) | (An)+ | -(An) | d(An) | d(An,Rn) | xxx.W | xxx.L | d(PC) | d(PC,Rn) | #xxx |
|--------|-----|---------|---|---|---|---|---|----|----|------|-------|-------|-------|----------|-------|-------|-------|----------|------|
| ASR | B,W,L | Dx,Dy | * | * | * | * | * | | | | | | | | | | | | |
| | B,W,L | #xxx,Dy | * | * | * | * | * | | | | | | | | | | | | |
| | W | ⟨ea⟩ | * | * | * | * | * | n | n | y | y | y | y | y | y | y | n | n | n |

The arithmetic shift right instruction shifts the contents of the destination right. The left-most bit (sign bit) is copied toward the right. The contents of the right-most bit shift out into the carry and extend CCR bits.

| Opcode | Ext | Operand | N | Z | X | C | V |
|--------|-----|---------|---|---|---|---|---|
| Bcc | | ⟨label⟩ | – | – | – | – | – |

The branch on condition instruction has many variations. In all cases if the condition under test is true, a branch to the ⟨label⟩ occurs. The maximum range of the conditional branch is ±32k bytes. Following is a list of all conditional branches and a description of the condition tested.

| | | |
|---|---|---|
| BCC | Branch if carry is cleared (carry CCR = 0) |
| BCS | Branch if carry is set (carry CCR = 1) |
| BEQ | Branch if equal or zero (zero CCR = 1) |
| BNE | Branch if not equal or not zero (zero CCR = 0) |
| BPL | Branch if plus (negative CCR = 0) |
| BMI | Branch if minus (negative CCR = 1) |
| BVC | Branch if overflow cleared (overflow CCR = 0) |
| BVS | Branch if overflow set (overflow CCR = 1) |
| BHI | Branch if higher (unsigned numbers) |
| BLS | Branch if lower or the same (unsigned numbers) |

BLE   Branch if less than or equal (signed numbers)
BLT   Branch if less than (signed numbers)
BGE   Branch if greater than or equal (signed numbers)
BGT   Branch if greater than (signed numbers)

| Opcode | Ext | Operand | N | Z | X | C | V | An | Dn | (An) | (An)+ | -(An) | d(An) | d(An,Rn) | xxx.W | xxx.L | d(PC) | d(PC,Rn) | #xxx |
|---|---|---|---|---|---|---|---|---|---|---|---|---|---|---|---|---|---|---|---|
| BCHG | | Dn,⟨ea⟩ | - | * | - | - | - | n | y | y | y | y | y | y | y | y | n | n | n |
| | | #xxx,⟨ea⟩ | - | * | - | - | - | n | y | y | y | y | y | y | y | y | n | n | n |

The bit change instruction inverts the bit position specified by the source immediate data or register contents. Before the bit is inverted it is tested, and the outcome of the test appears in the zero CCR bit.

| Opcode | Ext | Operand | N | Z | X | C | V | An | Dn | (An) | (An)+ | -(An) | d(An) | d(An,Rn) | xxx.W | xxx.L | d(PC) | d(PC,Rn) | #xxx |
|---|---|---|---|---|---|---|---|---|---|---|---|---|---|---|---|---|---|---|---|
| BCLR | | Dn,⟨ea⟩ | - | * | - | - | - | n | y | y | y | y | y | y | y | y | n | n | n |
| | | #xxx,⟨ea⟩ | - | * | - | - | - | n | y | y | y | y | y | y | y | y | n | n | n |

The bit clear instruction clears (to zero) the bit position specified by the source immediate data or register contents. Before the bit is cleared it is tested, and the outcome of the test appears in the zero CCR bit.

| Opcode | Ext | Operand | N | Z | X | C | V |
|---|---|---|---|---|---|---|---|
| BRA | | ⟨label⟩ | - | - | - | - | - |

The branch always instruction is unconditional, which means that a branch will always occur. The range of this branch is limited to within ±32k bytes. If a longer branch is required, a JMP instruction is used.

| Opcode | Ext | Operand | N | Z | X | C | V | An | Dn | (An) | (An)+ | -(An) | d(An) | d(An,Rn) | xxx.W | xxx.L | d(PC) | d(PC,Rn) | #xxx |
|---|---|---|---|---|---|---|---|---|---|---|---|---|---|---|---|---|---|---|---|
| BSET | | Dn,⟨ea⟩ | - | * | - | - | - | n | y | y | y | y | y | y | y | y | n | n | n |
| | | #xxx,⟨ea⟩ | - | * | - | - | - | n | y | y | y | y | y | y | y | y | n | n | n |

The bit set instruction sets (to one) the bit position specified by the source immediate data or register contents. Before the bit is set it is tested, and the outcome of the test appears in the zero CCR bit.

| Opcode | Ext | Operand | N | Z | X | C | V |
|---|---|---|---|---|---|---|---|
| BSR | | ⟨label⟩ | - | - | - | - | - |

The branch to subroutine instruction allows a branch to a subroutine that is stored within ±32k bytes. The branch to subroutine instruction pushes a copy of the contents of the program counter into the stack and then jumps to the ⟨label⟩.

| Opcode | Ext | Operand | N | Z | X | C | V | An | Dn | (An) | (An)+ | -(An) | d(An) | d(An,Rn) | xxx.W | xxx.L | d(PC) | d(PC,Rn) | #xxx |
|---|---|---|---|---|---|---|---|---|---|---|---|---|---|---|---|---|---|---|---|
| BTST | | Dn,⟨ea⟩ | - | * | - | - | - | n | y | y | y | y | y | y | y | y | n | n | n |
| | | #xxx,⟨ea⟩ | - | * | - | - | - | n | y | y | y | y | y | y | y | y | n | n | n |

The bit test instruction tests the bit position specified by the source immediate data or register contents. The outcome of the test is reflected in the value of the zero CCR bit.

| Opcode | Ext | Operand | N | Z | X | C | V | An | Dn | (An) | (An)+ | -(An) | d(An) | d(An,Rn) | xxx.W | xxx.L | d(PC) | d(PC,Rn) | #xxx |
|---|---|---|---|---|---|---|---|---|---|---|---|---|---|---|---|---|---|---|---|
| CHK | | ⟨ea⟩,Dn | * | U | - | U | U | n | y | y | y | y | y | y | y | y | y | y | y |

The contents of Dn are compared to the ⟨ea⟩, which is a two's complement integer. If Dn is less than zero or greater than the ⟨ea⟩, the processor initiates a CHK exception.

| Opcode | Ext | Operand | N | Z | X | C | V | An | Dn | (An) | (An)+ | -(An) | d(An) | d(An,Rn) | xxx.W | xxx.L | d(PC) | d(PC,Rn) | #xxx |
|--------|-----|---------|---|---|---|---|---|----|----|------|-------|-------|-------|----------|-------|-------|-------|----------|------|
| CLR | B,W,L | ⟨ea⟩ | 0 | 1 | - | 0 | 0 | n | y | y | y | y | y | y | y | y | n | n | n |

The clear instruction is used to place a zero into a register or memory location that is a byte, word, or long-word in size.

| Opcode | Ext | Operand | N | Z | X | C | V | An | Dn | (An) | (An)+ | -(An) | d(An) | d(An,Rn) | xxx.W | xxx.L | d(PC) | d(PC,Rn) | #xxx |
|--------|-----|---------|---|---|---|---|---|----|----|------|-------|-------|-------|----------|-------|-------|-------|----------|------|
| CMP | B,W,L | ⟨ea⟩,Dn | * | * | - | * | * | y | y | y | y | y | y | y | y | y | y | y | y |
|  | W,L | ⟨ea⟩,An | * | * | - | * | * | y | y | y | y | y | y | y | y | y | y | y | y |
|  | B,W,L | #xxx,⟨ea⟩ | * | * | - | * | * | n | y | y | y | y | y | y | y | y | n | n | n |
|  | B,W,L | (Ax)+,(Ay)+ | * | * | * | * | * | n | n | y | n | n | n | n | n | n | n | n | n |

The compare instruction compares the source and destination operand using subtraction, where the source is subtracted from the destination. Neither the source nor the destination changes as a result of the compare. The only change that occurs is a change in the CCR bits that reflect the difference.

| Opcode | Ext | Operand | N | Z | X | C | V |
|--------|-----|---------|---|---|---|---|---|
| DBcc |  | dn,⟨label⟩ | - | - | - | - | - |

The decrement and branch instruction is available in two basic forms: DBRA and DBcc. The DBRA form is a decrement and branch always, while the DBcc form is a conditional decrement and branch. In both cases the word-sized Dn register is decremented and a branch occurs to the ⟨label⟩ if Dn is not a minus 1 ($FFFF). With the DBcc, one other condition is tested: DBcc will branch only if the condition is false. That is, if the DBPL instruction is executed, a branch occurs only if the condition is negative and the Dn register is not a -1. The conditional decrement and branch instructions are really decrement and branch *UNTIL*. Following is a complete list of the DBRA and DBcc instructions.

DBRA    Decrement and branch always. Decrement Dn and branch to ⟨label⟩ if Dn is not -1.

DBCC    Decrement and branch until carry is cleared. Decrement Dn if carry is set, then branch to ⟨label⟩ if Dn is not -1; otherwise continue with the next instruction.

DBCS  Decrement and branch until carry is set. Decrement Dn if carry is cleared, then branch to ⟨label⟩ if Dn is not −1; otherwise continue with the next instruction.

DBEQ  Decrement and branch until equal. Decrement Dn if a not equal or not zero condition exists, then branch to ⟨label⟩ if Dn is not −1; otherwise continue with the next instruction.

DBNE  Decrement and branch until not equal. Decrement Dn if an equal or zero condition exists, then branch to ⟨label⟩ if Dn is not −1; otherwise continue with the next instruction.

DBPL  Decrement and branch until plus. Decrement Dn if minus, then branch to ⟨label⟩ if Dn is not −1; otherwise continue with the next instruction.

DBMI  Decrement and branch until minus. Decrement Dn if plus, then branch to ⟨label⟩ if Dn is not −1; otherwise continue with the next instruction.

DBVC  Decrement and branch until overflow is cleared. Decrement Dn if overflow is set, then branch to ⟨label⟩ if Dn is not −1; otherwise continue with the next instruction.

DBVS  Decrement and branch until overflow is set. Decrement Dn if overflow is cleared, then branch to ⟨label⟩ if Dn is not −1; otherwise continue with the next instruction.

DBHI  Decrement and branch until higher. Decrement Dn if lower or the same, then branch to ⟨label⟩ if Dn is not −1; otherwise continue with the next instruction.

DBLS  Decrement and branch until lower than or the same. Decrement Dn if higher, then branch to ⟨label⟩ if Dn is not −1; otherwise continue with the next instruction.

DBLE  Decrement and branch until less than or equal. Decrement Dn if greater than, then branch to ⟨label⟩ if Dn is not −1; otherwise continue with the next instruction.

DBLT  Decrement and branch until less than. Decrement Dn if greater than or equal, then branch to ⟨label⟩ if Dn is not −1; otherwise continue with the next instruction.

DBGE  Decrement and branch until greater than or equal. Decrement Dn if less than, then branch to ⟨label⟩ if Dn is not −1; otherwise continue with the next instruction.

DBGT  Decrement and branch until greater than. Decrement Dn if less than or equal, then branch to ⟨label⟩ if Dn is not −1; otherwise continue with the next instruction.

| Opcode | Ext | Operand | N | Z | X | C | V | An | Dn | (An) | (An)+ | -(An) | d(An) | d(An,Rn) | xxx.W | xxx.L | d(PC) | d(PC,Rn) | #xxx |
|---|---|---|---|---|---|---|---|---|---|---|---|---|---|---|---|---|---|---|---|
| DIVS | | ⟨ea⟩,Dn | * | * | – | 0 | * | n | y | y | y | y | y | y | y | y | y | y | y |

The signed division instruction divides the word-sized source into the long-word-sized destination. The quotient is found in the least significant word of Dn and the remainder is in the most significant word of Dn. If an attempt is made to divide by zero, a divide error exception is executed by the microprocessor. If the result overflows the quotient, the overflow CCR bit is set. Note that the sign of the remainder is the same as the sign of the quotient except in the case of a remainder of zero.

| Opcode | Ext | Operand | N | Z | X | C | V | An | Dn | (An) | (An)+ | -(An) | d(An) | d(An,Rn) | xxx.W | xxx.L | d(PC) | d(PC,Rn) | #xxx |
|---|---|---|---|---|---|---|---|---|---|---|---|---|---|---|---|---|---|---|---|
| DIVU | | ⟨ea⟩,Dn | * | * | – | 0 | * | n | y | y | y | y | y | y | y | y | y | y | y |

The unsigned division instruction divides the word-sized source into the long-word-sized destination. The quotient is found in the least significant word of Dn and the remainder is in the most significant word of Dn. If an attempt is made to divide by zero, a divide error exception is executed by the microprocessor. If the result overflows the quotient, the overflow CCR bit is set.

| Opcode | Ext | Operand | N | Z | X | C | V | An | Dn | (An) | (An)+ | -(An) | d(An) | d(An,Rn) | xxx.W | xxx.L | d(PC) | d(PC,Rn) | #xxx |
|---|---|---|---|---|---|---|---|---|---|---|---|---|---|---|---|---|---|---|---|
| EOR | B,W,L | Dn,⟨ea⟩ | * | * | – | 0 | 0 | n | y | y | y | y | y | y | y | y | n | n | n |
| | B,W,L | #xxx,⟨ea⟩ | * | * | – | 0 | 0 | n | y | y | y | y | y | y | y | y | n | n | n |
| | B | #xxx,CCR | * | * | * | * | * | | | | | | | | | | | | |
| | W | #xxx,SR | * | * | * | * | * | | | | | | | | | | | | |

The exclusive-OR instruction exclusive-ORs the contents of the source with the destination, leaving the result in the destination.

| Opcode | Ext | Operand | N | Z | X | C | V |
|---|---|---|---|---|---|---|---|
| EXG | | Rx,Ry | – | – | – | – | – |

595

The exchange instruction exchanges the contents of any two long-word-sized registers.

| Opcode | Ext | Operand | N | Z | X | C | V |
|---|---|---|---|---|---|---|---|
| EXT | W,L | Dn | * | * | – | 0 | 0 |

The sign-extend instruction sign-extends a byte to a word (EXT.W) or a word to a long-word (EXT.L).

| Opcode | Ext | Operand | N | Z | X | C | V | Dn | An | (An) | (An)+ | –(An) | d(An) | d(An,Rn) | xxx.W | xxx.L | d(PC) | d(PC,Rn) | #xxx |
|---|---|---|---|---|---|---|---|---|---|---|---|---|---|---|---|---|---|---|---|
| JMP | | ⟨ea⟩ | – | – | – | – | – | n | n | y | n | n | y | y | y | y | y | y | n |

The jump instruction allows a branch to any location in the memory system. Jump instructions are always unconditional and may be direct (JMP ⟨label⟩) or indirect (JMP A2).

| Opcode | Ext | Operand | N | Z | X | C | V | Dn | An | (An) | (An)+ | –(An) | d(An) | d(An,Rn) | xxx.W | xxx.L | d(PC) | d(PC,Rn) | #xxx |
|---|---|---|---|---|---|---|---|---|---|---|---|---|---|---|---|---|---|---|---|
| JSR | | ⟨ea⟩ | – | – | – | – | – | n | n | y | n | n | y | y | y | y | y | y | n |

The jump subroutine instruction allows a subroutine to be called at any location in the memory. This instruction is always unconditional and may be direct or indirect. The jump subroutine instruction places a copy of the contents of the program counter on the stack and then jumps to the address of the subroutine.

| Opcode | Ext | Operand | N | Z | X | C | V | Dn | An | (An) | (An)+ | –(An) | d(An) | d(An,Rn) | xxx.W | xxx.L | d(PC) | d(PC,Rn) | #xxx |
|---|---|---|---|---|---|---|---|---|---|---|---|---|---|---|---|---|---|---|---|
| LEA | | ⟨ea⟩,An | – | – | – | – | – | n | n | y | n | n | y | y | y | y | y | y | n |

The load effective address instruction computes the effective address of ⟨ea⟩ and loads that address into An.

| Opcode | Ext | Operand | N | Z | X | C | V |
|---|---|---|---|---|---|---|---|
| LINK | W,L | An,#xxx | – | – | – | – | – |

The link instruction pushes the contents of An onto the stack; then the contents of the updated stack pointer are loaded into An. Finally the displacement is added to the stack pointer to obtain a new stack frame.

| Opcode | Ext | Operand | N | Z | X | C | V | An | Dn | (An) | (An)+ | -(An) | d(An) | d(An,Rn) | xxx.W | xxx.L | d(PC) | d(PC,Rn) | #xxx |
|---|---|---|---|---|---|---|---|---|---|---|---|---|---|---|---|---|---|---|---|
| LSL | B,W,L | Dx,Dy | * | * | * | * | 0 | | | | | | | | | | | | |
| | B,W,L | #xxx,Dy | * | * | * | * | 0 | | | | | | | | | | | | |
| | W | ⟨ea⟩ | * | * | * | * | 0 | n | n | y | y | y | y | y | y | y | n | n | n |

The logical shift left instruction shifts the contents of the destination to the left. The left-most bit is shifted into the carry and extend CCR bits and the right-most bit is filled with a logic zero. If there is only one operand, the data are shifted one place. If there are two operands, the source specifies the number of places that the destination is shifted.

| Opcode | Ext | Operand | N | Z | X | C | V | An | Dn | (An) | (An)+ | -(An) | d(An) | d(An,Rn) | xxx.W | xxx.L | d(PC) | d(PC,Rn) | #xxx |
|---|---|---|---|---|---|---|---|---|---|---|---|---|---|---|---|---|---|---|---|
| LSR | B,W,L | Dx,Dy | * | * | * | * | 0 | | | | | | | | | | | | |
| | B,W,L | #xxx,Dy | * | * | * | * | 0 | | | | | | | | | | | | |
| | W | ⟨ea⟩ | * | * | * | * | 0 | n | n | y | y | y | y | y | y | y | n | n | n |

The logical shift right instruction shifts the contents of the destination to the right. The right-most bit is shifted into the carry and extend CCR bits and the left-most bit is filled with a logic zero. If there is only one operand, the data are shifted one place. If there are two operands, the source specifies the number of places that the destination is shifted.

| Opcode | Ext | Operand | N | Z | X | C | V | An | Dn | (An) | (An)+ | -(An) | d(An) | d(An,Rn) | xxx.W | xxx.L | d(PC) | d(PC,Rn) | #xxx | |
|---|---|---|---|---|---|---|---|---|---|---|---|---|---|---|---|---|---|---|---|---|
| MOVE | B,W,L | ⟨ea⟩,⟨ea⟩ | * | * | - | 0 | 0 | y | y | y | y | y | y | y | y | y | y | y | y | source |
| | | | | | | | | n | y | y | y | y | y | y | y | y | n | n | n | destination |
| | B | CCR,⟨ea⟩ | - | - | - | - | - | n | y | y | y | y | y | y | y | y | n | n | n | |
| | B | ⟨ea⟩,CCR | * | * | * | * | * | n | y | y | y | y | y | y | y | y | y | y | y | |
| | W | SR,⟨ea⟩ | - | - | - | - | - | n | y | y | y | y | y | y | y | y | n | n | n | |
| | W | ⟨ea⟩,SR | * | * | * | * | * | n | y | y | y | y | y | y | y | y | y | y | y | |
| | L | USP,An | - | - | - | - | - | | | | | | | | | | | | | |
| | L | An,USP | - | - | - | - | - | | | | | | | | | | | | | |
| | W,L | ⟨ea⟩,An | - | - | - | - | - | y | y | y | y | y | y | y | y | y | y | y | y | |

597

The move instruction moves the contents of the source into the destination. MOVE allows memory-to-memory transfers.

| Opcode | Ext | Operand | N | Z | X | C | V | An | Dn | (An) | (An)+ | -(An) | d(An) | d(An,Rn) | xxx.W | xxx.L | d(PC) | d(PC,Rn) | #xxx |
|---|---|---|---|---|---|---|---|---|---|---|---|---|---|---|---|---|---|---|---|
| MOVEM | W,L | ⟨rl⟩,⟨ea⟩ | – | – | – | – | – | n | n | y | n | y | y | y | y | y | n | n | n |
| | W,L | ⟨ea⟩,⟨rl⟩ | – | – | – | – | – | n | n | y | y | n | y | y | y | y | y | y | n |

The move multiple register instruction allows from one to all registers to be moved between the registers and memory.

| Opcode | Ext | Operand | N | Z | X | C | V |
|---|---|---|---|---|---|---|---|
| MOVEP | W,L | Dx,D(Ay) | – | – | – | – | – |
| | W,L | d(Ax),Dy | – | – | – | – | – |

The move peripheral instruction allows data to be moved between a data register and the contents of memory. The move peripheral instruction differs from a standard move because MOVEP accesses every other byte in memory, so that the address is always even or odd.

| Opcode | Ext | Operand | N | Z | X | C | V | An | Dn | (An) | (An)+ | -(An) | d(An) | d(An,Rn) | xxx.W | xxx.L | d(PC) | d(PC,Rn) | #xxx |
|---|---|---|---|---|---|---|---|---|---|---|---|---|---|---|---|---|---|---|---|
| MULS | | ⟨ea⟩,Dn | * | * | – | 0 | 0 | n | y | y | y | y | y | y | y | y | y | y | y |

Signed multiplication multiplies the word-sized source times the word-sized destination. The resultant product is found in Dn as a long-word-sized result.

| Opcode | Ext | Operand | N | Z | X | C | V | An | Dn | (An) | (An)+ | -(An) | d(An) | d(An,Rn) | xxx.W | xxx.L | d(PC) | d(PC,Rn) | #xxx |
|---|---|---|---|---|---|---|---|---|---|---|---|---|---|---|---|---|---|---|---|
| MULU | | ⟨ea⟩,Dn | * | * | – | 0 | 0 | n | y | y | y | y | y | y | y | y | y | y | y |

Unsigned multiplication multiplies the word-sized source times the word-sized destination. The resultant product is found in Dn as a long-word-sized result.

| Opcode | Ext | Operand | N | Z | X | C | V | An | Dn | (An) | (An)+ | -(An) | d(An) | d(An,Rn) | xxx.W | xxx.L | d(PC) | d(PC,Rn) | #xxx |
|--------|-----|---------|---|---|---|---|---|----|----|------|-------|-------|-------|----------|-------|-------|-------|----------|------|
| NBCD | | ⟨ea⟩ | U | * | * | * | U | n | y | y | y | y | y | y | y | y | n | n | n |

Negate BCD performs a ten's complement negation on the operand. This effectively changes the sign of a signed BCD number.

| Opcode | Ext | Operand | N | Z | X | C | V | An | Dn | (An) | (An)+ | -(An) | d(An) | d(An,Rn) | xxx.W | xxx.L | d(PC) | d(PC,Rn) | #xxx |
|--------|-----|---------|---|---|---|---|---|----|----|------|-------|-------|-------|----------|-------|-------|-------|----------|------|
| NEG | B,W,L | ⟨ea⟩ | * | * | * | * | * | n | y | y | y | y | y | y | y | y | n | n | n |

Negate performs a two's complement negation on the operand. This effectively changes the sign of a signed binary number.

| Opcode | Ext | Operand | N | Z | X | C | V | An | Dn | (An) | (An)+ | -(An) | d(An) | d(An,Rn) | xxx.W | xxx.L | d(PC) | d(PC,Rn) | #xxx |
|--------|-----|---------|---|---|---|---|---|----|----|------|-------|-------|-------|----------|-------|-------|-------|----------|------|
| NEGX | B,W,L | ⟨ea⟩ | * | * | * | * | * | n | y | y | y | y | y | y | y | y | n | n | n |

Negate with extend two's complements the operand with the extend CCR bit. This allows numbers that are wider than 32 bits to be negated.

| Opcode | Operand | N | Z | X | C | V |
|--------|---------|---|---|---|---|---|
| NOP | | - | - | - | - | - |

The no operation instruction performs no operation.

| Opcode | Ext | Operand | N | Z | X | C | V | An | Dn | (An) | (An)+ | -(An) | d(An) | d(An,Rn) | xxx.W | xxx.L | d(PC) | d(PC,Rn) | #xxx |
|--------|-----|---------|---|---|---|---|---|----|----|------|-------|-------|-------|----------|-------|-------|-------|----------|------|
| NOT | B,W,L | ⟨ea⟩ | * | * | - | 0 | 0 | n | y | y | y | y | y | y | y | y | n | n | n |

The not instruction one's-complements the operand.

| Opcode | Ext | Operand | N | Z | X | C | V | An | Dn | (An) | (An)+ | −(An) | d(An) | d(An,Rn) | xxx.W | xxx.L | d(PC) | d(PC,Rn) | #xxx |
|---|---|---|---|---|---|---|---|---|---|---|---|---|---|---|---|---|---|---|---|
| OR | B,W,L | ⟨ea⟩,Dn | * | * | – | 0 | 0 | n | y | y | y | y | y | y | y | y | y | y | y |
|  | B,W,L | Dn,⟨ea⟩ | * | * | – | 0 | 0 | n | n | y | y | y | y | y | y | y | n | n | n |
|  | B,W,L | #xxx,⟨ea⟩ | * | * | – | 0 | 0 | n | y | y | y | y | y | y | y | y | n | n | n |
|  | B | #xxx,CCR | * | * | * | * | * |  |  |  |  |  |  |  |  |  |  |  |  |
|  | W | #xxx,SR | * | * | * | * | * |  |  |  |  |  |  |  |  |  |  |  |  |

The OR instruction logically adds the contents of the source to the destination. Note that both the carry and extend CCR bits are always cleared by this instruction.

| Opcode | Ext | Operand | N | Z | X | C | V | An | Dn | (An) | (An)+ | −(An) | d(An) | d(An,Rn) | xxx.W | xxx.L | d(PC) | d(PC,Rn) | #xxx |
|---|---|---|---|---|---|---|---|---|---|---|---|---|---|---|---|---|---|---|---|
| PEA |  | ⟨ea⟩ | – | – | – | – | – | n | n | y | n | n | y | y | y | y | y | y | n |

The push effective address instruction calculates the effective address of the operand and then pushes that address onto the stack.

| Opcode | Ext | Operand | N | Z | X | C | V |
|---|---|---|---|---|---|---|---|
| RESET |  |  | – | – | – | – | – |

The reset instruction causes the rest pin connection to become active for 124 clocking periods. This instruction does not reload SSP and PC from the vectors stored in the vector table. After the reset pin connection has been placed at a logic zero, the next sequential instruction following reset is executed.

| Opcode | Ext | Operand | N | Z | X | C | V | An | Dn | (An) | (An)+ | −(An) | d(An) | d(An,Rn) | xxx.W | xxx.L | d(PC) | d(PC,Rn) | #xxx |
|---|---|---|---|---|---|---|---|---|---|---|---|---|---|---|---|---|---|---|---|
| ROL | B,W,L | Dx,Dy | * | * | – | * | 0 |  |  |  |  |  |  |  |  |  |  |  |  |
|  | B,W,L | #xxx,Dy | * | * | – | * | 0 |  |  |  |  |  |  |  |  |  |  |  |  |
|  | W | ⟨ea⟩ | * | * | – | * | 0 | n | n | y | y | y | y | y | y | y | n | n | n |

The rotate left instruction rotates the contents of the operand to the left. The left-most bit is copied to the right-most bit of the operand and also to both the carry and extend CCR bits. If one operand exists, the data are rotated one place. If two operands exist, the data located in the destination are rotated the number of places specified by the source operand.

| Opcode | Ext | Operand | N | Z | X | C | V | An | Dn | (An) | (An)+ | -(An) | d(An) | d(An,Rn) | xxx.W | xxx.L | d(PC) | d(PC,Rn) | #xxx |
|---|---|---|---|---|---|---|---|---|---|---|---|---|---|---|---|---|---|---|---|
| ROR | B,W,L | Dx,Dy | * | * | – | * | 0 | | | | | | | | | | | | |
| | B,W,L | #xxx,Dy | * | * | – | * | 0 | | | | | | | | | | | | |
| | W | ⟨ea⟩ | * | * | – | * | 0 | n | n | y | y | y | y | y | y | y | n | n | n |

The rotate right instruction rotates the contents of the operand to the right. The right-most bit is copied to the left-most bit of the operand and also to both the carry and extend CCR bits. If one operand exists, the data are rotated one place. If two operands exist, the data located in the destination are rotated the number of places specified by the source operand.

| Opcode | Ext | Operand | N | Z | X | C | V | An | Dn | (An) | (An)+ | -(An) | d(An) | d(An,Rn) | xxx.W | xxx.L | d(PC) | d(PC,Rn) | #xxx |
|---|---|---|---|---|---|---|---|---|---|---|---|---|---|---|---|---|---|---|---|
| ROXL | B,W,L | Dx,Dy | * | * | * | * | 0 | | | | | | | | | | | | |
| | B,W,L | #xxx,Dy | * | * | * | * | 0 | | | | | | | | | | | | |
| | W | ⟨ea⟩ | * | * | * | * | 0 | n | n | y | y | y | y | y | y | y | n | n | n |

Rotate left with extend rotates the contents of the operand to the left through the extend CCR bit. The left-most bit of the operand is moved into both the extend and carry CCR bits, and the right-most bit is loaded from the extend bit. If one operand exists, the data are rotated one place. If two operands exist, the data located in the destination are rotated the number of places specified by the source operand.

| Opcode | Ext | Operand | N | Z | X | C | V | An | Dn | (An) | (An)+ | -(An) | d(An) | d(An,Rn) | xxx.W | xxx.L | d(PC) | d(PC,Rn) | #xxx |
|---|---|---|---|---|---|---|---|---|---|---|---|---|---|---|---|---|---|---|---|
| ROXL | B,W, | L Dx,Dy | * | * | – | * | 0 | | | | | | | | | | | | |
| | B,W,L | #xxx,Dy | * | * | – | * | 0 | | | | | | | | | | | | |
| | W | ⟨ea⟩ | * | * | – | * | 0 | n | n | y | y | y | y | y | y | y | n | n | n |

Rotate right with extend rotates the contents of the operand to the right through the extend CCR bit. The right-most bit of the operand is moved into both the extend and carry CCR bits, and the left-most bit is loaded from the extend bit. If one operand exists, the data are rotated one place. If two operands exist, the data located in the destination are rotated the number of places specified by the source operand.

| Opcode | Ext | Operand | N | Z | X | C | V |
|---|---|---|---|---|---|---|---|
| RTE | | | * | * | * | * | * |

Return from exception returns from both interrupts and exceptions. This instruction reloads the status register and the program counter from the stack to effect a return.

| Opcode | Ext | Operand | N | Z | X | C | V |
|---|---|---|---|---|---|---|---|
| RTR | | | * | * | * | * | * |

Return and restore returns from a subroutine and reloads the CCR.

| Opcode | Ext | Operand | N | Z | X | C | V |
|---|---|---|---|---|---|---|---|
| RTS | | | – | – | – | – | – |

Return from subroutine returns from a subroutine by removing a long-word from the stack and placing it into the program counter.

| Opcode | Ext | Operand | N | Z | X | C | V |
|---|---|---|---|---|---|---|---|
| SBCD | | Dx,Dy | U | * | * | * | U |
| | | -(Ax),-(Ay) | U | * | * | * | U |

The subtract BCD with extend instruction subtracts the source operand from the destination operand with extend. This instruction is used to subtract two BCD with extend, which holds the borrow.

| Opcode | Ext | Operand | N | Z | X | C | V | An | Dn | (An) | (An)+ | -(An) | d(An) | d(An,Rn) | xxx.W | xxx.L | d(PC) | d(PC,Rn) | #xxx |
|--------|-----|---------|---|---|---|---|---|----|----|------|-------|-------|-------|----------|-------|-------|-------|----------|------|
| Scc | | ⟨ea⟩ | - | - | - | - | - | n | y | y | y | y | y | y | y | y | n | n | n |

The conditional set according to condition instruction sets the operand byte to $FF if the tested condition is true and to $00 if the condition is false. Following is a list of all set according to condition instructions.

SCC    Set if carry is cleared (carry CCR = 0)

SCS    Set if carry is set (carry CCR = 1)

SEQ    Set if equal or zero (zero CCR = 1)

SNE    Set if not equal or not zero (zero CCR = 0)

SPL    Set if plus (negative CCR = 0)

SMI    Set if minus (negative CCR = 1)

SVC    Set if overflow is cleared (overflow CCR = 0)

SVS    Set if overflow is set (overflow CCR = 1)

SHI    Set if higher (unsigned numbers)

SLS    Set if lower or the same (unsigned numbers)

SLE    Set if less than or equal (signed numbers)

SLT    Set if less than (signed numbers)

SGE    Set if greater than or equal (signed numbers)

SGT    Set if greater than (signed numbers)

| Opcode | Ext | Operand | N | Z | X | C | V |
|--------|-----|---------|---|---|---|---|---|
| STOP | | #xxx | * | * | * | * | * |

The stop instruction causes the microprocessor to stop executing a program until either a hardware reset or an interrupt or exception occurs. The stop instruction places the immediate operand into the status register when it is executed.

| Opcode | Ext | Operand | N | Z | X | C | V | An | Dn | (An) | (An)+ | -(An) | d(An) | d(An,Rn) | xxx.W | xxx.L | d(PC) | d(PC,Rn) | #xxx |
|--------|-----|---------|---|---|---|---|---|----|----|------|-------|-------|-------|----------|-------|-------|-------|----------|------|
| SUB | B,W,L | ⟨ea⟩,Dn | * | * | * | * | * | y | y | y | y | y | y | y | y | y | y | y | y |
| | B,W,L | Dn,⟨ea⟩ | * | * | * | * | * | n | n | y | y | y | y | y | y | y | n | n | n |
| | W,L | ⟨ea⟩,An | – | – | – | – | – | y | y | y | y | y | y | y | y | y | y | y | y |
| | B,W,L | #xxx,⟨ea⟩ | * | * | * | * | * | n | y | y | y | y | y | y | y | y | n | n | n |

The subtract instruction subtracts the contents of the source operand from the destination operand and places the difference into the destination.

| Opcode | Ext | Operand | N | Z | X | C | V |
|--------|-----|---------|---|---|---|---|---|
| SUBX | B,W,L | Dx,Dy | * | * | * | * | * |
| | B,W,L | -(Ax),-(Ay) | * | * | * | * | * |

The subtract with extend instruction subtracts the source from the destination with extend subtracted from the difference. This instruction is used when numbers wider than 32 bits are subtracted. The borrow propagates through the extend CCR bit.

| Opcode | Ext | Operand | N | Z | X | C | V | An | Dn | (An) | (An)+ | -(An) | d(An) | d(An,Rn) | xxx.W | xxx.L | d(PC) | d(PC,Rn) | #xxx |
|--------|-----|---------|---|---|---|---|---|----|----|------|-------|-------|-------|----------|-------|-------|-------|----------|------|
| SWAP | | Dn | * | * | – | 0 | 0 | | | | | | | | | | | | |

The swap instruction swaps the word halves of a data register.

| Opcode | Ext | Operand | N | Z | X | C | V | An | Dn | (An) | (An)+ | -(An) | d(An) | d(An,Rn) | xxx.W | xxx.L | d(PC) | d(PC,Rn) | #xxx |
|--------|-----|---------|---|---|---|---|---|----|----|------|-------|-------|-------|----------|-------|-------|-------|----------|------|
| TAS | | ⟨ea⟩ | * | * | – | 0 | 0 | n | y | y | y | y | y | y | y | y | n | n | n |

Test and set tests the byte-sized operand that changes the N- and Z-CCR bits. After testing, this instruction places a logic one in the most significant bit position of the operand.

| Opcode | Ext | Operand | N | Z | X | C | V | An | Dn | (An) | (An)+ | -(An) | d(An) | d(An,Rn) | xxx.W | xxx.L | d(PC) | d(PC,Rn) | #xxx |
|--------|-----|---------|---|---|---|---|---|----|----|------|-------|-------|-------|----------|-------|-------|-------|----------|------|
| TRAP   |     | #xxx    | - | - | - | - |   |    |    |      |       |       |       |          |       |       |       |          |      |

The trap instruction is a software interrupt. There are 16 different trap instructions (TRAP 0–TRAP 15).

| Opcode | Ext | Operand | N | Z | X | C | V | An | Dn | (An) | (An)+ | -(An) | d(An) | d(An,Rn) | xxx.W | xxx.L | d(PC) | d(PC,Rn) | #xxx |
|--------|-----|---------|---|---|---|---|---|----|----|------|-------|-------|-------|----------|-------|-------|-------|----------|------|
| TRAPV  |     |         | - | - | - | - |   |    |    |      |       |       |       |          |       |       |       |          |      |

The trap on overflow is a conditional interrupt. If the overflow CCR bit is set when this instruction is executed, an overflow exception is processed. If the overflow flag is cleared, this instruction performs a NOP.

| Opcode | Ext   | Operand | N | Z | X | C | V | An | Dn | (An) | (An)+ | -(An) | d(An) | d(An,Rn) | xxx.W | xxx.L | d(PC) | d(PC,Rn) | #xxx |
|--------|-------|---------|---|---|---|---|---|----|----|------|-------|-------|-------|----------|-------|-------|-------|----------|------|
| TST    | B,W,L | ⟨ea⟩    | * | * | - | 0 | 0 | n  | y  | y    | y     | y     | y     | y        | y     | y     | n     | n        | n    |

The test instruction tests the contents of the operand for zero and sign.

| Opcode | Ext | Operand | N | Z | X | C | V | An | Dn | (An) | (An)+ | -(An) | d(An) | d(An,Rn) | xxx.W | xxx.L | d(PC) | d(PC,Rn) | #xxx |
|--------|-----|---------|---|---|---|---|---|----|----|------|-------|-------|-------|----------|-------|-------|-------|----------|------|
| UNLK   |     | An      | - | - | - | - |   |    |    |      |       |       |       |          |       |       |       |          |      |

The unlink instruction loads the stack pointer from the address register; then the data are popped from the stack and placed into the address register. This instruction is used with the link instruction to unlink from a stack frame.

# 68000 Machine Language Instructions

**ABCD**  Add binary-coded decimal

1100 ddd1 0000 csss
- c field: 0 = data register to data register
  1 = memory to memory
- d field: destination data register if c = 0, destination address register if c = 1
- s field: source data register if c = 0, destination address register if c = 1

**ADD**  Binary addition

1101 dddo oomm mrrr
- d field: data register
- m field: effective address mode
- r field: effective address register
- 0 field:

| byte | word | long | operation |
|------|------|------|-----------|
| 000 | 001 | 010 | Dn = Dn + ⟨ea⟩ |
| 100 | 101 | 110 | ⟨ea⟩ = Dn + ⟨ea⟩ |

**ADDA**  Add address register

1101 dddo oomm mrrr
- d field: address register
- m field: effective address mode
- r field: effective address register
- 0 field:

| word | long | operation |
|------|------|-----------|
| 011 | 111 | An = An + ⟨ea⟩ |

**ADDI**  Add immediate

0000 0110 ssmm mrrr
- s field: size: 00 = byte, 01 = word, 10 = long-word
- m field: effective address mode
- r field: effective address register

ADDQ                           Add quick

0101  ddd0  ssmm  mrrr
  d field:    data field 0 = 8, 1–7
  s field:    size: 00 = byte, 01 = word, 10 = long-word
  m field:   effective address mode
  r field:    effective address register

AND                            Logical AND

1100  dddo  oomm  mrrr
  d field:    data register
  o field:    byte  word  long   operation

| byte | word | long | operation |
|------|------|------|-----------|
| 000  | 001  | 010  | Dn = Dn and ⟨ea⟩ |
| 100  | 101  | 110  | ⟨ea⟩ = Dn and ⟨ea⟩ |

  m field:   effective address mode
  r field:    effective address register

ANDI                           AND immediate

0000  0010  ssmm  mrrr
  s field:    size: 00 = byte, 01 = word, 10 = long-word
  m field:   effective address mode
  r field:    effective address register

ANDI                           AND immediate to CCR

0000  0010  0011  1100

ANDI                           AND immediate to SR

0000  0010  0111  1100

ASL                            Arithmetic shift left—data register

1110  ccc1  ssi0  0rrr
  c field:    count or register
  s field:    size: 00 = byte, 01 = word, 10 = long-word
  i field:    if 0, c field holds shift count; if 1, c field holds register number
  r field:    register shifted

ASL                            Arithmetic shift left—memory

1110  0001  11mm  mrrr
  m field:   effective address mode
  r field:    effective address register

ASR                          Arithmetic shift right—data register

1110  ccc0  ssi0  0rrr
   c field:    count or register
   s field:    size: 00 = byte, 01 = word, 10 = long-word
   i field:    if 0, c field holds shift count; if 1, c field holds register number
   r field:    register shifted

ASR                          Arithmetic shift right—memory

1110  0000  11mm  mrrr
   m field:    effective address mode
   r field:    effective address register

Bcc                          Branch on condition

0110  cccc  dddd  dddd
   d field:    8-bit displacement; if this field is zero, a 16-bit displacement is
            used in the following word
   c field:    condition codes
            0010 = high (BHI)
            0011 = low or the same (BLS)
            0100 = carry clear (BCC)
            0101 = carry set (BCS)
            0110 = not equal (BNE)
            0111 = equal (BEQ)
            1000 = overflow clear (BVC)
            1001 = overflow set (BVS)
            1010 = plus (BPL)
            1011 = minus (BMI)
            1100 = greater than or equal (BGE)
            1101 = less than (BLT)
            1110 = greater than (BGT)
            1111 = less than or equal (BLE)

BCHG                         Bit test and change—position in data register

0000  ddd1  01mm  mrrr
   d field:    data register containing bit position
   m field:    effective address mode
   r field:    effective address register

BCHG                         Bit test and change—position is immediate

0000  1000  01mm  mrrr
   m field:    effective address mode
   r field:    effective address register
   Note:     count is held in second word of this instruction.

BCLR                          Bit test and clear—position in data register

0000  ddd1  10mm  mrrr
    d field:     data register containing bit position
    m field:     effective address mode
    r field:     effective address register

BCLR                          Bit test and clear—position is immediate

0000  1000  10mm  mrrr
    m field:     effective address mode
    r field:     effective address register
    Note:        Count is held in second word of this instruction.

BRA                           Branch always

0110  0000  dddd  dddd
    d field:     displacement
    Note:        If displacement is zero, the next word contains a 16-bit
             displacement.

BSET                          Bit test and set—position in data register

0000  ddd1  11mm  mrrr
    d field:     data register containing bit position
    m field:     effective address mode
    r field:     effective address register

BSET                          Bit test and set—position is immediate

0000  1000  11mm  mrrr
    m field:     effective address mode
    r field:     effective address register
    Note:        Count is held in second word of this instruction.

BSR                           Branch to subroutine

0110  0001  dddd  dddd
    d field:     displacement
    Note:        If displacement is zero, the next word contains a 16-bit
             displacement.

BTST                          Bit test—position in data register

0000  ddd1  00mm  mrrr
    d field:     data register containing bit position
    m field:     effective address mode
    r field:     effective address register

BTST                      Bit test—position is immediate

0000  1000  00mm  mrrr
- m field:     effective address mode
- r field:     effective address register
- Note:      Count is held in second word of this instruction.

CHK                   Check register against boundary

0100  ddd1  10mm  mrrr
- d field:     data register
- m field:     effective address mode
- r field:     effective address register

CLR                     Clear operand

0100  0010  ssmm  mrrr
- s field:     size: 00 = byte, 01 = word, 10 = long-word
- m field:     effective address mode
- r field:     effective address register

CMP                  Compare data register

1011  ddd0  ssmm  mrrr
- d field:     data register
- s field:     size: 00 = byte, 01 = word, 10 = long-word
- m field:     effective address mode
- r field:     effective address register

CMPA                Compare address register

1011  ddds  s1mm  mrrr
- d field:     address register
- s field:     size: 01 = word, 11 = long-word
- m field:     effective address mode
- r field:     effective address register

CMPI                 Compare immediate data

0000  1100  ssmm  mrrr
- s field:     size: 00 = byte, 01 = word, 10 = long-word
- m field:     effective address mode
- r field:     effective address register

CMPM               Compare memory data

1011  ddd1  ss00  1rrr
- d field:     destination address register

s field:        size: 00 = byte, 01 = word, 10 = long-word
r field:        source address register

**DBcc**                        Test condition, decrement, and branch

0101  cccc  1100  1rrr
r field:        data register used as counter
c field:        condition codes
                0000 = true (DBT), never branches
                0001 = false (DBF or DBRA)
                0010 = high (DBHI)
                0011 = lower or the same (DBLS)
                0100 = carry clear (DBCC)
                0101 = carry set (DBCS)
                0110 = not equal (DBNE)
                0111 = equal (DBEQ)
                1000 = overflow clear (DBVC)
                1001 = overflow set (DBVS)
                1010 = plus (DBPL)
                1011 = minus (DBMI)
                1100 = greater than or equal (DBGE)
                1101 = less than (DBLT)
                1110 = greater than (DBGT)
                1111 = less than or equal (DBLE)

**DIVS**                        Signed binary division

1000  ddd1  11mm  mrrr
d field:        data register
m field:        effective address mode
r field:        effective address register

**DIVU**                        Unsigned binary division

1000  ddd0  11mm  mrrr
d field:        data register
m field:        effective address mode
r field:        effective address register

**EOR**                         Exclusive-OR

1011  ddd1  ssmm  mrrr
d field:        data register
s field:        size: 00 = byte, 01 = word, 10 = long-word
m field:        effective address mode
r field:        effective address register

EORI                          Exclusive-OR immediate

0000 .1010  ssmm  mrrr
    s field:      size: 00 = byte, 01 = word, 10 = long-word
    m field:    effective address mode
    r field:      effective address register

EORI                          Exclusive-OR immediate CCR

0000  1010  0011  1100

EORI                          Exclusive-OR immediate SR

0000  1010  0111  1100

EXG                          Exchange register

1100  sss1  mmmm  mddd
    s field:      source address or data register or data register if the exchange is
              between an address register and a data register
    m field:    mode: 01000 = data registers, 01001 = address registers, 10001
              = data and address registers
    d field:    destination address or data register or address register if
              exchange is between an address register and a data register

EXT                          Sign-extend

0100  1000  1t00  0rrr
    t field:      if 0, extend to word; if 1, extend to long-word
    r field:      data register

JMP                          Jump

0100  1110  11mm  mrrr
    m field:    effective address mode
    r field:      effective address register

JSR                          Jump to subroutine

0100  1110  10mm  mrrr
    m field:    effective address mode
    r field:      effective address register

LEA                          Load effective address

0100  ddd1  11mm  mrrr
    d field:      address register
    m field:    effective address mode
    r field:      effective address register

LINK                          Link and allocate

0100  1110  0101  0ddd
   d field:      address register

LSL                          Logical shift left—register

1110  ddd1  ssi0  1rrr
   d field:      immediate count or register containing shift count
   s field:      size: 00 = byte, 01 = word, 10 = long-word
   i field:      if i = 0, the d field contains the immediate shift count; if i = 1,
               it contains the data register number that holds the shift count
   r field:      the data register that is shifted

LSL                          Logical shift left—memory

1110  0011  11mm  mrrr
   m field:     effective address mode
   r field:      effective address register

LSR                          Logical shift right—register

1110  ddd0  ssi0  1rrr
   d field:      immediate count or register containing shift count
   s field:      size: 00 = byte, 01 = word, 10 = long-word
   i field:      if i = 0, the d field contains the immediate shift count; if i = 1,
               it contains the data register number that holds the shift count
   r field:      the data register that is shifted

LSR                          Logical shift right—memory

1110  0010  11mm  mrrr
   m field:     effective address mode
   r field:      effective address register

MOVE                         Move data

00ss  dddo  oomm  mrrr
   s field:      size: 00 = byte, 01 = word, 10 = long-word
   d field:      destination effective address register
   o field:      destination effective address mode
   m field:     source effective address mode
   r field:      source effective address register

MOVE                         MOVE to CCR

0100  0100  11mm  mrrr
   m field:     source effective address mode
   r field:      source effective address register

MOVE                    MOVE to SR

0100   0110   11mm   mrrr
  m field:      source effective address mode
  r field:      source effective address register

MOVE                    MOVE from SR

0100   0000   11mm   mrrr
  m field:      destination effective address mode
  r field:      destination effective address register

MOVE                    Move USP

0100   1110   0110   irrr
  i field:      if i = 0, address register copied to USP; if i = 1, address
              register is loaded from USP
  r field:      address register

MOVEA                   Move address register

00ss   ddd0   01mm   mrrr
  s field:      size: 11 = word, 10 = long-word
  d field:      address register
  m field:      effective address mode
  r field:      effective address register

MOVEM                   Move multiple register

0100   1d00   1smm   mrrr
  d field:      if d = 0, transfer is from register to memory; if d = 1, transfer
              is from memory to register
  s field:      size: 0 = word, 1 = long-word
  m field:      effective address mode
  r field:      effective address register
  Note:        Second word of this instruction contains the register mask.

Mask for all addressing modes except predecrement.
A7 A6 A5 A4 A3 A2 A1 A0 D7 D6 D5 D4 D3 D2 D1 D0
Predecrement mask:
D0 D1 D2 D3 D4 D5 D6 D7 A0 A1 A2 A3 A4 A5 A6 A7

MOVEP                   Move peripheral

0000   dddo   oo00   1rrr
  d field:      data register
  o field:      100 = transfer word from memory to register
              101 = transfer long-word from memory to register

110 = transfer word from register to memory
111 = transfer long-word from register to memory
r field:     address register

## MOVEQ                        Move quick

0111  rrr0  dddd  dddd
  r field:     data register
  d field:     8-bit data

## MULS                         Signed multiplication

1100  ddd1  11mm  mrrr
  d field:     data register
  m field:     effective address mode
  r field:     effective address register

## MULU                         Unsigned multiplication

1100  ddd0  11mm  mrrr
  d field:     data register
  m field:     effective address mode
  r field:     effective address register

## NBCD                         Negate binary-coded decimal

0100  1000  00mm  mrrr
  m field:     effective address mode
  r field:     effective address register

## NEG                          Negate

0100  0100  ssmm  mrrr
  s field:     size: 00 = byte, 01 = word, 10 = long-word
  m field:     effective address mode
  r field:     effective address register

## NEGX                         Negate with extend

0100  0000  ssmm  mrrr
  s field:     size: 00 = byte, 01 = word, 10 = long-word
  m field:     effective address mode
  r field:     effective address register

## NOP                          No operation

0100  1110  0111  0001

NOT                             Logical inversion

0100   0110   ssmm   mrrr
   s field:     size: 00 = byte, 01 = word, 10 = long-word
   m field:    effective address mode
   r field:     effective address register

OR                               Logical OR

1000   dddo   oomm   mrrr
   d field:     data register
   o field:     byte    word    long    operation
                000     001     010     Dn = Dn or ⟨ea⟩
                100     101     110     ⟨ea⟩ = ⟨ea⟩ or Dn
   m field:    effective address mode
   r field:     effective address register

ORI                             OR immediate

0000   0000   ssmm   mrrr
   s field:     size: 00 = byte, 01 = word, 10 = long-word
   m field:    effective address mode
   r field:     effective address register

ORI                             OR immediate to CCR

0000   0000   0011   1100

ORI                             OR immediate to SR

0000   0000   0111   1100

PEA                             Push effective address

0100   1000   01mm   mrrr
   m field:    effective address mode
   r field:     effective address register

RESET                           Reset system

0100   1110   0111   0000

ROL                             Rotate left without extend—register

1110   cccl   ssil   lrrr
   c field:     data register or rotate count
   s field:     size: 00 = byte, 01 = word, 10 = long-word
   i field:     if i = 0, c is an immediate count; if i = 1, c is a data register
                that holds the count
   r field:     data register rotated

ROL                 Rotate left without extend—memory

```
1110  0111  11mm  mrrr
```
  m field:     effective address mode
  r field:      effective address register

ROR                 Rotate right without extend—register

```
1110  ccc0  ssi1  1rrr
```
  c field:     data register or rotate count
  s field:     size: 00 = byte, 01 = word, 10 = long-word
  i field:      if i = 0, c is an immediate count; if i = 1, c is a data register
                that holds the count
  r field:      data register rotated

ROR                 Rotate right without extend—memory

```
1110  0110  11mm  mrrr
```
  m field:     effective address mode
  r field:      effective address register

ROXL                Rotate left with extend—register

```
1110  ccc1  ssi1  0rrr
```
  c field:     data register or rotate count
  s field:     size: 00 = byte, 01 = word, 10 = long-word
  i field:      if i = 0, c is an immediate count; if i = 1, c is a data register
                that holds the count
  r field:      data register rotated

ROXL                Rotate left with extend—memory

```
1110  0101  11mm  mrrr
```
  m field:     effective address mode
  r field:      effective address register

ROXR               Rotate right with extend—register

```
1110  ccc0  ssi1  0rrr
```
  c field:     data register or rotate count
  s field:     size: 00 = byte, 01 = word, 10 = long-word
  i field:      if i = 0, c is an immediate count; if i = 1, c is a data register
                that holds the count
  r field:      data register rotated

ROXR               Rotate right with extend—memory

```
1110  0100  11mm  mrrr
```
  m field:     effective address mode
  r field:      effective address register

RTE                          Return from exception

0100   1110   0111   0011


RTR                          Return and restore CCR

0100   1110   0111   0111


RTS                          Return from subroutine

0100   1110   0111   0101


SBCD                         Subtract binary-coded decimal

1000   ddd1   0000   irrr
   d field:     destination register
   i field:     if i = 0, data register subtraction; if i = 1, memory-to-memory
               subtraction
   r field:     source register


Scc                          Set according to condition

0101   cccc   11mm   mrrr
   m field:    effective address mode
   r field:     effective address register
   c field:    condition code
              0000 = true (ST)
              0001 = false (SF)
              0010 = high (SHI)
              0011 = lower or the same (SLS)
              0100 = carry clear (SCC)
              0101 = carry set (SCS)
              0110 = not equal (SNE)
              0111 = equal (SEQ)
              1000 = overflow clear (SVC)
              1001 = overflow set (SVS)
              1010 = plus (SPL)
              1011 = minus (SMI)
              1100 = greater than or equal (SGE)
              1101 = less than (SLT)
              1110 = greater than (SGT)
              1111 = less than or equal (SLE)


STOP                         Stop

0100   1110   0111   0010

## SUB                        Binary subtraction

1001  dddo  oomm  mrrr
- d field:   data register
- o field:   byte   word   long   operation
          000    001    010    Dn = Dn − ⟨ea⟩
          100    101    110    ⟨ea⟩ = ⟨ea⟩ − Dn
- m field:   effective address mode
- r field:   effective address register

## SUBA                       Subtract address register

1001  dddo  oomm  mrrr
- d field:   address register
- o field:   011 = word and 111 = long-word
- m field:   effective address mode
- r field:   effective address register

## SUBI                       Subtract immediate

0000  0100  ssmm  mrrr
- s field:   size: 00 = byte, 01 = word, 10 = long-word
- m field:   effective address mode
- r field:   effective address register

## SUBQ                       Subtract quick

0101  ddd1  ssmm  mrrr
- d field:   immediate data field
- s field:   size: 00 = byte, 01 = word, 10 = long-word
- m field:   effective address mode
- r field:   effective address register

## SUBX                       Subtract with extend

1001  ddd1  ss00  irrr
- d field:   destination register
- s field:   size: 00 = byte, 01 = word, 10 = long-word
- i field:   if i = 0, data register subtraction; if i = 1, memory-to-memory subtraction
- r field:   source register

## SWAP                       Swap register halves

0100  1000  0100  0rrr
- r field:   data register

TAS                            Test and set operand

0100   1010   11mm   mrrr
   m field:      effective address mode
   r field:       effective address register


TRAP                           Software interrupt

0100   1110   0100   vvvv
   v field:       vector number 0000–1111


TRAPV                          Interrupt on an overflow

0100   1110   0111   0110


TST                            Test operand

0100   1010   ssmm   mrrr
   s field:       size: 00 = byte, 01 = word, 10 = long-word
   m field:      effective address mode
   r field:       effective address register


UNLK                           Unlink

0100   1110   0101   1rrr
   r field:       address register

# The 68881/68882 Instruction Set

The following list contains the instructions allowed by the 68881/68882 coprocessor. Also listed are the subset of floating-point instructions allowed by the 68040 microprocessor. An asterisk (*) next to an instruction indicates that the instruction functions on the 68040 microprocessor. In this listing ⟨ea⟩ indicates the effective address, which can be any addressing mode except An. Also used as shorthand is a question mark extension (.?), which indicates any size data. Execution times for the instructions are not listed.

| FABS* | Absolute value |
|---|---|

Converts the source operand to an extended-precision absolute value.

```
FABS.?    ⟨ea⟩,FPn
FABS.X    FPn,FPn
FABS.X    FPn
```

| FACOS | Arc cosine |
|---|---|

Converts the source operand to an extended-precision arc cosine. The result is not defined if the source is outside the range of −1 to +1.

```
FACOS.?    ⟨ea⟩,FPn
FACOS.X    FPn,FPn
FACOS.X    FPn
```

---

FADD*              Addition

Converts the source operand to extended-precision number and adds it to
the destination register.

```
FADD.?      <ea>,FPn
FADD.X      FPn,FPn
```

---

FASIN              Arc sine

Converts the source operand to an extended-precision arc sine. The arc
sine is undefined if the source is outside −1 to +1.

```
FASIN.?     <ea>,FPn
FASIN.X     FPn,FPn
FASIN.X     FPn
```

---

FATAN              Arc tangent

Converts the source operand to an extended-precision arc tangent. The
results is in the range of $-\pi/2$ to $\pi/2$.

```
FATAN.?     <ea>,FPn
FATAN.X     FPn,FPn
FATAN.X     FPn
```

---

FATANH             Hyperbolic arc tangent

Converts the source operand to an extended-precision hyperbolic arc
tangent. This operation is undefined if the source is outside the range of
−1 to +1.

```
FATANH.?    <ea>,FPn
FATANH.X    FPn,FPn
FATANH.X    FPn
```

| FBcc* | Branch conditionally |
|---|---|

If the condition tested is true, a branch occurs to the label indicated. If the condition tested is false, no branch occurs and the instruction functions as a NOP.

```
FBcc.W     <label>
FBcc.L     <label>
```

| FCMP* | Compare |
|---|---|

Converts the source operand to extended-precision number and subtracts it from the destination. The result is not placed into the destination; instead, the floating-point condition code bits reflect the difference.

```
FCMP.?     <ea>,FPn
FCMP.X     FPn,FPn
```

| FCOS | Cosine |
|---|---|

Converts the source operand to an extended-precision cosine. If the source is not between $-2\pi$ to $+2\pi$, it is scaled to this range. If the source is greater than $10^{20}$, accuracy may suffer.

```
FCOS.?     <ea>,FPn
FCOS.X     FPn,FPn
FCOS.X     FPn
```

| FCOSH | Hyperbolic cosine |
|---|---|

Converts the source operand to an extended-precision hyperbolic cosine.

```
FCOSH.?    <ea>,FPn
FCOSH.X    FPn,FPn
FCOSH.X    FPn
```

---

FDBcc*                Test condition, decrement, and branch

---

This instruction tests the condition. If the condition is true, no operation is performed. If the condition is false, the data register (word-sized) is decremented. If the count becomes a $-1$, the instruction terminates. If the count is not a $-1$, a branch to the ⟨label⟩ occurs.

---

```
FDBcc       Dn,(label)
```

---

FDIV*                 Divide

---

Converts the source operand to an extended-precision number divided into the destination register.

---

```
FDIV.?      (ea),FPn
FDIV.X      FPn,FPn
```

---

FETOX                 $e^x$

---

Converts the source operand to an extended-precision number and calculates $e$ raised to that power.

---

```
FETOX.?     (ea),FPn
FETOX.X     FPn,FPn
FETOX.X     FPn
```

---

FETOXM1               $e^x - 1$

---

Converts the source operand to an extended-precision number and calculates $e$ raised to the power $x$ minus 1.

---

```
FETOXM1.?   (ea),FPn
FETOXM1.X   FPn,FPn
FETOXM1.X   FPn
```

---

FGETEXP          Get exponent

Converts the source operand to an extended-precision number and extracts the binary exponent. The binary exponent is stored in the destination register without the bias.

```
FGETEXP.?   <ea>,FPn
FGETEXP.X   FPn,FPn
FGETEXP.X   FPn
```

---

FGETMAN          Get mantissa

Converts the source operand to an extended-precision number and extracts the mantissa. The mantissa is stored as a floating-point number between 1.0 and 2.0.

```
FGETMAN.?   <ea>,FPn
FGETMAN.X   FPn,FPn
FGETMAN.X   FPn
```

---

FINT          Integer part

Converts the source operand to an extended-precision number so that the integer part is stored as an extended-precision floating-point number in the destination.

```
FINT.?      <ea>,FPn
FINT.X      FPn,FPn
FINT.X      FPn
```

---

FINTRZ          Integer par, rounded-to-zero

Converts the source operand to an extended-precision number so that the integer part is stored as truncated value.

```
FINTRZ.?    <ea>,FPn
FINTRZ.X    FPn,FPn
FINTRZ.X    FPn
```

---

**FLOG10**               Log$_{10}$

Converts the source operand to an extended-precision base 10 logarithm.

```
FLOG10.?    <ea>,FPn
FLOG10.X    FPn,FPn
FLOG10.X    FPn
```

---

**FLOG2**               Log$_2$

Converts the source operand to an extended-precision base 2 logarithm.

```
FLOG2.?    <ea>,FPn
FLOG2.X    FPn,FPn
FLOG2.X    FPn
```

---

**FLOGN**               Log$_e$

Converts the source operand to an extended-precision natural logarithm.

```
FLOGN.?    <ea>,FPn
FLOGN.X    FPn,FPn
FLOGN.X    FPn
```

---

**FLOGNP1**               Log$_e(X + 1)$

Converts the source operand to an extended-precision value plus 1, then the natural logarithm is formed from this number.

```
FLOGNP1.?    <ea>,FPn
FLOGNP1.X    FPn,FPn
FLOGNP1.X    FPn
```

---

**FMOD** Modulo remainder

Converts the source operand to an extended-precision number; then divides the destination by using the source as the modulo divisor.

```
FMOD.?      〈ea〉,FPn
FMOD.X      FPn,FPn
```

---

**FMOVE*** Move

Moves the source operand to the destination.

```
FMOVE.?     〈ea〉,FPn
FMOVE.?     FPn,〈ea〉
FMOVE.P     FPn,〈ea〉{Dn}
FMOVE.P     FPn,〈ea〉{#k}
FMOVE.L     〈ea〉,FPcr
FMOVE.L     FPcr,〈ea〉
```

---

**FMOVECR** Move constant ROM

Moves a constant from the ROM to a floating-point register.

```
FMOVECR.X   #ccc,FPn
```

---

**FMOVEM*** Move multiple registers

Moves the source to the destination.

```
FMOVEM.X    〈list〉,〈ea〉
FMOVEM.X    〈ea〉,〈list〉
FMOVEM.X    Dn,〈ea〉
FMOVEM.X    〈ea〉,Dn
FMOVEM.L    〈list〉,〈ea〉
FMOVEM.L    〈ea〉,〈list〉
```

| FMUL* | Multiply |
|---|---|
| Multiplies the source times the destination. | |
| FMUL.?   〈ea〉,FPn<br>FMUL.X   FPn,FPn | |

| FNEG* | Negate |
|---|---|
| Negates the source and stores it in the destination. | |
| FNEG.?   〈ea〉,FPn<br>FNEG.X   FPn,FPn<br>FNEG.X   FPn | |

| FNOP* | No operation |
|---|---|
| Performs no operation. | |
| FNOP | |

| FREM | IEEE remainder |
|---|---|
| Calculates the modulo remainder of the destination. | |
| FREM.?   FPn,〈ea〉<br>FREM.X   FPn,FPn | |

| FRESTORE* | Restore internal state |
|---|---|
| Restores the internal state of the coprocessor. | |
| FRESTORE   〈ea〉 | |

---

FSAVE*          Save internal state

Saves the internal state of the coprocessor.

```
FSAVE      (ea)
```

---

FSCALE          Scale exponent

Scales the destination.

```
FSCALE.?    (ea),FPn
FSCALE.X    FPn,FPn
```

---

FScc*           Set according to condition

Sets the destination to all ones if condition is true.

```
FScc.?      (ea)
```

---

FSGLDIV         Single-precision divide

Divides the destination by the source.

```
FSGLDIV.?   (ea),FPn
FSGLDIV.X   FPn,FPn
```

---

FSGLMUL         Single-precision multiply

Multiplies the destination by the source.

```
FSGLMUL.?   (ea),FPn
FSGLMUL.X   FPn,FPn
```

| FSIN | Sine |
|---|---|
| Finds the sine. | |

```
FSIN,?    <ea>,FPn
FSIN,X    FPn,FPn
FSIN,X    FPn
```

| FSINCOS | Sine and cosine |
|---|---|
| Finds the sine and cosine. | |

```
FSINCOS,?  <ea>,FPc:FPs
FSINCOS,X  FPn,FPc:FPs
```

| FSINH | Hyperbolic sine |
|---|---|
| Finds the hyperbolic sine. | |

```
FSINH,?    <ea>,FPn
FSINH,X    FPn,FPn
FSINH,X    FPn
```

| FSQRT* | Square root |
|---|---|
| Finds the square root. | |

```
FSQRT,?    <ea>,FPn
FSQRT,X    FPn,FPn
FSQRT,X    FPn
```

| FSUB* | Subtract |
|---|---|
| Subtracts the source from the destination. | |

```
FSUB,?     <ea>,FPn
FSUB,X     FPn,FPn
```

| FTAN | Tangent |
|------|---------|

Finds the tangent.

```
FTAN.?      (ea),FPn
FTAN.X      FPn,FPn
FTAN.X      FPn
```

| FTANH | Hyperbolic tangent |
|-------|--------------------|

Finds the hyperbolic tangent.

```
FTANH.?     (ea),FPn
FTANH.X     FPn,FPn
FTANH.X     FPn
```

| FTENTOX | Raise 10 to the X power |
|---------|-------------------------|

Raises the 10 to the power of the source.

```
FTENTOX.?   (ea),FPn
FTENTOX.X   FPn,FPn
FTENTOX.X   FPn
```

| FTRAPcc* | Conditional TRAP |
|----------|------------------|

Executes TRAP if condition is true.

```
FTRAPcc.W   #(data)
FTRAPcc.L   #(data)
```

| FTST* | Test operand |
|-------|--------------|

Tests the contents of the operand.

```
FTST.?      (ea)
FTST.X      FPn
```

| FTWOTOX | Raise 2 to the $X$ power. |
|---|---|
| Raises 2 to the power of the source. | |

```
FTWOTOX,?  <ea>,FPn
FTWOTOX,X  FPn,FPn
FTWOTOX,X  FPn
```

# 68000 Instruction Execution Times

This appendix lists all the 68000 instructions with the number of clocks required to execute each instruction. To determine the exact amount of time required to execute a given instruction, multiply the number of clocks required times the clock cycle time.

For example, a MOVE.B #2,D1 instruction requires 8 clocks to execute. If the clock is 8 MHz, the clock cycle time is 125 ns. The MOVE.B #2,D1 instruction then takes 8 × 125 ns or 1.0 μs to execute.

## Effective Address Calculations

Effective address times are indicated as the number of clocks required to access data for a particular addressing mode. Table D-1 lists each addressing mode with the number of clocks required to calculate the address and fetch or store the data.

**Table D-1  Effective Address Times**

| Mode | Byte, word | Long-word |
|------|------------|-----------|
| Dn | 0 | 0 |
| An | 0 | 0 |
| (An) | 4 | 8 |
| (An)+ | 4 | 8 |
| −(An) | 6 | 10 |
| d(An) | 8 | 12 |
| d(An,Rx) | 10 | 14 |
| XXX.W | 8 | 12 |
| XXX.L | 12 | 16 |
| d(PC) | 8 | 12 |
| d(PC,Rx) | 10 | 14 |
| #XXX | 4 | 8 |

**Table D-2   The Execution Times for the Byte and Word MOVE Instructions**

| Source | Destination | | | | | | | | |
|--------|-----|-----|------|-------|------|------|--------|-------|-------|
|  | Dn | An | (An) | (An)+ | −(An) | d(An) | d(An,Rx) | XXX.W | XXX.L |
| Dn | 4 | 4 | 8 | 8 | 8 | 12 | 14 | 12 | 12 |
| An | 4 | 4 | 8 | 8 | 8 | 12 | 14 | 12 | 12 |
| (An) | 8 | 8 | 12 | 12 | 12 | 16 | 18 | 16 | 20 |
| (An)+ | 8 | 8 | 12 | 12 | 12 | 16 | 18 | 16 | 20 |
| −(An) | 10 | 10 | 14 | 13 | 14 | 18 | 20 | 18 | 22 |
| d(An) | 12 | 12 | 16 | 16 | 16 | 20 | 22 | 20 | 24 |
| d(An,Rx) | 14 | 14 | 18 | 18 | 18 | 22 | 24 | 22 | 26 |
| XXX.W | 12 | 12 | 16 | 16 | 16 | 20 | 22 | 20 | 24 |
| XXX.L | 18 | 18 | 20 | 20 | 20 | 24 | 26 | 24 | 28 |
| d(PC) | 12 | 12 | 16 | 16 | 16 | 20 | 22 | 20 | 24 |
| d(PC,Rx) | 14 | 14 | 18 | 18 | 18 | 22 | 24 | 22 | 26 |
| #XXX | 8 | 8 | 12 | 12 | 12 | 16 | 18 | 16 | 20 |

## MOVE Instruction Execution Times

MOVE instructions offer a wide variety of addressing modes. Tables D-2 and D-3 list all the addressing modes that apply to these instructions, along with the number of clocking periods required to execute each one. The number of clocks includes the time required to fetch the instruction, calculate the effective address, and execute the instruction.

**Table D-3   The Execution Times for a Long-Word MOVE Instruction**

| Source | Destination | | | | | | | | |
|--------|-----|-----|------|-------|------|------|--------|-------|-------|
|  | Dn | An | (An) | (An)+ | −(An) | d(An) | d(An,Rx) | XXX.W | XXX.L |
| Dn | 4 | 4 | 12 | 12 | 12 | 16 | 18 | 16 | 20 |
| An | 4 | 4 | 12 | 12 | 12 | 16 | 18 | 16 | 20 |
| (An) | 12 | 12 | 20 | 20 | 20 | 24 | 26 | 24 | 28 |
| (An)+ | 12 | 12 | 20 | 20 | 20 | 24 | 26 | 24 | 28 |
| −(An) | 14 | 14 | 22 | 22 | 22 | 26 | 28 | 26 | 30 |
| d(An) | 16 | 16 | 24 | 24 | 24 | 28 | 30 | 28 | 32 |
| d(An,Rx) | 18 | 18 | 26 | 26 | 26 | 30 | 32 | 30 | 34 |
| XXX.W | 16 | 16 | 24 | 24 | 24 | 28 | 30 | 28 | 32 |
| XXX.L | 20 | 20 | 28 | 28 | 28 | 32 | 34 | 32 | 36 |
| d(PC) | 16 | 16 | 24 | 24 | 24 | 28 | 30 | 28 | 32 |
| d(PC,Rx) | 18 | 18 | 26 | 26 | 26 | 30 | 32 | 30 | 34 |
| #XXX | 12 | 12 | 20 | 20 | 20 | 24 | 26 | 24 | 28 |

## Standard Instruction Execution Times

Table D-4 gives the execution times of the standard instructions. Note that the effective address calculation times from Table D-1 must be added to the times given in this table.

## Immediate Instruction Execution Times

Table D-5 lists all the immediate instructions and the number of clocks required to execute them. Note that the effective address times from Table D-1 must be added to the times in this table.

## Single Operand Instruction Execution Times

Table D-6 list all the single-operand instructions, along with the number of clocks required to execute each of them. Note that the effective address times from Table D-1 must be added to memory addressed instructions to determine the number of clocks.

## Shift and Rotate Instruction Execution Times

Table D-7 gives all the shift and rotate instructions, along with the number of clocks required to execute each of them. Note that with the memory addressing mode, the effective address calculation times from table D-1 must be added. Also note that only a memory reference may be a word for these instructions.

## Binary Bit Manipulation Instruction Execution Times

Table D-8 lists all the binary bit manipulation instructions, along with the number of clocks required to execute each of them. Note that the effective address times from Table D-1 must be added to each instruction that uses memory addressing.

## Conditional Instruction Execution Times

Table D-9 lists the conditional instructions, along with the number of clocks required for execution.

## JMP, JSR, LEA, PEA, and MOVEM Instruction Execution Times

Table D-10 gives the number of clocks required to execute the JMP, JSR, LEA, PEA, and MOVEM instructions.

**Table D-4**    The Standard Instruction Execution Times

| Instruction | Size | ⟨ea⟩,An | ⟨ea⟩,Dn | Dn,⟨ea⟩ |
|---|---|---|---|---|
| ADD/ADDA | .B or .W | 8 | 4 | 8 |
|  | .L | 6** | 6** | 12 |
| AND | .B or .W | — | 4 | 8 |
|  | .L | — | 6** | 12 |
| CMP/CMPA | .B or .W | 6 | 4 | — |
|  | .L | 6 | 6 | — |
| DIVS | — | — | 158 | — |
| DIVU | — | — | 140 | — |
| EOR | .B or .W | — | 4* | 8 |
|  | .L | — | 8* | 12 |
| MULS | — | — | 70 | — |
| MULU | — | — | 70 | — |
| OR | .B or .W | — | 4 | 8 |
|  | .L | — | 6** | 12 |
| SUB | .B or .W | 8 | 4 | 8 |
|  | .L | 6** | 6** | 12 |

NOTE: * = data register address only and ** = address time is 8 for register direct and immediate.

**Table D-5**    The Immediate Instruction Execution Times

| Instruction | Size | #XXX,Dn | #XXX,An | #XXX,⟨ea⟩ |
|---|---|---|---|---|
| ADDI | .B or .W | 8 | — | 12 |
|  | .L | 16 | — | 20 |
| ADDQ | .B or .W | 4 | 8 | 8 |
|  | .L | 8 | 8 | 12 |
| ANDI | .B or .W | 8 | — | 12 |
|  | .L | 16 | — | 20 |
| CMPI | .B or .W | 8 | — | 8 |
|  | .L | 14 | — | 12 |
| EORI | .B or .W | 8 | — | 12 |
|  | .L | 16 | — | 20 |
| MOVEQ | .L | 4 | — | — |
| ORI | .B or .W | 8 | — | 12 |
|  | .L | 16 | — | 20 |
| SUBI | .B or .W | 8 | — | 12 |
|  | .L | 16 | — | 20 |
| SUBQ | .B or .W | 4 | 8 | 8 |
|  | .L | 8 | 8 | 12 |

**Table D-6**   The Single-Operand Execution Times

| Instruction | Size | Register | Memory |
|---|---|---|---|
| CLR | .B or .W | 4 | 8 |
| | .L | 6 | 12 |
| NBCD | .B | 6 | 8 |
| NEG | .B or .W | 4 | 8 |
| | .L | 6 | 12 |
| NEGX | .B or .W | 4 | 8 |
| | .L | 6 | 12 |
| NOT | .B or .W | 4 | 8 |
| | .L | 6 | 12 |
| Scc | false | 4 | 8 |
| | true | 6 | 8 |
| TAS | .B | 4 | 10 |
| TST | .B or .W | 4 | 4 |
| | .L | 4 | 4 |

**Table D-7**   The Shift and Rotate Instruction Execution Times

| Instruction | Size | Register | Memory* |
|---|---|---|---|
| ASR or ASL | .B or .W | 6 + 2n | 8 |
| | .L | 8 + 2n | — |
| LSL or LSR | .B or .W | 6 + 2n | 8 |
| | .L | 8 + 2n | — |
| ROR or ROL | .B or .W | 6 + 2n | 8 |
| | .L | 8 + 2n | — |
| ROXR or ROXL | .B or .W | 6 + 2n | 8 |
| | .L | 8 + 2n | — |

NOTE: * = word only and n = the shift count.

**Table D-8**   The Binary Bit Manipulation Instruction Execution Times

| Instruction | Size | Dynamic | | Static | |
|---|---|---|---|---|---|
| | | Register | Memory | Register | Memory |
| BCHG | .B | — | 8 | — | 12 |
| | .L | 8 | — | 12 | — |
| BCLR | .B | — | 8 | — | 12 |
| | .L | 10 | — | 14 | — |
| BSET | .B | — | 8 | — | 12 |
| | .L | 8 | — | 12 | — |
| BTST | .B | — | 4 | — | 8 |
| | .L | 6 | — | 10 | — |

**Table D-9**   The Conditional Instruction Execution Times

| Instruction | Displacement | Branch taken | Branch not taken |
|---|---|---|---|
| Bcc | byte | 10 | 8 |
| | word | 10 | 12 |
| BRA | byte | 10 | — |
| | word | 10 | — |
| BSR | byte | 18 | — |
| | word | 18 | — |
| DBcc | cc true | — | 12 |
| | cc false, count not expired | 10 | — |
| | cc false, count expired | — | 14 |

**Table D-10**   The JMP, JSR, LEA, PEA, and MOVEM Instruction Execution Times

| Instruction | Size | (An) | (An)+ | −(An) | d(An) | d(An,Rx) | XXX.W | XXX.L | d(PC) | d(PC,Rx) |
|---|---|---|---|---|---|---|---|---|---|---|
| JMP | — | 8 | — | — | 10 | 14 | 10 | 12 | 10 | 14 |
| JSR | — | 16 | — | — | 18 | 22 | 18 | 20 | 18 | 22 |
| LEA | — | 4 | — | — | 8 | 12 | 8 | 12 | 8 | 12 |
| PEA | — | 12 | — | — | 16 | 20 | 16 | 20 | 16 | 20 |
| MOVEM 〈ea〉 to reg | — | 12 | 12 | — | 16 | 18 | 16 | 20 | 16 | 18 |
| MOVEM reg to 〈ea〉 | — | 8 | — | 8 | 12 | 14 | 12 | 16 | — | — |

NOTE: For the MOVEM instruction, add 4 clocks per register transferred for each word and 8 clocks per register transferred for each long-word.

**Table D-11**   The Multiprecision Instructions and Execution Times

| Instruction | Size | Dn,Dn | −(An),−(An) |
|---|---|---|---|
| ADDX | .B or .W | 4 | 18 |
| | .L | 8 | 30 |
| CMPM | .B or .W | — | 12 |
| | .L | — | 20 |
| SUBX | .B or .W | 4 | 18 |
| | .L | 8 | 30 |
| ABCD | .B | 6 | 18 |
| SBCD | .B | 6 | 18 |

## Multiprecision Instruction Execution Times

Table D-11 lists the multiprecision instructions and the number of clocks required to execute each of them.

## Miscellaneous Instruction Execution Times

Tables D-12 and D-13 list the miscellaneous instructions, along with the number of clocks required to execute them.

## Exception Execution Times

Table D-14 lists the different types of exception and the number of clocks required to execute each of them.

**Table D-12   The Miscellaneous Instruction Execution Times**

| Instruction | Size | Register | ⟨ea⟩ |
|-------------|------|----------|------|
| ANDI to CCR | .B | 20 | — |
| ANDI to SR | .W | 20 | — |
| CHK | — | 10 | — |
| EORI to CCR | .B | 20 | — |
| EORI to SR | .W | 20 | — |
| ORI to CCR | .B | 20 | — |
| ORI to SR | .W | 20 | — |
| MOVE from SR | — | 6 | 8 |
| MOVE to CCR | — | 12 | 12 |
| MOVE to SR | — | 12 | 12 |
| EXG | — | 6 | — |
| LINK | — | 16 | — |
| MOVE from USP | — | 4 | — |
| MOVE to USP | — | 4 | — |
| NOP | — | 4 | — |
| RESET | — | 132 | — |
| RTE | — | 20 | — |
| RTR | — | 20 | — |
| RTS | — | 16 | — |
| STOP | — | 4 | — |
| SWAP | — | 4 | — |
| TRAPV | — | 4 | — |
| UNLK | — | 12 | — |

NOTE: Any memory addressing mode requires that the effective address calculations be added from Table D-1.

**Table D-13    The MOVEP Instruction Execution Time**

| Instruction | Size | Register to memory | Memory to register |
|---|---|---|---|
| MOVEP | .W | 16 | 16 |
| | .L | 24 | 24 |

NOTE: Any memory addressing mode requires that the effective address calculations be added from Table D-1.

**Table D-14    The Exception Execution Times**

| Exception | Clocks |
|---|---|
| Address error | 50 |
| Bus error | 50 |
| CHK instruction | 40* |
| Divide by zero | 38* |
| Illegal instruction | 34 |
| Interrupt | 44 |
| Privilege violation | 34 |
| Reset | 40 |
| Trace | 34 |
| TRAP instruction | 34 |
| TRAPV instruction | 34 |

NOTE: * = effective address time must be added to the number of clocks in this table.

# The VMEbus

single- and double-
height boards

data transfer bus
priority interrupt bus

utility bus
arbitration bus

The VMEbus, originally known as the VERSAbus, is an interfacing standard that is extremely popular with the 68000 family of microprocessors. It is found in many control applications because it is mounted in a rack panel that is easily incorporated in large control applications. The VMEbus is also designated the IEEE P1014/D1.2 standard and the IEC 821 bus. The designation VMEbus comes from VERSAbus which was reworked by Motorola and incorporates the specifications of Eurocard.

The VMEbus standard specifies a bus system that is applicable to all versions of the 68000 family of microprocessors. It specifies not only the bus connection and signals, but also the card size, backplane, and many other system parameters.

## Mechanical Specifications

The basic VMEbus card cage (Figure E-1) houses two different size printed circuit cards. One printed circuit card, called a *single-height board*, supports the 68000 or 68010 microprocessor. The other printed circuit card, the *double-height board*, supports any microprocessor in the Motorola 68000 family, including the 68040. The card cage and its backplane typically fit a rack panel that is 19 inches wide by 10 inches high. The backplane contains 21 connectors for up to 21 VMEbus interface cards. One of these cards contains the microprocessor and bus support and the remaining cards contain memory and I/O.

Figure E-2 illustrates the single-height VMEbus printed circuit board. Notice that the board is 6.3 inches by 3.9 inches and has one connector (P1). The connector contains three rows of 32 pins per row for a total of 96 connections. The actual component mounting area is smaller and typically measures 6 inches by 3.5 inches. This board is designed to support the 68000, 68008, or 68010 microprocessor.

Figure E-3 illustrates the double-height VMEbus printed circuit board. Notice that the board is 6.3 inches by 9.187 inches and has two connectors (P1 and P2).

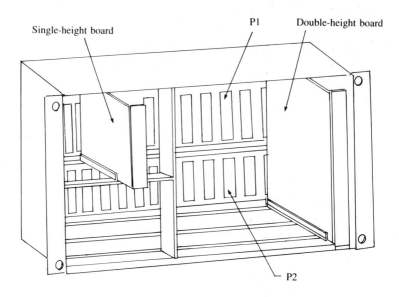

**Figure E-1   The VMEbus backplane.**

Each connector contain three rows of 32 pins for a total of 96 pins per connector. The actual component mounting area is smaller and typically measures 6 inches by 8.7 inches. This board is designed to support the 68020, 68030, or 68040 micro-processor.

The connectors (P1 and P2) contain 92 contacts each, arranged in three rows of 32 contacts each, as illustrated in Figure E-4. The contact rows are labeled A, B, and C.

The pin connections for connectors P1 and P2 are listed in Tables E-1 and E-2. Notice how the P1 signals correspond to the 68000, 68008, and 68010, while the P2

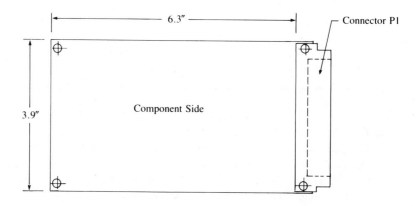

**Figure E-2   The single-height VMEbus printed circuit board.**

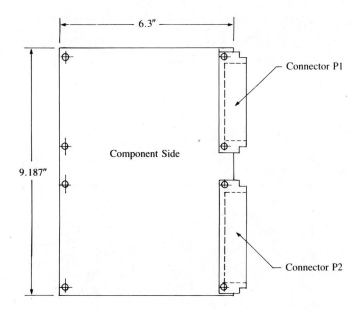

**Figure E-3**    **The double-height VMEbus printed circuit board.**

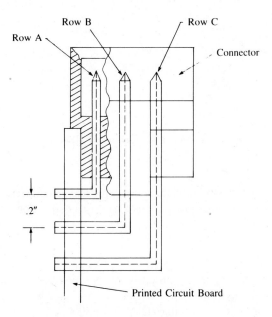

**Figure E-4**    **The 96-pin connector used for P1 and P2 on the VMEbus.**

Table E-1    The Pin Assignments for VMEbus Connector P1

| Pin | Row A | Row B | Row C |
|-----|-------|-------|-------|
| 1 | D0 | $\overline{\text{BBSY}}$ | D8 |
| 2 | D1 | $\overline{\text{BCLR}}$ | D9 |
| 3 | D2 | $\overline{\text{ACFAIL}}$ | D10 |
| 4 | D3 | $\overline{\text{BG0IN}}$ | D11 |
| 5 | D4 | $\overline{\text{BG0OUT}}$ | D12 |
| 6 | D5 | $\overline{\text{BG1IN}}$ | D13 |
| 7 | D6 | $\overline{\text{BG1OUT}}$ | D14 |
| 8 | D7 | $\overline{\text{BG2IN}}$ | D15 |
| 9 | GND | $\overline{\text{BG2OUT}}$ | GND |
| 10 | SYSCLK | $\overline{\text{BG3IN}}$ | $\overline{\text{SYSFAIL}}$ |
| 11 | GND | $\overline{\text{BG3OUT}}$ | $\overline{\text{BERR}}$ |
| 12 | $\overline{\text{DS1}}$ | $\overline{\text{BR0}}$ | $\overline{\text{SYSRESET}}$ |
| 13 | $\overline{\text{DS0}}$ | $\overline{\text{BR1}}$ | $\overline{\text{LWORD}}$ |
| 14 | $\overline{\text{WRITE}}$ | $\overline{\text{BR2}}$ | AM5 |
| 15 | GND | $\overline{\text{BR3}}$ | A23 |
| 16 | $\overline{\text{DTACK}}$ | AM0 | A22 |
| 17 | GND | AM1 | A21 |
| 18 | $\overline{\text{AS}}$ | AM2 | A20 |
| 19 | GND | AM3 | A19 |
| 20 | $\overline{\text{IACK}}$ | GND | A18 |
| 21 | $\overline{\text{IACKIN}}$ | SERCLK(1) | A17 |
| 22 | $\overline{\text{IACKOUT}}$ | SERDAT(1) | A16 |
| 23 | AM4 | GND | A15 |
| 24 | A7 | $\overline{\text{IRQ7}}$ | A14 |
| 25 | A6 | $\overline{\text{IRQ6}}$ | A13 |
| 26 | A5 | $\overline{\text{IRQ5}}$ | A12 |
| 27 | A4 | $\overline{\text{IRQ4}}$ | A11 |
| 28 | A3 | $\overline{\text{IRQ3}}$ | A10 |
| 29 | A2 | $\overline{\text{IRQ2}}$ | A9 |
| 30 | A1 | $\overline{\text{IRQ1}}$ | A8 |
| 31 | −12V | +5V STDBY | +12V |
| 32 | +5V | +5V | +5V |

signals are added for the 68020, 6803, and 68040. The P2 connector lists the row B pin connections only because rows A and C are user defined on this connector.

## Electrical Specifications

The signal lines on this bus are grouped into various buses. One of the more important of these buses is the *data transfer bus,* which consists of address, data, and control signals that are familiar from the 68000 microprocessor. The data transfer bus is comprised of most of the 68000 family signals.

**Table E-2** The Pin Assignments
for VMEbus Connector P2, Row B

| Pin | Row B |
|-----|-------|
| 1 | +5V |
| 2 | GND |
| 3 | [reserved] |
| 4 | A24 |
| 5 | A25 |
| 6 | A26 |
| 7 | A27 |
| 8 | A28 |
| 9 | A29 |
| 10 | A30 |
| 11 | A31 |
| 12 | GND |
| 13 | +5V |
| 14 | D16 |
| 15 | D17 |
| 16 | D18 |
| 17 | D19 |
| 18 | D20 |
| 19 | D21 |
| 20 | D22 |
| 21 | D23 |
| 22 | GND |
| 23 | D24 |
| 24 | D25 |
| 25 | D26 |
| 26 | D27 |
| 27 | D28 |
| 28 | D29 |
| 29 | D30 |
| 30 | D31 |
| 31 | GND |
| 32 | +5V |

Table E-3 lists the data transfer bus connections that appear on P1 and P2. It also contains a few lines that are new to the VMEbus: AM0–AM5, $\overline{\text{DS0}}$, $\overline{\text{DS1}}$, and $\overline{\text{LWORD}}$.

The AM0–AM5 signals are address modifier signals, similar to the function code bits of the 68000 family. These signal lines are not likely to be used in many applications.

The data selection lines ($\overline{\text{DS0}}$ and $\overline{\text{DS1}}$) and $\overline{\text{LWORD}}$ lines are used with A1 to select a byte of memory in a 32-bit-wide memory system. These lines are used to select memory as illustrated in Table E-4. Note that this table illusrates only the signals obtained for aligned word and long-word transfers.

Table E-3   The VMEbus Data Transfer
Signal Connections

| Address | Data | Control |
|---------|------|---------|
| A1–A31  | D0–D31 | $\overline{\text{AS}}$ |
| AM0–AM5 |      | $\overline{\text{DS0}}$ |
|         |      | $\overline{\text{DS1}}$ |
|         |      | $\overline{\text{LWORD}}$ |
|         |      | $\overline{\text{BERR}}$ |
|         |      | $\overline{\text{DTACK}}$ |
|         |      | $\overline{\text{WRITE}}$ |

The *priority interrupt bus* consists of the interrupt request lines ($\overline{\text{IRQ7}}$–$\overline{\text{IRQ1}}$), interrupt acknowledge ($\overline{\text{IACK}}$), and daisy-chain interrupt signals ($\overline{\text{IACKIN}}$ and $\overline{\text{IACKOUT}}$). The interrupt acknowledge cycle sends the request number back to the system address bus on address connections A3, A2, and A1. This is meant to be a signal to the interrupting device so that it can tell which interrupt level is being acknowledged.

The interrupt request pins are prioritized, with the $\overline{\text{IRQ7}}$ having the highest priority and $\overline{\text{IRQ1}}$ the lowest. The interrupt may be handled using either autovectors or user interrupts.

The daisy-chain signals ($\overline{\text{IACKIN}}$ and $\overline{\text{IACKOUT}}$) are used to expand the number of interrupts beyond 7. The daisy chain ensures that only one daisy-chain interrupting device receives the interrupt acknowledge signal when the interrupt request lines are cascaded.

The *utility bus* contains the main system control signals used to reset the microprocessor, provide the system clock, detect power failures, and transmit and receive serial data. The system clock (SYSCLK) signal is a 16 MHz, 50% duty cycle TTL signal. The serial clock (SERCLK) provides a fixed frequency clock

Table E-4   Selection Logic Signals

| Size | $\overline{\text{DS0}}$ | $\overline{\text{DS1}}$ | $\overline{\text{A1}}$ | LWORD |
|------|-----|-----|-----|-------|
| Long-word        | 0 | 0 | 0 | 0 |
| Word (bytes 0–1) | 0 | 0 | 0 | 1 |
| Word (bytes 2–3) | 0 | 0 | 1 | 0 |
| Byte 0           | 1 | 0 | 0 | 1 |
| Byte 1           | 0 | 1 | 0 | 1 |
| Byte 2           | 1 | 0 | 1 | 1 |
| Byte 3           | 0 | 1 | 1 | 1 |

NOTE: Byte 0 = D31–D24, byte 1 = D23–D16, byte 2 = D15–D8, and byte 3 = D7–D0. Misaligned transfers do not respond as illustrated; refer to Chapter 12 for more information on misaligned transfers.

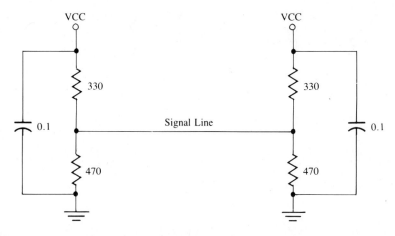

**Figure E-5  Bus termination for the VMEbus.**

signal that has a frequency of 2.9 MHz. The serial data line has various applications in VMEbus systems.

The $\overline{\text{ACFAIL}}$ line indicates that the ac power has failed. This signal is often used to initiate an automatic system backup when a power failure occurs.

The $\overline{\text{SYSRESET}}$ signal is operated with a push-button to allow the user to reset the system. It generates a hardware reset on the microprocessor.

The $\overline{\text{SYSFAIL}}$ signal is used to indicate a self-test failure. This line becomes a logic zero on a test error.

The *arbitration bus* is used for DMA transfers and consists of provisions for four channels, which use signals $\overline{\text{BRx}}$ to request a DMA, $\overline{\text{BGx}}$ to grant a DMA, and $\overline{\text{BGxOUT}}$ as a bus grant acknowledge signal. These correspond to the same inputs on the 68XXX microprocessors except for the 68040.

Each of the four channels often is connected to a daisy chain, permitting more than four channels of DMA to be requested at a time; as many as desired may be connected in daisy chain to each channel.

The backplane terminates all signal lines using the network illustrated in Figure E-5. Termination reduces signal distortion, provides pullups for open-collector signals, and causes tristated lines to become logic one levels.

# APPENDIX F

# *Answers to Selected Questions*

## Chapter 1

**1.** A microprocessor is a digital system that can perform data transfers, simple arithmetic, and decision making. The microprocessor is a programmable device that executes a program stored in its memory system.

**3.** See Figure 1-1.

**5.** The program and data are stored in the memory system.

**7.** Eight.

**9.** 1 M.

**11. (a)** Keyboard (input)
**(b)** Relay (output)
**(c)** Printer (output)

**13.** The address bus is used to provide the memory with the memory address and the I/O with the I/O address. In both cases the address selects either the memory location or I/O device.

**15.** 16 bits wide.

**17.** Zero.

**19.** Data transfer, arithmetic and logic, and decisions.

**21.** The address registers (A0–A7).

**23.** Address registers.

**25.** N = negative, V = overflow, Z = zero, C = carry, and X = extend.

**27. (a)** = 0001 0110
**(b)** = 0010 0101
**(c)** = 0101 1000
**(d)** = 1100 1010
**(e)** = 1111 1110

**29. (a)** 244　**(b)** 51　**(c)** 525　**(d)** 268,435,456

**31. (a)** $+27$  **(b)** $-97$  **(c)** $-128$

**33. (a)** 0001 0010 (packed)
   0000 0001 0000 0010 (unpacked)
  **(b)** 0000 1000 1001 0100 (packed)
   0000 1000 0000 1001 0000 0100 (unpacked)
  **(c)** 0001 0000 0000 0101 (packed)
   0000 0001 0000 0000 0000 0000 0000 0101 (unpacked)

**35.** HELLO

**37. (a)** $-255$  **(b)** $+0.5$  **(c)** $-4.46875$

## Chapter 2

**1.** source . . . destination

**3.** Immediate data.

**5. (a)** MOVE.B  D2,D5
  **(b)** MOVE.W  A3,D4
  **(c)** MOVE.L  D3,D1

**7. (a)** MOVE.B  D2,$2000
  **(b)** MOVE.W  $30000,A4
  **(c)** MOVE.L  $3,A2
  **(d)** MOVE.L  SP,$12000
  **(e)** MOVE.B  $3000,$2000

**9.** Any location in the entire memory system.

**11.** The MOVE.B $8000,D1 instruction copies the byte contents of location $FF8000 into D1 while the MOVE.B $008000,D1 instruction copies the byte contents of location $008000 into D1.

**13. (a)** MOVE.B  (A3),D2
  **(b)** MOVE.W  D4,(SP)
  **(c)** MOVE.L  (A2),(A3)
  **(d)** MOVE.B  (A3),$400F2
  **(e)** MOVE.W  #$33,(A6)

**15. (a)** A 66 decimal is moved into the byte-sized memory location addressed by A2 then A2 is incremented by 1.
  **(b)** The word-sized contents of the memory location addressed by A2 are copied into the location addressed by A3 then A2 is incremented by two.
  **(c)** The long-word contents of the location addressed by A1 are copied into the location addressed by A2 then both A1 and A2 are incremented by 4.
  **(d)** The word-sized contents of memory location $003000 are copied into the memory location addressed by A2, then A2 is incremented by 2.
  **(e)** The long-word contents of the memory location addressed by the stack pointer is copied into register D1, and the stack pointer is incremented by 4.

17. (a) Register A6 is decremented by 1, then the byte-sized contents of the location addressed by the new value in A6 are copied into D2.
    (b) Register A6 and A5 are both decremented by 2, then the word-sized contents of the location addressed by the new value in A6 is copied into the new location addressed by A5.
    (c) Register A4 is decremented by 4, then the long-word contents of the location addressed by the new value in A4 are copied into the location addressed by A3. Finally A3 is incremented by a 4.
    (d) The stack pointer register is decremented by 2, then a word-sized $88 is copied into the location addressed by the new value in the stack pointer.
    (e) Register A0 is decremented by 4, then the long-word contents of memory location $040000 are copied into the new location addressed by A0.

19. $028000.

21. The address in the data is relative to the program counter, which changes as a program is relocated.

23. MOVE.L  #3,D1
    MOVE.L  #2,D2
    MOVE.L  #5,D3

25. (a) $1602
    (b) $3A04
    (c) $2007
    (d) $1E02
    (e) $2C07

27. (a) $11D13000
    (b) $23F9000400000030000
    (c) $33FC100000034567
    (d) $2AE3
    (e) $31EB00224000

29. The MOVEQ instruction is coded only in machine language and is used to move a number between $00 and $FF (sign-extended) into a long-word data register.

31. (a) MOVEM.W  D0-D7,$30000
    (b) MOVEM.L  $20000,A0-A7
    (c) MOVEM.L  D1/D3-D5/A6,-(A3)
    (d) MOVEM.W  $30000,D0-D7/A0-A7

33. SWAP D3

## Chapter 3

1. Bytes, words, or long-words.

3. (a) Adds the long-word data in register D3 to register D4 and stores the result in register D4.

**(b)** Adds the word-sized data stored at memory location $2300 to register D3 with the sum stored in word-sized register D3.

**(c)** Adds the byte-sized data of 250 decimal to register D5 and stores the byte-sized sum in register D5.

**(d)** Adds the long-word contents of register D3 to the long-word contents of the memory location address by A3. The sum is stored in the memory location addressed by A3, then A3 is incremented by a 4.

**(e)** This instruction is not allowed because there can be no byte-sized address register.

5. ```
MOVE.W  $1000,D0
ADD.W   $1002,D0
ADD.W   $1004,D0
MOVE.W  D0,$1006
```

7. ```
MOVE.L  $1004,D0
ADD.L   $100C,D0
MOVE.L  D0,$1014
MOVE.L  $1000,D0
MOVE.L  $1008,D1
ADDX.L  D0,D1
MOVE.L  D1,$1010
```

9. **(a)** The byte-sized contents of register D2 are subtracted from D7. The difference is placed in byte-sized register D7.

**(b)** The contents of A6 are decremented by a 4. The long-word data stored at the memory location addressed by this new value in A4 are subtracted from D1. The difference is then placed into D1.

**(c)** A byte-sized 3 is subtracted from the memory location address by the sum of A4 and a sign-extended D2. The difference is then placed into this same byte of memory.

**(d)** The long-word number $44FF is subtracted from memory location $20000. The long-word difference is then placed into memory beginning at location $20000.

**(e)** The word-sized contents of register A6 are subtracted from the stack pointer. The sign-extended result is then placed into the stack pointer.

11. ```
SUB.W D2,$2000
SUB.W D2,$2002
SUB.W D2,$2004
```

13. ```
MOVE.L  $100C,D0
SUB.L   $1004,D0
MOVE.L  D0,$1014
MOVE.L  $1000,D0
MOVE.L  $1008,D1
SUBX.L  D0,D1
MOVE.L  D1,$1010
```

**15.** The MULU instruction performs unsigned multiplication, while the MULS instruction performs signed multiplication.

**17.** 32     16

**19.** 
```
CLR.W    D0
CLR.W    D1
MOVE.B   $3000,D0
MOVE.B   $3001,D1
MULU     D0,D1
MOVE.W   D1,$3002
```

**21.** When both bits being ORed together are zero.

**23.** 
```
OR.B    #$C0,D2
AND.W   #$F3FF,D2
EOR.L   #$81000000,D2
```

**25.** 
```
BSET  #7,$2000
BSET  #6,$2000
BSET  #5,$2000
BSET  #4,$2000
BCLR  #0,$2000
```

**27.** The logic right shift places a zero into the left-most bit, while the arithmetic right shift copies the sign-bit into the left-most bit.

**29.** 
```
LSR    $3000
ROXR   $3002
ROXR   $3004
ROXR   $3006
```

**31.** `CLR.W  D4`

**33.** `AND  #$FE,CCR`

**35.** `MOVE  CCR,$3000`

## Chapter 4

**1.** Short branch.

**3.** (a) $60EC
   (b) $60000082
   (c) $6000F060
   (d) $6000FF2C
   (e) $60FE

**5.** True.

**7.** BLT

**9.**
```
          TEST.L   D0
          BEQ      STEP1
          BPL      STEP2
          SUB.L    #1,D1
          BRA      ENDS
STEP1     NOT.L    D1
          BRA      ENDS
STEP2     ADD.L    #1,D1
ENDS      —
```

**11.**
```
          MOVE.W      #$2000,A0
          MOVE.W      #$7FF,D0
IT        CLR.B       (A0)+
          DBRA        D0,IT
```

**13.** The DBEQ instruction.

**15.** The condition "higher than."

**17.** A subroutine is a group of instructions that are stored in the memory once. The subroutine can be used as many times as necessary by calling it with the BSR or JSR instruction.

**19.** The BSR instruction places the return address on the stack and then jumps to the subroutine.

**21.** The RTS instruction returns from a subroutine by popping the return address from the stack into the program counter.

**23.**
```
EXG  D0,D4
EXG  D1,D5
EXG  D2,D6
EXG  D3,D7
```

**25.** The RTS instruction pops the program counter from the stack; RTR pops the CCR and program counter from the stack; and RTE pops the SR and program counter from the stack.

**27.** MOVE.L #$30100,A6

**29.** the entry pointer is one higher than the exit pointer.

**31.** The sum of A0 and D1.

**33.** Zero.

**35.** If overflow is set.

**37.** First subtract 4 from the stack pointer, then store the contents of A2 onto the stack. Next copy the contents of the stack pointer into A2. Finally, add a $-32$ to the stack pointer.

**39.** 32 bytes.

**41.** Absolutely nothing is accomplished by the NOP; it does, however, take time to execute.

## Chapter 5

**1.** Source, object.

**3.** A label table is generated and the opcodes are tested.

**5.** Label, opcode, operand, and comment.

**7.** (a) $56 (b) $38 (c) $41424344 (d) $00000001

**9.** It indicates to the assembler that the end of a pass has been reached.

**11.** (a) Label DATA is set equal to a 12 decimal.
   (b) Word-sized memory location LIST is set up as an array containing 100 words of data.
   (c) Long-word memory location ARRAY is set up as an array containing 200 long-words of data.
   (d) Memory beginning with location NUMB is set up containing 3 bytes of data: 12, 13, and 14.
   (e) Memory beginning with location NAME is set up containing 4 bytes of data: $4E, $61, $6D, and $65.

**13.** Terminal, process, predefined process, decision, input/output, and connector.

**15.**

```
          MOVE.W      #$3000,A0
          MOVE.W      #$4000,A1
          MOVE.W      #$5000,A2
          MOVE.W      #$5A,D0
LOOPS     MOVE.B      (A0),(A1)+
          MOVE.B      (A0)+,(A2)+
          DBRA        D0,LOOPS
```

**17.**

```
SUMS      MOVEM.L     A0/D1,-(SP)
          CLR.W       D0
          MOVE.W      #$3000,A0
          MOVE.W      #$F,D1
SUMS1     ADD.B       (A0)+,D0
          BCC         SUMS2
          ADD.W       #$100,D0
SUMS2     DBRA        D1,SUMS1
          MOVEM.L     (SP)+,A0/D1
          RTS
```

**19.**

```
SQUARE    MOVE.L      A0,-(SP)
          MOVE.L      #TABLE,A0
          AND.L       #$FF,D0
          ADD.L       D0,A0
```

```
              MOVE.B        (A0),D0
              MOVE.L        (SP)+,A0
              RTS
     TABLE    DC.B          0,1,4,9,16
              DC.B          25,36,49,64,81

21.  HOUR     MOVEM.L       D0-D2,-(SP)
              MOVE.W        #59,D2
     HOUR3    MOVE.W        #5999,D1
     HOUR2    MOVE.W        #7996,D0
     HOUR1    DBRA          D0,HOUR1
              DBRA          D1,HOUR2
              DBRA          D2,HOUR3
              MOVEM.L       (SP)+,D0-D2
              RTS

23.  TEST     MOVEM.L       A0/D0-D1,-(SP)
              MOVE.B        #$55,D1
              BSR           TESTE
              BNE           TESTE
              NOT.B         D1
              BSR           TESTS
     TESTE    MOVEM.L       (SP)+,A0/D0-D1
              RTS
     TESTS    MOVE.W        #$FFFF,D0
              MOVE.L        #$30000,A0
     TESTS1   MOVE.B        D1,(A0)+
              DBRA          D0,TESTS1
              MOVE.W        #$FFFF,D0
              MOVE.L        #$30000,A0
     TESTS2   CMP.B         D1,(A0)+
              DBNE          D0,TESTS2
              RTS

25.  LOOK     MOVEM.L       A0/D0,-(SP)
              MOVE.W        #$4000,A0
              MOVE.W        #$7F,D0
     LOOK1    CMP.L         #$30000000,(A0)+
              DBEQ          LOOK1
              BEQ           LOOK2
              AND           #$EF,CCR
              MOVEM.L       (SP)+,A0/D0
              RTS
     LOOK2    OR            #$10,CCR
              MOVEM.L       (SP)+,A0/D0
              RTS
```

```
        ;
27.     ;Assumes that A0 addresses data and D0 is the count
        ;Count is assume to be a word and greater than 1
        ;
SORTS       MOVEM.L         A0-A2/D0-D2,-(SP)
            MOVE.L          A0,A1
SORTS1      SUB.W           #1,D0
            BNE             SORTS2
            MOVEM.L         (SP)+,A0-A2/D0-D2
            RTS
SORTS2      MOVE            D0,D1
            MOVE.L          A1,A0
            MOVE.L          A1,A2
            ADD.L           #1,A2
SORTS3      CMP.B           (A0)+,(A2)+
            BHI             SORTS4
            MOVE.B          (A0),D2
            MOVE.B          -1(A0),(A0)
            MOVE.B          D2,-1(A0)
SORTS4      DBRA            D1,SORTS3
            JMP             SORTS1
```

## Chapter 6

**1.** 64-pin

**3.** 16M bytes

**5.** 8-bit data [or] 16-bit data

**7.** 8 bits.

**9.** The address, data, and control bus signals.

**11.** 8 or 12 MHz, depending on the version.

**13. (a)** A bus cycle consists of eight states that are used to read or write data.

   **(b)** Data transfer rate is the number of bus transfers per second.

   **(c)** A state is half a clocking period.

   **(d)** Memory access time is the time that the microprocessor allows the memory to acquire data. This is defined from the time that the address appears on the address bus until the data are read by the microprocessor.

**15.** At the end of $S_6$ or beginning of $S_7$.

**17. (a)** 505 ns    **(b)** 425 ns    **(c)** 334 ns    **(d)** 305 ns

**19.** The wait state generator is cleared whenever the $\overline{AS}$ signal is a logic one. This applies a logic one to the $\overline{DTACK}$ input of the microprocessor. When $\overline{AS}$

becomes a logic zero, the shift register begins to shift the serial input (a logic one) into the shift register. The output connection applied to the $\overline{\text{DTACK}}$ pin eventually becomes a logic one after a specified number of shifts. Whether the $\overline{\text{DTACK}}$ pin ever becomes a logic zero depends on whether the area of memory connected to the wait state generator becomes selected. If selected, $\overline{\text{DTACK}}$ goes low for a fixed number of clocks, which causes a fixed number of wait states.

**21.** The address of the first instruction executed is stored in vector numbers at memory locations \$000004–\$000007.

**23.** RESET.

**25.** An interrupt is a hardware-initiated subroutine jump.

**27.** The program that the microprocessor is currently executing.

**29.** A nonmaskable interrupt is an interrupt input that can never be disabled. The maskable interrupt input can be turned off or disabled.

**31.** A direct memory access is a data transfer that occurs without the use of the microprocessor. During a DMA, the microprocessor is disabled and an external DMA controller takes over the task of providing the memory with an address and selecting an I/O device.

**33.** The bus grant signal indicates to the DMA controller that the microprocessor has granted a DMA request applied to the $\overline{\text{BR}}$ pin.

**35.** Before the $\overline{\text{BGACK}}$ signal is activated, $\overline{\text{BGACK}}$ is tested to see whether it is a logic zero. If $\overline{\text{BGACK}}$ is a logic zero, then another device has access to the buses of the system.

## Chapter 7

**1.** The ROM.

**3.** The EPROM and the EEPROM.

**5.** The $\overline{\text{CE}}$ input is used to enable the memory component so that the $\overline{\text{OE}}$ connection can be used to read data or the $\overline{\text{WE}}$ connection (if available) can cause a write.

**7.** Data will appear at the output of a ROM if only $\overline{\text{OE}}$ and all the chip enable inputs are active.

**9.** Access time is the time required by a memory component to read data from a location. It is measured from the application of the memory address (if the device is enabled) to the time at which the data appear on the output connections.

**11.** 4096 locations.

**13.** 4k bytes.

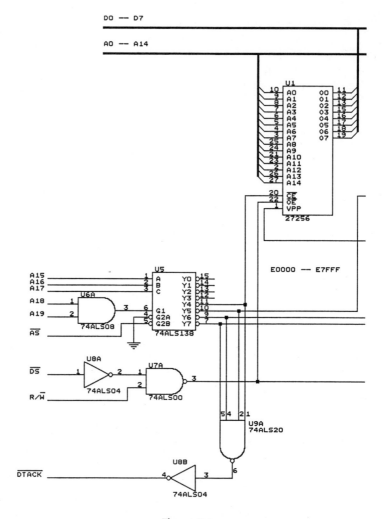

**Figure F-1**

**15.** When all the enable inputs of the 74ALS138 are active, the address inputs (A, B, and C) select which output becomes a logic zero.

**17.** See Figure F-1.

**19.** See Figure F-2.

**21.** The PROM decodes a memory address by storing the binary bit pattern for the required locations in the PROM.

**23.** See Figure F-3.

**25.** A 16-bit data transfer.

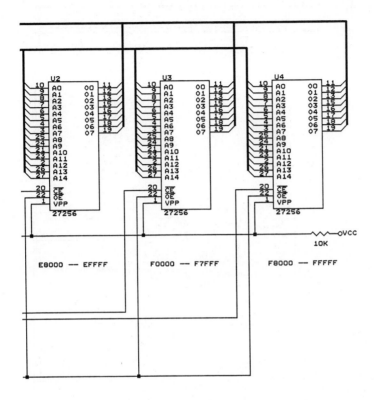

**Figure F-1**   Continued.

**27.** See Figure F-4.

**29.** See Figure F-5.

**31.** A refresh occurs when data within a DRAM are rewritten. Refreshes are required every 2 or 4 ms in most DRAM memory components.

**33.** The $\overline{\text{CAS}}$ (column address strobe) input.

**35.** The 74157 multiplexer connects the A inputs to the Y outputs whenever the select input is a logic zero. If the select input is a logic one, the B inputs are connected to the Y outputs.

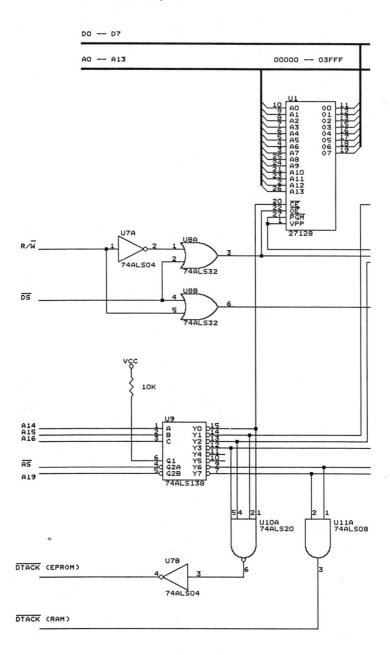

**Figure F-2**

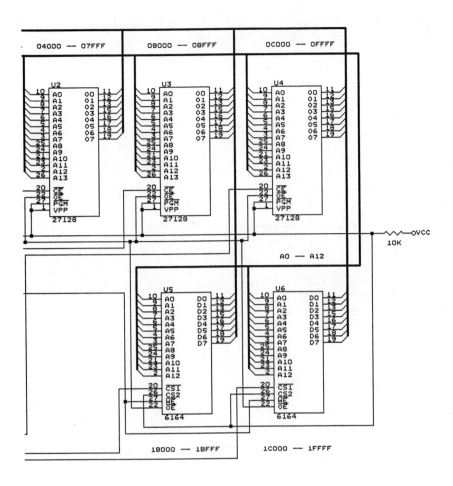

Figure F-2    Continued.

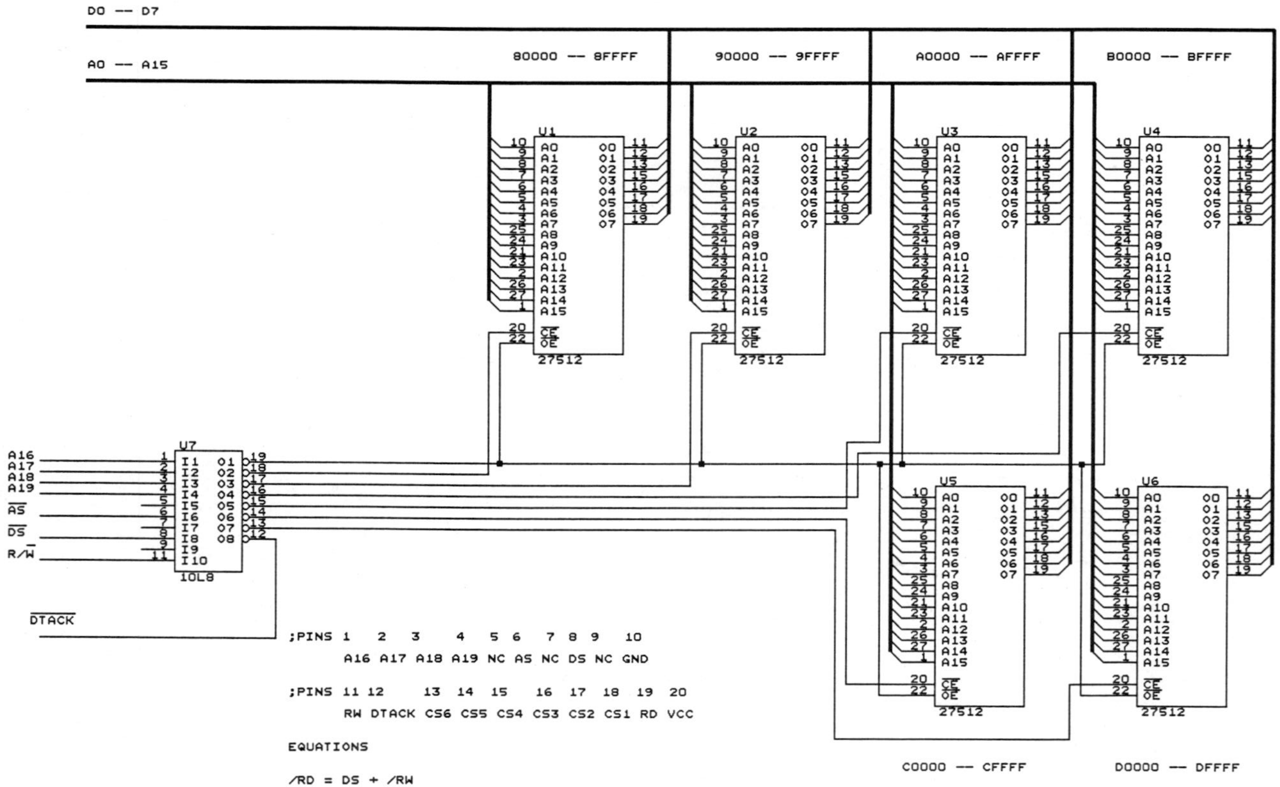

D0 — D7

A0 — A15

80000 — 8FFFF

90000 — 9FFFF

A0000 — AFFFF

B0000 — BFFFF

C0000 — CFFFF

D0000 — DFFFF

U1 27512
U2 27512
U3 27512
U4 27512
U5 27512
U6 27512

U7 IOL8

A16
A17
A18
A19
/AS
/DS
R/W

/DTACK

;PINS 1 2 3 4 5 6 7 8 9 10
A16 A17 A18 A19 NC /AS NC /DS NC GND

;PINS 11 12 13 14 15 16 17 18 19 20
R/W DTACK /CS6 /CS5 /CS4 /CS3 /CS2 /CS1 RD VCC

EQUATIONS

/RD = DS + /RW

/DTACK = /AS * A19  ; note /DTACK is low for \$80000 — \$FFFFF

/CS6 = /AS * A19 * A18 * /A17 * A16
/CS5 = /AS * A19 * A18 * /A17 * A16
/CS4 = /AS * A19 * /A18 * A17 * A16
/CS3 = /AS * A19 * /A18 * A17 * /A16
/CS2 = /AS * A19 * /A18 * /A17 * A16
/CS1 = /AS * A19 * /A18 * /A17 * /A16

**Figure F-3**

**37.** The $\overline{RAS}$ signal is first activated to strobe the row address into the DRAM. Next, the $\overline{CAS}$ input is activated to strobe the column address into the DRAM.

## Chapter 8

**1.** A three-state buffer such as the 74ALS244.

**3.** A latch such as the 74ALS374.

**5.** Whenever a switch is closed, it bounces back, opening the contacts. Also the contacts often bounce when the switch is open.

**7.** 10 mA.

**9.** Common anode and common cathode.

**11.** It is visible at most light levels. Also, it can be dimmed by changing the grid voltage.

**13.** To obtain power supply isolation.

**15.** Peripheral interface adapter.

**17.** Before the PDRA is programmed, the control register bit CRA must be cleared. This allows the PDRA to be programmed.

**19.** CLR.B  $41003
    MOVE.B  #$F0,$41002

**21.** See Figure F-6.

**23.** 90 mA.

**25.** See Figure F-7.

**27.** The number of bits, including start, stop, data, and parity, sent per second.

**29.** The count of the number of ones in a number expressed as an even number. If a number has 2 ones, it has even parity.

**31.** The $\overline{CTS}$ (clear-to-send) signal is used to request that the modem start sending data.

**33.** The $\overline{DSR}$ (data set ready) signal indicates that the data set (modem) is ready for operation.

**35.** A framing error occurs when the incorrect number of stop bits is received.

**37.** Between $-3.0$ and $-25$ V.

**39.**
```
SEND    MOVE.W      #19999,D0
        MOVE.L      #$50000,A0
LOOP    MOVE.B      (A0)+,$30000
        BSR         DELAY  ;wait for 1/2000 sec
        DBRA        D0,LOOP
        RTS
```

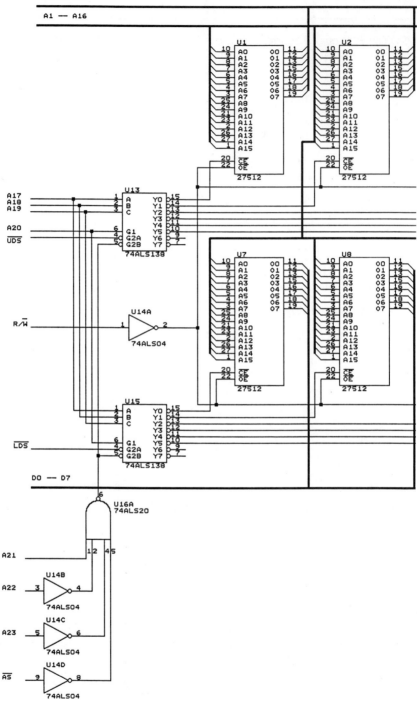

**Figure F-4**

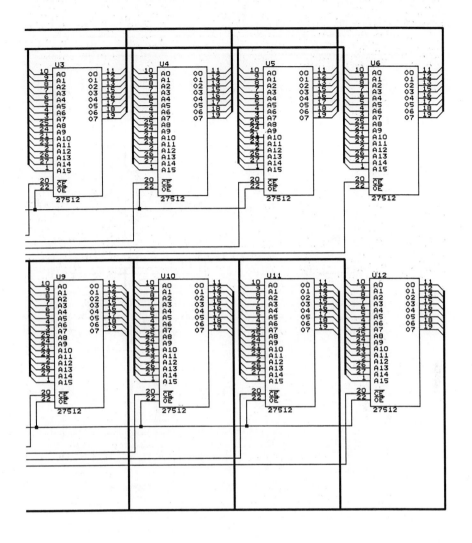

**Figure F-4** Continued.

665

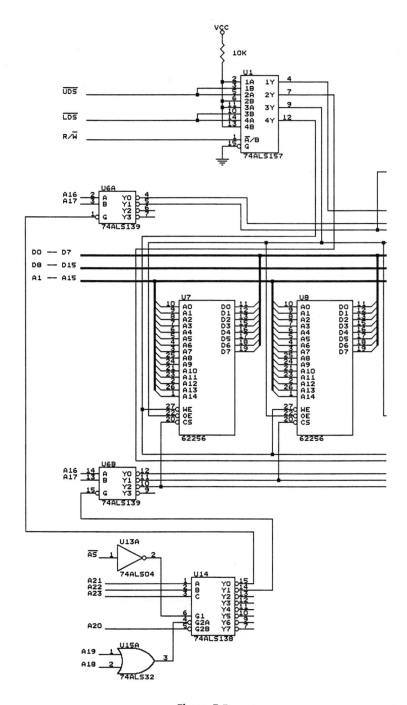

Figure F-5

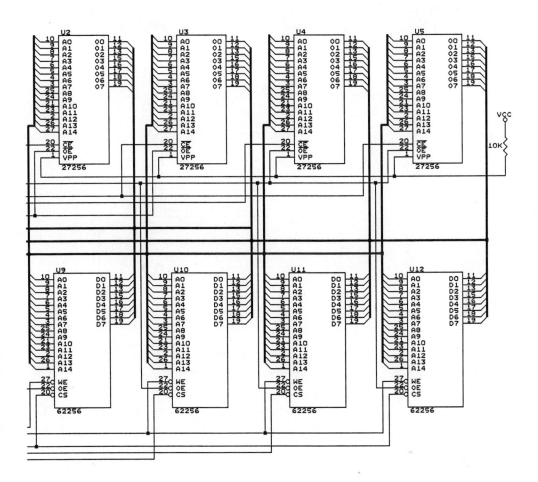

**Figure F-5   Continued.**

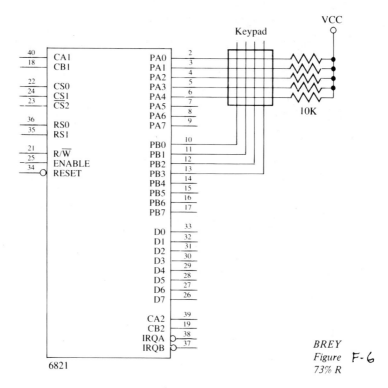

**Figure F-6**

**41.** See Figure F-8.

**43.** Stepper motor.

**45.** A full step moves the armature from pole to pole. The half-step moves the armature to a pole, then on to the next step between two poles.

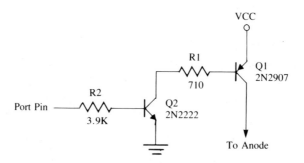

**Figure F-7**

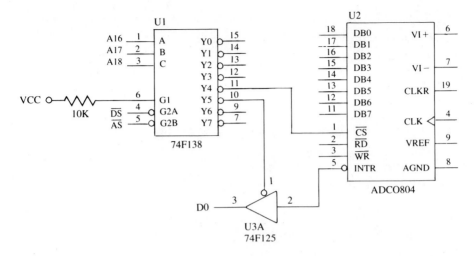

**Figure F-8**

**47. (a)** A dc motor is faster than a stepper.
  **(b)** A dc motor has more torque than a stepper.
  **(c)** A stepper is much easier to position than a dc motor.

## Chapter 9

 **1.** An interrupt is an exception that is caused by an external hardware event, whereas some exceptions originate in the software.

 **3.** There are 256 interrupt/exception vectors.

 **5.** The SSP is loaded from vector 0 and the PC is loaded from vector 1.

 **7.** An address error exception is caused by accessing a word at an odd memory address or a long-word at a non-long-word address. Access to an instruction stored at an odd address also causes an address error.

 **9.** Any instruction that is $AXXX causes a line emulator 1010 exception.

 **11.** The STOP, RESET, or any instruction that modifies the SR.

 **13.** The status register.

 **15.** RTE

 **17.** Level 4.

 **19.** $\overline{\text{VPA}}$

 **21.** Level 7.

 **23.** The $\overline{\text{DTACK}}$ signal is asserted in place of $\overline{\text{VPA}}$.

**25.** A spurious (unwanted) interrupt occurs when none of the $\overline{\text{IPL}}$ pins are low during interrupt acknowledge.

**27.** By software polling.

**29.** Change the ABCD instruction into ADD.

**31.** Empty occurs when both pointers are equal.

**33.** The data strobe signal sends data into the printer from the computer.

**35.** MOVE.B  #$30,CRB
  MOVE.B  #$38,CRB
  MOVE.B  #$30,CRB

**37.** The timer is 24 bits.

**39.** "Single-buffered" means that there is a latch in an output port.

**41.** Three.

**43.** CLR.B  $20000
  CLR.B  $20006
  MOVE.B  #$FF,$20002
  CLR.B  $20003

## Chapter 10

**1.** Bus arbitration occurs when more than one bus master vies for the system buses. The arbitration determines which device gains control of the system buses.

**3.** A direct memory access occurs when the microprocessor stops executing instructions and disconnects itself from the buses. Once disconnected, an external DMA controller transfers data between memory and I/O through the buses without the intervention of the microprocessor.

**5.** Read.

**7.** The $\overline{\text{BR}}$, $\overline{\text{BG}}$, and $\overline{\text{BGACK}}$ signals.

**9.** The 68440 and 68442 are two-channel DMA controllers, while the 68450 is a four channel DMA controller. Both the 68440 and 68450 are designed for a 16-bit microprocessor, while the 68442 is designed for a 32-bit microprocessor.

**11.** The $\overline{\text{DTC}}$ indicates when the data transfer is completed.

**15.** During the non-DMA mode, the DMA controller is programmed. During the DMA mode, the DMA controller has acquired the system buses and is transferring data.

**17.** The I/O device is often selected with the $\overline{\text{ACK}}$ signal during implicit addressing.

**19.** Explicit addressing must be used for memory-to-memory transfers.

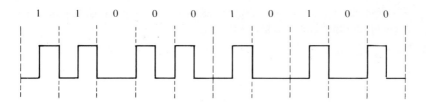

**Figure F-9**

**21.** The normal and error interrupt vector registers.

**25.** An array chain is sequential, while the linked array chain may be placed in noncontiguous areas of memory.

**27.** **(a)** A 5¼ inch floppy disk.
    **(b)** A 3½ inch floppy disk.
    **(c)** A concentric ring of data on the surface of a disk.
    **(d)** A portion of a track.
    **(e)** A pair of tracks, positioned as top and bottom on a floppy disk.

**31.** The term NRZ indicates that the magnetic field never returns to zero. This means that it is magnetized in one polarity for a logic one and the other for a logic zero. The main benefit of this recording technique is that no erase head is required to erase disk data.

**33.** See Figure F-9

**35.** A flying head is found in a hard disk drive. It is so named because it floats over the surface of the disk on a thin cushion of air.

**37.** A hard disk drive.

**39.** This means that the run of zeros is between 2 and 7.

**41.** RRL allows 50% more data to be stored on the same disk drive.

**43.** RRL.

**45.** The ROM CD is a read-only optical disk memory, while the WORM drive is a write-one-time optical disk device.

**49.** The device selection code is found on DB0–DB7.

**51.** 9 and 15.

**53.** Cyan, magenta, and yellow.

**55.** The smallest displayable spot on a video display.

**57.** 61 µs.

**59.** A logical address is the address generated by the software to access a memory location. The physical address is the address that appears at the address connections on the microprocessor to access memory.

**61.** F-line emulation.

**63.** $28000–$29FFF.

## Chapter 11

**1.** A coprocessor is a microprocessor that runs concurrently with any 68000 family memory.

**3.** 12 and 16.7 MHz.

**5.** $\overline{\text{DSACK0}}$.

**7.** This is a line F emulation instruction that is used to pass instructions to the 68881/68882 coprocessor.

**9. (a)** 0  10000100  0001010100000000000000000
   **(b)** 1  10000110  1001000100000000000000000
   **(c)** 0  10001000  1001000000011000000000000
   **(d)** 1  01111001  0100011110101110000000101

**11. (a)** $8003003000400000000000000000
   **(b)** $0010001567000000000000000000
   **(c)** $8002003600000000000000000000

**13.** The mode control byte selects the rounding mode and precision.

**15.** The N, Z, I, and NAN bits; they detect ±0, ±∞, ±NAN, and ±normalized or denormalized results.

**17.** The extensions are .B (byte), .W (word), .L (long-word), .S (single-precision), .D (double-precision), .X (extended precision), and .P (packed BCD real).

**19. (a)** 10 decimal is moved into FP2
   **(b)** π is loaded into FP1

**21.** FMOVEM.X WATER,FP0-FP2

**23.** PER FMOVE.S  D0,FP0
          FADD.S   D0,FP0
          FADD.S   D1,FP0
          FADD.S   D1,FP0
          FMOVE.S  FP0,D3
          RTS

**27.** This exception is due to a failure in coprocessor communications.

**29.** An underflow occurs when a number is too small to be represented as a floating-point number.

**31.** A busy state occurs when an FSAVE instruction is executed in the middle of a coprocessor operation.

## Chapter 12

1. There is no difference in the pinouts.

3. $000A0000 and $000A03FF.

5. MOVES.

7. Loop mode operation occurs for any 2-byte instruction followed by a DBcc instruction. This mode allows the software to execute completely inside the 68010 without any memory accesses to fetch the instructions.

9. 32.

11. The response placed in the $\overline{\text{DSACK}}$ pins determines the size.

13. 256 bytes or 64 long-words.

15. This pin disables the cache.

17. A trace can occur at the end of each instruction or at each branch.

19. The outer displacement consists of the last data added when the effective address is calculated.

21. A scaling factor is 1, 2, 4, or 8, multiplied by an index register. This allows the index register to index bytes, words, long-words, or 64-bit numbers.

23. (a) BFSET D2{1:5}
    (b) BFCLR D6{23:2}
    (c) BFTST D1{19:3}
    (d) BFCHG D7{2:3}

27. In addition to the 16-bit division found in earlier versions, the 68020 is capable of performing 32-bit division.

29. The compare and swap (CAS or CAS2) instructions compare and swap 1 or 2 operands. If the operands match, the update operand is written to the destination operand.

31. CHK, CHK2, and the TRAPcc vectors.

## Chapter 13

1. The 68030 contains a data cache and a memory management unit.

3. The write allocation bit (WA) selects whether the data cache is updated for write operations.

5. 3 clocks.

7. 2 clocks.

9. 5 clocks.

11. A page is a small section of the memory that can be any size (in the 68030) from 256 bytes to 32k bytes.

**13.** A logical address is an address that is generated by the software.

**15.** Five.

**17.** Two; the supervisor and user root pointers address the supervisor and user memory spaces.

**19.** Function code lookup offers another method of translating the logical address into a physical address by function code.

**21.** The address translation cache contains the last 22 translations; thus a new translation does not necessarily occur each time memory is addressed.

**23.** Yes, the smallest size block is 16M bytes and the largest is 4G bytes.

**25.** Using the PMOVE instruction.

**27.** CALLM and RTM.

**29.** The PCLK signal is twice the frequency of the BLCK signal.

**31.** Two.

**33.** The $\overline{\text{TS}}$ signal indicates the start of a transfer.

**35.** $\overline{\text{CIOUT}}$

**37.** Three.

**39.** 128.

**41.** Packed BCD real data.

**43.** Yes, multiple exceptions are processed differently.

**45.** At reset time, the $\overline{\text{CDIS}}$ pin is placed at a logic zero to select multiplexed mode.

**47.** This is the test data input pin; it allows test data to be input to the microprocessor.

**49.** The $\overline{\text{BR}}$ output connection is used to request access to the system buses.

**51.** With the 68000 microprocessor, the microprocessor is the bus master and controls the bus until it is asked for access through its $\overline{\text{BR}}$ input pin. With the 68040 microprocessor, the microprocessor is a bus slave and requests access through its $\overline{\text{BR}}$ output pin.

# Glossary

**Absolute long memory addressing** This form allows the programmer to access any memory location in the entire 680XX memory system.

**Absolute memory address** The actual memory location of the operand data. The address ranges are $00000–$FFFFF in the 68008, $000000–$FFFFFF in the 68000 and 68010, and $00000000–$FFFFFFFF in the 68020, 68030, and 68040 microprocessor.

**Absolute short memory addressing** This form uses a 16-bit memory address to access either the bottom 32K bytes of memory or the top 32K bytes.

**Access time** The time allowed by the microprocessor for the memory or I/O to access data, measured from where the address is output by the microprocessor to where it reads the data bus connections. Also, the amount of time it takes a memory component to access the data. This is usually given from the time the address is applied to the memory until the data appear on the output data connections.

**ACIA (asynchronous communications interface adapter)** A device that converts between parallel and serial data. The ACIA also allows the computer to control a modem.

**Acknowledge** A pin or indicator signal that indicates that the DMA controller is in charge of the memory and I/O space.

**Acknowledge, interrupt** An event indicating that an interrupt has been accepted by the microprocessor. The interrupt acknowledge signal is used to trigger a response to the interrupt request.

**ADC (analog-to-digital converter)** The ADC converts analog data into digital data for the microprocessor.

**Address** A hexadecimal number used to refer to a memory location in the memory system.

**Address bus** A common set of connections that carry the memory address from the microprocessor to the memory or the I/O. In the 68000 and 68010, the 24-bit address bus has 23 pin connections; in the 68008, the 20-bit address bus has 20 pin connections; and in the 68020, 68030, and 68040, the 32-bit address bus has 32 pin connections.

**Address connections** The pins on a memory component that are used to select a memory location within the memory. These are address connections multiplexed in a DRAM memory component.

**Address registers** A series of eight 16-bit registers that indirectly address memory data. The address registers (A0–A7) hold either a 16-bit sign-extended number or a 32-bit number; A7 is designated the SP (stack pointer) register. Two forms of the SP exist: the SSP or supervisor stack pointer (A7'), which is active in the supervisor mode, and the USP (A7), which is active in the user mode.

**Address strobe ($\overline{AS}$)**   Address strobe is a signal indicating that the address bus contains a valid memory or I/O address.

**Addressing mode**   Specifies how the microprocessor will treat the information used as an operand.

**AND**   Logical multiplication; yields a result of logic one only if both input bits are a logic one. The AND operation is often used to clear bits or turn them off.

**Arbitration**   Arbitration is the process of determining who gains access to the system memory and I/O buses.

**Arbitration bus**   A bus that is used for DMA transfers and consists of provisions for four channels.

**ASCII**   The American Standard Code for Information Interchange, a 7-bit code that is used to encode the letters, numbers, and special characters found in the English language. Modified forms exist for just about any language in the world.

**ASCII-Z string**   A series of ASCII characters (character string) that ends with a zero or null code.

**Assembler**   A program that converts symbolic source code into hexadecimal object code.

**Assembly language directives.**   see **Pseudo opcodes**

**Asynchronous communications interface adapter**   see **ACIA**

**Asynchronous serial data**   A form of digital data transmitted with a start bit and a stop bit. No clocking information is necessary for decoding data of this type at the receiver end of the system.

**Asynchronous transfer**   Data are transferred asynchronously with the $\overline{DSACK}$ control inputs on the 68020 microprocessor. The term means that there is no direct relation with the system clock and the transfer.

**Autovector interrupt**   A type of hardware interrupt requested with the $\overline{IPL}$ interrupt inputs. The 68000 family of microprocessors has seven different levels of au-

tovector interrupts. Autovector interrupts are requested if the $\overline{VPA}$ input is asserted in response to the interrupt acknowledge signal $\overline{INTA}$.

**Aware conditions**   Conditions that occur when numbers are compared that are not NANs. Comparing NANs is not considered to be an aware condition; it is considered to be unordered.

**.B**   An extension indicating that 8-bit bytes of data are being manipulated.

**Background program**   A program that executes without any attention from any other program. Background programs are normally interrupt driven and execute, often invisibly, as long as a system is powered.

**Backlit**   Describing an LCD display that is illuminated by a lamp placed behind it.

**Bank, memory**   An 8-bit-wide section of the memory that is used with the 68000, 68010, 68020, 68030, and 68040 microprocessors. Each byte of memory in the 68000 or 68010 is stored in either the upper or lower bank of memory. In the 68020, 68030, and 68040, there are four banks of memory.

**Baud**   A term indicating the number of bits (data bits, stop bits, parity bit, and start bit) transferred per second; usually called Baud rate.

**BCD**   The binary-coded decimal system, used to encode decimal data as a 4-bit binary number per decimal digit (0000–1001). BCD is stored as either a packed (2 BCD digits per byte) or unpacked (1 BCD digit per byte) number.

**Biased exponent**   A binary power of 2 that has a constant added. In single-precision format, the bias or constant added is 127 or $7F.

**Binary-coded decimal**   see **BCD**

**Binary-coded decimal floating-point**   A form of the floating-point number stored as a binary-coded decimal (BCD) number in scientific form. The opcode extension .P is used to designate this data form.

**Binary floating-point** A binary floating-point number contains a sign-bit, a biased exponent, and a significand that includes either an implicit or explicit one-bit. It may be single-precision, double-precision, or extended-precision. The opcode extensions for single, double, and extended precision are .S, .D, and .X.

**Binary scientific notation** Binary floating-point numbers or real numbers.

**Bit** One binary digit containing a one or zero. The term represents a contraction of BInary digiT.

**Bit field** A grouping of bits that are operated on with the bit field instructions of the 68020, 68030, and 68040 microprocessors. The bit field is defined by its starting bit and width.

**Borrow** Occurs after a subtraction and is held in the extend CCR (X-CCR) bit.

**Branch** A branch in the flow of a program to another instruction located elsewhere in the memory (termed a GOTO in a BASIC language program).

**Break character** Two complete asynchronous serial digit data 2 times of logic zeros or start bits. This character is normally used to break communications.

**Bubble sort** A sorting technique in which the smallest numbers appear to float or bubble to the top of a list.

**Burst** A DMA technique that places the microprocessor in a wait state for an extended period of time while a group of data are transferred, also using DMA techniques. Also a memory transfer technique in the 68030 and 68040 microprocessor in which 4 long-words of data are transferred in five clocking periods.

**Burst mode** A method of transferring multiple data using DMA techniques.

**Bus** A common set of signal lines that carry the same type of information. The address bus, for example, carries address information.

**Bus arbitration** The act of holding off a microprocessor or other controlling device so that an external microprocessor or controller can gain access to its memory or I/O space.

**Bus bandwidth** see **Data transfer rate**

**Bus conflict** Occurs whenever two or more memory or I/O devices are activated simultaneously. A bus conflict destroys any information present on the bus.

**Bus cycle** The time required by the 68000 to transfer one byte or word of data between itself and the memory or I/O. A bus cycle is measured in time, clocking periods, or clocking states.

**Bus master** A microprocessor, coprocessor, or DMA controller that is currently in possession of the system buses.

**Bus transfer** Data traveling to the memory or I/O from the microprocessor or from the microprocessor to the memory or I/O.

**Bus transfer time** The time needed to transfer a piece of data between the microprocessor and its memory or I/O.

**Byte** Generally 8 bits.

**Cache** A storehouse or reserve of data. In the 68020, an instruction cache is added to store instructions. In the 68030 and 68040, instruction and data caches are present to cache instructions and data.

**Cache disable input** An external pin which can disable the cache.

**Carry** Can occur after an addition and is held in the extend CCR (X-CCR) bit.

**CAS (column address strobe)** A signal used to send the column address into the column address latch within a DRAM. Also used to enable the DRAM to read or write data.

**CCR** The condition code register, which holds the condition code bits: N (negative), Z (zero), C (carry), V (overflow), and X (extend). The CCR bits generally indicate the effect of the most recently executed instruction.

**Centronics interface**   A type of printer interface used with many commercially available printers. This interface is a TTL level parallel interface standard.

**Chain**   A group of addresses and counts stored in a memory array. These commands can be stored in contiguous memory for an array chain or in any area of memory for a linked array chain.

**Checksum**   The sum of all the data on a ROM, which will remain constant except when an error is present.

**Clean ASCII file**   A file that does not contain control characters.

**Clear**   An instruction that clears the contents of any data register or any memory location using any effective addressing mode except program counter addressing.

**Clock period**   One complete cycle on the clock input pin is called a clock cycle or clock period.

**Common anode**   A term that applies to an LED display in which all the anodes of the internal LEDs are connected in parallel.

**Common cathode**   A term that applies to an LED display in which all the cathodes of the internal LEDs are connected in parallel.

**Common data connection**   see **Data connections, memory**

**Comparator**   A function that determines whether two bits are equal.

**Compare**   An operation that uses subtraction to modify the CCR bits. After a compare, the difference is lost.

**Complement**   see **Invert**

**Composite video**   A video signal that contains video, sync signals, and a color burst signal.

**Computed jump**   A programming technique that uses a number, located in one of the registers, to select from one of many programs.

**Condition code register**   see **CCR**

**Conditional branch**   A branch occurs only if the condition tested by the condition-al branch instruction is true. Conditional branch instructions test the carry, overflow, negative, and zero CCR bits.

**Connector symbol**   A symbol used to link sections of a flowchart and other symbols.

**Constant**   see **Immediate data**

**Control bus**   A common set of connections that thread to the memory and I/O, carrying control signals between them and the microprocessor. The most important control signal in the 68000 family of microprocessors is R/$\overline{\text{W}}$, which selects a read operation when it is a logic one and a write operation when it is a logic zero.

**Control connections, memory**   The memory control connections common to a ROM are $\overline{\text{CE}}$ and $\overline{\text{OE}}$. The connections common to the SRAM are $\overline{\text{CE}}$, $\overline{\text{OE}}$, and $\overline{\text{WE}}$. The connections common to DRAM are $\overline{\text{CAS}}$, $\overline{\text{RAS}}$, and R/$\overline{\text{W}}$.

**Control flow**   The aspect of a flowchart whih reveals the decision-making paths in a program.

**Controlling element**   see **Microprocessor**

**Coprocessor**   A device that, when connected to the microprocessor, performs operations concurrently with the microprocessor. Either a floating-point coprocessor or a memory management coprocessor is available to various members of the 68000 family.

**Coprocessor interface register (CIR)**   A register used for communications between the coprocessor and the microprocessor.

**CTS (clear to send)**   The signal from a modem indicating that the modem is ready to send information.

**Cylinder**   A group of tracks that are accessed together. For example, the upper and lower heads on a dual-sided disk comprise a cylinder.

**DAC (digital-to-analog converter)**   A device that converts digital information into an analog voltage.

**Daisy-chain**   A method of connecting interrupts or other events to the microprocessor so that if any event becomes active, the microprocessor is interrupted.

**Data bus** A common set of signal lines that carry data between the microprocessor and the memory or the I/O. The 68000 and 68010 have a 16-bit data bus; the 68008 has an 8-bit data bus; and the 68020, 68030, and 68040 have a 32-bit data bus.

**Data cache** The 68030 contains a 256-byte data cache and the 68040 contains a 4k byte data cache to store the most recently used data. This allows the microprocessor to access recent data quickly.

**Data connections, memory** The memory data connections are usually 8 bits wide on a ROM or a SRAM and often only 1 bit wide on a DRAM. The ROM and SRAM contain bidirectional common data connections, while the DRAM often contains separate data connections for input and output data.

**Data registers** Eight general-purpose registers (D0–D7) that hold a byte, word, or long-word of data.

**Data strobe** A connection that indicates that data are active on the data bus.

**Data transfer acknowledge ($\overline{\text{DTACK}}$)** A signal line indicating that the memory or I/O has received the data. This permits the microprocessor to continue with the execution of software.

**Data transfer bus** A bus that consists of address, data, and control signals that are familiar from the 68000 microprocessors.

**Data transfer rate** Generally defined as the number of bytes or words transferred per second through the data bus of a microprocessor; also referred to as bus bandwidth.

**DCD (data carrier detect)** Indicates that a modem has detected a digital serial transmission.

**Decoder** A device that selects memory devices in a memory system by using the address signals to pick out various memory components.

**Default** An option that will be performed unless the computer is programmed to do otherwise.

**Delimiter** A character, usually a comma, that separates two items in an assembly language statement.

**Demand system** A system where programs request memory areas from the memory management unit on access.

**Descriptor** Data that define a page of memory or the next level of translation in the next translation table.

**Destination** An operand used with the MOVE instruction that indicates where the information is being moved.

**Destination field** This field specifies the location to which the data are to be moved with the MOVE instruction.

**Direct address** A data or address register is considered to be a direct address in the 680XX microprocessors.

**Direct memory access (DMA)** The process in which the microprocessor is turned off and an external device gains access to the buses, where data are transferred between the memory and an I/O device without the intervention of the microprocessor.

**Direct memory access transfers** Hardware transfers that transfer data directly between the memory and I/O or between two memory locations.

**Direct register addressing** see **Direct Address**

**Displacement** The distance of the next instruction or data from the branch instruction or instruction that is addressing data. A short (8-bit) displacement is within $+129$ and $-126$ bytes from the branch and a long (16-bit) displacement is within $+32,769$ and $-32,766$ bytes from the branch instruction.

**DMA** see **Direct memory access**

**DMA acknowledge** see **Acknowledge**

**DMA mode**   A type of operation that transfers data with the DMA controller.

**DMA read**   The process of transferring data from a memory location to an I/O device.

**DMA transfer address**   Usually the address of the memory location at which data are transferred from or to during a DMA transfer.

**DMA transfer rate**   The number of bytes, words, or long-words transferred per second.

**DMA write**   The process of transferring data from an I/O device to a memory location.

**Don't care**   A binary bit that can be either a one or a zero. A don't care is usually represented as an X in a binary number.

**Double-buffered**   A term indicating that an input contains a latch to store input data and that an output also contains a latch. In double-buffered applications, handshaking is provided to indicate if data are available in these latches.

**Double-density**   A term that applies to floppy disks that use the MFM recording technique for storing data. They are said to store twice the data as a single-density (FM) disk.

**Double-height board**   A printed circuit card that supports any microprocessor in the Motorola 68000 family, including the 68040.

**DRAM (dynamic RAM)**   A memory component that stores data for only 4 ms before all locations must be refreshed. Its main advantage is that it has a much higher packaging density than the SRAM.

**DSR (data set ready)**   The signal indicating that the modem is powered up and ready to receive and transmit data.

**DTR (data terminal ready)**   A signal to the modem indicating that the data terminal is ready to operate.

**Dual in-line package (DIP)**   A device often used with digital and microprocessor integrated circuits. The DIP contains 2 rows of pins spaced either 0.3″ or 0.6″ apart.

**Dyadic operation**   An operation that has two parts, such as addition or subtraction.

**Dynamic bus sizing**   In the 68020 and 68030, a technique whereby the size of the bus can be changed to 8, 16, or 32 bits while the microprocessor executes a program. This allows different memory sizes and I/O buses to be used in a system.

**Dynamic memory error (soft memory error)**   A memory error that may occur only at times or as a result of a change elsewhere in the memory device.

**Dynamic random access memory**   see **DRAM**

**EEPROM (electrically erasable programmable read-only memory)**   A read-only memory that can be programmed and erased electrically within the unit that it operates.

**Effective address**   A generic term indicating that almost any addressing mode may be used for a particular operand; usually shown as ⟨ea⟩ in an instruction. Also often indicates the actual address used to access memory data.

**EGA (enhanced graphics adapter)**   A video standard that allows fairly high resolution color video displays.

**Enable**   To turn on or activate. This term is usually used with a memory component or a decoder.

**Entry pointer**   An address register used in a FIFO stack to address the current entry location in the stack.

**EPROM (erasable programmable read-only memory)**   A read-only memory programmed by the user with an EPROM programmer by storing charges on a floating gate located within the EPROM. The EPROM is erasable with an ultraviolet light source.

**EPROM programmer**   A device used to

program erasable programmable read-only memory.

**Equate** The assembler pseudo opcode (EQU) used to set a label equal to some value or other label.

**ESDI (enhanced small disk interface)** An interface to disk memory system that allows data transfer at a much higher speed than with the ST-506 MFM or RLL interface standard.

**Exception** A term indicating an interruption or exception to the normal processing path of a program.

**Exception handler** see **Handler; Interrupt service subroutine**

**Exchange** The term used whenever the contents of two 32-bit registers are exchanged.

**Exclusive OR** This function produces a logic one only if both inputs are different. Exclusive OR is used to invert bits or toggle them, or to compare numbers.

**Execution** The portion of a microprocessor's time spent performing the instructions fetched from a stored program.

**Exit pointer** An address register used in a FIFO stack to address the current exit location in the stack.

**Explicit addressing** A term used with DMA controllers to indicate that the DMA controller provides the address for the memory and I/O in two bus cycles. One bus cycle reads data from an I/O device or memory location and saves it within the DMA controller. The second bus cycle writes the data saved within the controller to an I/O device or a memory location.

**Explicit one-bit** A binary one that is stored with the binary fraction to form the significand. This bit appears only in the extended-precision form of a binary floating-point number.

**Extension** Many opcodes require a .B, .W, or .L extension to indicate byte, word, or long-word.

**Fanout** Usually described as the number of unit loads that an output pin is capable of driving.

**Fetch** The portion of the microprocessor's time spent extracting instructions from the stored program in the memory and decoding these instructions.

**FIFO (first in, first out)** A type of memory that retrieves stored data in the order stored. This type of memory is often called a queue or pipeline and is used to buffer low speed devices with high speed devices.

**Fixed disk** A hard disk is often called a fixed disk.

**Floating-point coprocessor** A device specifically designed as a coprocessor to manipulate floating-point numbers using floating-point arithmetic.

**Floating-point number** A number generally stored in 4 bytes of memory and containing three fields: sign, biased exponent, and fraction. Floating-point numbers are used to represent decimal whole numbers, fractions, and mixed numbers.

**Flowchart** A collection of graphic symbols used to indicate the flow or control structure of a program. Common flowcharting symbols found include process, predefined process, input/output, decision, terminal, and connector (see Figure 5-1).

**Fluorescent display** A display device that generates a blue-green light. Used in many systems because of the brightness of the light generated.

**Flush** A term used with cache memory. To flush a cache is to clear it of all data or instructions.

**Flying head** The head on a hard disk drive; so called because it rides on a film of air that is carried with the disk as it spins at 3000 rpm.

**Framing error** Occurs when data are received with the start and stop bits in the wrong place. This type of error normally occurs when data are received at the wrong Baud rate.

**Full duplex**   A term applied to a data communication system that can receive and transmit data simultaneously.

**Full-scale**   A term indicating the maximum output voltage of a digital-to-analog converter.

**Full-step**   Describing a stepper motor in which the armature is moved from one pole to another by the excitation currents in the field windings.

**Fully decoded (populated) memory**   A memory system that has or will eventually have its entire memory filled with memory and I/O.

**G**   A computer G is roughly a billion (specifically, 1,073,741,824; 1G = 1024M; 1M = 1024k; 1k = 1024.

**Global subroutines**   see **System subroutines**

**Glue**   The name often used for a PAL that interconnects other circuits components in a system.

**Half duplex**   A term applied to a data communications system that sends and receives data in one direction at a time.

**Half-step**   A term applied to stepper motors in which the armature is moved from pole to pole and also half-way between poles. This allows the stepper motor to be positioned to eight different discrete locations instead of four, as with full-steps.

**Halt**   The act of stopping the execution of all software in the 68000. Halt is caused by activating the $\overline{\text{HALT}}$ pin or by executing the STOP instruction.

**Handler**   A term designating a subroutine that processes an interrupt or an exception.

**Hard (memory) error**   see **Static memory error.**

**Hexadecimal**   A number represented in base 16. Values of a single hexadecimal digit range from 0–9 followed by A–F for the numbers 10–15. In the 680XX system, a

hexadecimal number is preceded by a dollar sign ($).

**Hexadecimal machine language**   The instruction in the microprocessor's native language: hexadecimal.

**Hidden refresh**   Describes a dynamic memory that is refreshed while the microprocessor is busy doing operations other than memory access.

**High density**   A term that applies to floppy disks that store 1.2M bytes on a $5\frac{1}{4}$ inch floppy and 1.44M bytes on a $3\frac{1}{2}$ inch floppy.

**Hit**   A term indicating that the instruction or data accessed from the memory system is already loaded into the instruction or data cache.

**Housekeeping registers**   Registers used by the microprocessor during the normal execution of software that are not generally directly accessible by the program. In the 68000 these registers are the program counter and the status register.

**IDE (integrated drive electronics)**   An interface standard used with hard disk drives; the disk controller electronics is located within the disk drive instead of in the computer system.

**Immediate data**   Data that exist as a constant and immediately follow the opcode in the memory.

**Implicit addressing**   A term used with DMA controllers to indicate that the DMA controller provides the address of the memory location used with a DMA transfer, but not the address of the I/O device. Instead, the DMA controller selects the I/O device with the $\overline{\text{ACK}}$ signal.

**Implicit one-bit**   A binary one that is not stored with the binary fraction for a floating-point number. It is implied to be present.

**Inclusive OR**   The term often given to the logic addition or the OR function.

**Index hole**   A hole through a mini-floppy

disk and its jacket that indicates the start of the first sector in a track of data (see Figure 10-23).

**Index register** A data or address register of word or long-word width that is added to another address register to form a memory address.

**Indirect addressing** A method of addressing memory data by using an address register to address (locate) the operand data in the memory.

**Indirect (addressing) with index** A type of indirect addressing that uses the sum of an 8-bit displacement, an address register, and the contents of any word or long-word address or data register to develop the address of the data.

**Indirect addressing with postincrement** A type of indirect addressing that automatically increments the contents of the address register after the data have been transferred.

**Indirect addressing with predecrement** A type of indirect addressing that decrements the contents of the address register before the data transfer occurs.

**Indirect jump** A jump instruction that jumps to the address stored in an address register.

**Initiator** A device on the SCSI bus that can initiate data transfers, for example, the host computer system that is attached to the bus.

**Input device** A device that allows data to be entered into the computer system from some external source.

**Instruction cache** A mechanism in the 68020 that is used to store 256 bytes of instructions in an internal memory. These instructions, once loaded, are executed at a very high speed. The 68030 contains a 256-byte instruction cache and the 68040 contains a 4k byte instruction cache.

**Integer** A binary whole number that either has a sign-bit (signed integer) or does not have a sign-bit (unsigned integer). With respect to the coprocessor, an integer is a signed whole number that is a byte, word, or long-word.

**Intelligent controller** A device that makes decisions and corrections as it controls a system.

**Interrupt** A technique whereby a program is interrupted to call a subroutine. There are software interrupts and hardware interrupts. An interrupt calls an interrupt service subroutine.

**Interrupt acknowledge** see **Acknowledge, interrupt**

**Interrupt service subroutine** A subroutine used by the interrupt to perform some useful task in response to the exception. After an interrupt service subroutine, control is passed back to the program that was interrupted.

**Invert** This involves changing the bits of a number from one to zero or from zero to one.

**I/O** Input/output devices accept a digital signal from the microprocessor or generate a digital signal for the microprocessor.

**Isolated I/O** A type of I/O interface where the microprocessor has special instructions for the I/O operations and even a separate area of addresses that are unique to I/O operations.

**Jump** A branch in the flow of a program to another instruction located elsewhere in the memory. The difference between a jump and a branch is the maximum distance of the instruction branched to in the program.

**k** A computer k is roughly a thousand and specifically 1024.

**.L** An extension indicating that 32-bit long-words of data are being manipulated.

**Label** A word constructed from alphabetic and numeric characters, used in place of a hexadecimal memory address when a program is written in symbolic assembly language.

**Label table**   A table formed during pass one of the assembly process that contains the labels and their actual memory locations in hexadecimal.

**LCD (liquid crystal display)**   A display device that shows information by aligning internal crystals with an electrostatic field.

**LED (light-emitting diode)**   A diode that is illuminated whenever current is passed through it. Such devices are used to construct segmented displays called LED displays.

**LIFO (last in, first out)**   A type of stack memory. A last in, first out memory is used to store data temporarily and also to return addresses for subroutines.

**Linear programming**   A programming technique in which a program starts at one location in memory and proceeds directly through memory without using a BSR or a JSR instruction.

**Link**   The act of obtaining a new stack area and a local storage area by using the LINK instruction.

**Listing (or print) file**   A file that prints the object program in addition to the source program.

**Local bus**   The bus connection of a microprocessor before the system bus buffers. This is the location of the coprocessor in a system.

**Local connection**   A term indicating that a device is connected to the microprocessor bus system before the bus buffers.

**Local subroutines**   These subroutines are often called with a BSR instruction, which has range limited to ±32K.

**Logical addition**   The term often given to the OR function.

**Logical memory**   The memory system as seen by the programmer. In most cases logical memory is 8 bits in width because each byte of memory is assigned a memory address.

**Logical memory address**   The address as it comes from a program and the microprocessor. A logical address does not always address the same physical address in a system that contains a memory management unit.

**Logical multiplication**   The term often given to the AND function.

**Logic inversion**   An instruction that inverts a number.

**Long address**   A 32-bit memory address.

**Long-word**   A 32-bit number in the 680XX microprocessor.

**Loop mode operation**   The 68010 operates in loop mode for tight loops that contain a 2-byte instruction followed by a DBcc instruction. This mode allows the 68010 to execute tight loops without memory references.

**Lower $\overline{\text{DS}}$**   A connection that indicates that the least significant 8 bits of the data bus are currently active.

**M**   A computer M is roughly a million (specifically, 1,048,576); 1M = 1024k; 1k = 1024.

**Machine language**   A language in binary, usually written as hexidecimal, that the microprocessor understands.

**Mantissa**   The part of a floating-point number that is a fraction.

**Maskable**   Describes a device or pin that can be turned off (masked off).

**Maskable interrupt**   An interrupt that can be turned off either by a software instruction or by the hardware.

**Mask-programmed ROM**   A type of memory programmed when it is manufactured by internally connecting circuits so that ones and zeros are permanently stored in the appropriate memory locations.

**Memory**   A system that functions to store programs and the data used by programs.

**Memory access time**   The time allowed for the memory to access data. This is equal to the time it takes for three complete 68000 clocking periods (six states) minus the time needed for the address to appear after $S_1$ ($t_{CLAV}$), minus the time required for data to be set up on the data bus before $S_7$ ($t_{DICL}$).

**Memory bank**   see **Bank, memory**

**Memory locations**   see **Address**

**Memory management unit (MMU)**   A part of the microprocessor that controls the access to and location of the logical memory.

**Memory-mapped I/O**   A type of I/O interface where the buffer times the application of the input data to ensure that data appear on the data bus only when its location is read from the memory.

**Memory-to-memory transfer**   A DMA technique that allows data to be moved between areas of memory without software intervention by the microprocessor.

**MFM**   see **Modified frequency modulation**

**Microcomputer**   A computer system that uses the microprocessor as the controller to access local memory and I/O.

**Microprocessor**   A digital machine that can perform simple arithmetic and logic operations, transfer data, and make simple decisions.

**Miss**   A term indicating that an instruction or data accessed in the memory system is not currently residing in the instruction or data cache.

**MMU**   see **Memory management unit**

**Mode**   Refers to the type of addressing selected for either the source or the destination operand.

**Mode field**   This field specifies how the data of the destination or source are addressed by the instruction.

**Modem**   Short for a modulator/demodulator, a device used to send and receive data transferred over telephone lines.

**Modified frequency modulation (MFM)**   A fairly common recording technique used to store data on the surface of a disk (see Figure 10-26).

**Monadic operation**   An operation that has only one part, such as sine or cosine.

**MOVE**   An instruction that takes the data specified in the source operand and moves it into the destination operand.

**NAN**   Not-a-number. The result of such coprocessor operations as infinity divided by infinity or any other operation that has no mathematical representation. see also **SNAN**

**Native**   The main conversational language of a system. The microprocessor views machine language as its native language.

**Negate**   A type of instruction used to two's complement a number.

**Nested subroutine**   A subroutine within a subroutine.

**Non-DMA mode**   A type of operation that causes the DMA controller to appear as a programmable I/O device to the microprocessor.

**Nonmaskable**   Describing a device that cannot be turned off (masked off).

**Nonmaskable interrupt**   An interrupt that cannot be deactivated (disabled).

**Non-return to zero (NRZ)**   A method of magnetizing the surface of a disk so that it is magnetized at the saturation level (see Figure 10-25). This automatically erases old data.

**Nonvolatile**   A manner of storage in which data or programs remain valid even after electrical power has been removed from the device.

**Nonvolatile memory**   A memory component that does not change such as a ROM.

**Not-a-number**   see **NAN**

**NOVRAM**   see **EEPROM**

**NRZ**   see **Non-return to zero**

**Object File**   A hexadecimal file that lists the object programs of a listing file.

**Object program**   The output of the assembler program that is in hexadecimal machine language.

**One's complement**   A function that changes the bits of a number from ones to zeros or from zeros to ones.

**Opcode**   An instruction to a microprocessor, such as MOVE or SWAP.

**Operand**   The data operated on by an instruction.

**Operand address**   The address of the operand.

**Operation**   An action resulting from a single computer instruction.

**Optical coupler**   Used to isolate systems. Optical couplers contain an LED and a phototransistor for electrical isolation.

**OR**   Logical addition; yields a result of zero only if both inputs are at their logic zero levels. OR is often used to set bits or turn them on.

**Ordered condition**   Occurs after a compare instruction when both numbers being compared are numbers (as opposed to NANs).

**Origin**   The start of a program or section of a program; ORG is one of the pseudo opcodes.

**Output device**   A device that accepts data from the microprocessor.

**Overflow**   A condition that occurs when the result of two signed numbers that are added is too large to be held in the destination operand.

**Overlay**   A space in the memory where an actual device appear again or is repeated.

**Overrun error**   A type of error that occurs in an ACIA when the data present are not removed before the next datum is received.

**Packed BCD**   Data that are stored as two BCD digits per byte.

**Page**   Normally, 256 bytes of memory. Using the MMU, a page may be 256, 512, 1024, 2048, 4096, 8192, 16,384, or 32,768 bytes in length. Note that the only allowable page sizes in the 68040 microprocessor are 4k and 8k bytes.

**Paged memory management unit (PMMU)**   see **MMU**

**Page frames**   Small physical areas of equal size into which the memory is divided.

**PAL (programmable logic array)**   A programmable logic element often is used as a decoder or other combinational logic circuit. Versions also contain flip-flops that can be used to develop synchronous machines.

**Parity**   A count of the number of ones, expressed as an even or an odd.

**Parity error**   A type of error indicating that an incorrect number of one-bits have been received in a data communications environment.

**Parsing**   The act of separating ASCII-coded data from an ASCII character string.

**Partially decoded (populated) memory**   A memory system that will never contain all the possible memory.

**PC**   see **Program counter**

**Peripheral interface adapter**   see **PIA**

**PGA**   see **Pin grid array**

**Physical address**   The actual physical memory address in the memory system. This address may be different from the logical address in a system that utilizes a memory management unit.

**Physical memory**   The memory system as it actually exists.

**Physical memory address**   The actual hardware memory address assigned to a memory location by the memory decoder.

**PIA (peripheral interface adapter)**   A device used to interface the microprocessor with parallel peripheral equipment.

**Pin grid array (PGA)**   An integrated circuit package.

**Pixel** A picture element; the smallest dot on a video display screen.

**PLD (programmable logic device)** A family of devices that are programmed with logic (e.g., the PAL, PLA, and GAL, which are all generic labels applied to PLDs).

**PMMU** see **Memory management unit**

**Polling** The act of asking an I/O device or other element if data are available.

**Postincrement** Incrementing the contents of an address register by 1 (byte), 2 (word), or 4 (long-word) after an instruction is executed.

**Predecrement** Decrementing the contents of an address register by 1 (byte), 2 (word), or 4 (long-word) before an instruction is executed.

**Predefined process** A subroutine.

**Prescaler** A device that divides by a fixed value, usually placed before a programmable timer (e.g., the prescaler inside the 68230 PI/T).

**Priority** As applied to interrupts. a device that is accepted first is said to have a higher priority.

**Priority interrupt bus** A bus that consists of the interrupt request lines, interrupt acknowledge, and daisy-chain interrupt signals.

**Print spooler** see **Spooler**

**Privileged instruction** An instruction that can be executed only in the supervisor mode of operation. If executed in the user mode, an interrupt occurs.

**Process symbol** A flowchart symbol used to indicate any process that appears in a program.

**Program counter (PC)** A register used by the microprocessor to locate the next instruction in a program.

**Program counter addressing** see **Relative address**

**Programmable/generic logic arrays** Devices, available in many different versions, that are used as decoders or other circuit elements.

**PROM (programmable read-only memory)** A read-only memory that is programmed by the user with a PROM programmer, which burns open tiny fuses inside the memory to store logic zeros.

**PROM programmer** A machine that programs read-only memory by burning open tiny fuses of nichrome of polysilicon inside the PROM.

**Propagation delay** The time a digital signal takes to move through a logic gate or a logic component.

**Pseudo opcodes (directives)** Special opcodes used to direct the assembly process, store constants in the memory, or reserve memory.

**Queue** A type of memory used to buffer data between a low speed device and a high speed device. Also referred to as a first in, first out memory.

**Quick** A term applied to certain instructions that allow an 8-bit sign-extended number to be used as a 32-bit immediate data operand.

**R/$\overline{\text{W}}$** Read/write is the main 680XX control signal; it commands the memory or I/O to do a read (logic one) or a write (logic zero).

**Random access memory (RAM)** Memory that can be written to or read from.

**$\overline{\text{RAS}}$ (row address strobe)** A signal that sends the row address into the row address latch through the address connections on a DRAM. Also used to cause the DRAM to refresh an entire row of data.

**RAS-only refresh** A refresh where only an RAS is used.

**Raster line** One complete line of video information on a video display screen.

**Read-only memory** see **ROM**

**Read/write/modify** A memory cycle

that, as it executes, cannot be intefered with by any other microprocessor in a shared system.

**Register field**   This field indicates which register, if any, is used for the destination or the source.

**Real number**   A binary floating-point number.

**Refresh**   The act of rewriting data in a DRAM.

**Refresh address**   The address that is sent to the DRAM to refresh a row of memory.

**Relative address**   An address that is relative to the program counter.

**Relocatable**   A program that is written using relative addressing; so called because it can be placed and executed anywhere in the memory without modification.

**Relocatable program**   A program that can be moved to any location in the memory because of displacement addressing.

**Repeat-until construct**   A programming structure that allows an operation to be repeated until some condition prevails. In the 680XX microprocessors, the decrement and branch instructions are used to execute a repeat-until construct.

**Reset**   A function in the microprocessor that initializes the microprocessor so that it begins execution of the program at a known location. In the 68000 series of microprocessors, a reset causes the machine to fetch the initial value of the supervisor stack pointer from memory locations $000000–$000003 and the initial value of the PC from locations $000004–$000007.

**Return address**   Normally, the contents of the program counter that are placed on the stack by a BSR or JSR instruction.

**Return instruction**   The instruction used to end a subroutine; so called because it will return from the subroutine by popping the stack into the program counter to retrieve the return address.

**RGB**   A term used to indicate a color moni-

tor. The letters RGB indicate red, green, and blue, the primary colors of light.

**Rigid disk**   A term often applied to a hard or fixed disk.

**RLL**   see **Run-length-limited**

**ROM (read-only memory)**   Memory that can only be read. This memory stores data permanently and is programmed by the manufacturer during construction.

**Root register**   A register in the memory management unit that is used to address the level A translation table.

**Rotate**   The act of shifting a number to the left or right with the bit that is shifted out of the register or memory location moved into the opposite end of the register or memory location.

**RS-232C**   An interface standard used in serial data communications environments.

**RTS (request to send)**   A signal sent to a modem to request that the modem set up for transmission in a half duplex system.

**Run-length-limited (RLL)**   A recording technique that limits the number of zeros in a row, allowing a higher storage density on the surface of the disk (see Table 10-3).

**Scaling**   When a register is scaled, it is multiplied by a factor of 1, 2, 4, or 8.

**Scratchpad memory**   A memory that can be accessed quickly and holds commonly used data.

**SCSI (small computer system interface)**   A hard disk memory interface standard that allows a high data transfer rate with multiple disk drives.

**Sector**   A portion of a track where data are stored. Today sectors are often either 512 or 1024 bytes long but can be any length (see Figure 10-23).

**Separate data connections**   see **Data connections, memory**

**Shadow**   see **Overlay**

**Shift**   The act of moving a binary number to the left or right.

**Short address**  A 16-bit memory address that is sign-extended into a full 32-bit address.

**Short format indirect descriptor**  Data that reside at the bottom level of the page translation table and contain the physical address of a page descriptor.

**Short format invalid descriptor**  Data that can be used at any level of the translation tree except at the root level. This descriptor indicates that the entry refers to an invalid section of the memory.

**Short format page descriptor**  Data that store the page address and may reside at any page translation table level.

**Short format table descriptor**  Data used to address a table of descriptors. It contains the physical base address of a descriptor table.

**Sign bit**  The left-most bit position of a byte, word, or long-word. A logic one in the sign bit indicates that the signed integer is negative and is stored in its two's complement form. A logic zero in the sign bit indicates that the signed integer is positive and is stored in its true form.

**Signed**  Numbers that have a plus or minus sign in front.

**Signed binary integer**  Used to store numbers that require an arithmetic plus or minus sign.

**Sign extension**  Whenever a word is moved into an address register, the sign bit is copied into the most significant 16 bits of the address register. If the word ranges between $0000 and $7FFF, a $0000 is placed in the most significant 16 bits; if it ranges between $8000 and $FFFF, a $FFFF is placed in the most significant 16 bits.

**Significand**  A term that refers to the fractional part of a floating-point number. In the case of the floating-point format presented for the coprocessor, the significand contains a binary fraction and either an implicit or explicit one-bit.

**Single-buffered**  A term applied to a latch

that appears in an output device when the output device contains no handshaking. Also referred to as latched output.

**Single-height board**  A printed circuit card that supports the 68000 or 68010 microprocessor.

**Size field**  This field specifies the size of a data transfer in bytes, words, or long-words.

**Slower memory component**  A memory device that requires a longer access time than the 6800 provides.

**Snooping**  An operation that allows the 68040 to keep current information in its caches even though it is not controlling the system buses.

**Soft memory error**  see **Dynamic memory error**

**Software fix**  A patch added to an existing program to correct a problem.

**Source**  An operand used with the MOVE instruction that indicates from where the information is being moved.

**Source field**  This field specifies the location from which the data are to be moved with the MOVE instruction.

**Source program**  A program written in symbolic assembly language.

**SNAN**  A signaling not-a-number; a NAN that is specifically indicated via the software.

**SP**  see **Stack pointer register**

**Spooler**  A device that holds information for an extended period of time for a system such as a printer. The spooler is usually constructed using a queue memory to hold the printer data.

**Spurious interrupt**  An interrupt that indicates a hardware error or an unwanted response to an interrupt request.

**SRAM (static RAM)**  A memory component that stores data statically for as long as power is applied.

**SSP**  see **Stack pointer register**

**Stack**  A section of memory and its associated registers used for temporary storage of information, operating on a last-in-first-out principle.

**Stack frame**  An area of memory created with the LINK instruction that contains a new stack and also local variable storage.

**Stack memory**  A special form of memory in which data are stored and retrieved from the memory location addressed by a stack pointer. This register is used mainly for linking to or from procedures and for storing data temporarily. There are two types of stack memory available: LIFO and FIFO. Each type reuses the same area of memory and is addressed by one (LIFO) or two (FIFO) pointers.

**Stack pointer (SP) register**  The 680XX has two stack pointers and two stacks. The SSP (supervisor stack pointer) addresses the supervisor stack and the USP (user stack pointer) addresses the user stack.

**Start bit**  A bit (logic zero) that indicates that a character frame has started.

**State**  Half a clocking period in the 68000 or 68008 microprocessor.

**Statement**  Each line of a source program. A statement is composed of four distinct fields of information: the label, the opcode, the operand, and the comment.

**Static memory error**  An error in which a bit is permanently stuck either high (1) or low (0); also called hard memory error.

**Status register**  Holds the system byte and the CCR register.

**Stepper motor**  A device that positions objects in discrete positions. Because it is a digital motor, it can easily be interfaced to the microprocessor to position objects.

**Stop bit**  A bit used for spacing between characters in an asynchronous communications system.

**Stored programs**  Programs stored in the computer system's memory allow the system to access instructions at a high rate of speed, giving the computer tremendous power and speed.

**Subroutine**  A grouping of instructions that usually perform one task and are stored in the memory once. A subroutine is used many times from a program by branching or jumping to it with the BSR or JSR instructions. The return is affected by using the RTS or RTR instruction.

**Supervisor stack pointer** see **Stack pointer (SP) register**

**Swap**  An exchange between the least and most significant halves of a data register.

**Symbolic instruction**  The written form of an instruction that we understand. For example, MOVE is a symbolic instruction.

**Symbolic memory addresses**  Labels used along with the actual machine language hexadecimal addresses.

**Synchronous transfer**  A memory system term meaning that data are transferred in synchronization with the $\overline{\text{STERM}}$ signal on the microprocessor. Synchronous transfers generally occur at a higher rate than asynchronous transfers.

**System bus**  A bus after it has been buffered.

**System byte**  Contains the system control bits that mask interrupts, select supervisor or user mode of operation, and select trace or single-instruction mode. The system byte is located in the status register.

**System subroutines**  Often called with the JSR function, these subroutines tend to be anywhere in memory.

**Table lookup**  A technique that uses tables of data to convert from one code to another.

**Target**  A device that performs services for the initiator and is usually a disk drive of laser printer.

**Terminal count**  The state of a counter which has returned to zero.

**Terminal symbol**  A flowchart symbol

used to indicate the START or END of a program or subroutine.

**Test access port (TAP)** Allows the microprocessor system to be tested through a 184-bit test boundary scan register that holds test information for the pin connections on the microprocessor.

**Timer** A programmable modulus counter, used to divide a clock frequency.

**Track** An area on a disk on which data are stored. A track is a concentric circle on the surface of the disk (see Figure 10-23).

**Translation table** A table that contains descriptors that refer to another translation table or to a physical memory address. Translation tables are used to convert logical addresses into physical addresses.

**Two's-complement** A method used to change the arithmetic sign of a signed binary number.

**Unconditional branch** A branch will always occur to the location indicated by the displacement. No conditions are placed on the branch.

**Underflow** Can occur after a signed subtraction to indicate that the result is invalid. The underflow is indicated by the overflow CCR bit.

**Unit load** One input connection on any logic circuit.

**Unordered condition** The condition that exists when one or both of the numbers compared are NANs.

**Unpacked BCD** Data that are stored as one BCD digit per byte.

**Unsigned** Numbers that do not have a plus of minus sign in front.

**Unsigned integer** A binary number that occupies a byte, a word, or a long-word.

**Upper $\overline{\text{DS}}$** A connection that indicates that the most significant 8 bits (D15-D8) of the data bus are inactive.

**User stack pointer** see **Stack pointer (SP) register**

**USP** see **Stack pointer register**

**Utility bus** A bus that contains the main system control signals used to reset the microprocessor, provide the system clock, detect power failures, and transmit and receive serial data.

**Vector** A 4-byte-long section of the memory that holds the address of the SSP or the PC after a reset. A vector also holds the address of the interrupt service subroutine.

**Vector base** The address of the starting point of the exception (interrupt) vector table in the memory system.

**VGA (variable graphics array)** A standard video display system that allows high resolution color video images to be displayed.

**Virtual memory** It exists in effect, but is not real. This is possible because any logical address can be mapped to any physical address.

**Volatile memory** Memory that changes whenever power is disconnected from the memory system. Examples include SRAM and DRAM.

**.W** An extension indicating that 16-bit words of data are being manipulated.

**Walking bit test** A special memory test used to test for dynamic errors.

**Word** A 16-bit number in the 680XX series of microprocessors.

**WORM** The name given to an optical disk that can be written to only once. It can be read as much as required, giving rise to the acronym WORM (Write Once/Read Mostly).

**Write through** A term used with a cache, indicating that when data are written to the memory, they are written to the memory and the data cache simultaneously.

**Zero wait states**   Operation of a memory system that requires no wait states from the microprocessor for normal function.

**$**   A dollar sign is used preceding a hex-idecimal value in all Motorola literature and throughout the industry.

**#**   A symbol used preceding immediate data.

# Index